THE RATE AND DIRECTION OF INVENTIVE ACTIVITY: ECONOMIC AND SOCIAL FACTORS

NATIONAL BUREAU OF ECONOMIC RESEARCH

Special Conference Series

The Rate and Direction
of Inventive Activity:
Economic and Social Factors

A CONFERENCE OF
THE UNIVERSITIES–NATIONAL BUREAU
COMMITTEE FOR ECONOMIC RESEARCH
AND
THE COMMITTEE ON ECONOMIC GROWTH
OF THE SOCIAL SCIENCE RESEARCH COUNCIL

A REPORT OF THE
NATIONAL BUREAU OF ECONOMIC RESEARCH, NEW YORK

PUBLISHED BY
PRINCETON UNIVERSITY PRESS, PRINCETON
1962

Printed in the United States of America

RELATION OF NATIONAL BUREAU DIRECTORS
TO PUBLICATIONS REPORTING CONFERENCE PROCEEDINGS

SINCE the present volume is a record of conference proceedings, it has been exempted from the rules governing submission of manuscripts to, and critical review by, the Board of Directors of the National Bureau. It has, however, been reviewed and accepted for publication by the Director of Research.

(Resolution adopted July 6, 1948, and revised November 21, 1949)

Contents

CONTENTS

CONTENTS

CONTENTS

THE RATE AND DIRECTION OF
INVENTIVE ACTIVITY:
ECONOMIC AND SOCIAL FACTORS

Introduction

RICHARD R. NELSON

THE RAND CORPORATION

The Background for the Conference

THE papers collected in this volume were presented at a Conference held at the University of Minnesota in the spring of 1960, and sponsored jointly by the Universities-National Bureau Committee for Economic Research, and the Committee on Economic Growth of the Social Science Research Council.

The developing interest in inventive activity which is reflected in the many papers presented at the Conference has stemmed from several roots. The growing body of research findings on productivity[1] turned the attention of economists interested in economic growth to the process of technological change. These articles showed that only a small fraction of the total increase in output per worker which had occurred in the American economy since the late nineteenth century could be explained by increased capital per worker. The lion's share had to be attributed to something else: to increased productivity or efficiency. The term increased productivity covers a wide number of different elements, and the operations by which increased productivity is defined and measured obscure a variety of economic phenomena. Better allocation of existing factor supplies (the process of dynamic adjustment) and capital formation in human beings (education, health, etc.) are two of the most important. But it seems obvious that technological change has also been an important ingredient.

Some of the crucial conceptual problems relating to the measurement and analysis of technological change were considered at a Conference on the Quantitative Description of Technological Change, held at Princeton in 1951 and sponsored by the Social Science Research Council. The 1951 Conference was concerned with innovation and diffusion as well as invention; its proceedings were not published as

[1] See for example: J. Schmookler, "The Changing Efficiency of the American Economy, 1869–1938," *Review of Economics and Statistics*, August 1952; M. Abramovitz, "Resource and Output Trends in the United States Since 1870," *American Economic Review*, May 1956; R. Solow, "Technical Change and the Aggregate Production Function," *Review of Economics and Statistics*, August 1957; J. Kendrick, "Productivity Trends, Capital and Labor," *Review of Economics and Statistics*, August 1956; B. Massell, "Capital Formation and Technological Change in U.S. Manufacturing," *Review of Economics and Statistics*, May 1960.

such although many of the papers were later published independently. This 1960 Conference was more narrowly focused, concentrating on inventive activity.

A second source of the heightened interest in inventive activity has been the cold war and the growing awareness that our national security may depend on the output of our military research and development effort—organized inventive effort for the purpose of creating more effective weapons. Closely related to the interest in military R and D is the growing concern with the technological race to which the Soviets have challenged us. The interest in inventive activity which stems from interest in defense and the space program has tended to be more micro-oriented than the interest stemming from concern with problems of economic growth. The studies generated have tended to be normative—analyses of conditions of efficiency (how resources should be allocated), rather than analyses of factors determining the actual allocation of inventive effort.[2]

A third source of the interest in inventive activity is the changing way that economists are coming to look at the competitive process. Increasingly the focus is on competition through new products rather than on direct price competition. And concurrently, normative considerations are shifting toward conditions of long-run growth rather than fixing on short-term Pareto optimality. In a sense these developments represent a renaissance of Schumpeter.[3]

Fourth, but strongly related to all the preceding points, the establishment of the National Science Foundation has been very important in focusing the attention of economists on R and D (organized inventive activity), and the statistical series the NSF has collected and published have given social scientists something to work with.

As the varied sources of interest in inventive activity suggest, the papers in this volume show a wide diversity of focus and method. All of them, however, are concerned with either the supply of factors which are allocated to inventive effort, the output of inventive effort (inventions themselves) or the input-output relationship (the production function). Social scientists studying the factors determining the

[2] See for example: B. Klein and W. Meckling, "Application of Operations Research to Development Decisions," *Operations Research*, May-June 1958; "Research and Development—Background Testimony," Hearings Before a Subcommittee on Government Operations, House of Representatives, 85th Congress, Government Printing Office, 1958.

[3] See for example: J. K. Galbraith, *American Capitalism—The Concept of Countervailing Power*, New York, Riverside Press, 1952; A. Berle, *Power Without Property—A New Development in American Political Economy*, New York, Harcourt Brace, 1959.

rate and direction of inventive effort are exploring territory which has been previously visited by only a few pioneers. The past few years, however, have been marked by the publication of a number of articles and books which have added considerably to our stock of knowledge about inventive activity. Both Schmookler and Nelson[4] recently have attempted to survey certain aspects of this literature. As a bench mark against which to judge the contributions made by the papers presented at this Conference, it seems useful to state briefly the conclusions reached by earlier authors.

Quantitative research on inventive activity had focused on patent statistics, R and D expenditure and employment, data and on counts of "important" inventions.[5] For a wide range of industries the cumulative time series of patents was found to be S-shaped, showing definite retardation as an industry matured. Further, the time path of the percentage of total patents issued which relate to a particular industry was bell-shaped, showing that inventive effort tends to shift its focus from industry to industry. The data showed a secular shift in inventive activity away from industries based on craft and simple mechanical engineering and toward industries based on physics and chemistry,[6] although the concept of an industry based on a certain type of knowledge was not clearly defined. The data also showed a significant increase in the proportion of patents granted to corporations as opposed to private individuals, reflecting the growing importance of industrial research and development. However, patent data and invention counts also indicated that the private inventor still is playing an important role.[7] Several writers were approaching the conclusion that the birth of new firms was an important part of the invention-innovation process.[8]

[4] Schmookler, "A Critique of Patent Statistics and a Review of the Literature" (awaiting publication, 1961); R. R. Nelson, "The Economics of Invention: A Survey of the Literature," *The Journal of Business* of the University of Chicago, April 1959.

[5] Schmookler, *ibid.;* Simon Kuznets, *Secular Movements in Production and Prices,* Boston, Houghton Mifflin, 1930; Robert Merton, "Fluctuations in the Rate of Industrial Invention," *Quarterly Journal of Economics,* 1935.

[6] A. B. Stafford, "Is the Rate of Invention Declining?" *American Journal of Sociology,* May 1952.

[7] Schmookler, "Inventors Past and Present," *Review of Economics and Statistics,* August 1957; Nelson, "The Economics of Invention"; and J. Jewkes, D. Sawers, R. Stillerman, *The Sources of Invention,* London, Macmillan, 1958.

[8] W. R. Maclaurin, *Invention and Innovation in the Radio Industry,* New York, Macmillan, 1949; R. Schlaifer and S. D. Heron, *The Development of Aircraft Engines and Fuels,* Harvard Business School, 1950; and A. A. Bright, *The Electric Lamp Industry: Technological Change and Economic Development,* New York, Macmillan, 1949.

The shifts in inventive activity which have been observed could be partially explained by changes in "demand" or, as some writers put it, "social need," although the verification of this relationship consisted primarily of examples. Economists writing about invention stressed the link between demand and profitability and were approaching a market theory of inventive activity. Sociologists and psychologists writing about invention tended to stress nonpecuniary incentives generated by social need. Although several writers seemed to hold these alternative views to be conflicting, more recent writers recognized that they were complementary.[9]

It was generally perceived that the number of people skilled in the appropriate arts and sciences, and the state of knowledge, were two of the most important factors determining the supply curve of inventions in particular fields.[10] However, major difficulties in defining the "state of knowledge" led to considerable confusion and prevented any useful test of this relationship. Writers who used as their examples the inventions of the nineteenth century tended to argue that formal scientific knowledge was unimportant to invention—what was important was general know-how about a technology.[11] Writers who used as their examples more recent advances in chemical and electronics technology tended to argue that, though scientific knowledge may not have been particularly important in the past, formal science was playing a major role in recent inventive activity. In a general way it was becoming recognized that the state of knowledge, however defined, was a very important factor determining the cost of making an invention.[12] Economists writing about invention were beginning to focus on the state of knowledge as affecting the probability calculations of inventors. Sociologists writing about invention were tending to stress the social aspects of knowledge. Some authors were beginning to treat invention as the creation of information, and were exploring feedback relations between information output and subsequent input.

[9] Schmookler, "The Level of Inventive Activity," *Review of Economics and Statistics*, May 1954; and S. C. Gilfillan, *The Sociology of Invention*, Chicago, Follet, 1935.

[10] Schmookler, "The Level of Inventive Activity"; Nelson, "The Simple Economics of Basic Scientific Research," *Journal of Political Economy*, June 1959; W. F. Ogburn, *Social Change*, New York, Viking Press, 1933; and C. Carter and B. Williams, *Investment in Innovation*, London, Oxford University Press, 1958.

[11] Gilfillan, *The Sociology of Invention;* Yale Brozen, "Research, Technology, and Productivity," in *Industrial Productivity*, L. R. Tripp, editor, Madison, Wisconsin, 1951.

[12] Nelson, "The Simple Economics of Basic Scientific Research"; Galbraith, *American Capitalism—The Concept of Countervailing Power*, p. 91.

It was generally agreed that inventive activity was a form of problem solving and, as such, was characterized by a considerable degree of unpredictability.[13] In this context, demand or social need was recognized as an important factor determining what problems people tried to solve, and the state of knowledge as affecting how, and with what success, people went about solving them.[14] The writers that stressed the unpredictability of problem solving behavior tended to argue against the possibility of a predictive theory of inventive activity. The writers that stressed the social and economic mechanisms for problem selection and solution tended to argue that general tendencies, if not specific inventions, could be predicted. Most writers who had examined inventive activity in any detail agreed on the sequential groping nature of the process and several people argued that a normative theory, or a positive theory based on rationality postulates, would have to take this phenomenom into account explicitly.[15]

Some Problems Treated in this Volume

Due to the large number of papers included in this volume and their diversity, it seems more useful to provide a guide to the reader by discussing some of the issues treated and some of the different points of view expressed than to present an annotated bibliography. In the discussion which follows a number of papers will be considered under two or more topic headings, and the order of treatment will follow the chapter sequence only roughly.

THE CLASSICAL ECONOMICS APPROACH AND THE BLACK BOX

Almost all the papers in this volume were written by economists and tend to reflect the economists' interest in economic growth and in problems of efficiency. This is certainly so of the papers in Part I, which deal with Problems of Measurement and Definition. Both Kuznets and Sanders are interested in defining inventive activity so that the outputs, "inventions," somehow measure an important contribution to technological change, and so that the inputs, resources directed toward inventive activity, may be fitted into a more or less

---

[13] Klein and Meckling, "Application of Operations Research," p. 24.
[14] A. P. Usher, *A History of Mechanical Inventions*, Cambridge, Harvard University Press, 1954.
[15] Nelson, "The Economics of Invention"; F. R. Bichowsky, *Industrial Research*, Brooklyn, Chemical Pub. Co., 1942; Schlaifer and Heron, *The Development of Aircraft*; Nelson, "The Economics of Parallel R and D Efforts," Research Memorandum RM-2482, The RAND Corporation, November 1959; Klein and Meckling, "Application of Operations Research."

classical economic analysis. Although the two authors differ quite markedly in the extent to which they believe that convenient and useful measures of inputs and outputs exist, the papers are very similar in point of view.

This point of view is essentially that of classical economic analysis, and many of the papers presented at this Conference are similar in that they are attempts to analyze inventive activity with the traditional tools of economics. Machlup's paper examining the supply curve of inventions and Fellner's paper on the profitability of various sorts of inventions certainly fit this mold.

Kuznets and Machlup point out, however, that there are some difficult problems involved in applying classical economics to inventive activity. One particularly important problem results from the fact that there may be great differences in the creativity and productivity of different inventors. How many average inventors does it take to equal one Edison? This fact seriously complicates the analysis of the supply of inventions and indicates that psychological and sociological data may be urgently needed for economic analysis of inventive activity.

MacKinnon's study indicates that such data may be obtainable and useful. MacKinnon examines the intellect and motives of a group of inventors and compares his results with existing data on other creative groups. His findings may have considerable bearing on the extent to which there is a sizable group of potential inventors which might be tapped by an increase in rewards, and hence on an analysis of the supply of inventions.

Minasian's paper presents encouraging evidence that classical economic theory can be applied fruitfully to inventive activity. Minasian's dependent variable is the one which is of real interest to most economists concerned with inventive activity—technological change. His independent variable is the one many economists would look to as the conveniently measured input to inventive activity—expenditure on R and D as defined by the National Science Foundation. He finds that a quite strong relationship exists between R and D expenditure and subsequent increases in productivity.

Save for analysis of the incentives of individual firms within competitive industries, the link between increased productivity and increased profits can be a quite complicated one. However, Minasian finds a strong relationship between increased productivity and subsequent profits for a firm. This result suggests that for some purposes economists may be justified in treating the allocation of resources to inventive activity within essentially the same framework as has been used to treat the allocation of production inputs. Fellner does just this. He is interested in how market incentives tend to "slant" inventions toward various factor saving configurations. Do high wage rates tend to stimulate inventions that are relatively labor saving? High interest rates, inventions that are relatively capital saving? Although he aks the question in terms of aggregative factors and factor prices, his analysis can easily be generalized in much greater factor detail. And although his conclusions are generally negative, his framework of analysis implies that inventors or R and D managers can predict the outcome of a particular inventive effort in considerable detail. Indeed they are able to predict what the new production function will look like. The assumptions Fellner requires are much stronger than the evidence provided by Minasian.

Several of the papers of Part V, particularly the Marshall-Meckling paper and the Klein paper, throw serious doubt on the ability of inventors to predict as closely as is required by the Fellner model. The concern of these papers is primarily with R and D efficiency, and the authors have attempted to look quite deeply at the insides of the black box—at the R and D process itself. The Marshall-Meckling paper shows that, in military R and D at least, the ability to predict the cost, performance, and development time of new inventions is sorely limited. Klein argues that this fact, plus the fact that as development progresses estimates get better, imply that the whole strategy of maximization in R and D may be different from that in production. If these conclusions are generally correct, prediction models based on the assumption of expected profit maximization, that is, models which attempt to explain changes in allocation by assuming optimal strategies on the part of entrepreneurs as a function of prices, etc., might well consider a wider class of behavior than is treated in classical economic analysis.

THE CONCEPT OF PARALLEL INVENTIVE EFFORTS

Klein argues that the type of uncertainty inherent in R and D implies that decision makers might be wise to run several R and D efforts in parallel. Since the concept of parallel inventive efforts, as formulated by Klein, Meckling and Marshall, and Arrow, and as described by Marschak, has few close analogies elsewhere in economic theory, it seems worthwhile to spell out the logic behind it.[16] Assume that a

[16] Nelson, "The Economics of Parallel R and D Efforts," *Review of Economics and Statistics*, November 1961.

certain value (a function of demand and cost variables) is attached to the successful invention of a device which meets specific requirements —say a long-range aircraft or a high quality soundscriber. Assume that a company or a group of inventors is interested in developing such a device and knows that there are a number of different possible designs that are likely to meet the requirements more or less adequately if enough inventive time and effort are expended. The utility, production cost, and invention cost of the different possible approaches are likely to differ significantly, but presently it is not at all clear which approach is best. However, it is expected that as work proceeds on any particular approach a great deal will be learned about its prospects and cost. Information and work accomplished are joint products.

It can be shown that it may be good strategy for the group of inventors initially to diversify their efforts and undertake parallel work on several alternative approaches—run them in parallel. Then, as information accumulates and more reliable rankings of the alternative designs are obtained, the effort should narrow down to the more promising designs. This conclusion is certainly intuitively reasonable, but the proof of it can be quite complicated.

Under certain assumptions it can be proved that the number of alternatives which should be run in parallel is larger (1) the greater the payoffs from successful invention, (2) the greater the rate of "learning," (3) the lower the costs of the initial stages of effort, and (4) the greater the "differences" in the alternative approaches.[17]

The concept of parallel inventive efforts has been studied formally only in the context of normative analysis for a company or organization. The extension to normative analysis for a society has not been undertaken, and the framework has not been used formally as part of a positive theory. However, the concept does suggest certain positive implications.

In particular, it might well be that a rightward shift in the demand curve for a particular product would have its major impact by increasing the number of independent efforts to invent close substitutes or reduce production costs. Schmookler's study of inventive activity in four industries supports this conjecture, and he presents an analysis of the incentive mechanism at work. Machlup also deals with the multiple effort nature of inventive activity and points out that an increase

---

[17] The rate of "learning" is defined as the rate of reduction in the expected squared error of estimate of a relevant parameter; the "differences" in alternative approaches are defined in terms of correlation coefficients.

in the number of parallel efforts might result partly in a greater number of new products or processes accepted by the economy, partly in greater speed in the achievement of a satisfactory breakthrough, and partly in a higher quality of inventions the economy finally accepts. One implication of this might be, as Machlup suggests that, as inventive activity in an area increases, the ratio of patents issued to resource inputs will fall because an increasing fraction of the resulting inventions will be duplicates, or near duplicates. And it well might be that by exploring just what *sorts* of responses are likely to occur as a result of an increase in expected profits, the predictive value of the theory could be significantly enhanced over the simple statement that inventive effort will increase.

PROFITS FROM INVENTIONS

The papers of Schmookler, Enos, Peck, Marschak, and Nelson indicate that, as a first approximation, one might ignore the complications suggested by Klein and try to explain the allocation of inventive effort by a quite simple maximization model. Schmookler is able to explain a considerable proportion of the variation in patenting in his four industries by variations of demand, and profitability. Enos finds that in the field of petroleum refining invention was extremely profitable, both ex ante and ex post. Peck finds that the different kinds of inventions in the aluminum industry were supplied by those groups of firms we would expect to be most likely to profit from them. Marschak finds that Bell Telephone Laboratories had a pretty good idea of what it wanted when it set out to develop a new communications system, and that the decision was quite rational (cost reduction oriented). Nelson shows that, even in a field with so complex a set of motives and controls and so uncertain an environment as basic research, similar circumstances prevailed. Thus the inventors of the transistor were looking for an amplifying device, among other things, and there were good reasons for their belief that a solid state amplifying device would yield significant practical payoffs.

Although these examples suggest that expected profit may be a very useful independent variable in a model explaining the allocation of inventive activity, they also suggest that a quite detailed and sophisticated analysis is required in order to understand where profit opportunities lie in the fields of invention. For example, in Marschak's study it is clear that the demand curve for communications capacity was shifting to the right, but the scarce factor whose opportunity cost was rising was the unused portion of the frequency band. The inventive effort was directed toward designing equipment to use previously unused frequencies. Although the initiation of the development is easily explained using the conventional language of economists, only someone quite familiar with the communications industry would think of frequency bands as a factor of production.

To further complicate the problem, Rubenstein's paper suggests that organizational factors may be very important in determining a firm's perception of, and reaction to, profit opportunites.

In order to have a useful theory relating inventive activity to perceived profit opportunities we must be able to answer the following kinds of questions: What factor costs are relevant to the profits from successful invention? Do the shapes of the supply and demand curves figure in an important way? What are the complements of invention? The substitutes?

The Thompson and Worley data reflect our present lack of understanding of the conditions underlying high R and D profitability. Thompson relates the geographical distribution of persons receiving patents to the extent of urbanization and to industrial structure. Worley explains the changing composition of the 100 largest R and D employers by relating R and D employment to the size of the firm, and to the industry involved. It is clear that some industries are much more R and D intensive than others but the reasons are not apparent. To say that in these industries R and D is extremely profitable is to beg the question. Brozen relates R and D profitability to past expenditure on basic research, but it seems worthwhile to ask why some industries have in the past spent more on basic research than others. To explain the differences we can fall back on institutional and cultural variables, or say that some industries are linked more closely to fundamental science than others. But what do we mean by that? It is not at all clear.

Schmookler's analysis suggests that invention and new capital equipment may be complementary relative to variable factors of production. This is scarcely a surprising result, but an important implication is that economists had better be wary in making any sharp conceptual split between capital formation and technological change as factors increasing output per worker. Clearly it will require a quite sophisticated type of analysis to disentangle the factors that contribute to high R and D profitability.

Adding to the difficulty of predicting and explaining where profitable opportunities lie is the problem of external economies, discussed by Arrow and others. This problem is more appropriately discussed under the topic "Invention and Policy," but it should be said here that, to the extent that different market structures and institutions affect R and D profitability, a predictive theory must consider these variables.

NONMARKET FACTORS

In his analysis of problems of public control, Markham raises the point that a very large fraction of our R and D effort is at least partially divorced from the incentives and controls of the market. On the demand side, the source of over half our R and D demand is the federal government. On the supply side, much R and D activity is conducted in organizations (universities, government laboratories, etc.) whose goals include many variables other than profits. It is important to understand these nonmarket controls and incentives.

Cherington's paper is a description of how military R and D decisions are made. It is a study of how a complex organization, attempting to maximize a welfare function involving many variables not easily measured by money and operating in an environment of great uncertainty, gains information and advice and comes to make choices.

Merrill's paper examines organization and the decision making process in basic science and in several other sectors that are linked only loosely to the market. He finds that the allocation of effort in basic academic science is determined in part by the interests of individual scientists and in part by the professional judgment of an elite who have considerable control over resources and rewards. The "welfare function" being maximized involves the conceptually vague but seemingly quite operational concept of promise to advance understanding. Nelson, in his study of the Bell Telephone Laboratories, shows that the mechanisms described by Merrill work in industrial basic research laboratories as well as in universities. Merrill also examines the structure of incentives and controls in medical research, in university engineering research, and in governmental agricultural research, all sectors where allocation is not directly guided by a market.

The Schmookler and Nelson papers present quite different evidence on the role that science plays in invention. Schmookler finds little evidence that advances in scientific knowledge contributed much to the inventions of the industries he has studied. To the extent that science did play a role it was a permissive one—as a reference book determining the skill with which persons concerned with practical problems were able to surmount them. Nelson's study shows science in a more active role, with advances in knowledge triggering inventive activity, generating a search for problems to which the new knowledge could be applied. It seems likely that the differences here reflect basic differences in the nature of the industries. The electrical communications industry is much more closely related to fundamental science than is railroading or papermaking. But this statement begs the question of what "closely related to fundamental science" means.

Siegel discusses a number of the relationships between science and invention. He attempts to relate both to the concept of information. A large number of the papers in this volume seem to be approaching the view that research and inventive activity are essentially activities aimed at creating information (see the Arrow comments). One would suspect that, in the future, research on the economics of invention will draw more intensively on the concepts of information being developed by economists, decision theorists, and mathematicians.

INVENTION AND POLICY

The notion that conditions for R and D efficiency may be quite different from conditions for production efficiency is reflected, but only partially, in the Arrow and Markham papers dealing with normative aspects and public policy. Arrow focuses on three important problems. One is the conflict between static conditions and longer-run efficiency conditions raised by the very low social cost of using knowledge, as opposed to the quite high cost of producing it. The problem is an old one in economics and in the past has been argued in the context of such examples as optimum bridge tolls. In R and D, however, certain special and quite complicated problems of appropriability of product seem particularly important. Arrow also is concerned with the welfare implications of the risk in R and D. It can be shown that to the extent that individuals can avert risks and no "insurance" is available, less will be spent on risky activities than is socially desirable.

A third major problem is that of external economies. Arrow, Kuznets, Machlup, Markham, Merrill, and Nelson all present arguments or evidence that, given existing institutions, inventive activity generates values which cannot be captured by the inventor. The problem seems particularly serious toward the basic research end of the spectrum.

Klein might argue that Arrow has not gone sufficiently far in admitting and examining the implications of certain properties of the knowledge producing industries, particularly the nature of the efficiency conditions. The problems raised by the efficiency of running parallel approaches may be particularly nasty. Is it efficient to run the invention industry as a lottery? If only one is to win the prize but each competitor can benefit from the ideas of the others, what mechanisms will generate an optimum flow of information? What of the many situations in which successful inventors and inventions spring from the ruins of unsuccessful ventures? To the extent that technological change builds on itself, what mechanisms can gain for an inventor some share of the profits from subsequent rounds of inventions to which his ideas contribute?

Markham is concerned with the conflict between antitrust policy and policies designed to sponsor a more rapid rate of technological change. The papers of this volume present conflicting evidence on the role of the large corporation. The Marschak and Nelson papers seem to indicate that in R and D size is a great advantage. It is difficult to imagine either the development of the T.H. system or the research which created the transistor being carried out in a small laboratory. These papers show that economies of scale seem to result from the ability of large laboratories to make profitable use of what would be external economies in a small laboratory, their ability to make profitable use of a wide range of expertness (division of labor), and their capacity to carry a large portfolio of projects (reduction of risk).

At first glance, Mueller's study seems to give conflicting evidence. He finds that only a small proportion of Du Pont's major product and process innovations stemmed from Du Pont inventions. (Three important exceptions are Dacron, Nylon, and Neoprene.) However, Mueller's evidence does not clash sharply with the theory that the large laboratory in the large and diversified company has a comparative advantage in many fields of inventive activity, for many of Du Pont's innovations stemmed from inventions of (other) large laboratories. Effective public policy certainly depends on better understanding of the economies and diseconomies of scale and diversification in the invention industry.

The organization of papers in this volume is significantly different from the order of presentation at the Conference. Further, because of duplication of content, or because the material is being published elsewhere, the following papers have been compressed considerably from their Conference versions: Brozen, Cherington, Machlup, MacKinnon, Rubenstein, Sanders, Siegel, and Worley. The more extensive versions of these papers can be obtained by writing to the authors.

PART 1
PROBLEMS OF
DEFINITION AND MEASUREMENT

Inventive Activity : Problems of Definition and Measurement

SIMON KUZNETS
HARVARD UNIVERSITY

Problems of Definition

INVENTIVE activity is limited in the following discussion to action concerned with technical inventions, yielding new products to be turned out and new devices to be used in economic production. We thus exclude social inventions, new methods of inducing human beings to compete and cooperate in the social progress—ranging from systems of pay and incentives or arrangements of work sequence within a firm to such far-reaching legal inventions as the modern corporation or the planning system of an authoritarian economy. The effects of social inventions on economic productivity are obviously major and profound, but the occupational groups connected with social inventions and the institutional arrangements for their production, selection, and application are so different from those involved with technical inventions that the two can hardly be treated together. And it need scarcely be mentioned that we also exclude creative work of an esthetic character, in which economic use is not the major aim or test.

Of the several characteristics usually formulated in defining technical inventions, the first discussed here is that an invention is a new combination of available knowledge concerning properties of the material universe. Two questions immediately arise. First, must the combination be new? Second, must it be of already known properties and processes without containing new discoveries?

The requirement of newness serves, presumably, to eliminate duplication in measuring the output of inventive activity, for clearly two inventions identical in character do not represent two distinct additions to the stock of technological knowledge. But if we are concerned with the *input* of inventive activity, if two identical inventions have been made independently of each other, and if we measure the productive factor involved by the capacity to produce inventions, then these two inventions signify a greater input of inventive activity and hence, all other conditions being equal, a greater supply of inventive

NOTE: I am indebted to Jacob Schmookler for helpful comments on an earlier version of this paper.

capacity than one invention. Furthermore, the supply of inventive capacity involved is not necessarily smaller than that represented by two independent and different inventions. It follows that an interest in the *input* of inventive capacity and a technological measure of inventive activity would require that an invention be defined as an *independently* derived rather than a new device; whereas an interest in the output of inventive activity as a contribution to technological knowledge would require that an invention be a new device, in the sense of constituting a real addition to the stock of available knowledge. Paradoxically, this may mean that a "borrowed" (to use a polite adjective) invention may be new, and an independent invention may be unborn if it has not yet become widely known. Inventions as a measure of input of inventive activity may thus differ from inventions as a measure of additions to the stock of knowledge both because of duplication of independent inventions and because of what might be called unknown or still-born cases.

The requirement that an invention be a combination of available and existing knowledge concerning properties of the material universe, with the implicit distinction between invention and discovery, has been criticized—partly because of the difficulty of drawing the distinction. More importantly, in that contrast, discovery is viewed as a process of unveiling something already existing, implying an indefensible theory of scientific knowledge. To be sure, much scientific work is devoted to discovering testable properties of the physical universe—assembling valuable information on coast lines, melting and boiling points, and so on. And yet it must be recognized that scientists in "discovering" their theories are in fact "inventing" them—for clearly the order which they bring into the structure of the universe is of their own contriving even though the test lies in an agreement between theoretical conclusions and observational data mirroring the real world. We may also admit that some scientific discoveries permit easy application without further invention and that many inventions involve, or quickly bring about, discovery of additional properties of the material universe; hence the distinction between these areas is far from sharp. Nor do we, in this analysis, have to accept patentability as the basis of the distinction, although it does reflect significant differences between technical inventions and scientific discovery.

Despite these difficulties it seems to me that the distinction should be retained for several important reasons. First, no problem of practicality or usefulness arises in scientific discovery. Any scientific finding

—whether it is specific information about the atomic weight of some organic compound or a wide-flung theory of nuclear structure, whether it is an accurate description of the coast line of the Persian Gulf or the most speculative theory of geological formation—is *potentially* useful, since any addition to our tested knowledge of the material universe is exploitable in economic production (the latter being a reshuffling of the material universe to make it better serve human purposes). Second, most scientific discoveries are immediately useless—certainly so far as the scientist is concerned, for he is not attempting the application of the results to useful ends even if he is aware of them, which often he is not. Third, the occupational groups, the institutional arrangements, and the individual motivations of inventors are quite different from those of scientists. Finally, since scientific discovery is usually general in character, each discovery provides a base for a wide variety of potential practical uses—technical inventions among them (the main reason for nonpatentability). At least since the second half of the nineteenth century, there have been many more scientific discoveries than inventions that could have been based upon them, and the lags between scientific discoveries and consequent inventions have been numerous. Conversely, there have been many inventions based on properties of the material universe, the knowledge of which has not been fully incorporated into the corpus of scientific theory. These lags and leads are indications that the two types of addition to knowledge have distinctly different properties. For more effective organization of the field of inquiry and sharper focusing of research, it would seem to me better to keep the line of distinction and restrict the definition of technical inventions to new combinations of existing knowledge designed for practical use in production—even at the danger of over-looking the contribution to knowledge that much inventive activity may supply.

A second characteristic claimed for a technical invention is that it must be the product of a mental effort above the average—although we do not insist on a flash of genius or any other presumably rare manifestation of man the contriver. The aim here is to distinguish between inventions and the host of improvements in technique that are made in the daily process of production and are the result of low-level and rather *obvious* attentiveness or know-how. Not that the cumulative effect of such obvious improvements on economic pro-ductivity is slight. It is merely that an invention is supposed to be of some minimum magnitude—magnitude not of economic impact but of input of some uncommon mental capacity of human beings.

Disregarding for the present the importance of this characteristic in connection with patent legislation or any other system of rewards, we may ask why the distinction between inventions and improvements is attempted. If we could measure the economic magnitude of each item from the most obvious improvement to the most major invention, would we still be interested in the distinction? The answer is "yes," if we assume that the upper segment of this range, i.e., the inventions which in fact provide the basis for the improvements, can only be produced by people with unusual equipment, and hence distinguishing them would lead to a more fruitful examination of the type of effort and corresponding type of personality involved. In particular, the distinction suggests that while inventions and improvements may be graded by their *economic* magnitude, no such continuity exists in the range of human ability involved; that there are qualitative differences between the effort and capacity associated with inventions and those associated with obvious improvements, so that no shift from the one to the other can be attained, no matter how much training, education, or other use of reproducible resources is thrown into the scale. The characteristic thus emphasizes the input side of inventive activity and implies that the distinctive factor can be identified and studied.

Whether this is a valid assumption, whether an effective line can be drawn between the capacity to produce inventions and that to make obvious improvements, and whether the particular type of ability connected with the former can be identified and studied, are questions best left to other papers in the conference. But it clearly affects the problem of measurement, and we shall return to it in the next section.

A third characteristic of a technical invention that may be suggested is that it be useful, i.e., that it be a practicable device which, when employed, would either reduce the cost of producing already established goods or make possible the production of new goods for which the demand is sufficient to cover costs. The reason for suggesting this characteristic is obvious enough, particularly to economists: we are interested in inventions because and insofar as they contribute to the growth of economic production. Yet one can easily envisage inventions that do not. For example, a new device for producing hairpins which is more costly—now and in the foreseeable future—than the presently used devices, is not useful in the sense in which we employ this term.

The difficulty with this criterion—and it has not been used in patent practice for some time—is that it requires knowledge concerning the economic effects of an invention after it has gone through a period of adaptation in pilot operation, and after an attempt has been made to apply it on an adequate scale to test its market potentialities. Many inventions never reach this stage; and practically all inventions when they are completed and even when they are recorded, are still far from the test of usefulness. To be sure, a patented invention must "work," i.e., the device must perform the task that the inventor claims for it; and the same test must be applied when unpatented inventions are recorded. But technical feasibility is a far cry from economic usefulness; and no assurance of the latter can be given at the time the invention is made. We must, therefore, shift the formulation to *potential* usefulness, although the question then arises as to whose judgment is to be accepted. The least demanding criterion would rely on the judgment of the inventor himself or of the firm under whose auspices he may be working. This standard does not provide a very firm base for identifying usefulness; but it at least permits an inclusive definition of inventions, on the assumption that they would not be made unless each inventor believed that his device was potentially useful in economic production.

But is this assumption valid? Are inventions made with this criterion clearly in mind? Or are many of them made out of sheer love of tinkering, pride of authorship, or instinct of contrivance without any regard to their potential usefulness in economic production? If the latter were the case there would be a vast disparity between the input of inventive activity and the output of potentially useful inventions, for there would be a vast number of inventions *not* designed for economic production. The disparity is large enough when we accept as the test of potential usefulness the judgment of the inventor or his firm; it would be enormous indeed if a great deal of inventive activity were not economically oriented. One may ask whether we should perhaps completely disregard the criterion of even potential usefulness and define an invention as *any* new device, employable in economic production, that represents some minimum mental effort. Yet, even if we did so, we would still have to make some assumptions as to the bearing of inventions on decreasing costs or on creating new products in the economy. Moreover, if we disregarded the criterion of usefulness we would be in fact removing an important part of invention as activity and as input. For it may be of the essence of invention that the search is not merely for a new device—which may be relatively easy—

but for a device that is more economical or attractively novel than existing ones. This is the major difficulty involved in inventing, the very aspect that may require that minimum effort discussed as the second characteristic. And while some inventive activity may be mere tinkering, and the potential usefulness of many inventions may be exaggerated, I would strongly urge that the criterion of usefulness be retained as a constituent characteristic in the definition of a technical invention; that a distinction be made at least implicitly between economically oriented inventive activity and noneconomically oriented tinkering; and that some attention be devoted to the different levels of judgment of potential usefulness in the analysis of both inventive activity and inventions. For this whole matter of usefulness has, to my view, obvious bearing upon a variety of questions concerned with measurement.

The Magnitude of an Invention

The preceding section led to a definition of inventive activity as being concerned with technical inventions, i.e. new combinations of existing knowledge in devices potentially useful in economic production and resulting from a mental performance above the average. The difficulties in measuring an activity so defined are perhaps obvious enough; but before we review the available indexes, it may be well to discuss explicitly the problems of measurement by dealing with the magnitude of a single invention.

It follows from the earlier comments that an invention has a technical and an economic side; and, of course, it has a past and a future. The combination of these two sets of aspects gives us four views of the magnitude of an invention: (1) the technical problem overcome— a view of the technical past; (2) the technical potential, i.e. the effect of the invention on further technical changes and the progress of technology in general—a view of the technical future; (3) the economic cost, i.e. the resources consumed or foregone in the "production" of the invention—a view of the economic past; and (4) the economic potential, i.e. the contribution of the invention to cost reduction or to the production of new goods in the economy—a view of the economic future. If we could set down meaningful figures for each invention under each of the four heads, the problem of measuring the input and output of inventive activity would be almost entirely removed, for any remaining difficulty of identifying inventions could be minimized. As an economist I would be willing to settle for meaningful quantities under (3) and (4). But knowing that no easy answers are available, I feel compelled to retain (1) and (2), for whatever help the examination of the technical problems and potentials of an invention may give us in considering its economic cost and contribution.

1. Consideration of the technical problem solved by an invention brings us right back to invention as the product of human performance of more than average quality. The difficulty is obviously related to the existing stock of knowledge; and it is assumed that such knowledge is accessible and that its possession is a necessary but not, in itself, sufficient condition of an invention. Given the search for an economically useful device as part of the task, the other condition is the ability to use the knowledge in some new and effective combination.

While a mere economist must tread warily here, it does seem to me that the magnitudes of the technical difficulties resolved by various inventions differ and, in that sense, different inventions represent different magnitudes of inventive capacity and of its input. To illustrate: Kay's flying shuttle, a useful modification in the handloom, represented the solution of a lesser technical problem than Arkwright's water-frame which mechanized spinning; Watt's separate condenser solved a greater technical problem than the earlier improvements in Newcomen's engine; and to use a modern example, the invention of an effective engine using nuclear power for air travel would represent the solution of a greater technical problem than the invention of another and better mechanical pen.

These are of course selected examples; a comparison of the technical problems resolved by Watt's inventions relating to the steam engine and Faraday's and his successors' on the electric generator would not yield unequivocal answers. All I am arguing is that above the threshold where obvious improvements cease and inventions begin the magnitudes of the technical problems resolved by inventions differ widely. Some of the problems are difficult and major because they are concerned with harnessing a new and previously intractable source of power; others, because they involve the conversion of a vast, complex, and time-consuming set of hand operations to machine operation; still others, because they are concerned with the displacement of a widely used but exhaustible material by a new one whose qualities, other than a suitability for various purposes, are still not well known. By contrast, the technical problems in other inventions seem to be of smaller magnitude, because they are modifications within the existing framework of technology and do not involve such new "large" elements as power, materials, or a complex set of manual operations.

Granted such differences between major and minor technical problems, I would argue next that the resulting major and minor inventions represent different levels of inventive activity. The only other explanation would be the gradualist and additive theory of inventions in which a major invention is the result of the long cumulative addition of small increments with the final inventor getting the credit; a minor invention is the sum of a shorter cumulative series. Inventions and inventors do, of course, depend upon the cumulation of knowledge—scientific discovery, past invention and improvements, and the state of the arts— but this dependence does not deny the proposition that specific inventive capacities vary, with the corollary that the difference between major and minor technical difficulties resolved by invention often represents different degrees of ability on the part of inventors. But as indicated in my earlier comments, I claim no knowledge of this subject which is quite fundamental in the whole problem of the supply of inventive capacity. It will, I hope, be dealt with by others. For the present I shall assume that the magnitude of an invention as represented by the technical problem resolved is correlated with the capacity of the inventive activity responsible.

2. Some inventions, representing as they do a breakthrough in a major field, have a wide technical potential in the sense that they provide a base for numerous subsequent technical changes. In this respect the invention of the first steam engine, which initiated a whole series of major technical changes and applications—what might be called subsidiary inventions—is vastly different from the invention of the safety match or the pocket lighter. This wide range is for our purposes the major characteristic relevant to the problem of measurement.

There is some positive correlation between the magnitude of the technical problem resolved by an invention and the magnitude of its technical potential. If an invention introduces a new industrial material of potentially wide use, or harnesses a new source of power, or mechanizes a wide variety of previously labor consuming operations, the very magnitude of the problem may mean that the first and pioneering invention has not overcome the difficulty fully, that much remains to be done by future inventions, and that the technical potential thus opened up is wide. But this association cannot be fully relied upon. A highly ingenious new device which overcomes a difficult technical problem may not provide a base for many further technical changes; while another invention that does not require comparable ingenuity

26

in overcoming a difficult *technical* problem may become a base for major subsequent changes in the technique of the process. I may be wrong in thinking that the Bessemer converter, measured by the magnitude of the technical problem resolved, was a "greater" invention than the open-hearth furnace; yet it was the latter and not the former that became the basis of modern steel technology, a foundation upon which a long series of technical improvements and changes has been built.

3. The economic cost of an invention can presumably be measured by the value of the resources used in producing it—the time of the inventor and his collaborators and the materials consumed, valued in terms of alternative uses or market prices.

Three questions are immediately suggested by this formulation. First, if *n* inventors are working on invention *X* and one is successful, we should presumably include the resources used by all *n* inventors, not just by the one successful. This creates no problem if the cost of a stream of inventions over a long period is to be measured since we could presumably use the input of all would-be inventors, successful and otherwise. But the specification of the cost of any single invention, or of a limited group of them, calls for the capacity to identify all the inventor inputs directed toward its attainment.

Second, how far *back* in the line of causation should we go in considering the cost? Should we include in the cost of an invention the resources devoted to securing the knowledge, via scientific research and discovery, that underlies it? Even if theoretically desirable, it would be impossible to specify fully the antecedent knowledge embodied in a given invention. But more important, if we treat inventive activity like other production activity, there is no more reason to charge it with the costs of scientific and other knowledge (except as it is already reflected in the value of a trained inventor's time) than there is to charge the production of any commodity—which is also based on a wide stock of antecedent knowledge—with such costs.

Third, there is the problem of specifying the completion of an invention and determining how far *forward* the cost calculation should be carried. If we adhere to the definition followed here, an invention is completed when it is shown to "work" and when a claim of possible economic usefulness is made for it. Substantiation of this claim might require a prolonged period of trial use and adaptation, a pilot operation, and sufficient mass application to permit most of the improvements that make for economical production. The economic cost of a tested invention may, therefore, be a large multiple of the cost of an untested invention; and it is important to distinguish between the two. Since many inventions are never fully applied and tested, it is only the economic cost of untested inventions that can be calculated for the whole universe of inventions; and it is the economic cost of untested inventions that corresponds to our definition of inventive activity. But it is useful to keep in mind the additional development costs involved in those inventions selected for application and service as innovations in productive activity.

4. The gross economic value of an invention to the inventor or the private user is either the capital sum received for it or the capitalized value of the returns that may be assigned to it. Such assignment and capitalization may call for complicated and imprecise procedures, but we are more concerned here with the economic contribution to society.[1]

If an invention involves an increase in productivity in turning out established goods, the gross magnitude of its economic contribution to society is the discounted value of the additional yield that it will permit. Given the data on such additional yield, its proper evaluation requires, however, either knowledge of or assumptions concerning the price elasticites of demand and supply.[2] If an invention involves a new product, a rough approximation to its economic magnitude seems to me to be possible only if the new product can be treated as a substitute for an old so that it again becomes feasible to estimate the additional yield and seek for a defensible economic basis for evaluating it.

Granted the difficulties of the type of approximation just noted, two further observations can be made. First, the estimate involves a forecast, the weight of which is greater the longer the future of an invention relative to its past (the future within the limits set by the discounting rate). With a large proportion of inventions made never reaching the development stage, the estimate of their gross economic contribution is purely a forecast; and that of their *net* contribution is

---

[1] It may be of interest to note that in estimating the returns from research and development expenditures the prevailing practices of firms follow rather rough and ready formulas, utilizing arbitrary percentages of sales or returns, arbitrary time periods over which to credit the invention or improvement with the effects, and perhaps no less arbitrary estimates of the probability of success (see, e.g., *Science and Engineering in American Industry: Final Report on a 1953–54 Survey*, National Science Foundation, 56–16, Washington, 1956, pp. 49–52).

[2] See the ingenious analysis for the cases of hybrid corn and related innovations in the paper by Zvi Griliches, "Research Costs and Social Returns: Hybrid Corn and Related Innovations," *Journal of Political Economy*, October 1958, pp. 419–431.

a double forecast, involving as it must some approximation to development costs still to be sustained. Even for inventions that have been selected for application as innovations, the estimate of the gross economic contribution to society is, within the limits set by the discount rate, necessarily a projection that has to embody numerous assumptions concerning future effects on production and the future behavior of market responses.

Second, if the invention is applied, it is likely to become the vehicle of a host of obvious and minor improvements (perhaps more so in the early phases than in the later) whose cumulative impact in reducing costs will be large indeed. Should we credit the original invention with all these improvements (denying credit to the latter) when assessing its economic contribution? The question has even wider ramifications. An invention introduced into a given industrial operation may not only give rise to improvements in that operation, but may also stimulate greater productivity elsewhere. For example, the standardization of cotton thread attained by the mechanization of spinning permitted some minor improvements in weaving (even before its mechanization) which would not have been possible with handspun thread. Should we credit the improvement in weaving to the invention of a mechanical spinning device?

An unequivocal answer is not easy. Although many inventions do provide bases for a host of obvious and minor improvements which otherwise could not have been made, it does not seem defensible to credit an invention with savings realized at times and places often remote from the original invention and inventor. The defensible answer, difficult as it might be to apply in practice, would be that the *acceleration* in the rate of minor improvements—over and above the usual run of obvious improvements in production processes—should be credited to the invention; and if we distinguish primary inventions from auxiliary inventions connected with them, it may be more justifiable to measure the economic contribution of a whole complex of related inventions. In that case the economic contribution would be measured by additions to output attained by the whole complex, *including* the *higher rate* (higher compared with industries unaffected by the new complexes) of obvious and minor improvements. The difficulties we would encounter if we used such a definition of economic contribution need not be emphasized. And yet in any rational calculation of economic returns from an invention some estimate of the contribution of the accelerated rate of minor improvements should obviously be taken into account—minor improvements in the process or product itself, from the standpoint of the firm; and both these and an accelerated rate of minor improvements elsewhere from the standpoint of society as a whole.

Several conclusions which emerge from this all too sketchy discussion of the magnitude of an invention seem particularly relevant to the problem of measurement.

First, inventions differ widely with respect to the magnitude of technical problem overcome, technical potential, and economic contribution. Untested inventions may differ widely with respect to economic cost and tested inventions surely differ widely with respect to their development costs.

Second, the magnitude of technical problems overcome may be positively correlated with the technical potential of an invention and the latter with its economic contribution. We may, therefore, assume, although none too securely, a positive association between the magnitude of technical problems overcome and the economic contribution of an invention.

Third, there is no reason to assume significant association between the economic cost to the inventor of a single untested invention and its potential economic contribution. However, some relation can be assumed if we assign to a given invention, or a related group of them, the total cost, including that of unsuccessful attempts. For if a given area seems to a wide group of inventors to be potentially profitable, the costs devoted to that area would be larger than those expended elsewhere and if the judgment is correct, economic costs of inventions would be large in areas where their potential economic contribution is large. This, of course, assumes free market operation in the matching of costs and potential returns and disregarding the effects of government subsidies, etc. And if we include development costs, there is more reason to expect that the cost of tested inventions would be positively associated with the potential economic contribution, for presumably—again on the assumption of free operation of market forces—the greater resources needed for development would flow in directions that seem most promising from the standpoint of potential economic contribution—as judged by the criteria of the given firm, although not necessarily by the criteria of social usefulness.

Measures of Input

The difficulties in the measurement of input are those involved in identifying the input and in evaluating it.

The major questions of identification may be stated as follows. Does the effective prosecution of inventive activity depend upon a certain relatively rare capacity of the human mind for which there is no possible substitute in the combined efforts of several less gifted individuals? Or is inventive ability widely distributed, even if at different levels, so that the body of potential inventors is limited only by the size of the adult population and the resources available for its education and by the time and facilities needed for effective inventing? Is there quantitative comparability in inventive capacity, i.e., can one man-hour of labor by a person at the x level of ability be equated to n hours by a person at the y level of ability, and so on?

If we assume wide variations in inventive ability and disregard for the moment the measurable resources involved in the educational and material facilities required for producing untested inventions, in order to measure the input in inventive activity—for the present in nonmonetary terms—we would have to: (1) spot individuals who, over a given period, engage in inventive activity; (2) ascertain the hours spent on such activity; and (3) weight these hours by some scale of inventive ability. Multiplying the hours by the appropriate weights we could then say that so many equivalent man-hours of inventive capacity have been "put-in" during the year.

The disparity between the data usually available and those suggested above can easily be gleaned from the literature. In his illuminating article, "Inventors, Past and Present,"[3] Jacob Schmookler presents findings for a small sample of persons to whom patents were granted during four weeks in October and November 1953. These findings are assembled with cross-section correlations of state data on patents and number of "technologists" (treated as would-be inventors), and defined in two ways: the narrower definition includes electrical, mechanical, chemical, industrial, mining, and metallurgical engineers, plus chemists, assayers, and metallurgists; the wider group includes also civil engineers, architects, designers, draftsmen, the very minor group of inventors proper, and surveyors. From our standpoint two of the conclusions are of particular interest. First, even in recent years, "invention remains primarily a part-time activity. Somewhat

---

[3] *Review of Economics and Statistics*, August 1957, pp. 321–333.

less than half of all inventions are made by full-time inventors, the rest being contributed by executives, line technologists, and individuals in a wide variety of other occupations working in their spare time"; second, "about half of inventions patented are still being made by individuals who lack college educations".[4] Thus, even if we disregarded the question of the comparability of man-hours of individuals endowed with different inventive capacities, and assumed that all man-hours were equivalent (or allowed only for differences associated with education, which apparently are not the most important), we would still have no measure unless we could estimate the part-time total of a large number of potential inventors.

But the problem of comparability is crucial, since it affects the whole question of supply of inventors and inventive activity. The limits to the possible supply obviously depend upon whether or not we assume a wide spread of inventive ability and gradation among the successive levels that would permit some quantitative comparison. Any light that professional study of human capacities can shed on this question would obviously be valuable. Moreover, we need far more empirical study than we have had so far of the universe of inventors; any finding concerning inventors, identified in either uniform or diverse fashion, would be of great value—not only for the measurement of input but also for public policy in regard to inventive activity. For the present, the number of "technologists" can give us an inkling of the temporal or spatial differences in input of man-hours of equivalent inventive capacity *only* on the assumptions that: (1) the proportion of technologists engaged in inventive activity and the average hours each devotes to it are constant in time or equal in space; (2) the man-hours of nontechnologists are in constant proportion to the man-hours of technologists over time or the same in space; (3) either all man-hours are equivalent, or the *average* man-hour has the same capacity weight for both technologists and nontechnologists, and is constant over time or the same in space. Clearly, these assumptions are unrealistic, although one would be hard put to it to assess the degree of unrealism. Does the average man-hour of nontechnologists have a lower weight as an index of inventive capacity than that of technologists, and if so, how much lower, and how has the coefficient changed over time? Has there been a rise over time in the proportion of technologists engaged in inventive activity? We do not have the answers to these questions, and must guess at the qualifications that the acceptance of the above

[4] *Ibid.*, p. 329.

assumptions impose on the use of the number of technologists as an index of physical volume of input of inventive activity.

Even if we could establish a scale and measure man-hours of inventive activity of equivalent capacity we would face the problem of valuation. How do we value these man-hours for comparison with other (material) resources employed in inventive activity and for comparison of the total with other inputs in the economy? Can we assume that compensation paid by the market to hired inventors (full- or part-time) or the revenue which the market secures to an independent inventor reflects a yardstick similar to that used for other resources in the economy? To be more specific, can we assume that the compensation of a hired inventor is determined by marginal productivity, with the flow of supply such that the marginal cost of an additional unit will not exceed or fall far short of the marginal return? Considering the difficulty of estimating the economic contribution of inventive activity suggested in the preceding discussion of the magnitude of an invention, the assumption of marginal productivity would surely strain one's credulity. On the one hand, one may argue that, in the aggregate, compensation to inventors, hired or independent, full-time or part-time, is well below any reasonable estimate of the assignable social product of their activity—partly because of the existence of non-pecuniary rewards, and largely because of the narrowness of the private market demand for many types of socially useful inventions. On the other hand, one may argue that, in some industries in which inventive activity is lavishly financed because of a general belief in a wide technical change potential, aggregate wages paid to employed inventors are too high (in comparison with other commodities and services) because of the inability of firms to distinguish between the fertile inventive mind and the educated hack. Since the market mechanism can so easily fail, one may wonder whether an increase in the real salaries of hired inventors actually means an increase in the input of inventive activity. It does represent an addition to the volume of resources devoted to sustain a particular group of people but it is no assurance of *any* rise in the input of inventive activity measured on some scale of inventive capacity.

This defect is inherent in the money measure of the input of any factor that cannot be effectively appraised by the market in terms of its quality or productivity. Obviously, it is a major deficiency of the available series on research and development expenditures by corporations, governments, and universities. Postponing for the moment consideration of other qualifications of the series, I would like to stress one implication of the argument above: that in dealing with the input of inventive activity an attempt must be made to go behind the money veil and to measure physical volume with allowance for quality differentials. True, such an approach would lead into the difficult field of inventive intelligence tests and personality studies and would, at best, yield a quantitative measure of inventive capacity not combinable with the dollar values of reproducible resources so much better evaluated by market prices. Such a measure would still be more useful than dollar value totals which reveal little about the productive factor involved. If, as is most likely, the supply of human talent is the bottleneck in inventive activity, and if we can derive acceptable measures of the input of this factor alone, we should eventually be able to study the effect of differences in its input, in combination with various amounts of material resources, on the output of inventions.

But to return to the series on research and development expenditures (R and D), they obviously suffer from limitations other than the inadequacy of the money yardstick in measuring the input of inventive capacity (the volume of inventive activity, as distinct from the volume of its output). To begin with, they exclude individual and independent inventors, whether full- or part-time; and in the light of Schmookler's study, the omission is substantial. Then, they include expenditures not only on applied research (which for practical purposes could be considered a fairly close approximation to inventive activity), but also on basic research (a small fraction of the reported total) and far more important, on development work. Development expenditures are probably far larger than expenditures on applied research proper, particularly among business corporations (whose outlays dominate the level and trend of R and D expenditures, including and excluding government financing). The line of distinction, although difficult to draw, is important: development expenditures begin when an invention, having been shown to "work," has been chosen for application (provided the technical problems of adjustment, prototypes, pilot operation, etc. permit extended operation, i.e., conversion of an invention into an innovation). Such expenditures are likely to be large because working out the patterns of operation, eliminating "bugs", and making successive trials and removing errors are all time consuming and require a great deal of material capital and skilled resources. I do not mean to disparage development work when I exclude it from inventive activity; it certainly makes demands upon ingenuity, technical knowledge, and ability. But it is a job of adjustment within given patterns of the production process; it is not original invention. And particularly important, the basis of decisions and the human personnel involved in development work are quite different from those involved in inventive activity. In studying this whole area of human endeavor, we probably would benefit by keeping the two activities—inventions or applied research, and development work—apart although naturally both would have to be studied in covering the full range from scientific discovery to economic innovation and spread.[5]

On the basis of this distinction and the implied definition of inventive activity (used throughout this paper), expenditures on applied research or inventive activity are probably a limited fraction of total R and D outlays. The actual fraction is a matter for guesswork, but the available data on the high ratio of development invention costs in those areas (aircraft, electronics, and the like) in which R and D expenditure totals loom large, suggest a fraction that does not exceed one-seventh.[6] If it is inventive activity that we wish to study, then we should not dim our view of it by using measures that are incomplete or so inclusive that inventive activity expenditures are only a small and probably variable fraction of the total.[7]

Measures of Output

The problems in measuring output of inventive activity are similar to those in measuring input: the difficulties of identification and of valuation. But much more data, quantitative and qualitative, are available on output than on input. The monographic and periodical literature that records at least the important inventions in various industries is far richer than that bearing directly upon activities,

[5] The apparently opposite stand taken by Willis H. Shapley on the need for distinguishing in the budgetary statistics between outlays on research and those on development stems, as I read it, from a view similar to that presented here, that *money* totals are a poor measure of input of inventive activity or of applied research ability (see his "Problems of Definition, Concept, and Interpretation of Research and Development Statistics," in *Methodology of Statistics on Research and Development*, National Science Foundation, 59–36, Washington, 1959, particularly pp. 12–13).

[6] After I made the guess cited in the text, an estimate was published by Dexter M. Keezer, Douglas Greenwald, and Robert P. Ulin, in their paper, "The Outlook for Expenditures on Research and Development during the Next Decade," *American Economic Review*, Papers and Proceedings, May 1960, pp. 355–369. The authors estimate the share of applied research in total R and D expenditures at between 22 and 22.5 per cent (see Table 3, p. 364).

[7] I do not mean to underestimate the difficulty of making the distinction in statistical collection. Nor are the observations above meant to minimize the high value of the new data in what is essentially a very difficult field.

characteristics, and origins of inventors and other information on input. Moreover, we have long statistical series on patents for a number of countries as well as voluminous unpublished data in the files of the national patent offices. Hence, instead of beginning with a further specification of the difficulties of proper measurement of output—which is perhaps unnecessary after our earlier discussion—we can immediately consider the data available, and begin with the statistics on patents.[8]

Before noting some of the limitations of the patent series, it would be well to point out its advantages. A patent is presumably issued after a test has been made of an invention's technical soundness, i.e., whether it matches the inventor's claim, and, in most countries, after a search has revealed that a similar invention has not already been patented. We may therefore assume—allowing for the fallibility of any human process—that a patent represents a new and technically feasible device. Furthermore, since it takes time and money to secure a patent, its issuance is evidence that someone—either the inventor or his backers—believes that the potential economic value of the patent warrants the expenditure. To be sure the costs are not large and some patents are taken out for their nuisance or blackmail value but unless the proportion of such patents is large or variable, the qualification they impose upon the statistics of patents as a count of new, technically feasible devices with some potential economic value is limited.

Note that these and subsequent comments refer primarily to patents issued—not to patent applications. Although some time distortion is introduced by the varying efficiency of the patent office into the series of patents issued as compared with applications, it is the issuance of a patent that assures a test of soundness and newness. Even that may be upset by subsequent challenge and litigation, and perhaps the series of patents issued net of upsets is the most unequivocal index of new devices of potential economic value. But there is no need to dwell here on technical details and on the possibilities of using one series as an approximation to the other.

The impressive advantages of patent issues as a measure of output of inventive activity, are offset by disadvantages under the heads of both identification and valuation. First, not all inventions are patented.

[8] The best recent discussion of the patent data is that by Jacob Schmookler in an unpublished paper, "A Critique of Patent Statistics and a Review of the Literature." I have profited greatly from it, although I disagree at points with Schmookler's conclusions.

Given the costs involved in securing a patent, the danger of competitive imitation resulting from the compulsory revelation of the new device, the cost of possible litigation in defending the patent, and the ability of an enterprise originating or possessing the new device to reap most of the benefit of pioneering without patent protection, the number of inventions that are not patented may be large. It has been suggested that the failure of the number of patents issued in this country to rise significantly since the 1920's may be due to an increasing volume of inventions for which no patent is sought. This hypothesis gains some support from the increasing proportion of patents assigned to firms, which implies that a growing number of inventions are originating under conditions in which a patent is not indispensable (as it is to an independent inventor) to assure the economic benefits to be derived. A contributory factor may be that many inventions are originating with large firms (which have the dominant proportion of private research departments) who fear that securing of patents may expose them to accusations of violation of anti-trust regulations. Another factor may be the growing financing of private research by government. Also relevant may be the increasing extent to which scientific discovery in some fields facilitates the development of alternative devices, so that patenting the pioneering device is no protection against effective competition. Whatever the reasons, there probably are variations in the extent to which the series of patents issued covers all the new technically feasible and potentially profitable inventions. It is also likely that the patent system in this country has become increasingly deficient in coverage in recent decades.

But the main difficulty with patent statistics is, of course, the enormous range in the magnitude of the inventions covered. Obviously, we cannot assume that one patented invention is, in any meaningful economic sense, equivalent to another. It is in this economic sense, the potential economic contribution of an invention, that we are naturally interested. As already indicated, the potential economic contribution of an invention when it is completed but before it has been tested and applied on an adequate scale is a rather conjectural quantity, and it would be difficult to attach such an estimate to each patent. Yet patented inventions do differ widely in their potential economic magnitude: a patent for a new corkscrew or plow sulky cannot be equated with one for a new gas combustion engine (although the former may eventually be economically more profitable, privately and socially, than the latter). Even at present, with a restricted and selective use of the patent system and a greater proportion of patents assigned to firms, one-third to four-tenths of all patented inventions do not reach commercial use by the end of the fifth year after patent issuance— a clear indication that for a substantial proportion of patents the implicit claim of economic usefulness is not confirmed. Furthermore, the range of economic contribution among patents that do find commercial use is very likely wide. To be sure, an ex post facto judgment of the economic potential of an invention in terms of its success in finding commercial use and of its contribution when used assumes that the economic contribution is properly determined by the play of market forces. It implicitly assumes that business firms are on the lookout for new inventions, appraise them tolerably well in terms of their potential, and then allocate resources to their development so that the maximum possible net contribution is realized. There may be flaws in this assumption since no human institution works that rationally, but I see no reasonable alternative to accepting it as a tolerable working rule— with the necessary qualifications for monopolistic action, human ignorance and folly, and for some inventions, the disparity between private and social return.

If individual patented inventions differ widely in economic magnitude, would the average for a large sample be constant over time or of approximately the same level across space? Would 1,000 patents, or the total for a given year (and they have been averaging 40,000 per year in this country in recent decades) have the same average economic value as the total twenty or fifty years ago; the same in New York state and in California; the same in this country and in the Netherlands? The answer cannot be given with assurance, but there are grounds for saying "no". The marked shift since 1900 in the distribution of patents from those assigned to individuals to those assigned to firms, the growing proportion of technologists among those securing patents, and the indication of a rise in the proportion of patents reaching commercial use all lead one to infer that there has been a secular rise in the average economic potential of a patent over the years, in this and perhaps in other countries. Other factors may have offset this trend, especially the nonpatenting of inventions directly exploitable by the originating firms, since it removes from the patent statistics one group of economically significant inventions. But the assumption that the raising and diminishing factors balanced each other in the long run, let alone in the short, is unwarranted; and the conclusion that the average economic magnitude per patent for any large group or the whole universe remained constant over time is unjustified. Indeed, the secular trends in the average values may have been quite marked. If so, it would be difficult to conceive that the averages are the same in different areas, industries, or other aggregates: each of these is a different compound of factors that produce trends over time, and it is unlikely that the balancing of these factors would produce equal average values. In short, one must conclude that the easily available statistics on the number of patented inventions are in units for which even the average economic value is variable—subject to significant trends over time and significant differences in space.

But this does not mean that the data are arbitrary and worthless. We need not assume that the trends over time and differences in space in the average economic values are so large as to overwhelm the indication that patent statistics may provide of the collective judgment of inventors and the resulting output differentials. To use an extreme illustration: if one patent is issued in area A and one thousand in area B, we could hardly conclude that the output of new inventions, measured by their potential economic contribution, is not larger in area B than in area A. Inventors are not complete ignoramuses and their flocking to area B would reflect a higher appraisal of economic potentialities there than in area A; and such flocking would include inventors with different capacities, up to the highest. Consequently, it would be dangerous to assume that the inventors in area B are idiots whose output is outweighed by that lone genius in area A. This reasoning may be completely wrong in any specific comparison, but it probably is valid in the overwhelming proportion of cases. In any event, it is presented here only as an example of the kind of assumption one must make concerning the responses and judgments of inventors as reflected in the patent statistics. The validity of the assumption used clearly depends on the characteristics of inventors, for it is they that determine the extent to which the collective judgment of inventors can be relied upon for an appraisal of the economic potential. If this collective judgment is not arbitrary but has some ascertainable relation to testable reality, it should be possible to interpret patent statistics as meaningful indexes of the output of inventive activity—despite the wide range in the economic contribution of individual patents or variations in the averages for large groups. The studies by the few scholars who have devoted attention to this material—Schmookler, Stafford, Sanders, and others—indicate that the data are neither arbitrary nor capricious, and that they can provide the basis for a great deal of insight into the distribution and even the volume of invention output.[9]

Three other comments can be made in this discussion of patent statistics. First, one can fairly say that even the easily available patent statistics have not been studied adequately. Despite the illuminating studies in this country by the scholars already mentioned and a handful of studies in other countries, I would conclude that the analysis has lagged far behind the accumulation of data. Of course, such a lag exists in practically every branch of empirical study of economic (and I suspect of all social) phenomena. The typical conjunction of the production of primary data by government and other agencies for administrative or general social intelligence purposes with the scarcity of scholarly analysts and of means at their disposal make a lag almost inevitable. Yet, while no precise measure of this lag is at hand, my impression is that it is much wider in the field under discussion, with specific reference to patent statistics, than in the study of many other production sectors in the economy. We are thus handicapped in attempting an appraisal of the possible yield of patent statistics because they have not been sufficiently analyzed.

Second, the mere number of patents, or even their classification by industry or process (and we have little of the latter) is only a fraction of the information in the files of the patent offices. At least in this country (I am not familiar with the situation in others), each patented device is described in some detail at the time of application and issuance. I am not a technologist and cannot fully appraise the value and potential uses of such information. But the latter is conceivably raw material for a more intensive study of the output of inventive activity than is possible on the basis of a mere count of patents or their summary grouping into several classes. And, of course, these additional data would permit identification of the patentors, and provide an initial step in the study of characteristics of inventors that is indispensable for a better analysis of the supply side of inventive activity.

Finally, one may fully admit that the patent data, summary or otherwise, are not a direct and efficient measure of the output of inventive activity, whatever analytically oriented definition of the latter we may agree upon. The relation is analogous to that between the primary

---

[9] It would seem to me that the data are better indexes of output than of input. Their defects as measures of output, i.e. of product of inventive activity, remain if they are considered as measures of input, since input must record differences in capacity for inventive activity. And they are a far more complete measure of output, since the input that failed to produce a patentable invention is not included.

data and the processes or totals implied in the analytically oriented definitions of many other areas of economic activity. The raw body of statistics does not contain data on output of capital goods or even on a clearly defined industrial sector, but we have been able to translate it into some rough but meaningful approximation to the concepts needed for analysis. The links connecting the original data with the analytical concepts were found only by intensive attempts to use the data. Some of the unexpected revelations that such studies provide are of immense value in identifying these links or in revising the concepts to render them operational without fatal loss of their analytical clarity and usefulness. This is but an elaboration of the comment above on the lag of analysis behind accumulation of patent data; but it specifies the service that the reduction of the lag through further study can make toward increasing the value of the data as measures of output.

Related to and supporting this conclusion is the possibility of using monographic and periodical literature (trade and industry journals, files, etc.) for a study of inventions that have been applied and have proved sufficiently important to deserve notice by historians and analysts interested in the development of specific industries and productive processes. These records register only a small proportion of the thousands of patented inventions in any one industry: they omit the host of inventions which are minor either in the technical or economic sense. But they can yield a fairly acceptable list of inventions that have proved important, with the possibility of distinguishing some order of importance. Too few such attempts have been made to establish a fully defensible basis of selection. But if the latter represents an acceptable consensus of experts in the field, the resulting selection is extremely useful, both for comparison with the yield of a study of all patents in a given area and particularly as a basis for more intensive analysis of successful inventions.

Concluding Comments

The gist of the discussion in this paper may be reduced to three propositions.

1. Despite the overlapping among scientific research and discovery, inventive activity, and design and development work, the attempt to distinguish inventive activity would mean a sharper definition of focus

and better research strategy. It would promise a more effective concentration of empirical data and analytical examination on the input of a distinctive ability, and on the output of a distinctive product. Of course, both the productivity of the input and the translation of the output into economic production depend upon and are affected by the other links in the chain from discovery to innovation. But granted that the study of inventive activity, like that of any process that is linked with others, can be useful only if there is a minimum parallel effort made on the other links in the chain, this does not mean that it is desirable to merge basic research, inventive activity, and development work into a fused mass and deal with the total input and output, without an attempt to differentiate among the three.

2. Proper measurement of the input in inventive activity requires some gauge of inventive capacity in addition to measures of reproducible resources, whether invested in education or in material capital. All these are needed, but the human ability resource is more crucial than the material capital and the money value of education. Money measures are of doubtful significance here. Disregarding the question whether this is a proper field for economists (it obviously is not), there is need, if relevant input measures are to be constructed, to draw upon the study of specialized human abilities.

3. No efficient measures of the output of inventive activity are available now. A variety of data—patent statistics, patent office files, selected lists of inventions in monographic and periodical literature—does exist but it has been barely utilized. According to preliminary indications provided by studies already made, it can with further work yield some quantitative indexes of the output of inventive activity—at least of rough trends and differences in the economic magnitude of new inventions in various fields at various times. The data are incomplete, since unpatented inventions escape attention; but they can yield far more information on trends and differences—to be linked with scientific discovery at one end and innovations at the other—than has been secured so far.

Judgments such as these can hardly be offered as firm conclusions. Discussion of definitions, the purpose of which is to delimit a field of inquiry through specifying its distinctive and constituent characteristics, can lead to no more than judgments whose relevance can be tested only by the development of research in the field. Likewise, discussion of problems of measurement can, unless much quantitative work in the field has already been done, lead only to suggestions that still have to stand the test of prolonged experimentation with the linkages between the available data and the desired quantitative counterparts of analytically defined concepts. The field under consideration has not reached the state of development in which canons of definition and measurement can be derived as conclusions distilled from already accumulated experience. Under the circumstances, all the propositions above can be advanced only as subjects for critical examination and debate; but more usefully as threads in the search for guidelines for further substantive research in the field.

COMMENT

JACOB SCHMOOKLER, University of Minnesota

When the other papers are considered against the background of Simon Kuznets' contribution, it seems clear that in many respects the conference is concerned not only with inventive activity as Kuznets defines it but with other kinds of knowledge-producing activity as well. The full range of activities covered can be delineated as follows.

1. APPLIED SCIENTIFIC RESEARCH. This may be defined as a planned search for new knowledge which is expected to have a practical pay-off. This term is intended to cover both basic research in industry and applied research as defined by the National Science Foundation. The NSF defines applied research as "Research projects which represent investigations directed to discovery of new scientific knowledge and which have specific commercial objectives with respect to either products or processes."[1] It defines basic or fundamental research (in industry) as "Research projects which represent original investigation for the advancement of scientific knowledge and which do not have specific commercial objectives, although they may be in fields of present or potential interest to the reporting company."[2] The reason for here including basic research in industry in the category of applied research is simply that such research is ordinarily expected to have an industrial application, though its precise character is not foreseen. Otherwise, firms would be unlikely to spend money on it.

NOTE: The author wishes to express his indebtedness to O. H. Brownlee for his criticisms of an earlier version of these comments.

[1] *Science and Engineering in American Industry: Report on a 1956 Survey*, National Science Foundation 59–50, Washington, 1959, p. 95.

[2] *Ibid.*

2. DEVELOPMENT. This may be defined as technical activity concerned with the nonroutine problems encountered in creating or improving industrial products or processes.[3]

In short, applied research is the search for new knowledge about natural or industrial products or processes with the expectation that the knowledge gained will be useful. Development is the effort expended in creating or improving industrial products or processes. The latter may or may not be based on knowledge gained in the former. As used here, applied research is concerned with the discovery, development, and creation of economically useful knowledge. The two activities combined represent the sum total of society's technology fostering efforts. "Pure research" stands apart from both, in that its primary purpose is the acquisition of knowledge for its own sake.

What is "inventive activity" and where does it fit in to this framework? We can define the term broadly and include all effort, from the initial exploratory work into the nature of phenomena carried on in the expectation that some use for the knowledge gained will result, to the formulation of the central properties of a new or improved product or process and the reduction of the idea to a form suitable for routine use in production. In that case, inventive activity is coextensive with applied research and development as defined above. Alternatively, we can so define it as to include only (a) the formulation of the central properties of the idea, and (b) its reduction to the point where it works, whether or not it works efficiently. The latter is essentially the definition which Kuznets proposes, and it corresponds substantially with the effort required to produce a patentable invention.

I shall use the second, Kuznetsian, definition on the ground that the character of such effort, certainly historically and probably currently as well, differs in many important ways, as Kuznets argues, from that involved in scientific discovery on the one hand or engineering development on the other. However, while Kuznets believes that inventive activity in this more restricted sense corresponds to that designated by the NSF as applied research, I gather from a conversation with

---

[3] The NSF defines development as "Technical activity concerned with nonroutine problems encountered in translating research findings or other general scientific knowledge into products or processes," *Ibid*. This definition unfortunately involves the unwarranted assumption that new or improved products invariably emerge from a prior scientific base.

Jacob Perlman, Head of the Office of Special Studies, that the problem is not simple. According to Perlman, inventions in patentable form generally come from the development phase, while the central ideas come from applied research. In my opinion, however, if the respondents to the NSF questionnaires follow the NSF definitions religiously, only activity expended on scientific discovery takes place in applied research and all invention takes place in development. Be that as it may, if research discovers what exists but was not known, while development creates what did not exist before, then invention is a phase of development. Separating research from invention is analytically useful, although in practice the two activities are often inseparable, so that the distinction is in one sense artificial.

Development as defined both here and by the NSF yields many minor and unpatentable improvements as well—improvements which I would call subinventions. Thus, the NSF definition of the activity includes "engineering activity required to advance the design of a product or a process to the point where it meets specific functional and economic requirements and can be turned over to manufacturing units. The design, construction, and testing of pre-production prototypes and models and 'engineering follow-through' in the early production phase is included. The development of designs for special manufacturing equipment and tools is included. . . ."[4] It therefore seems clear that while the problems dealt with in development are nonroutine, their solution often does not demand the creative faculty which the term invention implies. Whereas invention implies a result beyond that obvious to one skilled in the art, much development clearly does not.

To be sure, the degree of novelty required to constitute invention is open to dispute. To an outsider the paper bags, railroad rails, hayforks, etc., on which thousands of patents have been issued, might seem mere subinventions, and hardly inventions at all. Perhaps only those who have tried to make significant improvements in existing products or processes, or tried to produce nonroutine advances in any field of research, are likely to accept as proper the standard of novelty of the Patent Office.

Institutionally, invention is an activity engaged in by independent individuals, by corporations, and by governments. The objective is the improvement or creation of a specific product or process. The work requires examining the existing literature on the subject, theorizing,

[4] *Ibid.*, p. 98.

experimenting, formulating the essential properties of the new product or process, working it through to operational form so that subinvention can take over, washing out the test tubes, and sweeping up the floor.

Standing in a partially overlapping category are the applied research programs of industry and the production-oriented, knowledge-creating activities of nonprofit institutions. These two, of course, might be classified in separate categories. They are joined here only because both are production oriented, and are distinguished from development in that, while they are intended to improve production, the resulting knowledge usually must be further "processed" before that objective is achieved. Applied research in industry and production-oriented nonprofit research typically aim at illuminating whole classes of natural or industrial phenomena, not a single, specific commercial product or process. Thus, the scientific discovery that diabetes can be controlled by injection of insulin extracted from the normal pancreas of animals had to be followed by the invention and other development of means of producing insulin industrially. Similarly, as Nelson points out in his paper, scientific discoveries in solid-state physics had to be followed by development before the new knowledge could be put to industrial use. By definition, applied research includes research in engineering, soil science, aerodynamics, pharmacology, medicine, etc., in nonprofit institutions. Moreover, even nonprofit work in basic science motivated primarily by the prospective economic or military utility of the result should likewise be included.

The relevant distinction is *not* between basic and applied, but between pure and applied research. The results of basic research presumably illuminate an aspect of nature, the understanding of which is fundamental to some branch of knowledge. When undertaken with this objective as primary, it may properly be called pure research. However, if, as with most contemporary viral or nuclear research, the sponsors (if not the researchers) pursue the research with potential economic or military uses uppermost in mind, it is applied, not pure, research. Moreover, not all pure research is or is expected to be basic. A census of butterflies in a region would be surely pure but not necessarily basic research, for example.

The distinction between invention, other development, and applied research on the one hand, and pure research on the other is important to make, at least if one is interested in the theory of economic development. Sometimes, more out of convenience than conviction, modern economists have treated the growth of knowledge as autonomous. Yet, only a modest understanding of the phenomenon is needed to show that this assumption is at least partly false. Just as our knowledge of mineral deposits under the surface of the earth has been built up largely because of the possibilities of economic exploitation, so too, much of our knowledge of science and technology has been developed with a similar objective in view. Hence, the distinction between pure research on the one hand and other, knowledge-producing activities on the other corresponds to the distinction which students of economic development draw between exogenous and endogenous variables, and pure research is a relevant exogenous variable to the degree that the resulting findings prove sooner or later to affect the direction and rate of economic growth.

The volume and location of these activities inevitably is influenced by the role of economic objectives and the product- or process-specificity of the expected results. Pure research, because of the absence of an applied objective, derives its support almost entirely from, and takes place entirely in, nonprofit institutions. By contrast, invention and other development take place almost entirely under the auspices of the presumptive principal immediate beneficiary, because the re-sults take the form of specific products or processes, and are therefore in considerable measure appropriable directly by the sponsoring agent.

In contrast to development, the output of applied research, whether in the form of theories or data about natural or industrial processes and materials, is usually not product- or process-specific. This difference in specificity of results is associated with corresponding differences in their appropriability, which in turn helps explain the larger share of nonprofit institutions and trade association research organizations in the conduct of applied research.

Before we turn to a consideration of measurement problems, one final comment seems appropriate. The inherent uncertainty of each activity often takes the form of the attainment of unplanned results. In invention, a project designed to improve, say, automobile engines may yield as its major result a new metal alloy, an improved fuel, or a scientific discovery. Likewise, what was initially a project in basic science may produce instead a new invention, e.g. a cyclotron. The situation, again, is analogous to mineral exploration. Someone pros-pecting for gold may find iron or nothing; and vice versa, someone searching for iron or nothing may find gold. The discrepancy between

47

ex ante and ex post is thus very great in knowledge-producing activities, and it is one that students of the growth of knowledge must bear in mind.

Let me turn next to the measurement of output. I shall confine my remarks to the economic value. When we assign an economic value to an invention, it is its value after (not before) full development that is involved. I shall therefore treat invention and other development as one for the purpose of discussion. In short, I am discussing the value of the invention in the form in which it is actually used or produced by industry.

As Kuznets and Machlup have shown in principle, and Griliches in practice, we can estimate the social value of an invention. Moreover, if we wished we could estimate what its value would have been if different conditions prevailed. Of course, for some purposes (e.g., a comparison of two inventions far apart in time or space), it is not its absolute value which is relevant but its percentage effect on output, cost, or per capita income. If we can estimate the value of a single invention, I think we can, in principle at least, do likewise for a whole stream. The practical difficulties, however, are another story.

By contrast, there may be a theoretical reason why we could not ordinarily estimate the value of any other kind of knowledge and this reason applies, incidentally, to any comparable effort to assign a value to what Kuznets calls "the technical potential" of a given invention. The economic value of other kinds of knowledge derives, so far as I can tell, entirely from their contribution to specific inventions. The reason we may be unable to estimate the value of knowledge other than inventions is that each item of knowledge is by definition unique. Now, inventions are largely new combinations of existing knowledge. Hence, in many if not most cases, an item of knowledge entering into the making of an invention is indispensable to its creation. Without it, the specific invention would be impossible.

With each ingredient of an invention unique, it may be as impossible to assign a specific value to a single item within the particular complex of knowledge constituting the invention, as it is to assign a specific value to the wing of an airplane in flight. We could say that the value of the single item of knowledge in this particular combination does not exceed the value of the invention itself, but this is a different and not very useful thing.

One implication of this, which has long been recognized and in a sense eloquently pointed out by Ogburn and Gilfillan, is that the value of a given invention reflects not only the resources expended directly in its production but also the resources expended in producing the prior knowledge on which it is based. Hence, just as many American inventions rest on basic European discoveries and inventions, so it is possible that the intellectual effort of a given period may deserve far more credit than its direct output of inventions would suggest.

Now, despite the fact that we cannot place a value on individual items of knowledge other than inventions, it would still be very useful to study the frequency with which particular inventions or other pieces of knowledge reappear in a different guise in the course of technological progress. Kuznets is quite right in emphasizing the different technical potentials, the varying seminal quality, of different inventions. I am only emphasizing that other knowledge possesses an identical quality, and that while this quality merits study, it will elude measurement.

On the other hand, a private firm would certainly want to estimate the value to it of the new knowledge it generates. In this case, the appropriate thing for it to do is, presumably, to estimate the value to it of the inventions it makes, and assign this sum either to its R and D program as a whole, or to those phases of the program which fed the particular inventions. It might conceivably even form some crude estimate of the value of the inventions yet to come from the research the company has already performed. The limited time span and the narrow confines of the operation make these more sensible undertakings for a firm than for society. It is all the more reasonable for the firm, since it does not have to assign any value to the knowledge it uses from the public domain.

Let me turn now to a few brief remarks about the measurement of input. Kuznets is, of course, entirely right in emphasizing the desirability of nonmonetary measures here. What one would like would be estimates of the physical and human inputs used, each in some relevant, homogeneous unit. From such estimates one might want to construct estimates of the invention production function.

Unfortunately, unlike other production functions (except those for other knowledge-producing activities, such as market research or mineral exploration), every act of production here may change the production function itself. All production functions assume a given state of knowledge. The purpose of the inputs in this case, however, is to change the state of knowledge. Hence, successive acts of production may occur under unique production functions. Moreover, different projects at the same time operate under different production functions for a similar reason.

But even if we are interested only in the inputs independently of the production function, we still have the problem of the heterogeneity of inputs conventionally called by the same name. The occupations involved in invention and research are far more heterogeneous than are occupations in most fields. It is a tolerable approximation to regard one unskilled laborer as the equivalent of another, but it is hardly tolerable to view engineers or scientists in this fashion. And the median chemical engineer of 1950 is hardly comparable with the median chemical engineer of 1900. Perhaps most important of all, men differ vastly in terms of their creative talent, their possession and use of the "inventive faculty." While I would like to see, with as much refinement as possible, data on physical and human inputs, we may have to settle for careful estimates of expenditure on inputs. Such estimates at least indicate the share of national product devoted to increasing technical knowledge.

This problem of the heterogeneity of input probably reaches its most acute form, as indicated above, in the case of the inventive faculty itself. What we would like, while we are writing out our Christmas list, is a measure of this faculty in psychological terms, since the phenomenon involved is essentially psychological. I would assume that psychologists can or will ultimately be able to isolate the inventive faculty in its various forms, and that they can or will be able to rank those who possess any particular form of the faculty according to the degree to which they have it. Such information would be of great value to educators, employers, and—if it were available for large groups or over extended periods of time for representative samples—to students of economic growth.

On the other hand, such data will be of more limited use than one would like. For example, we would have difficulty inferring from the inventive faculty of an individual as shown by a test score how much of that faculty he exercised in making a given invention, since the use of a capacity may be less than the capacity itself.

What is worse, I do not think, from my limited reading on the subject, that we could rank all the inventors operating in a given period according to their inventiveness, because different fields of invention appear to demand different kinds of psychological abilities as well as different kinds of training.[5] The result is that Mr. X can make invention A but not invention B, while Mr. Y can make invention B but not invention A.

Worst of all, even if none of these problems existed, I do not believe that we could add together the psychological inventiveness test scores of the different inventors of a period and get a meaningful total—for the same reason that four men each with an I.Q. of 75 are not, in combination, twice as intelligent as one man with an I.Q. of 150. The differences among them are ordinal, not cardinal.

I am therefore forced to the reluctant conclusion that our interest in the distribution of the inventive faculty can be served only by studies like MacKinnon's of the psychological attributes of actual and potential inventors, and by studies of the factors which affect their development and functioning.

Let me summarize what I have tried to say. The conference is concerned with knowledge-producing activities of different kinds. Four broad categories may be distinguished: applied research, development, invention which is part of development, and pure research. Each of these provides knowledge inputs for the others and for itself. The differences among them run in terms of closeness to economic use, economic versus noneconomic motivation, and the degree of novelty (invention versus other development). The institutional differences and the extent of support accorded each activity largely reflect the differing appropriability of the results.

In principle and in practice we can and should try to get the best measures we can of the physical, human, and money cost of research and invention. We can likewise try to estimate the social returns from specific inventions. On the other hand, while we can study the inventive faculty in various ways with valuable results, one of those results will not be, in my judgment, an aggregate index of inventiveness, potentially or actually used, either for an industry or for the economy. Similarly, I do not see how we could assess the social value of that portion of knowledge which takes forms other than specific inventions.

[5] Cf. H. Stafford Hatfield, who argues that the psychological attributes needed for successful invention are different in inorganic chemistry from those demanded in organic chemistry. Hatfield, *The Inventor and His World*, New York, Penguin Books, 1948, p. 131.

Some Difficulties in Measuring Inventive Activity

BARKEV S. SANDERS

THE PATENT, TRADEMARK, AND COPYRIGHT FOUNDATION
OF GEORGE WASHINGTON UNIVERSITY

THIS paper is directed toward exploring some of the difficulties in measuring the rate of inventive activity. First, I examine the problems involved in trying to measure inventive activity through readily available information on inputs. Then I turn to the attempts to measure this variable through the rate of technological progress. Finally, I examine the use of patent statistics as a possible measure of inventiveness. The conclusions reached are negative. In my opinion none of the measures used to date is satisfactory even as a crude measure of inventiveness as such or inventive activity.

Measuring the Rate of Invention Through Input

Economists analyze input in terms of various factors of production, i.e., labor, capital and land. These have their respective units of measurement, units which we may regard as roughly uniform. To determine the degree of association between the input for inventions and the resulting inventions we must either (1) have some means to quantify inventions to test the association empirically, or (2) by definition agree to accept input as a measure of inventive activity, reconciling ourselves to the fact that this may be the closest approximation possible, or (3) develop some acceptable theory of inventions which can explain the nature and extent of the association between input and the end product which is invention.

However, there appears to be no commonly accepted unit of measurement for inventions, despite the fact that in many discourses on the subject one often encounters phrases implying that it is possible to quantify inventions by their number. Thus, in the Encyclopaedia Britannica, it is said:

> Many lists of the "world's greatest inventions" have been prepared, all widely different. The following list of seven has no unusual authority but is perhaps defensible.[1]

The list includes: (1) discovery of seeds and plants; (2) control of fire; (3) invention of pottery; (4) invention of writing; (5) invention

---

[1] "Inventions and Discoveries," Encyclopaedia Britannica, Vol. 12, 1949, p. 545.

of standards of measurement, i.e. weights, time, money; (6) the germ theory; and (7) tinned food. It may be noted that by and large these are not patentable inventions under the Patent Laws of the United States. More important, the way in which these inventions are considered makes it clear that they can not be regarded as equivalent units. Furthermore, since they are labeled as the most "important" inventions, it follows that other inventions are not equivalent to these. With a concept of invention consistent with this notion, it is difficult to see how one can establish any meaningful relationship between the number of inventions, and some measure of input, in view of the disparate units descriptive of the former.

A recent sociological treatise states:

> In the light of this principle of invention by combination, it becomes clear that the speed of cultural change depends upon five factors: (1) the number of culture elements from which new inventive combinations can be made; (2) the speed and completeness with which new inventions and discoveries are made known and made available to those who can make use of them; (3) the amount of improvement which each element is able to contribute; (4) the degree to which scientific methods are applied to the problems of cultural change; and (5) the intensity of the need or desire for the solution of various problems.[2]

The simple statement that the speed of inventions depends on the number of available cultural elements appears at first glance measurable, but as the author goes on to elaborate his views regarding the nature of these elements and the many facilitating factors which are deemed necessary so as to account for the present inventiveness, it becomes clear that such is not the case. If one were to adopt the theory elaborated by Hart as to what accounts for inventiveness, it is difficult to see how one could estimate the rate of inventions from the input, especially in the sense in which we are using that term here. Hart himself measures inventiveness in terms of its by-product, i.e. technological advance. In fact he seems to consider the two synonymous as we shall see when we consider the measurement of inventions or inventive activity in terms of output.

Despite the practical difficulties, one is led intuitively to believe that

---

[2] Francis R. Allen, Hornell Hart, Delbert C. Miller, William F. Ogburn, and Meyer F. Nimkoff, "Technology and Social Change," p. 49 ff.

there has to be some direct causal relationship between input and the frequency and extent of inventions, no matter how one measures the latter. Our economy certainly operates on the belief that there is this causal link between the two. Thus, the United States Congress increases research expenditures for specific diseases with the conviction that ways will thus be found to prevent or cure such diseases. We clamor for increased expenditures for space research to catch up with the Russians. Companies facing production difficulties increase their outlays for research with reasonable assurance that they will thereby find ways to overcome their problems. Our most successful corporations today are those with the highest proportionate expenditures for research and development.[3] Relatively higher "R" and "D" expenditures by chemical companies are believed to account for the increased proportion of chemical patents in relation to mechanical patents shown in Table 1.[4]

Intuitive relationships, however universally accepted, are not scientific proof of our ability to chart the course of inventions from the measurement of inputs. Empirical evidence of some apparent acceleration of inventions with increased input gives us no quantitative measure of the extent of this association or of the degree of acceleration in inventions with a specific increase in input; neither does it yield any clues as to the invariance of the functional relationship between input and the resulting inventions at different times.[5] No doubt there is a direct relationship of some kind, but we have no evidence that this relationship does not change. To measure inventions from input we need to know this. We need a much clearer understanding of the nature of inventive activity and a better perception of the intermediate steps linking inventive input with inventive output in different types of activities and at different times, before we can hope to measure or foretell the trends in invention or inventiveness from the measurement of relevant inputs. What we need most at this time is more

[3] Herbert Solow, "The Medicine Men of Kalamazoo," *Fortune*, July 1959, pp. 107–112, 164–168.

[4] *Science and Engineering in American Industry, Final Report on a 1953–1954 Survey*, National Science Foundation 56–16, Washington, 1956, especially pp. 21–28. *Proceedings of a Conference on Research and Development and its Impact on the Economy*, NSF 58–36, Washington, especially, Ralph E. Burgess, "Impact of Research and Development in the Chemical Industry," pp. 55–67.

[5] Even though it would be reasonable to assume that an increase in input would always mean some increase in inventive output at a given time, t_0, this does not mean that the identical increment in input at a later time, t_1, will have an increase equal to that produced at t_0.

TABLE 1

NUMBER AND PERCENTAGE DISTRIBUTION OF PATENTS ISSUED TO RESIDENT INVENTORS IN THREE BROAD CLASSES, DEMONSTRATING PROPORTIONATE CHANGES IN THE CLASSIFICATION OF PATENTS ISSUED IN DIFFERENT YEARS AND DIFFERENCES IN CLASSIFICATION ACCORDING TO ASSIGNMENT STATUS AND TYPE OF ASSIGNEE

YEAR OF ISSUE AND CLASSIFICATION	Total Issued	Total Assigned	NUMBERS Assigned Patents — To Individuals or Government	To Corporations Combined	To Corporations Initially	To Corporations Subsequently	Unassigned	PERCENTAGES — Total Issued	Total Assigned	To Individuals and to Government	To Corporations Combined	To Corporations Initially	To Corporations Subsequently	Unassigned
Total 3 years	1,848	1,236	119	1,117	1,065	52	612	100.0	100.0	100.0	100.0	100.0	100.0	100.0
Mechanical	1,297	757	90	667	623	44	540	70.2	61.2	75.6	59.8	58.5	84.6	88.2
Electrical	283	239	14	225	219	6	44	15.3	19.4	11.8	20.1	20.6	11.5	7.2
Chemical	268	240	15	225	223	2	28	14.5	19.4	12.6	20.1	20.9	3.9	4.6
Total 1938	636	438	47	391	364	27	198	100.0	100.0	100.0	100.0	100.0	100.0	100.0
Mechanical	472	299	41	258	237	21	173	74.2	68.3	87.2	66.0	65.2	77.8	87.3
Electrical	91	82	3	79	74	5	9	14.3	18.7	6.4	20.2	20.3	18.5	4.6
Chemical	73	57	3	54	53	1	16	11.5	13.0	6.4	13.8	14.5	3.7	8.1
Total 1948	440	292	26	266	258	8	148	100.0	100.0	100.0	100.0	100.0	100.0	100.0
Mechanical	278	146	15	131	124	7	132	63.2	50.0	57.7	49.2	48.0	87.5	89.2
Electrical	84	72	5	67	67	0	12	19.1	24.7	19.2	25.2	26.0	—	8.1
Chemical	78	74	6	68	67	1	4	17.7	25.3	23.1	25.6	26.0	12.5	2.7
Total 1952	772	506	46	460	443	17	266	100.0	100.0	100.0	100.0	100.0	100.0	100.0
Mechanical	547	312	34	278	262	16	235	70.8	61.7	74.0	60.4	59.2	94.1	88.4
Electrical	108	85	6	79	78	1	23	14.0	16.8	13.0	17.2	17.6	5.9	8.6
Chemical	117	109	6	103	103	0	8	15.2	21.5	13.0	22.4	23.2	—	3.0

SOURCE: The Patent Utilization Study of the Patent, Trademark, and Copyright Foundation of the George Washington University.

verifiable facts about the nature of invention and the factors which appear to inhibit or accelerate it.

So far we have considered whether we can determine the rate of inventions from the measurement of inputs. We have gone on the assumption that we are able to measure inputs in homogeneous and uniform units. But this assumption is not justified. We not only have no way to quantify the dependent variable (inventions), but we are far from having any precise measure of the independent variable (input) which is to be used as our yardstick. For instance, there is no satisfactory measure of over-all labor input for inventive activity. There is every reason to believe that over the decades the number of persons who give a considerable fraction of their time to inventive activity has increased; but what the rate of this increase has been we can not say. Even today, not all persons who produce inventions devote all, or perhaps even a major part of their working time, to inventing. Apparently, some inventions are still made by persons who give very little time to inventing, as such. We have practically no information on the number of persons in our population who have made inventions, and how much time they have given to inventing. It is astounding how incomplete our factual information is in these matters.

Productivity of labor in inventing depends on the technical skills and training of such labor. We believe there has been a progressive upgrading of the educational level of inventors over the course of time. The educational level of inventors of patented inventions in the sample of patents studied by the Patent, Trademark, and Copyright Foundation of the George Washington University confirms this belief. It shows a higher educational level for inventors of patented inventions in 1952 in comparison with that of 1938—a relatively short span of time. Since this is true for inventors of patented inventions, there is no reason to doubt it is true for inventors in general. Considering inventors of assigned patents in contrast to inventors of unassigned patents, the Foundation's Study shows very marked difference in the average educational level, in favor of inventors with assigned patents.[6]

---

[6] The educational level of inventors of assigned patents in the Patent Utilization Study is 16.0 and 16.7 years in terms of the mean and the median, respectively. The corresponding measures for inventors of unassigned patents are 12.3 and 12.5. It may be noted that according to the 1950 Census the average schooling for males age twenty-five and over in the United States was 9 years. For inventors see Barkev S. Sanders, "Patent Utilization," *Patent, Trademark, and Copyright Journal*, Conference Supplement, 1957, p. 74, and Table F on p. 155.

We may assume that similar differences have prevailed all along be-tween these two broad groups of inventors. Therefore, as the propor-tion of assigned patents has increased, signaling an increase in the number of inventors of assigned patents, there has been a parallel up-grading of the educational levels of inventors.[7] In other words, even if we could by some agreed-upon formula approximate the aggregate man-hours spent on inventive activity, the progressive change in the qualitative characteristics of inventors, with respect to their education-al levels and probably many other particulars as well, would still be an important factor to be taken into consideration in equating inputs over time.[8]

When we consider inputs in terms of capital, there can be no ques-tion but that the quality of the tools and equipment avilable for inven-tive activity has improved tremendously and is still improving.[9] It is also likely that the productivity of labor and capital inputs, so far as inventions are concerned, varies very markedly at different times and in different industries. It may be noteworthy in this connection that the National Science Foundation Study found little, if any, association between the number of patent applications pending and the expendi-tures in 1953 and 1954 for R and D reported by different industries.[10]

One does not overcome these shortcomings in the basic information on inputs for inventions or the qualitative changes in the labor and capital components, or the nonequivalent outputs for equivalent in-puts in different industries, or changing functional relationship be-tween input and invention over time, by shifting attention from specific factors of production to the annual expenditures for research and development or some related series that may serve as a common denominator. Such a shift, at best, camouflages the basic difficulties to which we have referred. The shift, in its turn, introduces the additional deficiencies inherent in the available expenditure series. Thus, the National Science Foundation series on research and development ex-penditures do not go very far back. More importantly, they are patently

---

[7] *Ibid.*

[8] The Patent Utilization Study shows that 90 to 95 per cent of assigned patents are developed by employees and the vast majority of such employees are required by contract to assign their inventions to the employer for patenting purpose. Barkev S. Sanders, Joseph Rossman, and James L. Harris, "Patent Acquisition by Corporations," *Patent, Trademark, and Copyright Journal*, Fall 1959, pp. 217–261.

[9] It should be noted that the training and selection of inventors itself involves capital outlays; in other words, the labor input which we consider is not free from some capital input, although the latter was not specifically allocated to inputs in invention.

[10] *Science and Engineering in American Industry, Final Report on a 1953–1954 Survey*, pp. 37–38.

incomplete since they do not attempt to include individual effort in inventive activity. They are restricted entirely to expenditures by corporate bodies and government. The series preceding the NSF data was constructed retrospectively and is subject to wide margins of error. The use of annual expenditures for R and D does not take into consideration qualitative changes in capital and labor or shifts in the industries responsible for the expenditures reported. No one would contend that the contribution of individual inventors as against "corporate" inventors, or the contribution of inputs by corporations and government, or by different industries have remained relatively constant over time. Therefore, this shift remedies none of the difficulties enumerated earlier; it merely adds others. Under these circumstances, about the only thing we can assert is that the fraction of total expenditures made by corporate entities and government—the recorded portion—has been increasing; at what rate (in any real and invariant sense) we do not know.

As for the quality and the completeness of the monetary series, even for the corporate and governmental segments the estimates are subject to a wide margin of error. In all probability, both the magnitude and the direction of the errors have changed from year to year and certainly over long stretches of time. It would be reasonable to assume that for the earlier years, for which the series had to be constructed retrospectively, expenditures are understated while in more recent years the tendency is toward overstatement. Independent of the systematic errors in constructing the series for the earlier years, these estimates are subject to large errors at any given time. For corporate agencies the amounts reported are subject to many judgmental considerations for different companies, and even for the same company at different times. Moreover, as relatively large expenditures for research and development have gained prestige for reporting companies, the scope of what is considered R and D expenditure has expanded. Such an expansion in the scope of reported expenditures is particularly likely to have occurred as a result of the amendments to the 1954 Revenue Act, which excepts corporate expenditures for research and development from Federal taxation.[11] It is notable that, only a fraction of the total amount spent for R and D is actually spent on inventions as such.

In view of these uncertainties, it should be obvious that even though

---

[11] Internal Revenue Code of 1954, Sec. 1235.

the evidence might be unequivocal that the amounts spent for inventions have increased, a large though unknown fraction of this increase is apparent rather than real. Aside from the large errors in the series of expenditures for R and D, at no time have we known what fraction of the total has been spent for inventions specifically and at what rate this fractional amount has changed in relation to the total.

Still another difficulty inherent in any series based on monetary units is the elasticity of the units recorded. The elasticity of the dollar is univerally known. What is not widely known, or at least not appreciated, even by many economists, is that deflating the dollars spent by the Consumer Price Index does not completely compensate for this elasticity.[12] In the case in point, the purchasing power of the dollar spent for personnel and equipment used specifically for inventions has changed at a rate different from the averages reflected in the Consumer Price Index.[13] We have, as of now, no appropriate deflation index as far as R and D expenditures are concerned. The National Science Foundation is acutely aware of this shortcoming.[14]

These basic limitations in both the dependent variable, inventions, and the independent variable, input for inventions (whether in terms of the actual factors of production or in terms of monetary outlays) cannot be overcome by the addition of other more or less associated variables to the monetary input so as to obtain a composite index, as has been tried.[15] In terms of our available insights and information it seems of dubious value at this time to attempt to estimate the trend of inventions from the available series of inputs for invention. It would appear that over the recent decades there has been a progressive increase in the input for inventive activity. But with increased inputs there have been concomitant transformations, the effects of which on the functional relationship between input and inventions can not be appraised at this time. Since the beginning of this century inventive

[12] Barkev S. Sanders, "Local Health Departments, Growth or Illusion?" *Public Health Reports*, January 1959, pp. 13–20.

[13] Barkev S. Sanders, "Discussion on Structures, Uses and Inadequacies of the Official Price Deflators," *Proceedings of the Business and Economic Statistics Section*, American Statistical Association, 1959, pp. 320–322.

[14] It is my understanding that at present the National Science Foundation is trying to develop an appropriate deflation index for R and D expenditures.

[15] I have in mind here specifically the as yet unpublished study of my good friend, S. Colum Gilfillan, in which he attempts to estimate inventive effort by a composite index which includes among other things the professional staff for R and D. The study was prepared for the Senate Subcommittee on Patents, Trademarks, and Copyrights of the Committee on the Judiciary of the United States Senate. Gilfillan has been generous enough to give me a copy of his manuscript to assist me in preparing the present paper, for which I am very grateful.

activity has shifted progressively from individual effort to organized effort. Table 2 shows this clearly with respect to patented inventions in the United States. It should be noted that much of this transition occurred in the first quarter of this century; there has been little, if any, consistent trend since 1940. Expenditures for research have shifted more and more toward larger organizational units. The input has come more and more from large corporate sources and from the Federal Government. In the case of the latter especially there are various restraints on any resulting patent rights.

In the meantime, the character of inventions has been changing (as we have shown earlier in Table 1) in terms of patented inventions in the United States in recent years. The solo inventor, whether working for a corporation or for himself, has been progressively replaced by groups of inventors; a natural corollary to the explosive growth of scientific knowledge and the consequent need for specialization.[16] What effects these and other changes have had on the productivity of input for inventions we do not know now. In the past very little attention has been given to the study and analysis of these relationships. The splitting up of knowledge through specialization in all probability reduces what we might call the conversion coefficient of input to invention, even if all other factors are held constant. It is quite possible that in terms of invention the productivity of the tax dollar is much lower than that of the corporation dollar, and the corporation dollar less productive than the dollar spent by individuals. Also, it is probable that the productivity of dollars spent for invention varies widely by industry and by the size of corporate entities, their organization and management patterns.

Moreover, we do not know whether or not there has been a progressive increase in the input requirement for inventions today, in comparison with inventions in the past. On the hypothesis that the more obvious and easily exploitable combinations of elements become exhausted, other things remaining equal, new inventions become more and more difficult, i.e. they require greater and greater input for a given volume of inventions, regardless of how we measure the latter. There is also the probability that in terms of factors of production, inputs of higher quality may be required, thus implying higher costs,

[16] The Patent Utilization Study shows that in 1938, 11 per cent of the assigned and 7 per cent of the unassigned patents had two or more inventors; in 1952, these percentages were 23 and 11, respectively. This trend is in line with other evidence of a progressive increase in teamwork. See George P. Bush, and Lowell H. Hattery, "Teamwork in Research," 1953.

TABLE 2

NUMBER OF PATENTS ISSUED TO CORPORATIONS, INDIVIDUALS, AND TO THE UNITED STATES GOVERNMENT, AND THE PROPORTION OF PATENTS ISSUED TO CORPORATIONS COMPARED WITH THAT ISSUED TO INDIVIDUALS, 1901–1957

Year of Issue	Number of Patents Issued				Percentage	
	Total[a]	Companies	Indi-viduals	U.S. Government	To Companies	To Indi-viduals
1957	42,744	26,627	15,154	963	62.3	35.5
1956	46,817	29,192	16,643	982	62.4	35.5
1955	30,432	17,828	11,914	689	58.6	39.1
1954	33,809	20,620	12,531	658	61.0	37.0
1953	40,468	23,524	16,284	658	58.2	40.2
1952	43,616	24,375	18,538	695	55.5	42.5
1951	44,326	24,468	19,192	659	55.2	42.8
1950	43,040	23,442	18,960	622	54.5	44.0
1949	35,131	19,663	14,957	485	56.0	42.6
1948	23,963	13,752	9,812	352	57.4	49.7
1947	20,139	12,117	7,784	155	60.2	38.7
1946	21,803	14,071	7,444	147	64.3	34.2
1945	25,695	16,245	8,981	87	63.6	35.0
1944	28,053	17,414	9,636	106	62.2	34.3
1943	31,054	18,546	11,654	48	59.7	37.5
1942	38,449	23,305	14,534	62	60.7	37.8
1941	41,109	24,744	16,322	43	60.2	39.7
1940	42,238	24,571	17,624	40	58.2	41.7
1939	43,073	24,440	18,582	50	56.7	43.2
1938	38,061	21,698	16,303	59	57.0	42.9
1937	37,683	21,655	15,994	33	57.5	42.4
1936	39,782	23,110	16,639	33	58.1	41.8
1935	40,618	22,839	17,757	22	56.2	43.7
1934	44,420	24,660	19,731	29	55.5	44.4
1933	48,774	26,010	22,813	51	53.3	46.6
1932	53,458	27,147	26,274	37	50.8	49.1
1931	51,756	25,110	26,618	28	48.5	51.4
1930	45,226	21,500	23,726	—	47.6	52.4
1929	45,267	19,900	25,367	—	44.0	56.0
1928	42,357	19,000	23,357	—	44.9	55.1
1927	41,717	16,300	25,417	—	39.1	60.9
1926	44,733	16,100	28,633	—	36.0	64.0
1925	46,432	16,100	30,332	—	34.7	65.3
1924	42,574	13,400	29,174	—	31.5	68.5
1923	38,616	11,600	27,016	—	30.0	70.0
1922	38,369	11,000	27,369	—	28.7	71.3
1921	37,798	10,700	27,098	—	28.3	71.7
1916	43,892	12,150	31,742	—	27.7	72.3
1911	32,856	8,100	24,756	—	24.7	75.3
1906	31,170	6,420	24,750	—	20.5	79.5
1901	25,546	4,650	20,896	—	18.2	81.8

SOURCE: *Historical Statistics of the United States*, Revised Edition, 1960, Chap. W, Series W 66–75, p. 599.

[a] We have used the basic figures as published even though they are not always internally consistent. The differences are negligible, however. The percentages have been computed.

even though this may not become apparent in terms of labor input as such.

When we top all of these uncertainties and difficulties with the perceptive difficulty as to what it is really that we are trying to measure, it should be evident that no sober student of this phenomenon will venture any firm opinion as to whether increases in input for inventions, signify proportionate increases in inventions over time.

We would like to see continued attention given to the compiling and improving of the quality of available information with respect to the national effort going into inventions. We believe that neither the quality nor the completeness of the information which we have now, nor our conceptual understanding of the functional relationship between input and inventions, are such as to enable us to determine from apparent trends in input the trends in inventions.

Ultimately, we may find that the only practical approximation to inventive activity is in terms of input for invention. There is all the more reason to try to purify this series and reduce the types of errors to which it is currently subject.

Measuring the Rate of Invention Through the Rate of Technological Progress

Instead of using input other students of invention have attempted to measure the rate of invention through technological changes, which they regard as the output of inventive activity.

The logic of measuring inventions in terms of technological progress, as the resultant of invention, is quite as justifiable as the attempt to measure it in terms of inputs. Both of these approaches are also in conformity with folk wisdom[17] Both are used by science. Thus, in physical sciences it is not uncommon to measure some force, such as electricity, in terms of its effect, whether by the lighting of an incandescent lamp, the heating of an oven, or the output of a generator. However, these analogies are not quite valid; the transmutation of inventions into technological progress implies a series of intermediate steps which may not remain invariant over time. As my good friend Colum Gilfillan points out in his work for the Senate Subcommitte on Patents, Trademarks, and Copyrights:

[17] Thus the relationship between input and inventions is reflected in the Biblical axiom: "Whatsoever a man soweth, that shall he also reap." (Galatians, Ch. 6, Vs. 7). Notice, however, that this is not quantified. The relationship between invention and technological progress is reflected in the statement: "Ye shall know them by their fruits." (Matthew, Ch. 7, Vs. 16).

Progress and productivity depend on many other things—the use and disuse of old inventions, the importation of foreign ones, innovations other than inventions, mistakes public or private, the supply of capital and land, the discovery or exhaustion of resources, the education and quality of labor. . . .[18]

In connection with patented inventions, the present writer, while a graduate student at Columbia University, did extensive work in attempting to correlate patented inventions in specific industries with economic measures of productivity, but dropped the whole matter, being unimpressed with the coefficients of correlation obtained (after the removal of secular trends in relation to time). These coefficients of correlation seldom exceeded 0.3 or 0.4, and literally thousands were computed. But even these relatively low coefficients were obtained after much trial and error with different lags and leads between the series that were being correlated. The question of how much of the apparent association was real, and how much accidental, allowed no great confidence to be placed in the end results. But even if one took the coefficients at their face value, they would be of little help in forecasting the dependent variable from a knowledge of the independent variable.[19] Similar efforts by Jacob Schmookler were no more impressive in this respect.[20]

As to the prediction of inventions from technological progress, the evidence presented by Hornell Hart and others who have followed his lead may appear impressive and significant but it provides us with no useful formula for our specific problem. In reality, Hart and his followers have never attempted to measure inventions. Hart is merely trying to establish the thesis that man's technological and cultural progress has been accelerated over time. Specifically, archeological and historical information show relatively little change in technology in early times but a progressive acceleration of change in recent times, and every indication that this acceleration is continuing. For instance, in considering the rise of maximum speeds Hart points out that from the beginning of man until about 1700 B.C. man's fastest mode of locomotion was by means of his own two feet. At that date the horse made

[18] Gilfillan, *op. cit.*

[19] The highest coefficients of determination thus obtained were of the order of 0.09 to 0.16. If one took into consideration the sampling errors, the predictive value of these relationships would be nil.

[20] "Technical Change and Patent Statistics," Conference on Quantitative Description of Technological Change, sponsored by the Committees on Economic Growth and on Social Implications of Atomic Energy and Technological Change of the Social Science Research Council, 1951.

its appearance in history and dominated the speed records until A.D. 1829, when the steam locomotive outstripped it. The pace of locomotives continued to increase but at a decelerating rate and by 1910 the speed record was taken by the automobile. Although the maximum speed of the automobile continued to increase, by 1921 the lead was lost to the airplane. It is taken for granted that the accelerated breaking of speed records in recent years is *per se* a measure of inventive activity.

Hart believes that in measuring the rate of technical change he is measuring the rate of invention but the student of inventions is interested primarily in the rate of the inventive process as such. An invention to him means a new configuration of objects and forces that will result in a new product or process to meet some human need; if not entirely new, it generally excels in quality, or in some other attribute, products or processes already known. The extent of its novelty, which might be described as the conceptual jump between the previously known and the new configuration, is the essence of what we may call the "amount of invention." We have devised no objective yardstick for the measurement of this quantity and may never be able to devise one.

In other words, Hornell Hart does not differentiate the elements which some students of invention have labeled innovation and diffusion, and other intermediaries, such as those which Gilfillan mentions, which contribute along with invention to the end process of technological or cultural progress. If we are ready to do without these conceptual distinctions between invention and the intervening processes connecting invention with technological progress, then we had better turn to the economists' concept of increased productivity. In increased productivity we have a more or less appropriate common denominator in terms of economic value, or market price of goods and services. With such a concept we should be able to compare and combine varying rates of change in different fields into some overall index of productivity. It must be realized, however, that in doing this we will have to abandon the narrower concept of invention, substituting in its place some measurable end product far removed from the initial act of inventing. It is quite possible, of course, that this may be the nearest we shall ever be able to come to measuring invention.

Perhaps we should illustrate how alien Hart's thinking is to our specific concept of inventive activity by citing one of the illustrations which he uses to demonstrate man's accelerating technological progress. After giving the following table which illustrates the accelerating rate with which life expectancy per decade has been increasing:

Dates	Gains per Decade in Expectation at Birth
2000 B.C. to 200 B.C.	0.02
200 B.C. to A.D. 1840	0.79
1840 to 1910	1.9
1910 to 1940	2.4
1940 to 1955	3.9

He proceeds to observe:

> If increases in expectation of life at birth were to continue to accelerate along the trend indicated by the above figures, the average expectation of American babies born in the year 2000 would be approximately 100 years.
>
> The increase in expectation of life has been grouped in this section as one of four examples of technological acceleration. . . .[21]

It should be obvious to anyone that there is a wide gulf separating inventions that influence the longevity of man from their widespread adoption and use so that they affect significantly the life expectancy of large populations. Moreover, there are many external factors such as diet, mode of living, the organization and effectiveness of medical care, personal hygiene and cleanliness, and accidental hazards, to mention only the more important ones, which decidely influence life expectancy. But these considerations do not concern Hart. Following Ogburn,[22] he takes it for granted that inventions are a recombination of different elements in the culture base, and that the rate of these recombinations depends on the number of elements available. As Hart puts it, "Inventions breed inventions."

We must conclude, of necessity, that this approach to measuring inventions is of little avail, at least now. It is possible that with appropriate analytical tools the time may come when we shall be able to do better in correlating at least major inventive periods with subsequent technological changes, as cause and effect. We certainly have not been able to do this so far to any significant degree.

It is conceivable that simultaneous analysis, in terms of input on the one hand and output as technological progress on the other, may

[21] Allen *et al.*, *op. cit.*, p. 34.
[22] William F. Ogburn, *Social Change*, 1922.

prove more effective than either approach used by itself. This possibility has not been explored adequately. In any event, we need more reliable series to measure both input and output, and also a sharper crystallization of our concept of what it is that we are trying to measure, before much progress can be hoped for.

Of course, if one were ready to accept the theory of invention propounded by Ogburn there might be little reason to develop techniques, or more complete information, on input and output series for measuring inventions along the line which we have considered. According to Ogburn inventions are inevitable combinations of elements in the culture that are ripe to occur. If true, theoretically one should be able to develop a function, based on a properly conceived mathematical model, that could prognosticate the rate of new inventions at any point in time. However, Ogburn's theory of invention is far from validation. It fails completely to explain why some cultures prove much more dynamic than others, irrespective of the extent of the cultural base. It fails to account for plateaus that are frequent in the course of any art or even for an entire culture complex. It fails to consider the obvious fact that invention takes place in the mind of an individual; individual minds have not changed much, and the mind can encompass only a small fraction of the culture base in a culture such as ours. The strongest evidence in support of the cultural inevitability of inventions is the "frequent" occurrence of duplicate inventions more or less simultaneously. But, finding several hundred duplicates in literally millions of inventions, is hardly solid evidence for a theory, the postulates of which run counter to historical and much other evidence.[23]

If inventing is essentially not much more than the permutation and combination of the elements in the cultural base, as Ogburn and others have theorized, then how is one to account for the small number of persons who are inventors? Why has not the number and proportion of inventors increased with the expansion of the cultural base? More specifically, there are thousands of persons in positions where their advancement and prestige depends to a large extent on the patentable inventions which they are able to develop. According to the cultural

---

[23] I am not unaware of the contribution which my associate, Dr. Rossman, made to this line of evidence by pointing out the frequency of interference in the Patent Office as an indication of multiple inventions. It should be observed, however, that an interference does not necessarily mean duplicate inventions, but merely the fact that one or more claims of two or more patent applications overlap or are deemed to be the same.

base theory of invention, with an expanding cultural base such inventors should be able to acquire larger and larger numbers of patents year after year. But that is not what happens. In fact, there is no evidence that the productivity of persons who are hired primarily to invent is greater today than some fifty or sixty years ago, notwithstanding the fact that the cultural base has expanded tremendously in the intervening period.[24]

The theory seems untenable to me. Therefore, I see little prospect of arriving at a solution to the problem via some theoretical formulation of the nature of inventions. On the contrary, I am of the belief that if there is a solution it can only come through empirical study of inventions, and related phenomena. Of special importance are studies focused on the acceleration and retardation of inventiveness, as we are able to infer these, however inadequately, from our analyses of inputs and outputs. If there is a solution to our problem, it can come only through intensive empirical studies. In such studies, series of patented inventions have a special role to play because of their ready availability.

We have already indicated that students of invention have often restricted themselves to the study of patented inventions. There are, as we have just mentioned, unquestionable advantages to such a limitation. In patents we have identifiable inventive acts which have met at least the minimum criteria of novelty and utility, the two prerequisites for a patentable invention. The question arises again: can we measure the rate of inventions in terms of patent statistics?

Patents as a Basis for Measuring Inventive Activity

In this century a number of students have attempted to use the number of patent applications or the annual number of patents issued as a possible measure of inventiveness, inventive activity, or other related concepts. The most persistent of this group has been Jacob Schmookler, who has argued at length and repeatedly that patent statistics are, in terms of the number of patents applied for, a useful measure of inventive activity. Schmookler has drawn many conclusions about inventive activity from patent data. Unfortunately, these conclusions

[24] The Patent Utilization Study of the Patent, Trademark, and Copyright Foundation of George Washington University includes analyses of information for the first time bearing on these and related problems of the productivity of inventors. This phase of the study has not been completed as yet.

and assertions are not supported by valid empirical evidence, and in the opinion of this writer they are unwarranted and unsound.[25]

It seems to me that in order for patent applications to serve as a useful index of inventive activity two conditions must be closely approximated: (1) The proportion of inventive activity resulting in patented inventions must have remained essentially invariant over the span of time during which patents are deemed to serve as a useful index; and (2) The input per average patent must have remained similarly invariant. Neither of these propositions can be established to be true and, indeed, what we know tends to negate them.

With respect to the first condition, we know that through the decades the ascendancy of different industries has shifted. Since the inclination of different industries in relation to patentable inventions varies widely it would be reasonable to assume that the proportion of inventive activity which has gone into patented inventions has not remained constant. In the 19th century most of the inventions were made by individuals, and an individual as a rule has no means of using his invention except by patenting it and selling it to someone who can exploit it. However, this is not the case with many corporations. Therefore the proportion of corporate inventive activity that goes into patented inventions is likely to differ from that of individual inventors.

Through the decades public attitudes and legal attitudes toward patent protection have oscillated; such shifts in all probability have influenced the economic value of patents and in turn the proportion of corporate and individual inventive activity going into patented inventions.[26]

The Patent Utilization Study shows that, at least in recent years, a large proportion of the assigned patented inventions that are put to

[25] In the original paper which I submitted to the Conference I documented my criticism of Schmookler by extensive quotations from his different published works. The publications committee of the conference has excised these pages. The Schmookler articles which were quoted from included: "The Interpretation of Patent Statistics," *Journal of the Patent Office Society*, February 1950, pp. 123–146; "Technical Change and Patent Statistics"; "The Utility of Patent Statistics," *Journal of the Patent Office Society*, June 1953, pp. 407–412; "Patent Application Statistics as an Index of Inventive Activity," *Journal of the Patent Office Society*, August 1953, p. 539; "The Level of Inventive Activity," *Review of Economics and Statistics*, May 1954, pp. 183–190.

[26] H. R. Meyers, "The United States Patent System in Historical Perspective," *Patent, Trademark and Copyright Journal*, Spring 1959, pp. 33–52. Daniel H. Kane, "Patentable Invention and Our Political Economy," *Journal of the Patent Office Society*, February 1950, pp. 89–96. Both these articles show that the attitude of the courts has shifted from time to time with respect to the upholding of litigated patent rights, and Meyers attributes this to shifts in public attitudes.

use have been utilized before the patent application. Even if we assume that this practice is not new, at least it is pretty much confined to assigned inventions, which represented a small proportion of patents forty or fifty years ago. We have indicated in Table 2 the shift from individual inventors to hired inventors. Other things being equal, the practice of pre-application use of inventions would tend to reduce the proportion of inventions that are patented as a result of at least two factors.

1. Industrial use of an invention will bring out any limitations inherent in it, and if these are serious enough no patent application will be filed. This will tend to increase inventive activity which does not result in patented inventions in relation to inventive activity which gives rise to patents.

2. The patent laws of the United States prohibit the patenting of an invention if it has been in commercial use for more than twelve months. It is probable that some inventions which are put to use before patent application may inadvertently be used too long and thereby be disqualified. To the extent that this occurs, it again would increase the proportion of inventive activity which does not result in patent applications. It may be observed that early industrial use of an invention may also negatively influence the decision to pursue a patent application in instances where such use helps to make obsolete a device by stimulating substitute inventions of higher quality.

With the growing size of our markets, certain types of inventions can be exploited by hitting the market once. Inventions of this type which at one time would have been patented will not be patented today, thus reducing the ratio between inputs and the number of patented inventions.

Until recently the interval between a patent application and the granting of a patent was increasing, to the extent that this lag was reducing the economic value of some patents and it was exercising a depressing influence on applications. With growing hazards governing the outcome of patent litigation and the rising costs of such litigation some inventions which under more auspicious circumstances would have been patented, may not be patented. And as we have indicated the attitude of the courts has gone through several up and down cycles affecting the proportion of inventive activity going into patents.

The tradition of patenting has varied widely among different professional groups; as the relative importance of these groups has changed over time the proportion of inventions which are patented has changed in response. In companies which are narrowly specialized many inventions may not be patented because they fall outside of a given line. Many of the inventors who responded positively to the question as to whether they had had inventions which were not patented gave this as the reason why.

The growing share of government in research and development work and, to a lesser extent, the increased importance of other non-profit agencies have radically shifted the patent yield from R and D expenditures. While on a large scale this influence may be comparatively recent, its roots go back to the establishment of land-grant colleges in 1870, and government financed agricultural research. There are undoubtedly additional factors which over the decades have altered the proportion of inventive activity that goes into inventions that are patented. And Schmookler's thesis has no basis if this is the case.

The second prerequisite if patents are to serve as a useful index of inventive activity is that input per average patentable invention be uniform. Here, again, the evidence tends to invalidate the assumption.

There is every reason to believe that the average input per patent has been markedly different for unassigned patents as compared with assigned patents. And since the proportion of assigned and unassigned patents has changed over time, the average input per patent has changed in all probability. Bearing on this, one of the facts on which information was sought in the Patent Utilization Study was the lapse of time from the moment when the invention was conceived to the moment when it was ready for patent application. The replies received show a very wide range. But the mean duration is about 9 months for inventors with assigned patents and over 20 months for inventors with unassigned patents. This disparity is corroborated by information of an entirely different nature reported by inventors of assigned and unassigned patents. The average number of patents held by inventors with unassigned patents in the sample was 9, for inventors with assigned patents this average number was 25.[27] These relationships could imply widely different inputs for patented inventions made by individual inventors in comparison to those made by employee inventors.

The National Science Foundation study of expenditures by industries for R and D shows wide differences in the amount spent in 1953 and 1954 in relation to the number of patents owned, or the number of patent applications filed. The range per patent application is from a low of about $11,000 for petroleum products and extraction to a

[27] See Sanders, "Patent Utilization."

high of about $24,000 for professional and scientific instruments. The variations would be still wider if we considered corporations by size as well. With respect to expenditures per patent owned the range is from about $3,000 for machinery to almost $8,000 for chemicals and allied products. Here, too, the range would widen if corporation size was taken into consideration. These findings suggest marked variation in inputs per patent for different industries. It would be reasonable to assume that such differences have prevailed all along, and since the industrial origin of patents has varied widely over the decades, it would seem unreasonable to assume that the input per average patent has remained constant.

The changes in the types of inventions and in the education and training of inventors over the last century would lead one to infer that the quality of patented inventions has changed progressively, and such changes are also associated with changing inputs per patented invention or patent application.

If the Schmookler thesis on patent statistics were correct, it would follow that the probability of obtaining a patentable invention with a specified input has not changed. However, if the total volume of inventive activity increases sharply, the probability of multiple inventions based on the same idea (interference) will increase and obsolescence of inventions aborning will also increase. It would follow, therefore, that as inventive input increases, other things being equal, the number of patented inventions per unit of input will tend to diminish.

The Patent Utilization Study shows a marked increase in the proportion of patents with two or more inventors. The mean time lapse for these patents with two or more inventors is not significantly shorter than that reported by single inventors. Therefore the increased proportion of patents with multiple inventors (see footnote 16) would imply an increase in the input per average patent.

These are only a few of the many factors that influence markedly the input-per-patent ratio and tend to nullify any fixed proportion between input and the number of patents. It seems futile to try to show gross relationships between input and patents, and patents and productivity without a penetrating study of the forces which have operated and are still operating on these variables. It requires sheer faith to maintain that a random sample of 1,000 patents in force in 1900 is equivalent to a similar sample of patents in force now in terms of inventive content, input, or any other factor of interest to social scientists. Moreover, without such comparability in units, it is difficult to see what significance to attach to the decline in the number of patent applications filed and the number of patents issued.

Another student of inventions who proposed to answer the question whether the number of patents might be used to measure inventiveness was Rupert Maclaurin.[28] A pertinent observation of his was:

> The problem of comparison is peculiarly difficult because the degree to which inventions are prolific at any given time depends in large measure on the state of the art in which the firm is working. For example, consider cases where there has been a major breakthrough in fundamental science, such as that which followed the work of Ampere, Von Helmholz, Maxwell, Faraday and others in laying the foundations of Electrical Revolution. Any firm operating on the crest of a technological revolution can be expected to produce a far larger number of new inventions than could be achieved by inventors of comparable intelligence working in an industry in which no such breakthrough had taken place.[29]

More specifically, on the question of whether patents measure invention, Maclaurin concluded:

> This brings us to the question that is often raised as to whether the number of patents issued represents an effective measure of the inventive record. *I believe that we have to answer this question negatively.* Some measure can be obtained from getting a complete record of the patents issued to a particular firm or in a particular industry, and some rather crude comparisons can be made between firms and between industries on this record. There are, however, a number of serious weaknesses in any analysis based on this kind of statistical evidence.[30]

[28] Rupert W. Maclaurin, "The Sequence from Invention to Innovation, with Emphasis on Capital Supply and the Entrepreneur," Conference on the Quantitative Description of Technological Change, 1951.

[29] *Ibid.*, pp. 1–2.
I am inclined to account for the growth curve pattern of inventions in a given line thus: When there is a breakthrough, such as the one to which Maclaurin referred, many inventors flock to the new area, there is a period of building up, and the number of patents starts to increase. However, in spite of the increased manpower and resources, new inventions begin to require larger and larger inputs in the field and a decline finally sets in. As time goes on this decline is compounded because the supply of new inventions is becoming exhausted and no new inventors and resources are brought in; in fact some abandon the field in favor of greener pastures. This brings the cycle to a close.

[30] *Ibid.*, p. 2. Emphasis added.

I fully subscribe to the above views as to the relationship between patents and inventions. The weaknesses that Maclaurin went on to discuss are:

1. The distinction between fundamental research and engineering art. This is essentially the question we raised regarding the constancy of the proportion of inventions patented.

2. The distinction between basic patents and improvement patents. This is analogous to our consideration of the question of homogeneity of patents in a more specific and restricted sense.

3. The historical changes in the methods by which industrial companies apply for patents. In this connection Maclaurin cited the following:

> For example, in the early days of the telephone industry, it was customary to pay inventors on the basis of the number of patents that they were granted during a year. This led to curious results. When some new problem demanded solution, a group of inventors in the company was brought together for a conference to discuss the broad objectives. They would then go off into their individual cells and produce as many possible answers to the problem as they could think of; in the final analysis, they would try to split up their inventions into a host of particular patents. This proved unsatisfactory for the company because such patents are much more difficult to sustain in the courts. The Telephone Company, preferring a general solution, abandoned its practice of giving inventors a premium for the number of patents taken out and changed its policy to offering bonuses for outstanding work.[31]

4. The different emphasis given to patents by companies equally interested in research. On this point his observation was as follows:

> For example, a company which is patent-minded and anxious to develop a licensing position is much more likely to spend substantial sums on patent development; and while, of course, it is not possible to produce patents out of thin air, the presence of an able group of attorneys in a concern who are constantly on the

---

[31] *Ibid.*, pp. 3–4.

alert for possible new inventions is much more likely to result in an "impressive" list of patents.[32]

Summary and Conclusions

In studies aiming to determine trends in inventing, an important prerequisite is a precise definition of what it is that one is trying to measure.

In view of the fact that, at least as of now, we know of no objective way to determine inventiveness directly it follows that our prospect of measuring it will have to depend on indirect methods. I have, therefore, examined and tried to appraise three different indirect approaches that have been employed to measure inventive activity.

Of the three approaches considered, the measurement of inventive activity by way of inventive input is perhaps the most direct and the most defensible logically. However, historically our available information regarding inputs is too incomplete and too inaccurate an index to be of much value at present. It is hoped that, with a sharper definition of what constitutes inventive activity and the extension and refinement of our information regarding inventive inputs, we may be able eventually to measure inventive activity from inputs with some degree of accuracy. But in all probability at no time can we hope to have a precise index of inventiveness or inventive activity.

The second approach, which also seems rational, at least in the abstract, is to measure inventiveness or inventive activity in terms of its outcome, technological advance. But the measurement of technological advance *per se* presents many practical problems. Therefore, it is difficult for me to see, for instance, how one can use the approach advocated by Hart to measure inventiveness. If the measurement of output proves a useful approach, it would seem to me it would have to be in terms of increased labor productivity as a result of inventiveness. But as we indicated, this would not be merely measuring inven-

[32] *Ibid.*, p. 4.

The importance of the emphasis which a company places on patents, and the influence of this on patent productivity of its employees was brought to my attention very forcefully recently. A friend of mine, who is an electronics engineer, worked for a large corporation for over ten years engaged in research work on atomic reactors. This particular company works exclusively on government contracts, and has had no interest in patents. In the ten or more years during which my friend worked for this company he had two disclosures, one of these in collaboration with a colleague. Less than two years ago he transferred to another company, doing similar work, also on a government contract; this other company was not restricted to government contracts and emphasized patents in all its departments. During the first year of his employment for this company my friend had six disclosures. This illustrates how deceptive input could be as an index of patents, since eventually a certain proportion of these disclosures may end as patents.

tiveness but also the speed of its adoption and the extent of its use. In other words, this would mean the abandonment of the conceptual purism of the rate of inventions *per se*, separate and distinct from innovation and the dissemination of its use (which some call imitation). But even in this restricted sense, our present-day measures of productivity are too crude and subject to too wide margins of errors to serve as a useful index of inventiveness.

Theoretically, it might be possible to reduce the margin of error in measuring inventiveness if the input and output approaches could be used simultaneously. It is believed that such a dual approach, if it could be evolved, would have compensatory factors in it so that errors would tend to offset one another; also inconsistencies between the input and output series might become apparent in cases where conflicting results were obtained.

The third method, that of using the number of patent applications or the number of patents issued as the index of inventive activity is least defensible, Its use by a number of students must be attributed to its ready availability. As I have tried to show there is no sound basis to assume that decade after decade the quality of patents has remained constant. Furthermore, there is no basis for assuming that inventive activity leading to patents has remained constant in relation to inventive activity in general, including that which gives rise to unpatentable inventions and those not patented for one reason or another.

In my opinion, none of the three approaches so far has demonstrated its effectiveness in measuring inventiveness or inventive activity. The conclusions arrived at by those who have followed more or less the approach which we have described as using inputs, though without too clear an appreciation of this fact, is that there has been an acceleration of inventiveness, though not in the sense in which Hart and his followers have claimed, i.e. following an exponential curve. Gilfillan does get a more or less straight line on a logarithmic grid, which would mean an exponential function, but the slopes of his graphs are decidedly more gentle than those described by Hart. As against these findings, if one considers the productivity of labor as the yardstick of inventiveness as distinct from inventive activity, the indication is that there has been no drastic change in trend, which has been on the whole upward but with a gentle slope of about 3 per cent per year. The preceding approaches all indicate increases though with markedly varying slopes. If one considers the number of patents as the criterion of increase or decrease in inventiveness, there has been a decline. Which of these four different courses comes nearest to describing the true rate and direction of change in inventions, including inventions that are patented, we cannot state with any degree of confidence. If I were to hazard a guess, I would be inclined to guess that inventiveness has increased perhaps paralleling roughly the increase in the productivity of labor as far as this country is concerned, though this would not be true for technologically backward countries. Inventive activity has increased more steeply in the United States than elsewhere though how steeply I would not attempt to define, since a considerable part of what is regarded as a measure of R and D is spurious rather than real.

Even though I question the utility of the patents count as an index of inventiveness, or inventive activity, I think that patents as verified inventive acts present a unique resource for study and understanding of the inventive process. A firsthand study of patented inventions should give the social scientist a unique opportunity to follow inventions and attempt to assess the social and economic impact that they have on our society. Study of patentees gives one an opportunity to study inventors, their characteristics, their method of work, influences which stimulate them and circumstances which tend to affect their productivity. It is somewhat surprising that, despite the lip service which many social scientists have given to the role of inventions and inventors in our lives, very little has been done by way of basic studies to understand the phenomenon of invention and the specific traits and characteristics of inventors. It would seem that for an understanding of inventive activity and its trends an intensive study of patents and inventors responsible for these patents should provide us with deeper insights for appraising changes in inventive trends. Yet when social scientists have become interested in patents, it has usually been in the readily available statistics of patent applications or patents issued; often the motive has been advocacy of changes in patent policies, on premises not always based on objectively verifiable facts.[33] In other words, the contribution of social scientists to our understanding of inventiveness has so far added much to the heat of argumentation and very little to the light of understanding. A firsthand study of patents ought to help us to reverse this imbalance.

[33] In his scholarly work: "An Economic Review of the Patent System," Fritz Machlup after seventy-nine pages comes to this realistic conclusion: "No economist, on the basis of present knowledge, could possibly state with certainty that the patent system, as it now operates, confers a net benefit or a net loss upon society." Study of the Subcommittee on Patents, Trademarks, and Copyrights of the Committee on the Judiciary, United States Senate, 85th Congress, 2nd Session, Committee Print, 1958, p. 79.

COMMENT

JACOB SCHMOOKLER, University of Minnesota

While it is not entirely clear just what Sanders means by invention, inventiveness, or inventive activity, in preferring direct measures of inventive input and output to patent statistics his logic is impeccable. No one will dispute that accurate measures of a thing are always better than an uncertain *index* of it. There is just one difficulty. While we have the uncertain index, we do not have accurate measures. What is more we cannot get them for years past which is the only period I have been concerned with. When such data as Sanders prefers are available, I shall be the first to abandon patent statistics in their favor. In the meantime, much as we might prefer caviar, we had better settle for plain bread when that is all we can get.

The question, therefore, is not whether to use statistics of aggregate patents granted or applied for, but how. Having discussed years ago[1] other shortcomings of patent statistics as well as many of those to which Sanders now calls our attention, I cannot but agree with many of the items on his bill of particulars, and I welcome some of the new ones he has added to the list. The most important point to be made about the biases in the patent data is that except during the years since 1940, which I shall discuss later, their influence on the aggregate was probably slow-moving and gradual. Thus, it is probably correct that the propensity to patent differs among different industries, different occupations, etc. Hence, the ratio of the number of patents applied for in one period to the corresponding number in a period long before has no necessary relation to the relative amounts of inventive activity (however defined) in the two periods. Moreover, the relative importance of different industries and occupations changes considerably *within* business cycles. This suggests that year-to-year fluctuations in, say, total patent applications would also be difficult to interpret. I have recommended against the use of the data for such periods.[2] On the other hand, and this is the important point, the relative importance of different industries and occupations does not change much from one business cycle to the next. Nor is the joint effect of other presumptive biases likely to be large from one business cycle to the next. Hence, it seems probable that a substantial difference between the

---

[1] Cf. my papers cited by Sanders.

[2] Cf. my "Patent Application Statistics as an Index of Inventive Activity," *Journal of the Patent Office Society*, August 1953, p. 550.

number of patents applied for in, say, one five-year period and those in the next five years ordinarily represents a difference in the same *direction* in the volume of inventive activity.

In short, as I stated many years ago, "statistics of patents applied for by Americans are a useful indicator of fluctuations in American inventive activity for the period 1869–1938, but . . . their utility as an index of secular *trend* cannot be assessed for want of suitable evidence.[3] Nothing Sanders points out invalidates this position, and this is all I have ever contended on behalf of the aggregate data. As indicated, however, I sympathize with his unwillingness to use the data as an index of long-term trends. Of course, as we learn more about the characteristics of the aggregate data and ascertain which of the potential biases have substance, we may also be able to estimate the extent of each bias. In that case we may be able to adjust the data and use them to measure the trend, and perhaps even annual fluctuations.

In the meantime, however, we should realize that the biases are probably so strong in the post 1940 period that use of the data even as an index of intermediate period fluctuations in inventive activity in the last two decades is risky. The protracted war depleted the personnel of the Patent Office, the patent bar, and related private services. The proportion of direct, usually unpatented, government invention rose considerably. Even more important, large firms, and perhaps others to a lesser extent, curtailed their use of the patent system for a number of more or less related reasons. Chief among these were (1) a vigorous antitrust policy initiated in the late 1930's under which tens of thousands of patents held by large firms were thrown open to compulsory licensing, (2) the development of judicial attitudes casting doubt on the very patentability of ideas produced in corporate research and development programs,[4] (3) the great growth of government-

---

[3] "The Level of Inventive Activity," *Review of Economics and Statistics*, May 1954, p. 184. Italics in original.

[4] The proportion of patents held invalid in infringement suits before U.S. Circuit Courts of Appeal ran to 70 per cent or higher from 1940 through 1957. Such a rate of invalidation is without parallel since 1891 when these courts were established. Prior to 1891 the Supreme Court heard appeals concerning patents. During the heyday of agrarian unrest and antitrust agitation in the 1880's and 1890's, the high court also invalidated the great bulk of the patents on whose validity they passed. Cf. H. R. Mayers, "The United States Patent System in Historical Perspective," *Patent, Trademark, and Copyright Journal*, Spring 1959, Appendixes A and B esp. In the earlier years, of course, independent inventors were overwhelmingly the source of inventions, and whatever the legal hazards, they usually had to have patents to make much from their inventions. Hence, the high invalidation rate in the late nineteenth century probably had far less effect on patenting than now when many corporate managers usually consider patents rather unimportant anyway.

financed corporate R and D, accompanied generally by a government lien on the resulting product which usually diminished the incentive to patent, (4) the prolonged delays at the Patent Office in processing applications, and (5) a growing belief among corporate managers that a headstart usually provides all the protection the innovator either needs or can hope for, so that patents seemed less valuable than before.[5] Presumably in consequence of those developments, while corporate R and D expenditures rose several-fold, patents taken out by firms increased by only one-fifth from 1940 to the mid-1950's.

Thus, after 1940 a number of factors diminish if they do not destroy the utility of the data as a reflection of inventive effort. Conceivably, however, certain segments of the data, e.g. patents by independents, may be used as an indication of those phases of inventive activity to which they relate; and further research may reveal bases for adjusting the balance.

The serviceability of the data for the pre-1940 period, however, is considerable, This is precisely the period for which data on R and D expenditures are poorest. More important, this period covers the development of the American economy from its "take-off" phase to "maturity". While the data suffer from real or presumptive biases of indeterminate magnitude, when used with care, skepticism, and imagination they can throw light on important aspects of economic growth which are unlikely to be illuminated by any other means.

Their utility for this period can perhaps be best understood by means of an analogy. Suppose that for the period 1870 to 1940 we had no national income data. Could we then draw useful inferences about the course of national income over that period from statistics on railroad ton-miles of freight carried? The answer is, of course we could—even though we know that the proportion of the nation's freight carried by rail changed over the period, and even though we know that a ton-mile of freight may represent either a ton of sand carried one mile or a pound of gold carried two thousand miles. The case of patent statistics is entirely analogous.

I shall take time to discuss only two specific points which Sanders raises. The first of these concerns his contention that a rising average level of education of inventors indicates that the quality of inventive input has risen. When we say one inventor is better than another, we

---

[5] These developments will be discussed in my forthcoming "A Critique of Patent Statistics and a Review of the Literature" to which Kuznets referred.

may mean that the inventions of the first are better than those of the second. And when we say that one invention is better than another, we mean either that one is economically more valuable than the other, or that it leads to more valuable later inventions than the other one does.

If this is what we mean, then it seems reasonable to assume that at any moment of time, the quality of inventive input in a given field varies, on the average, with the educational level of the inventors (although the degree of association between quality of product and education of the inventor would probably vary greatly among fields). This, I think, is the most we are entitled to affirm as plausible at this stage of our knowledge. For a very simple and compelling reason we cannot maintain that the well educated inventors in field X today represent an input of a higher quality than either (1) the modestly educated inventors of field X of yesterday, or (2) the modestly educated inventors of field Y today. The reason is that the state of knowledge in X today differs from that of X yesterday or Y today. Hence, the inventions in X today may be inferior to those in X yesterday or Y today. Since this is true, how can we say, merely on the basis of educational attainment, that the inventive input in X today represents a higher quality than that in X yesterday or Y today?

Quite the contrary—for if we judge quality of input by value of output there are grounds for conjecturing that the rising educational level of inventors signifies a declining rather than a rising quality of inventive input. The growing complexity of science and technology demand an ever-higher educational preparation of those who would advance them further. The rising educational qualifications of inventors and the increase in group research may fundamentally represent an accommodation to the demands of a more complex state of knowledge, but there is no reason to suppose that this accommodation has exceeded the requirements of the situation, and it may well have fallen behind them.

On the other hand, if we define the quality of inventive input simply in terms of the creative power of the men involved, e.g. as measured by some hypothetical psychological test, then I know of no evidence which indicates that the better educated inventors of today possess this capacity in greater measure than did the less well educated inventors of yesterday. Here, too, it is conceivable that the drift of quality in this sense has been down, not up.

My final comment concerns Sanders' comparisons between patents held or pending and corporate R and D expenditures. Sanders' statement that "the National Science Foundation Study found little, if any, association between the number of patent applications pending and the expenditures in 1953 and 1954 for R and D reported by different industries" is misleading. The NSF did not undertake to measure the association. In point of fact, the coefficient of correlation (r) between patents pending and R and D expenditures reported by the NSF is 0.83 for the six industries, with the three size classes of firms in each, for which data are provided.[6] Thus the correlation involves eighteen pairs. Since this coefficient means that 68 per cent of the variation in patents pending among the groups was associated with variation in 1953 R and D outlays, it indicates that Sanders' statement on the subject is highly erroneous.

The coefficient is higher than I would have expected for a number of reasons. In the first place, I would have imagined that the great disturbances in patenting behavior, with their uneven incidence among industries and firms of different sizes, would have impaired the association more. In the second place, the great majority of the patents pending in one year are for inventions made in earlier years. In view of the turbulent changes in corporate R and D activity which occurred during the Korean war, the normal association between patents pending and the R and D activity of a given year would be reduced. Finally, as indicated in my comments on Simon Kuznets' paper, a good deal of corporate R and D activity is not directly, or even indirectly in many cases, devoted to inventive activity as defined by Kuznets, i.e. to the production of patentable invention. However we wish to define inventive activity, it is expenditures on inventive activity in the Kuznetsian sense which one would expect to find associated closely with patents. Corporate R and D activity includes scientific research per se at one extreme and engineering development at the other. The production of patentable inventions begins toward the close of what the NSF calls applied research and terminates some time after the beginning of what it defines as development. The wide variations between industries and between firms of different sizes in the relative proportions of what the NSF defines as basic research, applied research, and develop-

---

[6] The original data appear in *Science and Engineering in American Industry: Final Report on a 1953–1954 Survey*, National Science Foundation 56–16, Washington, 1956, Tables A-34 and A-35.

The coefficient of rank correlation between these variables, Spearman's rho, is 0.80.

ment[7] and the existing uncertainty as to the precise location of pure inventive activity alone provide grounds for anticipating a less than perfect association between the output of patentable inventions and aggregate R and D expenditure.

In view of these considerations, a coefficient of correlation of .83 between the number of patents pending in 1953 and the 1953 R and D outlays of eighteen groups of firms suggests that it is quite reasonable to use the total number of patent applications as an indicator of fluctuations in inventive activity—especially for periods of intermediate duration in the years before 1940 when the correlation was in all probability higher.

COMMENT

S. COLUM GILFILLAN

All the economists at this conference seem to agree that an index of inventive output, i.e., successful invention, is much needed but impossible to obtain. Not knowing it was impossible I prepared one, together with subtotals for a dozen measures of inventive input, most of which go back to 1880, an unusually early date. For my measure of output I took the number of articles and books by Americans abstracted yearly in such indexes as *Chemical Abstracts* and *Engineering Index*, and for input, the number of engineers, chemists, and physicists in the principal societies and in training (lagged), and the professional grade staffs in organized R and D, combining them with suitable weights. As shown in chart 1, the curves, with one minor exception, are strikingly similar; steep and straight on the ratio scale. The combined inputs increased 226-fold in 1880–1955, but output 86-fold, suggesting the diminishing returns which Machlup and Kuznets expected. Patents to Americans went up but $2\frac{1}{2}$ times, showing that they are quite worthless for long-time measurement of invention, although they might perhaps be used for consideration of short-time peaks, with more caution than Schmookler has used. As for counts from lists of "important inventions", which Schmookler trusts less, they are still farther from true measures, registering virtually no

---

[7] Thus, in 1956 basic research varied from 1.7 per cent of total R and D expenditures in "other manufacturing industries" to 10.7 per cent in chemicals. Applied research varied from 8.0 per cent in the aircraft industry to 41.7 per cent in chemicals, and development varied from 90.0 per cent in the former to 47.6 per cent in the latter. *Science and Engineering in American Industry: Report on a 1956 Survey*, National Science Foundation 59–50, Washington, 1959, Appendix Table A-6.

CHART 1

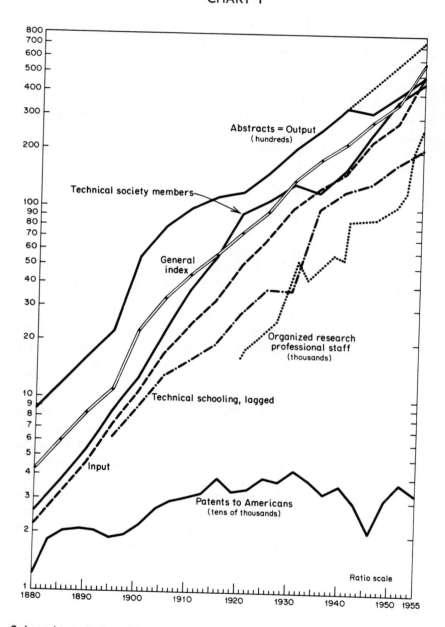

Subtotals and General Indexes on American Inventing and Invention-Oriented Research, 1880–1955

progress at all. To Sanders' objection that the abstracts are often duplicative, I would reply that this might be an advantage, meeting the demand others have expressed at this conference for a way to distinguish or properly weight the important as opposed to the trivial inventions, since the more important the more duplication of notices. My findings will be summarized in the summer issue of *Technology and Culture*, and published in full by the Senate Subcommittee on Patents, for whom I am writing a book on Invention and the Patent System.

COMMENT on Sanders and Kuznets

HERMAN I. LIEBLING, National Science Foundation

Inasmuch as references have been made by Barkev Sanders and Simon Kuznets to the National Science Foundation series on total national research and development expenditures, I should like to cover several points concerning these statistics. I will limit my comments to these particular aspects, leaving for another occasion the more general problems of measuring inputs and outputs of scientific endeavors, also considered in these two papers, and in which we are deeply engaged.

Referring to expenditure series on research and development as camouflage for unresolved difficulties in measuring inputs into inventive activity, Sanders appears to direct his fire at series preceding those of the Foundation, although it would seem that any such series logically comprises a target for his criticism. Thus, while he suggests as a limitation that "the National Science Foundation statistics on research and development do not go very far back," his underlying substantive complaint is that "they are patently incomplete since they do not attempt to include individual effort. . . ." This latter characteristic, of course, is a condition irrelevant to the period encompassed by the time series, and, indeed, his real concern is revealed by his criticism that the research and development expenditure series "does not take into consideration qualitative changes in capital and labor or shifts in the industries responsible for the expenditure reported."[1] Basically, then, his criticism is of a conceptual nature; on the one hand it refers

---

NOTE: The opinions expressed here are the views and conclusions of the author, and do not necessarily represent official views.

[1] It should be noted that shifts in industry research and development expenditures in fact are reported by various NSF industry reports covering the years 1953–57 (NSF 56–16, NSF 59–60, and NSF 60–59).

to the lack of homogeneity implicit in money measures of inputs, and on the other to the restriction of coverage to "corporate bodies and government."

These are fundamental conceptual criticisms of R and D money series, shared to some extent by Kuznets, and again discussed in connection with comments on the latter's paper. It may be noted now that expenditure measures which require surmounting a test of pure homogeneity in terms of quality of inputs would rule out from economic analysis not only measures of inputs into science but also, perhaps, nearly all measures of industry factors of production presently included in our widely utilized national income and expenditure figures. It does not seem necessary to defend these latter statistics; to the contrary, these expenditure series continue to be useful for a large variety of purposes, even in their "impure" state.

On statistical grounds, Sanders states that the estimates of the R and D monetary series "are subject to a wide margin of error," without distinguishing the several available series on these expenditures. Whatever deficiencies may characterize other R and D series, which Sanders states were constructed "retrospectively," the official NSF series from 1953–54 to 1959–60, widely publicized since its release in December 1959, was not so constructed. On the contrary, the NSF series represents the results of comprehensive fact-finding surveys undertaken in four separate sectors of the economy, including government, industry, colleges and universities, and nonprofit institutions. In contrast with other work in this field, the Foundation figures are distinctive in employing uniform concepts and definitions in the measurement of research and development expenditures in the sectors noted above, and have provided a substantial volume of integrated and detailed information on the breakdown of outlays by type of research, scientific field of effort, source of financing, etc., which satisfies widespread needs of private and public agencies and individuals. What Sanders states may have been applicable some years ago, but much has been done to remedy the situation in recent years.

Sanders states that the private industry sector data also are subject to a wide margin of error due to "many judgmental considerations" among different companies, although he does not give figures regarding the size of the error, as he does in the federal government sector. This is perhaps a safer course, but documentation of the extent of the error would have been desirable.

We in the Foundation would agree that the process of estimating research and development expenditures is fraught with difficulties; that many improvements in the technique will emerge as increased experience is gained with the surveys; and that revisions of estimates may become necessary, as they do in most statistical series of a complex nature. However, on the basis of our present experience with the surveys of industrial research and development, which have been conducted by at least two separate government agencies as well as by a private group, survey estimates of aggregate expenditures for overlap years have been satisfactorily close. Rather than giving cause for despair, the experience gained from the NSF surveys of industry R and D expenditures has been increasingly revealing of the nature and scope of scientific efforts; and substantial grounds exist indicating that the surveys will continue to yield usable results along these lines. Of course, modification and improvement of concepts and procedures—which are constantly under study—may require changes in the future. Conferences such as these will benefit our deliberations on these matters.

We would agree with Sanders that a need for deflators of research and development expenditures exists to correct for changing purchasing power of research budgets, so that we may tear off the "money veil" disguising the course of real inputs into research and development. We agree that such a deflator needs to take into account the specific elements in such budgets, not only the personnel and equipment costs that he mentions, but also the expendable materials and supplies and indirect costs as well. A special purpose index of costs is indeed required for deflation; no sensible economist to our knowledge has recommended using the consumer price index for this purpose, as Sanders states. Toward this objective, efforts by the National Science Foundation are well under way to make available a special purpose deflator for research and development outlays.[2]

Turning now to the comments of Professor Kuznets on the research and development expenditure series, we proceed with the benefits of the accumulated wisdom he has provided in the pioneering work on concepts and methodology underlying the national income and product statistics. No modern economist may consider himself fully trained without exposure to the conceptual fundamentals of income and wealth measurements in which Kuznets has played such an important role. In this tradition, we shall ask that he apply no more

---

[2] We are presently accelerating the work on deflation by enlisting under contract as a collection agency the forces of the U.S. Bureau of Labor Statistics.

difficult criteria of measurement to the research and development series than have been applied to the national income and product statistics.

Kuznets notes accurately that the R and D expenditures series excludes efforts of individual and independent inventors, whether full or part time. In explanation, we note that in the construction of any complex set of statistics, attention must be given to its operational requirements in obtaining a successful measure, often requiring the adoption of certain conventions. These problems confronted the national income statisticians, who were compelled to make certain exclusions and omissions on these grounds. Thus, in the well-known example of housewives, their services contribute substantially to individual and national welfare, yet because the market place is not a test of their services, no actual or imputed value is given to their services in estimates of the national income. It is by now perhaps a hoary joke that if one marries one's housekeeper, the national income declines by the amount of her wages.

Other areas of difficult statistical measurement are excluded. Thus, by the same token if the "do-it-yourself" trend is as large as reported, the substantial omissions resulting from values created by the man who models or remodels his basement, who undertakes to supervise the construction of his home, etc., are missing from the national accounts. To proceed to other well-known areas, the production of "radio sets has its counterpart in the hobbies of the radio amateur, commercial shaves are akin to self-administered ones and the educational services of teachers often are supplemented by those of parents."[3]

These matters are complicated by another distinction relating to the differentiation of work and play (of special relevance to individual inventors), which has been discussed at length in the substantial literature on national income theory in terms of inclusion as economic activity. Furthermore, part of this discussion refers to the restriction of the definition of economic activity to those things which require the use of scarce factors of production, according to which leisure-time and part-time invention or in fact any inventive activity for which no compensation is paid could be excluded.[4] To cut across these problems and establish some type of operational requirements, the official national income statistics use an operational definition of economic

[3] U.S. Department of Commerce, *National Income, A Supplement to the Survey of Current Business*, Washington, 1958, p. 30.
[4] Milton Gilbert and Irving B. Kravis, *An International Comparison of National Products and the Purchasing Power of Currencies*, Paris, 1954, p. 67.

production those activities "reflected in the sales and purchase trans-actions of the market economy."[5] The concept of research and development expenditures used by NSF generally conforms to this definition, and efforts are under way to integrate them further into the national accounts. The point raised by Kuznets troubles us, but we see no easy solution. We find some comfort in the fact that the exclusion of these individuals appears more important historically than at present.

There is still another point on which Kuznets applies somewhat more rigorous standards to the research and development series than he does to the national income methodology we have learned from him. He is troubled that inputs measured in money do not accurately portray the true amount and quality of changes in the volume of inventive manhours. Changes in real wages paid to employed inventors may not portray a trend because "of the inability of firms to distinguish between the fertile inventive mind and the educated hack"—a major deficiency of the R and D series, according to Kuznets. This raises an important point concerning the special objective of Kuznets and that of the NSF series. Before approaching it, however, it should be noted that Kuznets himself adds that the defect he notes "is inherent in the money measure of input of any factor that cannot be effectively appraised by the market in terms of its quality or productivity." We agree that measurement of the productivity of inputs of research and development is difficult, just as the productivity of any skilled input or of physical capital continues to be troublesome in economic analysis. Thus, is he not applying a more rigorous test to research and development than to other inputs?

Kuznets has defined the concept of inventive activity to conform to his special need, excluding in the process activities associated with inventive activity by his usage. One must agree that each analyst is free to choose his particular definition to suit his particular purpose. Thereby, he excludes a large part if not nearly all that is called basic research, because this usually results in discovery rather than in invention, which he distinguishes by the test of practicality or useful-ness. Development is also excluded because these activities concern application of the invention, not original invention.

As noted previously, Kuznets is entitled to use whatever definitions he finds useful. However, we believe (1) that relevant studies do not suggest that the type of personnel involved in the three phases of basic and applied research and development differ markedly, and (2) that

---

[5] *National Income*, p. 30.

the three markets for scientists and engineers are competitive. On the contrary, the studies of supply and demand for scientists and engineers indicate that we are dealing with a mobile labor force, large sections of which are responsive to various economic supply and demand forces which result in redeployment of available scientific personnel in these three fields. Indeed, Fritz Machlup has argued that too many of our scientists have shifted from basic to applied research and development.[6] Colleges and universities complain of the loss of scientific personnel to industrial activities in applied research and development and to military development work.

George B. Kistiakowsky, Science Advisor to President Eisenhower, recently noted that "many creative scientists have moved from the laboratory benches to the ranks of engineers. Fortunately, this has been a two-way flow. The engineers have undertaken to support basic scientific advances through the construction of great scientific instruments."[7] However, he does note also that the work, if not the personnel, of scientists is not the same as that of the engineer and that more basic scientific research is indispensable to technology.

Without going too deeply into the matter, it may be useful to indicate that the NSF series on R and D expenditures is designed to measure the scope of the scientific effort for government policy purposes. Against this perspective, we find useful measures which include components of basic and applied research and development.

Kuznets has written a challenging and stimulating paper. Not all the many issues he raises can be adequately discussed within the limited time available. There are a number of problems connected with his concepts of the measurement of inputs and outputs of scientific research in which we are interested and we believe that the publication resulting from the Conference proceedings will provide a vehicle for further studies.

[6] Fritz Machlup, "Can There Be Too Much Research?" *Science*, November 28, 1958, pp. 1320–1325.
[7] Excerpt from an address reproduced in *Science News Letter*, March 19, 1960, p. 187.

PART II
THEORY AND
MACRO-QUANTITATIVE ANALYSIS

The Economics of Research and Development

JORA R. MINASIAN

THE RAND CORPORATION

Introduction

THE PROBLEM AND THE SUMMARY OF RESULTS

THE contribution of productivity changes to economic growth has attracted much attention in recent years. Real income per capita in the United States roughly quadrupled from 1869–78 to 1944–53. Per capita inputs of labor and capital weighted by their relative contribution in the base period (the nineteen twenties) increased only by some 14 per cent.[1] This suggests that there has been a substantial increase in the net national product that can not be explained by the increases in inputs, conventionally measured.

The rate of growth in productivity has neither been uniform over time nor the same for different industries. For example, although none of the industries studied by Kendrick[2] experienced a decline in productivity over the long period from 1899 to 1953, there are several which show declines during subperiods. During approximately ten year subperiods the average annual rates of change in the productivity ratios of the thirty-three industries Kendrick studied range from (–4 per cent) to at least 9 per cent. The interindustry differences persist

NOTE: This paper is a reproduction, with minor omissions, of a Ph.D. dissertation, "The Economics of Research and Development," Department of Economics, University of Chicago, 1960.

This study was carried out while I was a member of the Econometrics Workshop at the University of Chicago, and was made possible by a grant from the Ford Foundation. I am indebted to many faculty members and students in the Department of Economics of the University of Chicago. I would like to single out for special thanks C. Christ, who directed my work, G. Stigler, M. Bailey, Y. Grunfeld, A. Harberger, and J. Rothenberg. I am grateful to L. Sjaasted for his valuable editorial help.

I would also like to thank my wife, Diane, who not only helped directly in the preparation of the dissertation but enabled me to remain in the University at an earlier stage of my career at her expense.

The author bears the full responsibility for all the shortcomings of this paper. Neither the persons nor the organizations mentioned above necessarily agree with any of the statements made.

[1] Moses Abramovitz, *Resource and Output Trends in the United States Since 1870*, Occasional Paper 52, New York, National Bureau of Economic Research, 1956.

[2] John W. Kendrick, *Productivity Trends: Capital and Labor*, Occasional Paper 53, New York, NBER, 1956.

for all subperiods. By comparison, the annual rate of change for the 1899–1953 period as a whole ranges from zero to 6 per cent.

Why do productivity changes differ among industries and over time? What are the factors leading to increased productivity?

This study advances the general hypothesis that *productivity increases are associated with investment in the improvement of technology and the greater the expenditures for research and development the greater the rate of growth of productivity.*

In principle, there are two ways of obtaining productivity increases: (1) economies of scale; and (2) either a change in the state of the arts and sciences—that is, improvement of the available technology—or utilization of better techniques which are already known. In the first category belong all the factors associated with change of scale and identified with movements *along* the cost curve. All possible factors that shift the production function (and thus the cost curve under constant prices and scale) fall in the second category.

We have empirical information which suggests that industrial organization (degree of competition) is correlated with growth in productivity.[3] This is an important explanatory variable. However, its main contribution is the light it sheds on the question of the industrial organization most favorable to innovation and economic progress. Although there is disagreement on that question, there is general agreement among economists that innovation by the entrepreneur achieves technological change and increases productivity.

Economies of scale, industrial organization, and quality of the labor force are relevant variables which can account for some of the unexplained increase in net national product. However it is usually agreed that the greater portion of this increase has resulted from technological changes causing a substantial increase in productivity.

One of the main variables singled out by quite a few economists has been research and development activity carried out by the firm. Research and development represents investment in knowledge which in turn affects the technology which improves productivity. However our only knowledge of this process consists of vague theoretical postulates and hypotheses which have not been subjected to empirical tests, which is why this study came about.

In trying to fill this gap in our knowledge, I have undertaken an empirical analysis of the relationship between productivity increase

---

[3] George J. Stigler, "Industrial Organization and Economic Progress," Paper read at 25th Anniversary of the Social Science Research Building, University of Chicago.

and research and development expenditures, and tested some alternative hypotheses. This is a cross-section study on the firm level. Eighteen firms in the chemical and allied products industry and five firms in the drug and pharmaceutical industry constitute the sample. The observed value of each variable for the cross-section study is based on the period 1947–57 because of lack of earlier data for most firms.

We can conclude from this study that, beyond a reasonable doubt, causality runs from research and development to productivity, and finally to profitability. With the possible exception of differential monopoly power (the test of its influence was not conclusive) no other factor tested was able to compete effectively with, or even to complement substantially, the relationships found between the above variables.

In the remainder of this section some conceptual problems are discussed. Next, we define our hypothesis and proceed to a discussion of our variables, measurements thereof, and sampling considerations. Finally, we test our main hypothesis, and consider alternative hypotheses of profitability, investment, economies of scale, and monopoly pricing. We also test for returns to research and development expenditures.

SOME CONCEPTUAL PROBLEMS

In principle we would like to have firms identical in all respects except the independent variables under consideration. The fewer and the weaker the influential variables which are not taken into account explicitly, the more reliable the results. The firms constituting our sample are not homogeneous with respect to scale or to diversification of production. I will consider a few broad conceptual difficulties at this point and introduce more specific ones as we progress.

Crossing Industry Boundaries

One of the reasons we must be cautious in generalizing the results of this study is our lack of knowledge about the cost of innovation. Does it cost the same amount to achieve an innovation which will result in a given percentage increase in productivity, regardless of the nature of production or the industry? Since we do not know the facts, I have analyzed firms in the two industries separately.

The external effects on the industry may not fall uniformly on all firms in the industry since the output mixes of the firms are different.

To the extent that this happens, external effects will influence the results. Due to the difficulty of designing a meaningful test for differential external effects, we have not allowed for this influence; this must be borne in mind when interpreting the results.

Scale

Scale has three different connotations in this study: (1) scale signifying economies of scale in production, (2) scale signifying economies of scale to research and development, and (3) scale in terms of correlation where both dependent and independent variables are positively correlated with scale.

1. I have already mentioned the case of economies of scale and have recognized it to be a possibly important variable.

2. If we admit the possibility that the research and development expenditure required to reduce average cost by X per cent is independent of output, then the returns from research and development to the industry will increase with industry output. However, for the firm, returns to research and development will not increase as its relative share of industry output increases, if it can monopolize the information and sell it on a perfect market.

3. Scale in the third role is analogous to the trend in time series data. It can be handled either by including a scale variable (when using *absolute* research and development expenditures) in the function, or by deflating research and development by a suitable size variable.

The scale of operation is not only a simple question of size; it is also positively correlated with the number of products produced. That is to say, firms are diversified to different extents. Therefore, in most cases scale also represents diversification, to the discussion of which we now turn.

Diversification

The varying degree of diversification among firms raises two important problems. The first concerns the construction of index numbers. I will deal with this and other index number problems later. However, it should be noted in passing that the greater the degree of diversification the more appropriate become Bureau of Labor Statistics indexes of wholesale prices and wage rates. The second problem is whether there are research and development economies resulting from diversification of output. There is a strong belief that a dollar spent on research and development yields a higher return, the greater the degree of diversification of output. One may think of four reasons for such a belief:

1. Unanticipated findings will be more readily recognized and therefore utilized. This proposition sounds plausible but there is no way to test it. However, one would expect random findings of the nature postulated to be a small portion of all findings and, also, the more diversified firms will probably have more independent projects with less effective communication among researchers. However, if diversification of research and development increases with diversification of output, and specialization of researchers goes up with output, the larger firms may have the advantages associated with specialization of function.

2. A particular finding may require a specialized test which may not be available to a less diversified concern. The lack of specialized services within the firm might be a deterrent but obviously not a completely effective one, in view of the rise of independent industrial laboratories during recent decades, which will supply these services at a price.

3. The finding may not be in line with the concern's existing activities, hence it may not be used. If the finding is worthwhile, there are two alternatives available to the firm. One is to produce the product or utilize the new process in its own production. The other is to sell or rent the finding. The firm is equally happy with both choices if it can patent its finding and sell it in a perfect market.

4. Knowledge created may be used in the production of more than one product. This requires a note of clarification about the ambiguities involved in the term diversification. There are two kinds of diversification which are fundamentally different for the purposes of this study: diversification in kinds of products among which knowledge of production is transferable; and that in which it is not transferable. When we speak of economies of diversification, we should mean diversification of the transferable kind. Then, it is not at all clear which way the economies of diversification run. If diversification is taken to be the consequence of past research, then the economies of diversification are nothing but the result of the knowledge thus accumulated, a simple case of return to past research and development expenditures. However, if one chooses the second definition of diversification, it is not

clear to the writer why and how economies of diversification will come into the picture.[4, 5]

These propositions will not be tested directly. The above discussion indicates the difficulty of finding a variable which can be used in testing them. However, if scale of operation is positively correlated with diversification, a test for scale will be a partial test of the diversification hypotheses.

The Hypothesis

The production function of a firm summarizes the technological conditions under which the firm operates and shows the maximum quantity of output that can be produced with given quantities of each of the factors of production that are used. Ordinarily, output, X, is related to inputs of labor, L, and capital, K, in a production function of the form

$$X = f(L, K) \tag{1}$$

which is often assumed to be homogeneous of the first degree. All variables are measured as dollar magnitudes deflated by price indexes. The derivation of such a function is especially complicated when the economy is characterized as progressive over time. The difficulties that arise may be classified in two categories:

1. The inputs, even adjusted to a constant dollar basis, are not homogeneous over time because of quality changes in labor and capital.

2. Given the quantities of inputs, free of the problem in 1 above, varying quantities of output can be produced depending on the knowledge of the arts and sciences available and used in the process of production—that is, the existing technology utilized. However, technological change may alter the desired quality of inputs as well as the combination of inputs and the scale of operation.

One can use more relevant indexes in dealing with the first problem, although we are still short of correct indexes. On the second problem,

---

[4] Here I am abstracting from the case in which the product whose price is lower now, because of greater productivity, may be used in the production of other products thus lowering the prices of the latter and increasing their sale. Growth in the output of these other products may give rise to economies of scale.

[5] Diversification of the second kind creates a measurement problem. If the proportion of research and development funds allocated to each product differs from the proportion of other inputs, then an average research and development measure may not accurately describe the intensity of the research and development activity.

neither the theory nor the empirical knowledge is rich. The problem of measurement aside, the production function is characterized by under-specification of inputs, i.e. the impact of technological changes is not explicitly incorporated in the process of estimation. Thus the conventional approach, i.e. using equation 1 with no explicit allowance for changes in technology, tends to correlate the output with wrongly identified inputs. This can cause biased estimates of coefficients of the specified variables, namely, labor and capital.

The conventional production function ought to be rewritten. In general, we may express the production function as

$$X_t = f(L_t, K_t, P_t) \tag{2}$$

where X_t, L_t, K_t, and P_t represent output, labor, capital, and productivity (a parameter shifting the production function), respectively, at time, t. Furthermore, if we assume the case of neutral change in technology, we can rewrite 2 as

$$X_t = P_t f(L_t, K_t) \tag{3}$$

Ample attention has been focussed on the role of the entrepreneur in allocating resources under competitive and stationary conditions in economic literature. However, in a changing economy another important task should be assumed, namely, the investment in knowledge to obtain improved or new technology. Thus, in a changing economy the great economic force of innovation arises from a decision variable of the firm. It is an economic decision, so we are interested in knowing its costs and returns. Its costs may be thought of as expenditures on research and development; its returns as some part of the increased output unexplained by the conventional production function. The role of technology is to change the parameters of the conventional production function, and expenditures on research and development may be viewed as the cost of making such changes. Our equation 3 expresses this process in a manner that enables us to approximate these changes with a single variable.

In equilibrium, the marginal return *ex ante* on a dollar spent on labor, capital, or research and development should be the same. But the only data we have in this study are the annual expenditures on research and development and indexes of productivity (obtained using equation 3). We can do no more than estimate the gross effect of the one on the other. We cannot identify any particular development project with any subsequent growth in productivity. Nor even can we say which particular experiments were successful and which were not. Nevertheless, we know that a firm, under the dictates of rational behavior, will seek to maximize the present value of its expected return. Therefore, under a changing economy the firm will invest in research and development in order to create new products and processes and to improve the old products so that it may compete better in the market, stay in business and reap a monopoly profit, or both.

An interesting implication is that the research and development program of a firm reflects the effort or costs of the firm in the direction of obtaining efficiency. Logically, therefore, one would expect that a change in the productivity of the firm would be somehow related to its research and development activities. Consequently, we propose the general hypothesis: *The greater the research and development expenditures, measured in several ways to be described below, the greater is the subsequent rate of growth in the productivity of a firm.*

For the reasons outlined, research and development expenditures will be viewed as a variable shifting the production function over time. It is not clear how this variable should be measured in a sample where firms are neither equally diversified in kind and number of products produced, nor equal in scale of operation. These differences create great difficulties in determining an appropriate measure of research and development. If, in fact, research and development has the postulated effects, the measure thereof must have the power of discriminating among firms with respect to differences in productivity, without reflecting other influences which may be hidden in the statistic.

One has to ask whether the cost of a given percentage increase in productivity is the same for different products and different scales of output. If it is, then, given demand conditions, the return to research and development expenditure is higher the larger the total value of the product.[6] Furthermore, as stated in the introduction, the problem of diversification enters into the picture. I have not tested for the effect of diversification for lack of a meaningful measure of that variable. In this study research and development measures are deflated by two alternative size-of-firm variables to standardize the firms for the effect of scale. The scale measures utilized are (1) a weighted average of real labor and capital inputs, the weights being determined by Euler's theorem (discussed below); and (2) the real gross stock of plant and equipment.

[6] This assumes the technology can be monopolized by the developing firm.

I have chosen these scale variables because research and development expenditure is expected to shift the production function and, therefore, its ratio to inputs going directly into the production function is important.[7] Alternatively, looking at research and development as an input of production, one can see the ratio as an analytical measure to be interpreted by the law of variable proportions. It should be noted that the above measures do correct for the diversification effect if scale is a positive function of diversification (with perfect correlation). But they do not correct for differences in the cost of the given technology if there are differential innovation costs depending on the type and kind of product.

Finally, it is certain that the effect of research and development takes place with a lag. In fact research and development is a good example of a distributed lag. In the study of cross-sectional differences among firms with respect to the rate of change in productivity, we are interested in finding a measure of research and development which reflects the intensity of this activity. Because of the short period for which data are available and other data deficiencies (discussed in detail further on), I have chosen two simple measures of research and development activity for each firm. One measure is an average of recent research and development expenditures divided by a weighted average of recent inputs of labor and capital. The other is the same numerator divided by an average of recent figures for real gross plant and equipment. More specifically the following estimation methods were used:

$$R_i = \frac{\sum\limits_{t=47}^{56} (R.D.)_t}{\sum\limits_{t=47}^{56} (L^a K^{1-a})_t} \tag{4}$$

$$R_k = \frac{\sum\limits_{t=47}^{56} (R.D.)_t}{\sum\limits_{t=47}^{56} K_t} \tag{5}$$

[7] Renting or purchasing new technologies will also shift the production function. Royalties paid by the firm indicate the extent of this influence and will be tested in the section dealing with empirical results.

where R.D., L, and K, represent real research and development expenditure, labor, and the real gross stock of plant and equipment, respectively.

Two comments on these measures are appropriate. First, if the time-shape or the lag of research and development has not changed, measures 4 and 5 are fairly good estimates of what we want since a relatively long span of time is used. On the other hand, if the time shape has changed, then clearly a distributed lag is far superior to these measures. Second, these measures will not distinguish between opposing tendencies if research and development expenditures increase over time and then decrease over time, so that the average for the period remains the same. However, both R_i and R_k are positively correlated with time for all firms in this period.

Equations 4 and 5 will define the intensity of research and development activity for the firms and one of them will constitute an important independent variable in our analysis.

The dependent variable in this study is the rate of growth of productivity. This choice introduces a few methodological advantages. First of all, one of the most troublesome questions, that of labor quality, has been defined away. This problem arises because of our inability to take into account the increase in the value of the labor hour over time which is assumed to result from rising standards of education and health. It does not bother us since we are interested in explaining the differences in the rate of growth in productivity among firms in the same industry. There is no reason to believe that the consequences of the increased quality of the labor force will differ among industry members. Thus whatever the effect of this change may be, it is expected to be uniform for all the firms. Second, this measure depends on the experience of a firm over the period and not at a particular point in time; thus the role of fortuitous and random elements is minimized.

The rate of growth in productivity for each firm will be estimated by the following method.

Assume a production function homogeneous of the first degree in labor and capital and the case of neutral change in technology over time. Furthermore, assume this function to be of the Cobb-Douglas form. Thus we have

$$X_t = P_t L_t^a K_t^{1-a} \tag{6}$$

where X_t, P_t, L_t, and K_t represent value added (or output), productivity, labor, and capital, respectively, in time, t. Therefore,

$$P_t = \frac{X_t}{L_t^a K_t^{1-a}} \tag{7}$$

The change in productivity between two periods can be obtained by

$$\frac{P_t}{P_{t-1}} = \frac{X_t \, L_{t-1}^a \, K_{t-1}^{1-a}}{X_{t-1} \, L_t^a \, K_t^{1-a}} \tag{8}$$

The rate of growth in productivity for an individual firm will be estimated by regressing $\log_e \dfrac{P_t}{P_o}$ on time. That is:

$$\frac{P_t}{P_o} = C \, e^{rt} \tag{9}$$

where r is the slope of the regression line and the rate of growth of productivity. P_o is the value of P at the beginning of the period.

We can compute a by using Euler's theorem which states that if the production function is homogeneous of the first degree and the factors of production are paid their marginal products, the total payments will exhaust the product. Thus from value added, a will be obtained by the share of labor:[8]

$$a = \frac{\text{Wage bill}}{\text{wage bill + profits before taxes (adjusted by other income or expense not related to production, i.e., dividends received or paid) + interest paid + depreciation.}} \tag{10}$$

This assumes that the firms are in equilibrium every year. Of course, this may not be true. However, a is taken as the average for the sample

---

[8] This formulation assumes that taxes on profits are paid by the owner(s) of the firm, so the contribution of capital to production is gross of taxes. An alternative formulation may be to assume that benefits derived from taxes are shared by labor and capital according to their relative shares of input. On this view point, the weights may be determined by using value added net of taxes in the denominator of equation (10), and then using value added gross of taxes in the numerator of equation (6). We will test the research and development hypothesis using rate of growth in productivity and the weights obtained by both formulations. We will find that the results of the study do not depend on the choice of the formulation.

period. For the firms observed, there is no systematic tendency or trend in the annual values of *a* over the period.[9]

We will obtain the rate of growth in productivity for each firm from 9 and correlate these rates cross-sectionally with the measures of research and development obtained from 4 and 5 above. In the next section the sample, the data, and the measurements of the variables will be discussed.

The Sample, the Nature of Data, and the Estimation of Variables

THE SAMPLE

Ultimately we will concern ourselves with interpreting our results and deriving statistical inferences. Therefore it is important to know the process by which the sample was obtained.

It is to be mentioned that the general and the main hypothesis was formed before data became available. The first survey of company annual reports revealed that the greatest likelihood of success in finding research and development data was with chemical and pharmaceutical firms. Realizing the dangers of crossing industry lines, I concentrated on firms classified within these two industries.

Moody's Industrial Manual was consulted. For none of the firms investigated were research and development expenditures shown. A second item which seemed equally difficult to obtain was wage and salary expenditures. To reduce the data problem, a sample of 85 firms was chosen for investigation on the basis of the completeness of the accounting information published in *Moody's*. Out of 85 firms contacted by letter, 19 supplied all the data requested, 6 supplied all but research and development expenditures, 13 all but research and development and wage and salary expenditures, 7 supplied all data but for a shorter period of time than 1947–57, 12 supplied all but wages and salaries, and 28 did not reply.

The method of choosing the 85 firms and the pattern of response make our sample strictly a nonrandom one. Instead of hypothesizing inconclusively about the motives or conditions which generated this sample, I would like to emphasize that the results of this study should be interpreted strictly as applicable to the sample.

---

[9] The assumption of constant returns to scale is made as a way out of measurement problems rather than as an economic principle. This assumption will be tested in the section on empirical results.

THE DATA

As we are interested in some physical measure of productivity, we need to eliminate price changes. We want to obtain real magnitudes of output, value added, labor, capital, and research and development expenditures and to use them in the manner described in equations 4, 5, and 9 above. The dollar values of these variables are deflated as described below.

Real Output and Real Value Added

Sales adjusted by the changes in the beginning and ending inventories of finished products equals output. We use the denominator of equation 10 as an approximation of value added. A better estimate could have been obtained if data on raw materials consumed had been available.

A growth measure using value added reflects the contribution of labor and capital better than one using gross output (including materials' value) because raw materials may not have remained a constant proportion of the output over time. Also, to the extent that firms purchase semifinished goods to be processed and sold, i.e., vertical integration, the gross output figures distort the picture. The proportion of output which comprises this type of good, its behavior over time, its magnitude among firms, and the extent of processing may differ and thus output may not reflect the true contribution of labor and capital inputs. However, value added will be immune to these variations.

The general problems of index number construction are well known and need not be mentioned here. However, two specific aspects of the subject should be dealt with since their importance is magnified in this study. In the first place we are studying the production function of the firms, so we need prices at the manufacturers' level. Second, since the study is carried out on the firm level, our choice of a price index should be such that a set of varying weights assigned to different products will approximately reflect the product mix produced by the firms.[10]

The first criterion above necessitates the use of a wholesale price index. Therefore, the BLS wholesale price indexes of the chemical

---

[10] New products must be entered into the product mix, but choice of the relevant price creates a problem. As the product becomes well known the price may rise because of increased demand, but if monopoly power over a new product falls over time, the price will fall. These problems will be discussed in more detail subsequently.

industry broken into subcategories were investigated. As there are substantial differences in the pattern of change in the wholesale price indexes of these subcategories, it was imperative to match the output mix of the companies with the appropriate subclass price indexes.

Data on the output mix of the firms by broad categories of products were available only for 1954–57. Except for five pharmaceutical firms, the relative output weights were determined on this basis and price indexes computed for each firm. Both output and value added figures were then deflated by these price indexes, since no information on materials consumed and the prices thereof was available to be used in the construction of value added price indexes.

The drug and pharmaceutical wholesale price index used was derived from two BLS wholesale price indexes: one for drugs, pharmaceuticals, and cosmetics and one for cosmetics alone. The weights used by the BLS in combining drugs and pharmaceuticals with cosmetics were 3/4 and 1/4, respectively, in both 1953 and 1957. Using the following relation, the price index for drugs and pharmaceuticals was derived:

Price index of drugs and pharmaceuticals, and cosmetics = 3/4 (price index of drugs and pharmaceuticals) + 1/4 (price index of cosmetics)

then,

Price index of drugs and pharmaceuticals = 4/3 (price index of drugs, pharmaceuticals, and cosmetics) − 1/4 (price index of cosmetics).

This wholesale price index was used to deflate both the output and the value added of the pharmaceutical firms.

Labor

Total wages, salaries, and other employee compensations such as vacation time, sick leave, insurance, retirement funds, etc., are taken as the contribution of labor to production. We would have liked to exclude that part of the wage bill which is attributable to research and development activity; however, this breakdown was not available. This is not important as research and development expenditures are only from 1 to 6 per cent of total wage payments. In equation 9 labor is weighted at roughly 60 per cent of total inputs. Aproximately 70 per cent of the total research and development expenditures are wages and salaries and the rest, materials costs and depreciation on laboratories. Thus the relative effect of being unable to exclude research and development wages and salaries is very small.

The firm's wage rate was obtained by weighting the BLS index of the average hourly earnings of subclasses in the total chemical, drug, and pharmaceutical industries by the same weights used in construction of the price indexes. The total wage bill is deflated by these wage rate indexes.

Although this deflation does not correct for changes in the productivity of the labor force over time, it will correct for differences existing at a point of time, if the relative wage rates represent the relative service inputs.

Plant and Equipment

We need service flows of capital for our production function but these data are not available. One may think of three alternative measures of service flow of capital: (1) depreciation, (2) stock of capital net of depreciation, and (3) gross stock of capital. Measures 1 and 2 are clearly affected by tax rules and, above all, are the result of an accounting method which is, or may be, completely arbitrary. This criticism does not apply to measure 3. However, there are a number of other difficulties associated with this concept. First, if the durability of plant and equipment changes over time, the service flow of gross capital stock will vary with time, since for a given per-annum service flow the price of the capital good should be a positive function of durability, *ceteris paribus*. Second, the per-annum service flow of a given stock of capital will vary depending on how intensively the capital is used. Since the period of our study is relatively short (1947–57), we can realistically assume that changes in durability are minor. I have no conclusive evidence on the second problem.

I will assume that there is a constant relationship between service flows and the stock of capital. More specifically, my choice assumes that changes in the durability of plant and equipment, the interest rate,[11] and the hours "worked" by the capital per week did not affect the relationship during so short a period as 1947–57.

I have chosen gross plant and equipment as a measure of capital for two reasons. (1) Gross stock was chosen under the assumption that as long as the capital was not retired the service flow was maintained via repairs and maintenance. It is felt that the error involved in this

---

[11] The interest rate is relevant to the extent that changes in it, while leaving the flow unaltered, will alter my measure of the *stock* of capital, which is in value terms. While flows only are relevant to my problem, we measure those flows by the value of the stock, hence we must worry about the interest rate.

procedure is much less than that likely to occur in trying to correct the service flow by some arbitrary percentage representing presumably lesser productivity due to obsolescence, breakdowns, etc. (2) Choice of plant and equipment instead of a concept inclusive of land, minerals, and other current assets, i.e. inventories, cash, etc., is based on the possibility that some firms hold such properties for long-run considerations which are not necessarily relevant to current production.[12] In summary, then, the gross plant and equipment at the year end will represent the capital entering into the production function in that year. The method of construction of this variable is given below.

Data on gross plant and equipment at the beginning of the year, gross investment, and gross retirement, broken down by categories and types, are given in the Annual Reports—Form 10-K, submitted to the Securities and Exchange Commission by publicly owned firms. These reports date back to 1934 when the Securities Exchange Act was passed. In order to construct a continuous series, we need an estimate of the stock of capital in 1934.

We have estimates of gross plant and equipment, in money terms, for January 1, 1934. The gross national product implicit deflators for new construction and durable equipment change but little during 1919–29, with the exception of one or two years. Therefore, the 1929 indexes are not bad indexes for the preceding decade. I have deflated gross plant and equipment at the beginning of 1934 by the 1929 price indexes for new construction and durable equipment, respectively.[13] Each year's gross additions to plant and equipment have been deflated by the price index of that year and added successively to the stock of real plant and equipment of the initial year. It has been assumed that generally the retired capital was the oldest. Therefore, the 1929 GNP implicit deflators were used to deflate the retirements of the years 1934–46. Retirements of 1947–57 were assumed to have been purchased during 1940–47. So each of the two price indexes of this latter period were weighted by the relevant gross private domestic

---

[12] It may, however, be argued that total gross capital is the more relevant concept, since (1) total resources available determine productivity in a given year, and (2) long-run considerations are important because we are interested in the rate of growth in productivity. It will be found later that the results of the study do not depend on the particular choice of a capital concept.

[13] Changes in book values of fixed assets of a few firms for which data were available for 1929–33 were investigated. Four firms had positive changes ranging approximately from 4 to 10 per cent and three firms negative changes of 5 to 20 per cent of fixed assets in 1934. Most of the positive change took place in 1930.

investments for 1940–47 to obtain an average deflator. This weighted average deflator was then used to deflate retirements of 1947–57.[14]

So long as the GNP implicit price deflator reflects the technological changes in capital, that is, the quality changes, we have corrected for the changes in the efficiency of capital. But to the extent that it does not reflect these changes over time and quality has improved, our capital stock is under estimated in recent years. The effect of this is especially important if the capital of different firms has undergone different rates of technological improvement over time and/or the magnitude of capital investment has varied among firms.

Research and Development Expenditures

Research and development expenditures are deflated by the GNP implicit price deflator and used in the manner described by equations 4 and 5. In addition to deflation, there are other problems associated with this variable. Ideally, we would like it to measure the expenses incurred for activities which do not enter the production function directly and do not represent advertising or promotional activities. There are four possible sources of difficulties with this variable: (1) true expenditures may be distorted for publicity purposes; (2) the tax rule may influence the accounting procedures used; (3) the definition of research and development activity may not be the same for all the firms; (4) some research and development may be government financed.

1. I agreed not to identify the firms in the study in order to persuade them to supply the data. It is therefore difficult, considering the number that did not respond, to rationalize the first proposition. Given that the costs of reporting are almost zero, one might expect firms to reveal the data and to compete with each other in inflating the figures, if it were true that this type of advertising is profitable.

2. The effect of tax rules can be a real one. Clearly, if treatment of these expenditures for corporate tax purposes has changed over time, the behavior of this item over time will be affected. If this is the only source of error, the ranking of the firms does not necessarily change with respect to measures defined by equations 4 and 5. However, we

---

[14] The deflation of retirements is a poor approximation. However, its effect is not significant, since (1) none of the firms retired more capital during 1934–46 than they held in 1933, and (2) retirements during 1947–57 amounted to 5 to 15 per cent of gross investments during this period. There were few mergers. Only one of them amounted to more than 3 per cent of the plant and equipment of the firm in the year of merger. In this case the plant and equipment of the new firm was measured as described in the text. In the rest of the cases, the price paid for the capital was deflated by that year's price indexes.

would expect some "padding" of research and development expenditures if they were fully deductible, and the incidence of this padding might not be the same for all firms. As a matter of fact, since 1954 all research and development other than laboratory and equipment investments have been fully deductible.

3. It is frequently thought that the definition of research and development is not the same among firms. In three interviews, controllers, after consulting their data sheets, told me that the most liberal definition of research and development expenditures would inflate their figures from 10 to 20 per cent.

Let us take 20 per cent as the maximum error of measurement in research and development expenditures. The range over all eighteen chemical firms of the research and development measure R_i defined by equation 4 is from 1 per cent to 11 per cent. However, for most firms it is between 2 and 8 per cent. Let us use 5 per cent to illustrate our point. This means that if the numerator of equation 4 is inflated by 10 per cent, the measure itself will be inflated to 5.5 per cent. If we take 20 per cent as the maximum inflation figure, we increase our measure by one percentage point. Table 1 shows the frequency distribution of firms with respect to the measure of 4.

TABLE 1

FREQUENCY DISTRIBUTION OF FIRMS, BY RESEARCH AND DEVELOPMENT
EXPENDITURES DEFLATED BY AVERAGE TOTAL WEIGHTED INPUTS
OF LABOR AND CAPITAL, CHEMICAL FIRMS

| | *Percentage Interval* | | | | | | | | | | |
	1–2	2–3	3–4	4–5	5–6	6–7	7–8	8–9	9–10	10–11	Total
Number of firms	1	1	4	4	2	2	2	0	1	1	18

A scatter diagram with the rate of growth in productivity on the vertical axis and the measure of research and development on the horizontal axis was investigated. The points lie around a positively sloped line. Even a 20 per cent error, which will affect the adjacent cells of the frequency table above, will not alter the positive character of the relationship. However, there is no way to tell whether the degree of correlation will increase or decrease.

4. Few firms that supplied research and development expenditures in their annual reports specified that government sponsored research and development were excluded. The firms that supplied this informa-

tion upon request were asked to give only the concern's expenditures on research and development but it is not certain that they did so. It can be seen from National Science Foundation surveys[15] that the government finances only about 8 per cent of the total research and development in the chemical industry. Furthermore, if we assume realistically that relatively large firms are the recipients of government contracts, we can be reasonably sure that although this source of discrepancy increases the variation in the measures of research and development it does not give rise to any spurious correlation since, as will be seen, the correlations between size and the research and development measures are not strong.

In conclusion, then, although errors of measurements may exist, it is unlikely that they have an appreciable influence on the results.

The Empirical Results

TEST OF THE HYPOTHESIS

HENCEFORTH, the rate of growth of productivity will be denoted by $\dot{P}$. As indicated earlier, the basic data from which the rate of growth in productivity is obtained for each firm is the time series measure of its productivity. For the chemical industry these time series are available from 1947 to 1957 for thirteen firms, from 1948 to 1957 for four firms, and from 1949 to 1957 for one firm. $\dot{P}$ was obtained by using output and, alternatively, value added in equation 9 with P_o being the value of P in the earliest year of the series, either 1947 or 1948 or 1949. Chart 1 shows the behavior of the measures of productivity of the eighteen chemical firms over the years 1947–57. Chart 2 summarizes the same information for five drug and pharmaceutical concerns for 1947–57.

The boxes at the bottom of Charts 1 and 2 supply us with information about the pattern of change in the productivity measures. The great majority of firms had an increase in productivity during 1947–50, 1952–53, and 1954–55, and a general decline during 1953–54. Approximately 50 per cent of the firms had increases and the rest, decreases in their productivity during the remainder of the period. These patterns of change do not coincide exactly with business cycle years.

These patterns of change raise grave problems in choosing a period for obtaining rates of growth of the productivity of the firms. As we

[15] *Science and Engineering in American Industry, Final Report on a 1953–1954 Survey,* National Science Foundation 56–16, 1956.

CHART 1

Indexes of Productivity Measures, Using Output, Solid Lines, and Value Added, Broken Lines, Chemical Firms

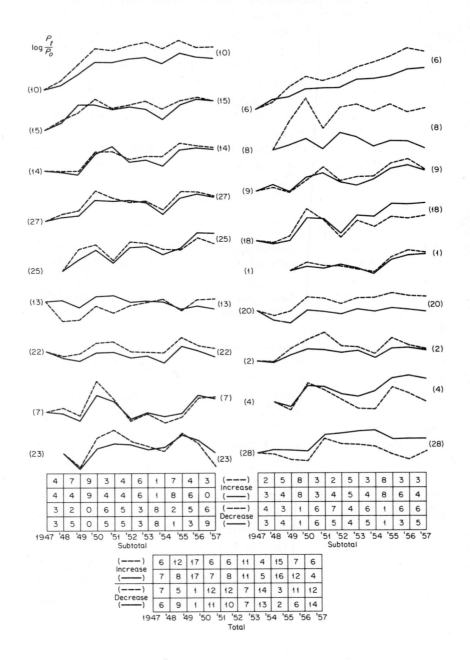

CHART 2

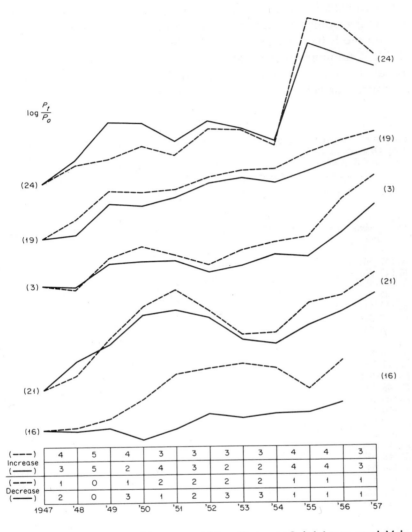

$\log \dfrac{P_t}{P_0}$

	4	5	4	3	3	3	3	4	4	3
(----) Increase (——)	3	5	2	4	3	2	2	4	4	3
(----)	1	0	1	2	2	2	2	1	1	1
Decrease (——)	2	0	3	1	2	3	3	1	1	1
	1947	'48	'49	'50	'51	'52	'53	'54	'55	'56	'57

Indexes of Productivity Measures, Using Output, Solid Lines, and Value Added, Broken Lines, Drug and Pharmaceutical Firms

expect research and development to affect productivity only with a lag, we want to explain productivity changes by means of previous research and development. As data on such expenditures are not available before 1947 for most of the firms in the sample, we are forced to break up 1947–57 and use research and development in the early years to explain the productivity changes in later years. We would expect that some lags may give better results than no lag at all, depending on the behavior of research and development activity over time. Table 2 summarizes the regression results of the rates of growth of productivity (using value added) and the research and development measures for lags ranging from zero to five years.

TABLE 2

SIMPLE r^2's OF THE RATE OF GROWTH OF PRODUCTIVITY ($\dot{P}$) AND AVERAGE RESEARCH AND DEVELOPMENT DEFLATED BY A WEIGHTED AVERAGE OF TOTAL INPUTS (R_i), AND AVERAGE RESEARCH AND DEVELOPMENT DIVIDED BY REAL GROSS PLANT AND EQUIPMENT (R_k), FOR LAGS RANGING FROM ZERO TO FIVE YEARS, CHEMICAL FIRMS

Independent Variables	$\dot{P}$ (47–57)	$\dot{P}_1$ (48–57)	$\dot{P}_2$ (47, 48, 52, 55, 56, 57)	$\dot{P}_3$ (49–57)	$\dot{P}_4$ (50–57)	$\dot{P}_5$ (51–57)	$\dot{P}_6$ (52–57)
R_i (47–56)	0.668	0.593	0.619				
R_k (47–56)	0.734	0.701	0.604				
R_i (47–55)				0.533			
R_k (47–55)				0.654			
R_i (47–54)					0.389		
R_k (47–54)					0.521		
R_k (48–55)					0.508		
R_k (49–56)					0.508		
R_k (50–57)					0.510		
R_i (47–53)						0.452	
R_k (47–53)						0.442	
R_k (48–54)						0.429	
R_k (49–55)						0.429	
R_k (50–56)						0.424	
R_k (51–57)						0.413	
R_i (47–52)							0.270
R_k (47–52)							0.163
R_k (48–53)							0.174
R_k (49–54)							0.180
R_k (50–55)							0.182
R_k (51–56)							0.181
R_k (52–57)							0.181

$\dot{P}$ = Rate of growth in productivity (using value added), equation (9).

$$R_i = \frac{\sum (\text{R.D.})_t}{\sum (L^a K^{1-a})_t}$$ = Average research and development expenditures deflated by a weighted average of total inputs. The years relevant to each R_i are indicated in the brackets.

$$R_k = \frac{\sum (\text{R.D.})_t}{\sum (K)_t}$$ = Average research and development expenditures deflated by average gross plant and equipment. The years relevant to each R_k are indicated in the brackets.

TABLE 3

SIMPLE r^2'S OF R_k MEASURE OF RESEARCH AND
DEVELOPMENT IN 1949, 1952, AND 1955,
CHEMICAL FIRMS

	R_k (1952)	R_k (1955)
R_k (1949)	0.973	0.951
R_k (1952)		0.968

See Table 2 above for the definition of R_k.

First note that the r^2's of the three rate of growth of productivity variables, $\dot{P}_4$, $\dot{P}_5$, and $\dot{P}_6$, with measures of research and development expenditures are highest when research and development is lagged by three, four and two years, respectively.

Second, note that the r^2's of the rate of growth of productivity variables $\dot{P}$, $\dot{P}_1$, $\dot{P}_2$, and $\dot{P}_3$, with research and development measures decline almost monotonically as we shorten the period upon which the change in productivity is based. The shorter periods begin with Korean war years of 1950–52, include the recession of 1953–54, and end with the five months recession of 1957. There is no reason to expect that all firms will be affected to the same extent in these years. In fact we have seen that even the directions of the change in productivity among the firms were different during the years 1950–52 and 1955–57. Therefore, we would expect the influence of research and development on productivity to be overshadowed by the effects of these "abnormal" years and the idiosyncrasies of price changes, to be discussed later. These effects or errors will assume increasingly heavier weights as we shorten the period; affecting the slope of the regression line—the rate of growth of productivity—more and more.

A logical question now is, if we know that certain years contain errors, why use longer periods in order to minimize the effect of the errors when we can eliminate them entirely by excluding these particular years? This alternative was not chosen for two reasons. One reason was the lack of a satisfactory rule for discarding years. One might first disregard the recession years, then perhaps the Korean war years, leaving presumably full employment years. That is, we might disregard the years 1949, 1950, 1951, 1953, 1954, and possibly also 1957. The regression results obtained when the rate of growth of productivity was calculated using data on 1947–48, 1952, and 1955–57 are presented in Table 2. The r^2 of the rates of growth of productivity for these years ($\dot{P}_2$) with R_i is 0.62 and that with R_k is 0.60. This compares well with 0.67 and 0.73 when all the observations in the period are used.[16]

The second reason for not excluding the years containing errors was, how justifiable is it to eliminate recessions and war years and leave "normal" years untouched? Although one may very well call these years normal for the economy—they were characterized by full employment, etc.—it is questionable that these years would be "normal" for all firms in the chemical industry. It should be noted that we found above that changes in the productivity measures did not correspond exactly with business cycle years. Furthermore, firms had different experiences even in "normal" years. Rather than remove the recession years, it might be more meaningful to look at a complete cycle(s). If the business cycle affects the relationships we are investigating, looking at only parts of a cycle will bias our results; for purposes of generality, we would favor a complete cycle. These considerations persuaded us to choose the method that utilized all the observations in calculating our rate of growth of productivity.

The regression results of the rates of growth using value added in equation 9 and two alternative measures of research and development expenditures defined by equations 4 and 5 are summarized in Table 4. Both regression coefficients are significant at the 1 per cent two-tail level. The regressions indicate that the greater the ratio of research and development expenditures to total inputs or to gross real plant and equipment the greater the rate of growth of productivity.

[16] After the surrender of Germany in 1945, confiscated German patents were made available (at no cost) to U.S. firms. It has been speculated that the effects of these patents may be present in my measure of productivity, as the patents may have been assimilated as late as 1947 or 1948. It seems unlikely that these effects will alter my results for two reasons. In the first place, it is not obvious that the acceptance of these free patents by firms in the same industry should be correlated with the independent variables, hence it should not negate the results. On the other hand, to the extent that the acceptance does affect productivity but is uncorrelated with the independent variables, the unexplained variance of the dependent variable is increased. Secondly, the lag between the availability of these patents and the impact on productivity would arise only from investment in plant and equipment, as there is no lag analogous to that of research and development where it takes time to develop technology. Thus this German patent effect was perhaps worked off by 1947.

Further, for five firms for which research and development data is available before 1947, the behavior of R_k before 1947 was similar to its behavior since that date. Also note Table 3, where we see very high correlations between R_k (for all eighteen firms) for the years 1949, 1952, and 1955. This evidence leads one to believe the research and development activity for 1945 and 1946 did not differ greatly from that of years for which we have data. Thus, even if there is a substantial lag between research and development and $\dot{P}$, our results should not be altered by previous research and development, since we believe our 1947–57 measure of R and D to summarize the immediately preceding period as well.

TABLE 4

SIMPLE REGRESSION COEFFICIENTS AND THEIR STANDARD ERRORS, AND THE COEFFICIENTS
OF DETERMINATION OF THE RATE OF GROWTH OF PRODUCTIVITY ($\dot{P}$)
AND TWO ALTERNATIVE MEASURES OF RESEARCH AND DEVELOPMENT
(R_i AND R_k), CHEMICAL FIRMS

Independent Variable	Dependent Variable $\dot{P}$ Regression Coefficients and Standard Errors	r^2
R_i	0.250 (0.044)	0.67
R_k	0.294 (0.044)	0.73

See Table 2 above for definitions of $\dot{P}$, R_i, and R_k.
Figures in parentheses are standard errors.
With the exception of average gross plant and equipment (K), which is $1,000, the
variables are measured in percentages.

In order to investigate the sensitivity of the results to a different
formulation of the share of labor (footnote 8) and a different concept
of capital (footnote 12), $\dot{P}$ was adjusted for these effects and the results
obtained are summarized in Table 5.[17] It can be seen that the results

TABLE 5

SIMPLE REGRESSION COEFFICIENTS, COEFFICIENTS OF DETERMINATION OF RATES OF
GROWTH OF PRODUCTIVITY ($\dot{P}^*$, $\dot{P}^{**}$, $\dot{P}^{***}$), AND A MEASURE OF
RESEARCH AND DEVELOPMENT (R_k), CHEMICAL FIRMS

Dependent Variable	Independent Variable R_k Regression Coefficients	r^2
$\dot{P}^*$	0.294	0.733
$\dot{P}^{**}$	0.293	0.732
$\dot{P}^{***}$	0.293	0.731

$\dot{P}^*$ = The rate of growth in productivity using the share of labor obtained by an
alternative formulation.
$\dot{P}^{**}$ = The rate of growth in productivity when total gross capital is used instead of
gross plant and equipment.
$\dot{P}^{***}$ = The rate of growth in productivity when total gross capital and the share of
labor determined by alternative formulation are used.

of this study do not depend upon the particular concept of capital
employed or the formulation of the share of labor. Furthermore, to
test for the effects of royalties paid (footnote 7), residuals of the regression line of $\dot{P}$ on R_k were plotted against the average ratio of royalties

[17] For details of this adjustment see Jora R. Minasian, "The Economics of Research
and Development," unpublished Ph.D. dissertation, University of Chicago, 1960,
pp. 33–34.

paid to research and development expenditures. A positive relation was expected but the result was equivocal.[18]

Three broad questions can be asked at this point: (1) Are there any omitted variables which may cause the rate of growth in productivity to be positively correlated with research and development expenditures? That is, are rates of growth in productivity and research and development positively correlated only because each one of them is so related with some other causal variable(s) not introduced in the regression equation? (2) Are there other variables which belong in the regression equation because they can explain some of the changes in the productivity measure that are unexplained by research and development? (3) Is there a variable that causes research and development, and affects $\dot{P}$ only via research and development?

In the pages that follow, the method is to insert additional variables in the regressions of productivity change on research and development expenditures. These variables will include profitability, gross investment, and a few scale measures. We shall see if these additional variables increase the explanation of the dependent variable, and if they, any or all of them, reduce the significance of the research and development variable.

ALTERNATIVE HYPOTHESIS, PROFITABILITY

The first general alternative hypothesis states that profitability is the important variable which determines research and development expenditures and is associated with the rate of growth in productivity, and that the observed correlation between rate of growth of productivity and research and development activity is spurious. In this study the term profitability will be defined as profits deflated by a size variable, gross plant and equipment.

The general hypothesis is that profits play the role of a budget restraint. The implications are: (1) initial profitability should be better correlated with final research and development than vice versa; (2) research and development may or may not affect productivity, but being a "superior consumption good" will be "consumed" by highly profitable firms; and (3) if profitability determines research and development, which in turn affects $\dot{P}$, which finally controls profitability, then profitability at the end of the period should be significantly correlated with initial profitability.

Let us investigate the simple coefficients of determination of the

[18] *Ibid.*, Graph 15, App. I.

relevant variables. Table 6 gives these coefficients for profitability and research and development variables.

TABLE 6

SIMPLE r^2's OF THE RATE OF GROWTH OF PRODUCTIVITY ($\dot{P}$), AVERAGE RESEARCH AND DEVELOPMENT DEFLATED BY A WEIGHTED AVERAGE OF TOTAL INPUTS (R_{iB}) AND (R_{iE}), AVERAGE RESEARCH AND DEVELOPMENT DEFLATED BY REAL GROSS PLANT AND EQUIPMENT (R_{kB}) AND (R_{kE}), AND PROFITABILITY IN 1947–50 (I_B), IN 1955–56 (I_E), CHEMICAL FIRMS

	R_{iB}	R_{kB}	R_{iE}	R_{kE}	I_B	I_E
$\dot{P}$	0.60	0.72	0.71	0.73	0.01	0.52
R_{iB}	—	—	0.72	—	0.01	0.34
R_{kB}	—	—	—	0.93	0.09	0.72
R_{iE}	—	—	—	—	0.01	0.36
R_{kE}	—	—	—	—	0.10	0.74
I_B	—	—	—	—	—	0.21

$\dot{P}$ = See Table 2 above.
R_{iB} and R_{kB} = Same as R_i and R_k in Table 2 but for 1947–50 instead.
R_{iE} and R_{kE} = Same as R_i and R_k in Table 2 but for 1955–56 instead.

$$I_B = \frac{\text{Net income after taxes}+\text{interest payments}}{\text{Real gross plant and equipment}} \times \frac{1}{4} = \text{profitability in 1947–50.}$$

I_E = Same as I_B above but for 1955–56 instead.

First, note that the r^2's of the two research and development measures at the beginning of the period R_{kB} and R_{iB} with profitability at the end of the period I_E are, respectively, 0.34 and 0.72, while the r^2's of profitability at the beginning of the period I_B with the two measures of research and development at the end of the period R_{iE} and R_{kE} are, respectively, 0.01 and 0.10. These results indicate that the research and development at the beginning of the period explains profitability at the end of the period much better than profitability at the beginning of the period explains the research and development expenditures at the end of the period. This is exactly the opposite of implication 1 of the alternative hypothesis of profitability.

Second, note that the r^2 of the rate of growth in productivity $\dot{P}$ with average research and development expenditures deflated by total weighted inputs, 1955–56, R_{iE} is 0.71, and that of $\dot{P}$ with average research and development expenditures divided by total gross plant and equipment, 1955–56, R_{kE} is 0.73, while the r^2 of the rate of growth in productivity with profitability in 1947–50 I_B is only 0.01. Also note that the r^2's of the rate of growth in productivity with the two research and development measures for 1947–50, R_{iB} and R_{kB}, are 0.60 and

0.72, respectively, while the r^2 of the rate of growth of productivity with the profitability measure in 1955–56, I_E, is only 0.52. The above results indicate that the research and development of both the beginning and the end of the period explain the rates of growth in productivity better than the profitability at the end of the period and much better than the profitability at the beginning of the period, which is inconsistent with implication 2.

Finally, note that the r^2 between initial and final profitability, I_B and I_E, respectively, is only 0.21, which is not significant at 5 per cent (one tail). Thus, implication 3 of the alternative hypothesis also fails to be borne out. To the contrary we see that the correlations (r^2's) between initial research and development and initial profitability are only 0.01 and 0.09; while between final research and development and final profitability the r^2's are 0.36 and 0.74. It seems research and development affects profitability, rather than the other way around; our simple correlations tell us to reject the alternative hypothesis in favor of the one advanced in this study.

To obtain a more conclusive test of this alternative hypothesis, profitability and research and development measures are introduced as two different independent variables in regression equations with the rate of growth in productivity as the dependent variable. If research and development is the effect of profitability, we should expect lagged profits to steal away the explanatory power of research and development when both are present in a multiple regression.[19] The results of eight such regressions are summarized in Table 7.

In regressions 1 and 2 the partial regression coefficients of I_B are not significant even at the 20 per cent two-tail level, and one in 2 has the wrong sign. However, both the R_{iE} and R_{kE} variables have partial regression coefficients significant at the 1 per cent two-tail level, explaining 70 per cent and 76 per cent, respectively, of the variation in the rate of growth in productivity, while lagged profitability explains less than 0.1 per cent and 10 per cent, respectively, of the variation.

Regressions 3 and 4 use lagged research and development measures, R_{iB} and R_{kB}, and profitability at the end of the period, I_E. Again, partial regression coefficients of R_{iB} and R_{kB} are significant at the 1 per cent two-tail level. The partial regression coefficient of I_E is significant at the 1 per cent two-tail level in regression 3; it is not significant at even the 20 per cent two-tail level in regression 4 and in addition it has

---

[19] Or perhaps we might find a high multiple coefficient of determination but insignificant coefficients for both variables because of high multicollinearity.

the wrong sign. In terms of partial coefficients of determination, R_{iB} and R_{kB} both explain approximately 40 per cent of the variation in the rate of growth of productivity, while profitability at the end of the period explains, at best, 27 per cent of the variation.[20]

TABLE 7

MULTIPLE REGRESSIONS OF THE RATE OF GROWTH OF PRODUCTIVITY ON RESEARCH AND DEVELOPMENT AND PROFITABILITY VARIABLES CONTAINED IN TABLE 6, CHEMICAL FIRMS

Regression Number and Dependent Variable	Independent Variable						R^2
	R_{iB}	R_{kB}	R_{iE}	R_{kE}	I_B	I_E	
(1) $\dot{P}$			0.181 (0.030) 0.703		0.002 (0.018) 0.001		0.707
(2) $\dot{P}$			0.291 (0.042) 0.759		(−)0.023 (0.017) 0.106		0.762
(3) $\dot{P}$	0.213 (0.066) 0.399					0.034 (0.014) 0.274	0.712
(4) $\dot{P}$		0.449 (0.138) 0.413				(−)0.000 (0.022) 0.000	0.719
(5) $\dot{P}$	0.306 (0.065) 0.598				0.002 (0.021) 0.001		0.603
(6) $\dot{P}$		0.476 (0.073) 0.740			(−)0.021 (0.018) 0.088		0.743
(7) $\dot{P}$			0.138 (0.033) 0.543			0.028 (0.012) 0.253	0.781
(8) $\dot{P}$			0.290 (0.083) 0.447			(−)0.005 (0.022) 0.003	0.735

See Table 6 for definitions of the variables.

In each regression, the partial regression coefficient is given in the first row, its standard error (in parentheses) in the second row, and the partial coefficient of determination in the third row. None of the multiple coefficients of determination are corrected for degrees of freedom. The results of further multiple regressions will be presented in the same manner.

[20] Relationships, theoretical and empirical, between research and development and profitability are investigated later on in this section.

Finally, it is interesting to test the following two propositions: first, that the effect of research and development on $\dot{P}$ takes place with a lag, and, second, that the lag between profits and research and development may be shorter than the period used in the above regressions, i.e., 1947–50 to 1955–56. Regressions 5 and 6 use both lagged research and development and lagged profitability. Here again both measures of research and development expenditures have partial regression coefficients significant at the 1 per cent two-tail level. The profitability variable has partial regression coefficients insignificant even at the 10 per cent two-tail level. Regressions 7 and 8 use end-of-period values for both variables and the results are similar to those of 5 and 6, except that profitability is significant when measured at the end of the period. This is consistent with a belief that productivity affects profitability.

It is, therefore, concluded that the alternative hypothesis of profitability is false. Furthermore, the above results indicate that it is more probable that profitability is the result of past research and development activity, than the other way around.

ALTERNATIVE HYPOTHESIS, INVESTMENT IN PLANT AND EQUIPMENT

It might be expected that the rate of growth of productivity $\dot{P}$ would be explained by investment in plant and equipment because a firm without research and development may have gained in $\dot{P}$ through expansion, and new capital incorporates new technologies provided by the producers of the capital which may not have been corrected for in our measure of capital.[21] Therefore, we might expect a positive correlation between $\dot{P}$ and investment in plant and equipment.

---

[21] "Opportunity" is another alternative hypothesis which states that research and development expenditures are determined by still another factor, that is the technical possibilities which may vary among firms. Therefore, the firm will indulge in such activity only if its production processes readily lend themselves to improvement. This seems illogical. If returns are high to research and development for particular product mixes, a firm should (and would) carry on such activity whether it produces such mixes or not, as it can either alter its mix to take advantage of the resulting improvement, or sell that improvement to a firm that can use it directly.

Strictly speaking, we have three cases: (1) assume that there is no mobility in the industry—ill-fated firms can not change their product mix—thus the ranking of the firms with respect to research and development does not change over time, (2) there is mobility, thus the ranking of firms does change over time, and (3) research and development creates opportunities and the intensity thereof is governed by subjective probabilities and the risk preference functions of the decision makers.

We saw in Table 3 that the ranking of the firms did not change during the period which is consistent with propositions 1 and 3. I believe, however, that profit motives are strong and there is mobility in the market, which leaves me to conclude in favor of case 3 above.

The reasons that led us to deflate research and development by a size variable now lead us to deflate investment in plant and equipment by a size variable. The simple coefficients of determination are given in Table 8.

TABLE 8

SIMPLE r^2'S OF THE RATE OF GROWTH OF PRODUCTIVITY ($\dot{P}$), AVERAGE RESEARCH AND DEVELOPMENT DEFLATED BY A WEIGHTED AVERAGE OF TOTAL INPUTS (R_{iB}) AND (R_{iE}), AVERAGE RESEARCH AND DEVELOPMENT DEFLATED BY REAL GROSS PLANT AND EQUIPMENT (R_{kB}) AND (R_{kE}), AND AVERAGE GROSS INVESTMENT DEFLATED BY A WEIGHTED AVERAGE OF TOTAL INPUTS (G_B) AND (G_E), CHEMICAL FIRMS

	R_{iB}	R_{kB}	R_{iE}	R_{kE}	G_B	G_E
$\dot{P}$	0.60	0.72	0.71	0.73	$(-)0.02$	0.00
R_{iB}	—	—	0.72	—	$(-)0.00$	$(-)0.01$
R_{kB}	—	—	—	0.93	$(-)0.02$	$(-)0.09$
R_{iE}	—	—	—	—	$(-)0.03$	$(-)0.01$
R_{kE}	—	—	—	—	$(-)0.05$	$(-)0.11$
G_B	—	—	—	—	—	0.00

See Table 6 above for definitions of ($\dot{P}$), (R_{iB}), (R_{iE}), (R_{kB}), and (R_{kE}).

$$G_B = \frac{\sum\limits_{t=47}^{50} (G.I.)_t}{\sum\limits_{t=47}^{50} (L^a K^{1-a})_t} = \text{Average gross investment in plant and equipment deflated by a weighted average of total inputs, 1947–50.}$$

$$G_E = \frac{\sum\limits_{t=55}^{56} (G.I.)_t}{\sum\limits_{t=55}^{56} (L^a K^{1-a})_t} = \text{Average gross investment in plant and equipment deflated by a weighted average of total inputs 1955–56.}$$

The r^2's of the rate of growth in productivity $\dot{P}$ with two measures of research and development R_{iE} and R_{kE} are 0.71 and 0.73, respectively, while the r^2 of $\dot{P}$ and average investment deflated by total weighted inputs in 1947–50, G_B, is 0.02. Furthermore, the r^2's of the rate of growth in productivity $\dot{P}$ with R_{iB} and R_{kB} are, respectively, 0.60 and 0.72, while the r^2 of $\dot{P}$ with G_E is 0.00. It should be emphasized that none of the r^2's of $\dot{P}$ with investment measures, both at the beginning and at the end of the period, are significant at even the 20 per cent two-tail level.

In addition, the r^2's of the investment measure at the beginning of the period G_B with R_{iE} and R_{kE} are, respectively, $(-)0.03$ and $(-)0.05$, while the r^2's of R_{iB} and R_{kB} with G_E are, respectively, $(-)0.01$ and $(-)0.09$. Furthermore, the r^2's of G_E and G_B with R_{iE}, R_{kE} and R_{iB},

R_{kB}, respectively, are $(-)0.01$, $(-)0.11$, $(-)0.00$ and $(-)0.02$. These results suggest that the decision to invest in plant and equipment and the decision to invest in research and development may be competitive in nature since they are negatively correlated. Again it should be emphasized that none of the r^2's relevant to the investment hypothesis are significant even at the 20 per cent two-tail level.

Multiple regression analysis, used in testing the profitability hypothesis, is also used for testing the investment hypothesis. The results of eight such regressions are summarized in Table 9.

TABLE 9

MULTIPLE REGRESSIONS OF THE RATE OF GROWTH OF PRODUCTIVITY
ON RESEARCH AND DEVELOPMENT AND INVESTMENT VARIABLES
CONTAINED IN TABLE 8, CHEMICAL FIRMS

Regression Number and Dependent Variable	Independent Variable						R^2
	R_{iB}	R_{kB}	R_{iE}	R_{kE}	G_B	G_E	
(1) $\dot{P}$			0.183 (0.031) 0.702		0.001 (0.001) 0.002		0.707
(2) $\dot{P}$				0.278 (0.043) 0.732	0.003 (0.008) 0.012		0.737
(3) $\dot{P}$	0.311 (0.064) 0.613					0.008 (0.012) 0.026	0.613
(4) $\dot{P}$			0.499 (0.063) 0.805			0.024 (0.009) 0.309	0.805
(5) $\dot{P}$	0.304 (0.063) 0.608					$(-)0.007$ (0.009) 0.041	0.615
(6) $\dot{P}$			0.448 (0.073) 0.714			$(-)0.001$ (0.008) 0.001	0.719
(7) $\dot{P}$			0.184 (0.030) 0.720			0.009 (0.011) 0.045	0.720
(8) $\dot{P}$				0.311 (0.035) 0.841		0.027 (0.008) 0.401	0.841

See Table 8 for definitions of the variables.

See Table 7 for a description of the manner in which results are presented.

In regression equations 1 and 2 the partial regression coefficients of G_B are not significant even at the 20 per cent two-tail level. However, the partial regression coefficients of both R_{iE} and R_{kE} are significant at the 1 per cent two-tail level. Furthermore, the partial regression coefficient of G_E is insignificant even at the 20 per cent two-tail level in regression 3 while it is significant at the 1 per cent two-tail level in regression 4. Both R_{iB} and R_{kB} have partial regression coefficients significant at the 1 per cent two-tail level. Regressions 5 and 6 use investment and both the research and development measures at the beginning of the period. Both partial regression coefficients of G_B have the wrong sign and are not significant at even the 20 per cent two-tail level, while both R_{iB} and R_{kB} are significant at the 1 per cent two-tail level.

Finally, in regressions 7 and 8, which use end-of-period data, investment is highly significant in 8 but not in 7, while research and development measures are significant in both.

The complete failure of investment to be related to either research and development or $\dot{P}$, and the complete lack of correlation of beginning period investment with $\dot{P}$ in the multiple regressions, are viewed as sufficient evidence to dismiss the investment hypothesis that a firm without research and development may have gained in $\dot{P}$ through expansion. However, the significant results in regressions 4 and 5 where end of period investment and R_{kB} and R_{kE}, respectively, were used are consistent with the hypothesis that $\dot{P}$ affects investment (research results are commercialized) which may also be coupled with underestimation of capital in the sense that improvements in capital have not been corrected for.[22]

ALTERNATIVE HYPOTHESIS, ECONOMIES OF SCALE

Economies of Scale to Production

Our measure of the rate of growth, utilizing the assumption of constant return to scale, might show too large a productivity increase if there were economies of scale to production.

Our dependent variable is the rate of growth in productivity over

---

[22] A change in productivity caused by research and development will have two effects on the stock of capital as measured. The substitution effect will indicate a low gross stock while the scale effect will dictate a large stock. A priori, we cannot say which effect is stronger so we cannot predict the effect of research and development on future investment in the firm.

the period. If there are economies of scale then we may expect some measure of the *increase in scale* to steal away the research and development variable's ability to explain $\dot{P}$. To test this hypothesis the percentage change in real output was correlated with the rate of growth in productivity. The simple r^2 of the rate of growth of productivity $\dot{P}$ with the percentage change in real output (1947–56) is 0.023, which is not significant even at the 10 per cent two-tail level. Because of this and similar insignificant results obtained in multiple regressions for an alternative measure, presented below, we did not compute the multiple regressions of $\dot{P}$ on research and development and the percentage change in output.

Economies of Scale to Research and Development

It is said that large firms are in a position to conduct research activity more effectively, presumably, because of economies of scale, diversification, and financial strength, as well as the uncertainty of the results and the waiting time involved.

Three scatter diagrams, the rate of growth of productivity $\dot{P}$ on average value added, $\dot{P}$ on average total weighted inputs, and $\dot{P}$ on average gross plant and equipment, were investigated. The three scatter diagrams were almost identical, indicating that all the measures reflect size equally well. Furthermore, the relationship could not be improved by a simple nonlinear function. To test this hypothesis, we chose average gross plant and equipment.

We have also investigated the percentage net increase in gross plant and equipment during this period in order to see whether the rate of change in size has any explanatory power. In this form it also incorporates something from the investment hypothesis and is another, perhaps inferior, variable reflecting the economies of scale to production.

The r^2's are given in Table 10. The r^2 of the rate of growth in productivity $\dot{P}$ with average gross plant and equipment K is 0.01 and that of $\dot{P}$ with percentage net additions to gross plant and equipment $\dot{K}$ is $(-)0.07$. Furthermore, the r^2 of research and development deflated by total weighted inputs 1947–56, R_i with K is 0.03 and that of R_i with $\dot{K}$ is $(-)0.04$. These r^2's are $(-)0.00$ and $(-)0.15$, respectively, when research and development expenditure divided by gross plant and equipment R_k is used. None of the r^2's are significant at the 5 per cent two-tail level.

TABLE 10

SIMPLE r^2's OF THE RATE OF GROWTH OF PRODUCTIVITY ($\dot{P}$), AVERAGE RESEARCH AND
DEVELOPMENT DEFLATED BY A WEIGHTED AVERAGE OF TOTAL INPUTS, 1947–56 (R_i),
AVERAGE RESEARCH AND DEVELOPMENT DEFLATED BY REAL GROSS PLANT AND
EQUIPMENT, 1947–56, (R_k), AVERAGE GROSS PLANT AND EQUIPMENT, 1947–56 (K), AND
PERCENTAGE NET ADDITIONS TO GROSS PLANT AND EQUIPMENT, 1947–56
($\dot{K}$), CHEMICAL FIRMS

	R_i	R_k	K	$\dot{K}$
$\dot{P}$	0.67	0.73	0.01	(−)0.07
R_i		0.74	0.03	(−)0.04
R_k			(−)0.00	(−)0.15
K				0.02

See Table 2 above for definitions of variables ($\dot{P}$), (R_i), and (R_k).

$$K = \frac{\sum\limits_{t=47}^{56} K_t}{10} = \text{Average gross plant and equipment in 1947–56.}$$

$$\dot{K} = \frac{\sum\limits_{t=47}^{56} (\text{G.I.} - \text{R.})_t}{48} = \text{Average percentage net additions to gross plant and equipment in 1947–56. } R = \text{Retirement.}$$
$$\frac{\sum\limits_{t=47}^{} K_t}{2}$$

The results of the multiple regressions appear in Table 11. Neither
of the partial regression coefficients of average gross plant and equipment in regression equations 1 and 2 is significant at even the 20 per
cent two-tail level. On the other hand, both measures of research and
development R_i and R_k have partial regression coefficients significant
at the 1 per cent two-tail level in regressions 1 and 2, respectively.
Furthermore, while neither of the partial regression coefficients of
$\dot{K}$ in regression equations 3 and 4 are significant even at the 20 per
cent two-tail level, both measures of research and development R_i and
R_k are significant at the 1 per cent two-tail level. Finally, regressions 5
and 6 include, in addition to research and development measures,
average plant and equipment K and percentage net addition to gross
plant and equipment $\dot{K}$.

Comparison of regressions 1 and 2 with 5 and of 3 and 4 with 6
reveals that the results do not change when K and $\dot{K}$ are simultaneously
present in the regression equations. Therefore, the independent variable, research and development, not only yields statistically significant
results; it also accounts for practically all the explained variance of
the dependent variable. That is, the additional independent variables

TABLE 11

MULTIPLE REGRESSIONS OF THE RATE OF GROWTH OF PRODUCTIVITY ON RESEARCH AND
DEVELOPMENT AND ECONOMIES OF SCALE VARIABLES CONTAINED IN TABLE 10,
CHEMICAL FIRMS

Regression Number and Dependent Variable	Independent Variable				R^2
	R_i	R_k	K	$\dot{K}$	
(1) $\dot{P}$	0.253 (0.046) 0.668		(−)0.001 (0.004) 0.009		0.671
(2) $\dot{P}$		0.296 (0.044) 0.747	0.003 (0.003) 0.055		0.749
(3) $\dot{P}$	0.244 (0.046) 0.654			(−)0.001 (0.002) 0.028	0.677
(4) $\dot{P}$		0.306 (0.049) 0.722		0.001 (0.002) 0.024	0.741
(5) $\dot{P}$		0.305 (0.050) 0.730	0.003 (0.003) 0.047	0.001 (0.002) 0.017	0.753
(6) $\dot{P}$	0.247 (0.049) 0.649		(−)0.001 (0.004) 0.004	(−)0.001 (0.002) 0.023	0.679

See Table 10 for definitions of the variables.

See Table 7 for a description of the manner in which results are presented.

have not increased the total explanation significantly. This can be seen by examining the partial coefficients of determination of these additional independent variables, or by examining the simple r^2's in conjunction with the multiple coefficients of determination.[23]

The choice of the value added rather than the gross output measure was justified in the preceding section. Although, a priori, we should expect a less satisfactory relationship using gross output, it is still interesting to see the effect on the main results. Tables 12 and 13 contain the results of simple and multiple regressions of the rate of

[23] Minasian, *op. cit.*, App. II contains similar multiple regression results for a subset of 1947–57 where research and development is lagged by three years. The results, in terms of partial coefficients of determination, for research and development are similar to those discussed in the section on profitability above; the lagged relationships offer less explanation, however, see discussion presented there. $\dot{K}$ performs similarly to the results in the text, but K improves, has a negative sign, and is not significant.

TABLE 12

SIMPLE r^2's OF THE RATE OF GROWTH OF PRODUCTIVITY ($\dot{P}$****), AVERAGE RESEARCH AND DEVELOPMENT DEFLATED BY A WEIGHTED AVERAGE OF TOTAL INPUTS, 1947–56 (R_i), AVERAGE RESEARCH AND DEVELOPMENT DEFLATED BY REAL GROSS PLANT AND EQUIPMENT, 1947–56 (R_k), AVERAGE GROSS PLANT AND EQUIPMENT, 1947–56 (K), AND PERCENTAGE NET ADDITIONS TO GROSS PLANT AND EQUIPMENT, 1947–56 ($\dot{K}$), CHEMICAL FIRMS

	R_i	R_k	K	$\dot{K}$
$\dot{P}$****	0.18	0.13	0.02	0.02
R_i		0.74	0.03	(−)0.04
R_k			(−)0.00	(−)0.15
K				0.02

See Table 10 for definitions of variables (R_i), (R_k), (K), and ($\dot{K}$).

$\dot{P}$**** = Rate of growth in productivity (using output), equation (12).

TABLE 13

MULTIPLE REGRESSIONS OF THE RATE OF GROWTH OF PRODUCTIVITY (USING OUTPUT) ON RESEARCH AND DEVELOPMENT AND ECONOMIES OF SCALE VARIABLES CONTAINED IN TABLE 12, CHEMICAL FIRMS

Regression Number and Dependent Variable	Independent Variable				R^2
	R_i	R_k	K	$\dot{K}$	
(1) $\dot{P}$****	0.129		0.001	0.003	
	(0.068)		(0.005)	(0.003)	0.235
	0.205		0.001	0.061	
(2) $\dot{P}$****		0.154	0.003	0.004	
		(0.079)	(0.005)	(0.003)	0.244
		0.214	0.018	0.099	

See Table 12 for definitions of the variables.

growth in productivity, based on output $\dot{P}$****, on average gross plant and equipment K, the percentage net additions to gross plant and equipment $\dot{K}$, and the two measures of research and development, R_i and R_k.

Comparison of the first rows of the Tables 10 and 12 indicates the differences in the r^2's when the dependent variable uses value added and output, respectively. It can be seen that the r^2's of average gross plant and equipment K and percentage net additions to gross plant and equipment $\dot{K}$ are approximately the same with both measures of productivity, i.e. nearly zero. However, the r^2's for both measures of research and development and the rate of growth in productivity are substantially larger when the dependent variable is derived from value added than from output, as is expected. They are 0.67 and 0.73 using value added but become 0.18 and 0.13, respectively, when the rate of growth in productivity is measured by output.

Comparison of the multiple regression equations in Tables 11 and 13 reveals that, in terms of the partial coefficients of determination, the variables size and the percentage change in size perform a little better where the dependent variable uses output rather than value added. However, neither partial regression coefficient is significant at the 10 per cent two-tail level. Furthermore, both measures of research and development have partial regression coefficients barely significant at the 5 per cent two-tail level. But, in terms of partial coefficients of determination, they explain much less when the dependent variable uses output than when it uses value added. Finally, the multiple coefficients of determination are much smaller when output rather than value added is used.

We can conclude, therefore, that the main findings using value added are somewhat reinforced when output is used. However, we have a much stronger relationship in the former than in the latter case, in the level of significance of both the partial regression coefficients and the multiple and partial coefficients of determination.

We have so far analyzed firms in the chemical industry. We can not, unfortunately, do the same with the pharmaceutical firms since there are only five included in the sample. Since we have but three degrees of freedom at most, no correlations or regressions were computed. Scatter diagrams of some of the most important relationships were investigated. It is not an exaggeration to state that the findings seem to be compatible with those obtained above, with the case of returns to scale being an exception. It should, however, be emphasized that such inferences about the pharmaceutical firms are based upon the assumption that the pattern would remain the same if the sample size were increased; therefore they are highly tentative.[24]

ALTERNATIVE HYPOTHESIS, MONOPOLY PRICING

It will be recalled that our measures of value added and output are deflated to convert them to real terms. The effect of monopoly pricing on the deflation should be made clear. When a firm introduces a new product at a monopoly price, our price index (used for deflation) may not be affected, but our output and value added measures will be inflated. Thus our productivity estimate for that year may be an over-

[24] *Ibid.*, pp. 50–53.

statement. Now if the firm loses its monopoly on this product over time, value added will fall relative to the price index, pushing the productivity measure down.

It should be recognized that when a new product is introduced in a given year, the price index of that year is not affected, whether this product is included in the price index or not. However, if the product has been linked into the price index and its price changes in subsequent years, the price index will be affected. The extent of the change depends on the relative weight attached to the product in the index. We will consider three cases of this pricing effect on our measure of productivity to bring out the general type of result likely to be obtained.

The first case is when a new product is introduced and maintained indefinitely at a price higher than the long run competitive market price. Our measure of productivity for that year, when the price index is used to deflate the output or value added of the firm, will reflect the following influences. Since the price index is unaffected by the new product, the productivity measure for the firm involved will show an increase in the initial year which will be maintained indefinitely. The extent of the increase will depend on the relative portion of output represented by this new product and the extent to which the price of this product exceeds the competitive price. The productivity measure for the firms which did not participate in the production of the new product will be unaltered by that product, if it is not an input for older products.

The second case occurs when a new product is introduced by a firm (or firms) at a competitive market price. Under this circumstance, assuming the same input-output relation for the new and old products and assuming that the general price index represents competitive prices, the firms' measure of productivity also will be unaltered by this development.

Case three involves a new product priced monopolistically at first but competitively later, and linked into the price index. When the price of the new product decreases to a competitive level, the price index will decline accordingly. In the first year the effects are identical to case one above. In the following years, the productivity measure for firm(s) enjoying temporary monopoly power over the new product will decrease and that for firms which are not involved with producing the new product will increase. These results hold strictly, if some firms produce the new product *only* and the rest produce *only* the old.

In reality, we have more than one product introduced during this period by all firms, which complicates the situation. If we assume that the new products are priced monopolistically when they are introduced but approach competitive prices as time goes on, the crucial question is whether, during the period in question, the firms have gained *more* in monopoly power through the introduction of new products than they have lost through competition in the market on products previously introduced. This depends on the following conditions: (1) The proportion of total output or value added devoted to new products each year; (2) The time lapse, if any, between the introduction of the new product and the loss of monopoly power; (3) The extent to which the price charged by the firm exceeds the competitive price; (4) The relative weights attached to new and old products in both the general and the firms' own price indexes.

It can be seen that the more intense the conditions postulated under 1, 2, and 3 above are, the more the rate of growth in the measure of productivity reflects monopoly pricing. However, the effect of condition 4 works both ways. If the general price index links new products as they are introduced into the market, if these new products are introduced at monopoly prices but tend toward competitive ones over time, and if the extent of monopoly power is constant (3, above) the general price index will have a downward bias for the purpose of deflating value added. This downward bias will be constant over time—affecting all the observations on productivity for all years by a constant; thus not affecting the slope, i.e. the rate of growth of productivity—if the net rate of gain in monopoly power (gain on new products minus the loss on previously introduced products) is zero for each firm. Therefore, our estimates of $\dot{P}$ for any firm will be affected by monopoly pricing if there is a net change in monopoly power. For example, if some firms gain in monopoly power and some lose so that the average is unchanged, over time the bias of the general price index will increase for the former and decrease for the latter. If new products are introduced into the index at competitive prices, the productivity measure will be affected only by changing monopoly power over time (condition (3) above).

Two chemical firms indicated the percentage of their annual sales arising from new products. For the years that we have these data, no trend over time in these percentages is apparent. Furthermore, these percentages are in the order of magnitude of 3 to 5 per cent. 35 per cent of the 1958 sales of three firms were for products introduced since

1945. One of these three firms provided its own weighted average price index, using relative quantities of products sold as weights. We computed the rate of growth in productivity of this firm using its own price index and compared it with the one based on our estimated price index. The two measures of $\dot{P}$ obtained had a ratio of the order of 1.05. P based on our estimated price index was used in the regressions. Two other firms supplied their own price indexes for a few years. There was a very close correspondence in both the absolute change and the direction of change between these and the price indexes estimated for these firms.

Finally, the weighted price indexes constructed for each of the chemical firms were ranked according to the extent of the increase between 1947 and 1957. The smallest range was from 100 in 1947–49 to 85 in 1957 and the highest from 100 in 1947–49 to 141 by the end of the period. Spearman rank correlation between the rate of growth in productivity and the percentage change in the price indexes during 1947–57, assigning the lowest rank to the smallest percentage change, had a simple coefficient of determination of (−)0.04 which is not significant at the 35 per cent two-tail or the 75 per cent one-tail level. Therefore, our price indexes cannot be the cause of such correlation.

Considering the evidence given in this section, it seems that monopolistic pricing has not affected our measure of the rate of growth in productivity so much as to make the latter primarily a measure of changes in monopoly power. Nevertheless, we cannot presume that this disposes of the problem.

We are interested in finding a variable which will reflect the effects of idiosyncrasies in price changes in general and in monopoly prices in particular, and then in using it as another independent variable to explain the rate of growth in productivity. A plausible candidate for such a variable is the trend in the profitability of a firm over time. Since it depends on changes in supply and demand conditions and on the pattern of monopoly prices, the trend of profitability will be affected to a different extent if the rates of losses or gains of monopoly power are different among firms.[25] Profitability is defined as net profits

---

[25] Note that the role of the trend of profitability as an independent variable will not be affected whether it is taken relative to a competitive industry or an average for the economy, since we will be in essence subtracting or dividing (depending on how the deviations are expressed) the variable by a constant. Furthermore, the general behavior of the economy during 1947–57 will affect the firms differently depending on the shapes of their cost curves which are not identical at least because of differences in monopoly position.

THEORY AND MACRO-QUANTITATIVE ANALYSIS

after taxes (adjusted for other financial income and expenses, i.e., dividends received and paid), plus interest payments deflated by the implicit price deflator of GNP divided by gross plant and equipment.[26]

The reason for adding the trend of profitability to a multiple regression equation as an independent variable when the rate of growth in productivity is the dependent variable should be made clear. The trend of profitability does not belong in the regression equation as an explanatory variable *if* our measure of the rate of growth in productivity does *not* reflect idiosyncrasies of price changes, since, a priori, the chain of causation runs from productivity to profitability. However, we want to test for the effect of possible idiosyncrasies of price changes on our measure of productivity. Therefore, if the dependent variable is affected by such price changes, the trend of profitability belongs in a multiple regression equation *if* it also reflects the price changes which, by assumption, have not been eliminated by the price indexes used.

The regression results are summarized in Tables 14 and 15. The r^2 between the trend of profitability I and the rate of growth in productivity $\dot{P}$ is 0.60, and the r^2's between I and the two measures of research and development R_i and R_k are respectively 0.30 and 0.46. Furthermore, the r^2's of I with K and $\dot{K}$ are 0.00 and $(-)0.06$, respectively, which are not significantly different from zero at the 10 per cent two-tail level.

Multiple regression equation 3 utilizes K, $\dot{K}$, and I as independent variables. The partial regression coefficients of K and $\dot{K}$ are not significant at even the 10 per cent two-tail level. However, the partial regression coefficient of I is significant at the 1 per cent two-tail level. In terms of the partial coefficient of determination, the trend of profitability explains 57 per cent of the variation in the rate of growth of productivity.

Multiple regression equations 4 and 5 contain, besides K and $\dot{K}$, both variables I and R_i (and alternatively R_k) as independent variables. Partial regression coefficients of I are significant at the 1 per cent two-tail level in both regressions 4 and 5. *Both* measures R_i and R_k obtain

[26] A more accurate concept of profitability would use as its base all of the capital of the firm rather than just gross plant and equipment. Using an all-inclusive concept of capital will yield different results if the time paths of net plant and equipment, inventories, cash, etc., are dissimilar among the firms. Such a measure was developed and used in place of gross plant and equipment. It is to be noted that the conclusions arrived at in this section are supported by the alternative measure of capital stock, as the levels of significance are similar. See Minasian, *op. cit.*, App. III, for the construction of the measure and the results of the regressions.

TABLE 14

SIMPLE r^2'S OF THE RATE OF GROWTH OF PRODUCTIVITY ($\dot{P}$), AVERAGE RESEARCH AND DEVELOPMENT DEFLATED BY A WEIGHTED AVERAGE OF TOTAL INPUTS, 1947–56 (R_i), AVERAGE RESEARCH AND DEVELOPMENT DEFLATED BY REAL GROSS PLANT AND EQUIPMENT, 1947–56 (R_k), AVERAGE GROSS PLANT AND EQUIPMENT, 1947–56 (K), PERCENTAGE NET ADDITIONS TO GROSS PLANT AND EQUIPMENT, 1947–56 ($\dot{K}$), AND THE TREND OF PROFITABILITY, 1947–57 (I), CHEMICAL FIRMS

	K	$\dot{K}$	I	R_i	R_k
$\dot{P}$	0.01	(−)0.07	0.60	0.67	0.73
K		0.02	0.00	0.03	(−)0.00
$\dot{K}$			(−)0.06	(−)0.04	(−)0.15
I				0.30	0.46
R_i					0.74

See Table 10 for definitions of variables ($\dot{P}$), (R_i), (R_k), (K), and ($\dot{K}$).

$$I_t = \frac{\text{(Net income after taxes + interest payments + adjustments—as before)}_t}{\text{deflated by the GNP implicit price deflator}}{\text{(Real gross plant and equipment)}_t}$$

= The profitability in year t.

The trend of profitability for an individual firm is obtained by regressing $\log e\ I_t/I_o$ on time. That is:

$$\frac{I_t}{I_o} = C\,e^{rt}$$

where r is the slope of the regression line and the trend of the profitability. I_o is the value of I in 1947.

partial regression coefficients significant at the 1 per cent two-tail level in regressions 4 and 5. In terms of partial coefficients of determination, I explains 46 per cent of the variation in the rate of growth in productivity in regression 4 and 25 per cent of the variation in regression 5, while the research and development measures R_i and R_k explain, respectively, 55 per cent and 53 per cent of the variation in regressions 4 and 5.

What do these results mean? First, it is apparent that both measures of research and development are stronger independent variables than the trend of profitability. Second, if both variables, the rate of growth in productivity and the trend of profitability, were purely the by-products of idiosyncrasies of price changes, the measure of research and development would have become a statistically insignificant independent variable. Third, if idiosyncratic price changes were the result of changes in monopoly pricing power and if research and development represented this effect better than the trend of profitability, then both independent variables would summarize the same effects, and either the weaker one would become statistically insigni-

135

ficant or, if they were equally strong, the regression coefficient of both would become insignificant.

TABLE 15

MULTIPLE REGRESSIONS OF THE RATE OF GROWTH OF PRODUCTIVITY ON RESEARCH AND DEVELOPMENT, ECONOMIES OF SCALE, AND MONOPOLY PRICING VARIABLES CONTAINED IN TABLE 14, CHEMICAL FIRMS

Regression Number and Dependent Variable	Independent Variable					
	K	$\dot{K}$	$\dot{I}$	R_i	R_k	R^2
(1) $\dot{P}$	0.003	0.001			0.305	0.753
	(0.003)	(0.002)			(0.050)	
	0.047	0.017			0.730	
(2) $\dot{P}$	(−)0.001	(−)0.001		0.247		
	(0.004)	(0.002)		(0.049)		0.679
	0.004	0.023		0.649		
(3) $\dot{P}$	0.001	(−)0.001	0.189			
	(0.004)	(0.002)	(0.044)			0.611
	0.009	0.018	0.574			
(4) $\dot{P}$	0.002	0.001	0.087		0.224	
	(0.003)	(0.002)	(0.041)		(0.059)	0.815
	0.035	0.018	0.252		0.526	
(5) $\dot{P}$	(−)0.001	(−)0.000	0.117	0.173		
	(0.003)	(0.002)	(0.035)	(0.043)		0.825
	0.006	0.005	0.457	0.552		

See Table 14 for definitions of the variables.

See Table 7 for a description of the manner in which results are presented.

We have, however, a result where both independent variables are statistically significant. It seems that two interpretations could rationalize the result.

One, the rate of growth in productivity and the trend of profitability are positively correlated since each is affected by the idiosyncrasies of price changes. Thus, to the extent that the rate of growth in productivity is attributable to such uncorrected price changes, an indication of this effect is given by the partial regression coefficient of the trend of the profitability variable. Therefore, under this interpretation, the role of this variable in the regression equation is that of *correcting* our measure of productivity.

Two, there will be a significant positive correlation between the trend of profitability and the rate of growth in productivity, so long as there are other forces affecting the trend which are not summarized by research and development. Factor(s) of production specific to the firm, such as differential entrepreneurial capacity, may be such forces. Furthermore, there are efficiencies obtained from better organization and there are also changes which take place continuously on the production line. To the extent, however, that these changes are obtained through either research and development directly or through other variables for which research and development is an instrumental variable, we have accounted for such forces. However, there is no a priori reason to believe that such is the case. Thus, productivity and profitability may be affected by some types of change independent of research and development, and thus be correlated in the regression beyond their correlation with research and development.

The significant positive correlation between the rate of growth in productivity and the trend of profitability is not prima facie evidence of the existence of idiosyncrasies of price changes—differential behavior of monopoly pricing being a facet—in our productivity measures. However, even if we interpret the results as a case for the existence of such an effect, we see that there is substantial variance in the dependent variable left unexplained by the variable, the trend of profitability.

We can summarize the results of this section to this point thus: we can not conclude whether the significance of the trend of the profitability variable is due to the differential behavior of monopoly power over the period, or to other factors which may have affected both the rates of growth in productivity and the trend values not summarized by the research and development variable.

It should be emphasized that this trend variable at best tests for the changes in monopoly power in the period only. It does not test the level of monopoly power in the industry. If the monopoly power, regardless of how strong it was, had stayed constant, the rates of growth of productivity variables would be immune from errors caused by monopoly considerations. All the observations on productivity for a firm for all years will be inflated or deflated by a constant which, of course, does not affect the slope—the rate of growth of productivity.

RETURNS TO RESEARCH AND DEVELOPMENT EXPENDITURES

Under the "profitability" hypothesis, we saw that lagged research and development explained end-of-period profitability better than vice versa; this suggests that research and development does affect profitability. The logical question, then, is: does research and development explain not only differences in levels of profitability but also differences in profitability time paths among firms?[27] Strictly speaking, a positive correlation between research and development and the rate of growth in productivity does *not* imply a positive correlation between research and development and the trend of profitability, since the latter will depend crucially on the industrial organization and the lags in adjustment to a change in the system. Therefore, we may look at the degree of correlation as an indication either of type of industrial organization or of lags of adjustment present in the industry (see, however, footnote 27).

The dependent variable of our analysis now becomes the trend of profitability $\dot{I}$. The simple coefficients of determination are those given in Table 14. The results of the multiple regression equations are given in Table 16. Average gross plant and equipment K and percentage net additions to gross plant and equipment $\dot{K}$ are utilized as independent variables in regressions (1) through (5). It can be seen that neither variable is significant even at the 10 per cent two-tail level in any of the multiple regressions. The highest partial coefficients of determination for K and $\dot{K}$ are, respectively, 1 per cent and 2 per cent regressions 1 and 2.

Regressions 1 and 2 contain two alternative measures of research and development, R_i and R_k. Both partial regression coefficients are significant at even the 1 per cent two-tail level. In terms of partial coefficients of determination, R_k and R_i explain approximately 43 per cent and 27 per cent of the variation in the dependent variable, respectively.

The above results indicate that the larger the research and development effort the greater the trend (value) in profitability. Strictly speaking, the profitability of all firms but four decreased over time. Therefore, if we think of the highest absolute trend value as zero, the above statement is true. Otherwise we have to restate the relationship in the following way: the larger the research and development the smaller the decrease in profitability. Furthermore, this result indicates that there exists a positive gross return to research and development expenditures.

Multiple regression technique may be used to shed some light on the

[27] To the extent that there are differences in research and development expenditures among firms and since investment in research and development is excluded from our capital base, there is some spurious correlation between research and development and the trend.

TABLE 16

MULTIPLE REGRESSIONS OF THE TREND OF PROFITABILITY (l) ON RESEARCH AND
DEVELOPMENT, ECONOMIES OF SCALE, MONOPOLY PRICING, AND THE RATE
OF GROWTH OF PRODUCTIVITY VARIABLES CONTAINED IN TABLE 14,
CHEMICAL FIRMS

Regression Number and Dependent Variable	Independent Variable					R^2
	K	$\dot{K}$	$\dot{P}$	R_i	R_k	
(1) l	0.008	0.001			0.937	
	(0.018)	(0.011)			(0.288)	0.470
	0.012	0.000			0.431	
(2) l	(−)0.001	(−)0.007		0.630		
	(0.021)	(0.012)		(0.281)		0.315
	0.000	0.023		0.265		
(3) l	(−)0.000	(−)0.002	3.033			
	(0.016)	(0.009)	(0.698)			0.603
	0.000	0.004	0.574			
(4) l	(−)0.000	(−)0.002	2.916		0.049	
	(0.017)	(0.010)	(1.393)		(0.497)	0.603
	0.000	0.003	0.252		0.001	
(5) l	0.002	(−)0.002	3.911	(−)0.334		
	(0.016)	(0.009)	(1.184)	(0.362)		0.627
	0.002	0.005	0.457	0.061		

See Table 14 for definitions of the variables.

See Table 7 for a description of the manner in which results are presented.

direction of the effects. For example, in our problem, we are certain
that research and development will affect profitability if it affects
productivity. Thus when the trend of profitability is the dependent
variable, we can look at research and development (independent variable) as an instrumental variable for the rate of growth of productivity.
Therefore, when both research and development and the rate of
growth of productivity are introduced into the multiple regression
with the trend of profitability as the dependent variable, research and
development should lose its explanatory power. We would expect
this result so long as the simple coefficients of determination between
the dependent and the two independent variables are not of approximately the same magnitude, and so long as the two independent variables do not have substantial correlation between them. In the latter
case the matrix of variance covariance will become larger and larger
tending to give statistically insignificant answers. Having this point

in mind, let us examine the results of multiple regressions (3) through (5) in Table 16 above.

Multiple regression equation 3 contains the rate of growth in productivity $\dot{P}$ in addition to K and $\dot{K}$. The variable $\dot{P}$ has a partial regression coefficient significant at even the 1 per cent two-tail level. Multiple regression equations 4 and 5 include $\dot{P}$ and R_i and, alternatively R_k as independent variables in addition to K and $\dot{K}$. It can be seen that in both regressions the two alternative measures of research and development become statistically insignificant. However, the rate of growth in productivity has a partial regression coefficient significant at even the 1 per cent two-tail level in both regressions 4 and 5.

This result is consistent with our belief that research and development affects profitability if the aforementioned conditions are present in the system, only by *first* affecting productivity.

Conclusion

We have seen that in no single test was the hypothesis advanced in this study disproved. The relevant research and development expenditure was found to be a highly significant independent variable explaining not only the rate of growth in productivity but also the trend of the profitability of eighteen chemical firms in the sample.

In hope of shedding some light on the chain of causality involved, we tested alternative hypotheses that increases in productivity might be explained by profitability or investment. Both hypotheses were rejected. Furthermore, investment in plant and equipment showed a consistent, but not statistically significant, negative correlation with investment in research and development. This suggests that the two types of investment are competitive rather than complementary in nature. We also found that lagged research and development explains end-of-period profitability better than end-of-period research and development is explained by lagged profitability; this suggests that research and development does affect profits.

We also investigated the relationship between the growth in productivity and the rate of change in output, average plant size and, essentially, the rate of growth in plant size. Nowhere did we find a statistically significant relationship. Once we eliminated the statistical illusion of size, we found that firms which spent relatively large sums on research and development were not typically large. In addition, these firms were the highest ranking in productivity gains. We did not find conclusive evidence to dispute the hypothesis that the differential behavior of monopoly power among firms over time may have affected our productivity measure.

We have seen that research and development expenditures explain, significantly, both the level and the trend of profitability. We have concluded that this result indicates that there are gross returns to research and development expenditures. However, the form of the function chosen does not lend itself to estimation of absolute magnitudes of net returns.

Finally, scatter diagrams were investigated for five firms in the drug and pharmaceutical industry. If the pattern of the results obtained for these five firms prevails as sample size increases, we can probably conclude that the above conclusions will also hold for drug and pharmaceutical firms with the exception of the findings about returns to scale.

What can we infer from our results? It will be recalled that the sample was strictly a nonrandom one. Therefore, our conclusions apply only to the firms in the sample; if the sample is representative our conclusions are applicable to the chemical industry. Because of differences among industries, it would be reckless to generalize these results to cover the entire economy (we have no information on relative innovating costs and returns for the latter). Further, all differentials in productivity should not be attributed to research and development expenditures, since these are by nature residuals and may well catch many irrelevant factors such as royalties paid. The test for the royalties hypothesis was inconclusive, perhaps because of poor data. Additional work in this direction may be useful.

The Supply of Inventors and Inventions

FRITZ MACHLUP

PRINCETON UNIVERSITY

THE word "supply" customarily has two different meanings: it means either a quantity actually made available or a schedule of quantities hypothetically made available as a function of one or more independent variables, particularly as a function of the price offered for the good or service in question while other conditions are assumed to be unchanged. In the following discussion of the supply of inventions, supply is to be understood in the second sense: it refers to hypothetical variations in the flow of new inventions becoming available for eventual industrial application in response to variations in the compensation society offers to those who undertake the production of inventions.

Lest we expect from this analysis more than it can yield, we shall note that even the best clues it may afford concerning the flow of inventions would help us toward only a very partial understanding of the determinants of realized technical progress. For, ordinarily, the tempo of effective advance in the productivity of resources will be determined by other things besides the supply of new inventions; in particular, by the rate of actual innovation, which does not depend solely on the rate of invention, and by the rate of the general adoption or imitation of improved technologies, which may be the most decisive variable involved. However, awareness of the fact that answers to many questions are needed does not make any one of them superfluous.

The analysis of the supply of inventions divides itself logically into three sections: (1) the supply of inventive labor—the chief input for the production of inventions; (2) the input-output relationship— the technical "production function" describing the transformation of inventive labor into useful inventions; and (3) the supply and cost of useful inventions—the output obtained from the use of inventive labor. All this, of course, follows the pattern by which the supply of any economic good is analyzed in modern economic theory.

The Supply of Inventive Labor

No unambiguous numerical estimates of the elasticities of supply of inventive talent and effort over substantial ranges can be derived from any data now available or likely to become available in the foreseeable future. Very general statements will have to do for our present purposes. What is needed here are educated guesses, intelligent judgments about the relative scarcity of the supply of qualified personnel and the possibilities of new recruitment and of increased efforts on the part of a given work force.

WHY INVENTORS INVENT

Why inventors invent; what nonpecuniary motivations they may have; whether pecuniary returns are necessary to secure inventive effort beyond a point; whether the size of the pecuniary returns significantly influences the amount of effort devoted to inventive activity; whether increased lucrativeness of inventing attracts proportionately increased personnel; whether increased personnel and increased efforts are likely to yield proportionately increased inventive capacity —these are some of the questions to be examined.

Inventions are sometimes made by accident, not as a result of special purposive efforts. But since even an accidental invention calls for some work—at least for its formulation or description—we may regard inventing as a special effort of labor, capital, and enterprise, and inquire into the motivations behind the expenditure of this effort.

Without trying to present an exhaustive list, we distinguish (1) inventing for fun, (2) inventing for fame, (3) inventing for the service of mankind, and (4) inventing for money. Perhaps we should add (5) inventing as an expression of the "instinct of workmanship"[1] or of the "instinct of contrivance."[2]

There are those who would not see much difference between exertion "for the fun of it"—motive 1—and exertion for the sake of "getting the job done"—motive 5. From a psychological and sociological point of view the difference is perhaps significant. But from the point of view relevant to this analysis, the inventor who enjoys every minute of his activities—as a game or sport, as it were—and the

[1] Thorstein Veblen, "The Instinct of Workmanship and the Irksomeness of Labour," *American Journal of Sociology*, September 1898, pp. 187–201. Id., *The Instinct of Workmanship and the State of the Industrial Arts*, New York, Macmillan, 1914.

[2] Frank W. Taussig, *Inventors and Money-Makers*, New York, Macmillan, 1915, p. 17.

144

inventor who takes pains toiling and sweating over the problems which his instinct of workmanship dictates that he solve, have in common that they ask nothing in return for their efforts.

The only return expected by the person who exerts himself inventing in order to serve humanity—motive 3— is the successful completion of his projects and the feeling that this will contribute to social progress and the happiness of man. The return expected by the fame seeking inventor —motive 2—does not cost society much, because the recognition which it can show for the valuable inventions, the honors which it can bestow upon the great inventor, do not absorb any part of its productive capacity or of its national product, no matter how much productivity may increase as a result of the new inventions. (There will of course be a social cost measured by the alternative uses of the inventors' time and effort. But we are discussing here the compensations received by the inventors.)

The inventors who do their work as amateur sportsmen, workmanlike professionals, applause-seeking stars, or high-minded public servants require no money rewards—though they may be willing or even anxious to accept pecuniary advantages if such are given to other inventors under the institutional arrangements adopted by society. Any income they derive from their inventive activity is, therefore, in the nature of pure economic rent, that is, a payment not needed to call forth their efforts. What part of all inventive activity undertaken in our society is actually of this variety is anybody's guess. It may be only an insignificant fraction of the total inventive effort or it may be a substantial portion, at least of the labor effort of the highest qualities of inventive personnel. Certainly it cannot be the whole, simply because, if for no other reason, most people could not afford to spend much of their time on inventive work if it did not pay. Thus, undoubtedly some part of the labor devoted to the production of new inventions is supplied only in consideration of the pecuniary compensation that is held out to such labor.[3]

Beyond a certain point, the supply of inventive effort will depend on the offer (or hope) of pecuniary compensation. Thus, the supply

---

[3] Polled by questionnaire, 710 individual inventors reported on their motivation: 193 of them listed "love of inventing," 189 listed "desire to improve;" as against these 382 amateurs, sportsmen, and idealists, only 167 answered that "financial gain" had been their motive. But in answer to a different question, 265 of the 710 inventors, or 38.2 per cent, reported that they were earning their livelihood by inventing. See Joseph Rossman, "The Motives of Inventors," *Quarterly Journal of Economics*, 1931, pp. 522, 526.

curve will start rising. Will this rise be gentle or abrupt? How elastic will the supply of inventive labor be once it becomes a function of pay? A judicious answer first requires that we distinguish among the concepts of labor force, labor time, labor energy, labor quality, and labor effectiveness.

EXTRA EFFORT AND OVERTIME

Although the distinction between *labor time* and *labor energy* is relevant for many problems, we need not complicate our argument, and may assume that the labor energy expended per hour will not be affected by the amount of compensation.

The distinction between *labor force* and *labor time* is relevant because there may be some elasticity in the supply of inventive labor merely because of changes in the number of hours worked per man. This would be socially significant because an increase in inventive labor, to the extent that it is only at the expense of people's leisure, would not encroach upon alternative productive activities. Persons with a bent for tinkering and inventing, busy with other jobs during their regular hours, may be willing to devote more of their free evenings and week-ends to inventive activity. Scientists and engineers employed in research and development may be willing to work overtime. But, however important that possibility might be in times of emergency for the implementation of "crash programs" in research and development, long-run programs designed for "progress in general" cannot successfully be based on the continuous and continual supply of overtime labor. The other source of supply of extra labor hours—the spare time of amateur researchers and tinkerers— can possibly be drawn upon regularly. (To have mobilized these individual inventors is perhaps one of the achievements of the patent system in times past.) But it is a very limited source of supply, probably fully exhausted in the earliest phase of the rising supply curve of inventive labor. We may conclude that the possible sacrifice of leisure cannot be counted on to provide substantial amounts of labor for additional inventive activity; and it will therefore be no serious mistake to think of new recruitments to the inventive labor force, diverting labor from other occupations, as the only significant element in the elasticity of supply of inventive labor.

Thus, when we speak of the supply of inventive labor we shall not stop to differentiate between the size of the inventive labor force and the amounts of time and energy expended per man but shall simply think of the total amount of inventive labor as some number of men (or man-hours); indeed we shall, for the sake of simpler expression, use the term inventive labor force as equivalent to the total effort devoted to the search for inventions.

QUALITY DIFFERENCES AND NEW RECRUITMENT

We must not, however, neglect differences in *labor quality*; they are particularly important in the case of researchers and inventors. It would seem that the blend of training, experience, originality, tenacity, and perhaps genius which makes a man a potentially successful inventor is too "special" to permit the economic theorist to make his customary assumption of "homogeneity of productive resources"— unless he has very good excuses. Whether his trick of translating different qualities into one standard quality ("efficiency units" or "corrected natural units") can serve a good purpose here, will have to be examined. Off hand, a statement that five hours of Mr. Doakes' time were the equivalent of one hour of Mr. Edison's or two hours of Mr. Bessemer's would sound preposterous. But if such "misplaced concreteness" is avoided, the device may prove helpful in abstract arguments.

Inasmuch as the problem of differences in the quality of inventive talent concerns us chiefly in connection with new recruits to the inventive labor force, the speed with which the recruitment is to be accomplished will be an important consideration. The time element is always significant in elasticity problems; it is particularly so regarding entry into an occupation such as "inventing", for which training and experience are essential.

A distinction between the short run and the long run is the customary device for focusing attention on important differences in the length of time allowed for certain reactions to given changes. Present membership in the labor force may be made the criterion for the distinction between short-run and long-run supply of inventive labor. The short-run supply curve would then depict the rates of compensation necessary to secure an expansion of the inventive work force through transfers from other fields and occupations; the long-run supply curve would depict the rates at which an expansion can be secured through both transfers of persons already in the labor force and recruitment of persons entering the labor force for the first time.[4]

The short-run supply function of inventive labor expresses the ease or difficulty of drawing on trained, though probably less experienced, personnel; for the most part, these will be persons now engaged in teaching or fundamental research who can be induced to switch to applied research and development work. The long-run supply function must reflect consideration of the teaching capacity of the universities and institutes of technology, and of the pool or flow of potentially qualified students. Obviously, the elasticity of the long-run supply is greater than that of the short-run supply; it will be largely a matter of letting public knowledge of job openings and of differential earnings potentials steer young students into the natural science and engineering departments of the institutions of higher education. The question is whether, in both the long run and the short, additions to a given amount of inventive labor—additions in response to higher pay— are apt to be of lower quality.

The Short-Run Supply

Some of the clues that come to mind when one reflects on the question of quality differences in connection with the short-run supply of inventive labor seem to be contradictory. There is the case of the academic scientist who, bribed into industrial research, out-invents the most seasoned inventors. The success stories of former university professors as salaried inventors employed in industrial research and development work may be presented as evidence in support of an argument that the quality of new members of the inventive labor force need not be below the previous average, and may even be above it— at least as long as there are still professors that can be lured from their academic posts. (This reservation is significant; it shows again that much depends on where one "starts" adding to the force already employed, that is, on how many more researchers can be obtained in further raids on college and university faculties.) The validity of the evidence, however, may be questioned on several grounds: that the cases cited were exceptions to the rule; that many of the new members

---

[4] It is convenient to think of the new entrants into the labor force as equal in number to those leaving the labor force through death or retirement. This simplification is designed to separate the problem of allocation from the problem of population growth. This does not mean that a long-run supply curve of this sort will be less relevant in an analysis of the allocation problem of a growing total labor force; but the supply curve of any particular kind of labor would have to be in terms of percentage shares of the growing labor force. For the sake of simpler expression it is customary to discuss resource allocation under the assumption of a given labor force, even for the long run.

of industrial research staffs had previously been engaged in inventive work of a more fundamental nature and that their transfer from academic to industrial positions was in fact not a net addition to the inventive work force; that many of these transfers were made in response, not to the lure of money, but to appeals to undertake tasks of immediate usefulness in a national emergency.

The opposite contention can also be defended; that as a rule the qualifications of new transfers to the inventive work force will be inferior to those of persons who have entered it earlier for less pay. Such an argument may be based on rather broad generalizations about "typical" human attitudes: that ordinarily people prefer to do things they are good at. The person who prefers to teach or write, and who will only by much higher rates of compensation be attracted to the engineer's draftboard or the industrial laboratory, is probably less qualified for inventive work than the "tinker and contriver" who follows an almost irresistible drive to find and try new devices. Regardless of whether more weight is given to deductions from such speculative assumptions or to inductive generalizations from individual observations, one will have to yield to the common-sense judgment that a point must exist beyond which further transfers to the research and development work force cannot possibly be of the same quality. The number of trained people in the labor force is limited and if research and development staffs are to be expanded close to that limit or beyond it, less qualified persons will have to be included.

The Long-Run Supply

Regarding the long-run supply of inventive labor, is there any presumption that those who are attracted only by higher rates of pay are less qualified than those willing to work for less? Youngsters, at the time when they choose their professional training, may not yet have developed preferences consistent with their aptitudes. They may have a preference for one thing but superior aptitude for another. Better earnings prospects might then bring into the field young people not less qualified than those who would have chosen it even with poorer earnings prospects. If this should be a valid argument in speculating about the long-run supply of inventive labor, it certainly cannot be valid for unlimited amounts of labor. For in calculations of the potential supply of inventive labor, innate ability undoubtedly counts as much as training, if not much more. The popular hero worship for inventors may grossly exaggerate the scarcity of inventive genius but to suppose that mere training can produce any desired amounts of inventive capacity is a worse exaggeration in the opposite direction. One may, of course, steer more young people toward inventive work, but one must not expect them all to be of equal caliber.

If additional personnel is attracted to the inventive labor force only by higher rates of compensation and if, by and large, the newcomers are less qualified than those who are willing to work for less, the elasticity of the "effective supply" of inventive labor is held down by both factors, preference and aptitude. If the supply of inventive labor expressed in terms of natural units (man-hours) is not very elastic, it will certainly be still less elastic if expressed in terms of units corrected for differential qualification.[5]

Higher rates of pay (or expected pay) might, at some point, call forth hardly any more inventors, but merely more associate inventors and assistant inventors, that is, talents not apt to produce independently, but only to assist the leading men, taking off their shoulders some of the work that can be assigned, and thus releasing some of their time and thought for the really creative tasks. The aggergate capacity to produce new inventions can thus be increased through additions to the inventive labor force, regardless of whether the additional men are working independently of or in collaboration with those previously at work.[6] But the addition of thousands of hours of work of assisting specialists (engineers, researchers, etc.) may mean merely hundreds of hours added to really inventive activity or capacity,[7] and the latter can therefore be expanded only at a greatly increased money cost.

This does not say anything about the prospect that increased amounts of inventive talent put to work will actually produce new inventions in proportionately increased amounts. The supply we have been discussing is merely that of talent and effort ready to be put to

[5] The technique of "corrected natural units" is used here only as an analogy, not as a measuring device. A supply curve in terms of "corrected natural units" is not only less elastic than a supply curve in natural units but also smaller (to the left of it) over at least a part of its course.

[6] In a sense, another errand boy hired for an industrial research laboratory would be an addition to the inventive labor force inasmuch as he may enable the staff to work with fewer interruptions. However, if we go that far in expanding the concept of "inventive labor", some of our earlier generalizations concerning its supply in terms of natural units would lose validity. It is preferable to confine the concept to the professional personnel.

[7] "The real moving spirits are few and the rest pedestrian, although of course useful, supporters. Quantity cannot make up for quality and little purpose is served in lamenting the absence of what are in fact unattainable levels of intellectual coordination when there are always too few minds of the highest calibre and there is a limit to the help that can be afforded them in their original thinking." John Jewkes, David Sawyers, and Richard Stillerman, *The Sources of Invention*, London, Macmillan, 1958, p. 162.

work—the input, not that of the actual product of this talent and effort—the output, in the form of workable inventions.

THE SOCIAL COST OF THE ADDITIONAL LABOR IN INDUSTRIAL RESEARCH

The additional money outlay required to secure a small addition to the inventive labor force is no fair indication of the social cost involved. The money outlay includes the surplus, or rent, accruing to inventive personnel who would have been willing to work for less than the rate of compensation that is actually paid in order to attract more people to research and development work. These rent payments do not themselves signify the use of more resources; and only the cost of additional resources, in terms of alternatives foregone, constitutes a social cost. The increased rent payments are merely transfers of income from one part of society to another; they are losses to "society exclusive of inventive personnel," and gains for the members of the "inventive labor force" (who are of course part of "society as a whole").

The social cost of inventions is determined by the value of the most valuable alternative output that could be produced with the same input. But the price paid for any sort of input will reflect the social value of its potential output only where the resources are acquired in competitive markets and where the market prices of all alternative outputs reflect their full contributions to economic welfare. It is very doubtful that these conditions are met in the case of the resources required for the production and development of inventions. With regard to the alternative uses of the resources, chiefly basic research and higher education, the social benefits resulting are far above any private benefits conferred on their "buyers." The market prices of education and basic research and the compensations paid to scholars are no more commensurate with the social value of the services rendered than the market prices of inventions and the compensations paid to inventors are with the social value of inventions. Thus, the compensations needed to attract additional labor into the business of inventing do not reflect the social values of education and basic research that are foregone by the transfer of personnel.[8]

---

[8] For a preliminary discussion of the alternative costs of education, basic research, and industrial research, all competing for the same productive resources, see my article "Can There Be Too Much Research?" *Science*, 1958, pp. 1320–25. A more detailed treatment, including relevant statistical information, will be found in "The Allocation of Scientific Personnel" a doctoral dissertation by Vladimir Stoikov, submitted to the Johns Hopkins University (May 1960).

The Production of Inventions

To regard a study of the supply of inventive labor as a prerequisite of a study of the cost and supply of inventions is to assume that there is a quantitative relationship between the input of labor and the output of inventions. The implications are that inventions are "produced," that the volume of production can be measured or at least "sized up" to the extent necessary to make it meaningful to speak of an increase and a decrease in the flow of new inventions, and that changes in output depend on changes in input, at least partially. These assumptions should not be made without attempting to justify them.

One might take the position, and defend it on good grounds, that it is impossible even to define invention, let alone identify, count, or weight inventions for purposes of measuring the quantity produced by inventive effort. And if it is meaningless to quantify the output, it must be meaningless to assert or posit the existence of a quantitative relationship between input and output. Or, one might take a less negative position and grant the possibility of quantifying the inputs and outputs, at least roughly or merely for purposes of constructional reasoning, but at the same time hold that the incidence of accidents in making inventions is too great to legitimize, even provisionally, the assumption of a "production function," a functional relationship between input and output. These issues are discussed in other papers of this volume.

Assuming that it makes sense to quantify the input, i.e. inventive labor plus equipment and whatever else is needed, as well as the output, i.e. new technical inventions, will a model that assumes a functional relation between input and output be relevant in an interpretation of the real facts concerning the flow of inventions?

An affirmative answer—at least to the extent that an increase in input will, as a rule, produce an increase in output—is implied in the theory that invention can be "stimulated" by patent systems or subsidization. Even more than that is implied in the familiar arguments about the need or desirability of increased industrial research and development: they implicitly deny, on the one hand, that a very small increase in research will suffice to produce a vast increase in inventions and, on the other, that a huge increase in research will produce but a trivial increase in inventions. Thus there has always been an implicit acceptance of a sort of "production function" affirming a positive correlation between input and output and expressing certain constraints which exclude extreme values of the input-output ratio.

These constraints have long been thought to apply only to the "invention industry" as a whole. For individual producers of inventions no functional dependence of output upon input seemed to hold: a most extravagant increase in input might yield no inventions whatsoever, and a reduction in inventive effort might by a fluke result in the output that had in vain been sought with great expense. As in a lottery, individuals would still make plans involving high stakes on the basis of a probability calculus that applied only to the whole population of gamblers, not to any single one. The making of inventions would be a lucky accident, nothing the individual firm could count on. The inventive process, however, has become more methodical than it used to be in earlier times, more systematic, mechanized, and routinized,[9] until it now seems that the probability calculus applies to individual producers of inventions, even to medium- and small-scale establishments.[10] All of the large firms and a good many smaller ones, in the industries in which technology has been advancing rapidly, regularly allocate funds for research and development, and one could hardly assume that they do so as a sheer gamble, without rational and reasonable expectations of a satisfactory return. They have learned that research expenditures can be profitable, and this implies that they expect inputs of inventive labor and complementary resources to produce workable new inventions.

All production functions involve probability distributions of some sort, with more or less wide deviations from the norm resulting from such factors as variations in the performance (speed, accuracy) of human operations, differences in the quality (purity, strength, consistence) of materials, unevenness in the operation (speed, accuracy) of tools and machines, fluctuations in the supply (quantity, pressure, tension) of energy, changes in weather (precipitation, humidity, sunshine, winds), etc. The deviations are notoriously great in agricultural

[9] "The greatest invention of the nineteenth century was the invention of the method of invention." Alfred North Whitehead, *Science and the Modern World*, London, Macmillan, 1925, p. 120.

[10] "In the larger firms of today, the flow of new ideas for product and process innovation results, not from the chance inspiration of exceptional individuals, but from a deliberate decision by management to spend money on research and development. There is still a great need for the inspiration of genius, but much routine discovery and improvement waits simply for the investment of sufficient resources." Charles F. Carter and B. R. Williams, *Industry and Technical Progress: Factors Governing the Speed of Application of Science*, London, Oxford University Press, 1957, p. 108.

production, with its dependence on weather (rainfall, frosts), insects, fungi, etc. This does not prevent anybody from basing theoretical as well as practical considerations upon production functions for agricultural products. Both the individual farmer and the government adviser on farm policy assume for their plans—the former for his private production plan, the latter for some national program—that the use of more land, more seed, more fertilizer, and more labor would increase output by certain quantities. Perhaps there is less uncertainty in the production plan for an entire region or country than there is for an individual farm because of the likelihood that positive and negative deviations will cancel out in the larger "population."

That chance, luck, and accident play an unusually large role in the "invention industry" need not preclude the existence of sufficient regularities in the production of inventions to permit expression of the relationships in the form of production functions. What does, however, complicate matters in the invention industry is the extreme heterogeneity of the product as well as of the producing units. May one assume much similarity in the input-output relations that are relevant for individual inventors (self-employed free lancers), small teams of experts specializing in research and consultation work in particular fields, large independent or cooperative research laboratories, scientific or engineering departments of universities, governmental research agencies, and research and development divisions of large industrial concerns? Is it reasonable to expect much similarity in input-output relations in the inventive work in aeronautics, electronics, nuclear physics, chemical engineering, automotive mechanics, etc.? Can one justify the assumption that there is some reasonably stable ratio of successful to unsuccessful tries in the mass of all inventive work with its uncertain composition?

To ask these questions is to suggest negative answers. Contrary to other industries where the probable errors are larger for individual producers than for the industry as a whole, the "invention industry" is apt to present smaller dispersions in the probability distributions for the individual producers. The individual firm undertaking inventive work in a certain field and attempting to solve some problems related to more or less circumscribed objectives is quite capable of setting out with fixed budgets, appropriations, and time schedules, that is, with a specification of the inputs believed necessary to achieve the goal, to produce the inventions wanted. This is true for the small independent research outfit (producing nothing but inventions) as well as for a research organization integrated with a firm that also produces other products, particularly the kind of product for which the wanted inventions would be most useful. But to develop a production function for "inventions in general" for the "invention industry as a whole" seems an impossible task, especially if nothing is said about what kinds of inventions are sought.

Such a disappointingly negative conclusion, however, implies an excessively literal interpretation of the term "production function." One need only remember the universally accepted proposition that "agriculture operates under diminishing returns" to realize that no definite, numerically specifiable production function for agricultural output is referred to in the context. Obviously, there cannot be one definite aggregate production function for a variable composite of barley, wheat, rye, corn, rice, cotton, tobacco, potatoes, carrots, spinach, and all the rest, produced on land of all grades and locations, by farms of all sizes. Yet, a statement concerning constant or diminishing returns in the agriculture of a certain country at a certain time makes perfectly good sense. The unit of output would be some "homogenized bushel of produce" and the shape of the production function would merely illuminate the general nature of such quantitative relationships as are relevant to the problem at hand. It is in this sense that one may speak of the invention industry and of its output, which evidently is not homogeneous but which can be "homogenized" for the sake of reasoning and discussion. To repeat, the production function of inventions in general in the invention industry as a whole is only an abstract construction designed to characterize some quantitative relationships which are regarded as empirically relevant.

THE RATE OF INVENTIVE OUTPUT IN THE ECONOMY AS A WHOLE

What does the production function look like? Are there ranges of increasing and diminishing returns in the production of inventions in the economy as a whole? Is there an optimum point or range in the resource allocation to the "invention industry"? Is the total inventive effort in the economy more likely to be of such dimensions that it would be more efficient if it were expanded or if it were cut down? Not that efficiency in the production of inventions—that is, the smallest possible number of researchers and developers per invention—should be regarded as an end in itself. If society were getting as many inventions per year as it wanted, it would be foolish to push for more just because this would raise the average output per inventive worker. Similarly, if the flow of inventions was inadequate and society wanted to increase it, it would be foolish to hold back just because the increase would lower the average per inventive worker. But, even if the possibility of improving the input-output ratio in the production of inventions (by expanding it under increasing returns or curtailing it under diminishing returns) cannot be a decisive factor in society's decision concerning the desired flow of inventions, it is nevertheless something to be taken into account.

Superficially it might appear that the question of increasing or decreasing returns to inventive effort in the economy as a whole is the same as, or related to, the frequently discussed question of the acceleration or retardation of the rate of invention in the course of time. There have been two schools of thought on the subject of the effect of the flow of inventions upon the ease of making further inventions. According to the "acceleration school," the more that is invented the easier it becomes to invent still more. This is deduced from the assumption that every new invention furnishes a new idea for potential combination with vast numbers of existing ideas; and from the mathematical proposition that the number of possible combinations increases geometrically with the number of elements at hand. According to the "retardation school," the more that is invented, the harder it becomes to invent still more. This is deduced from the assumption that there are limits to the improvement of technology. In its extreme form this thesis states that the more that has been invented the less there is left to be invented.

Although this issue concerning the historical—past or future—change in the potential rate of technological progress will presently be shown to be irrelevant to the question of the potential returns to inventive effort at any particular time, it is worth while reflecting about it. There is no a priori reason why the possibilities of technological development should be either narrowly limited or virtually limitless. Nor is there any legitimate basis for inductive inferences from the relatively brief periods in which accelerated or retarded rates of inventive accomplishment were observed.

In periods of depression prophets of technological stagnation were usually listened to with greater attention, and repeatedly over the last hundred years persons recognized as authorities at the time told the world that all important inventions had already been made and no further inventions of great import could be expected. Such pessimistic predictions of the future of technological exploration look particularly comical to a reader who has the advantage of hindsight, for they were made before the automotive, electrical, radiomagnetic, and nuclear revolutions of technology had occurred. Thus the predictions were surely wrong at the time they were made. There is little inclination to accept such predictions as correct at the present.

Prophets of an ever-increasing flow of inventions have also been disappointed. Even if patent statistics (which show a drastic decline in patenting relative to the manpower employed in research and development) are rejected as a yardstick for the flow of inventions, no evidence has been presented to support the thesis that the rate of inventive accomplishment has been increasing relative to the size of the population, the labor force, or the inventive work force. There are indications that inventing is becoming increasingly expensive in terms of man-hours. But this need not be taken as counterevidence to the assertion that inventing becomes easier over time; it may merely be indicative of overly intensive efforts to achieve too much in a short time. And this brings us back to the question of increasing and decreasing returns to inventive activity at a given time.

These are two essentially different issues: one refers to the shape of the production function (in the invention industry) at a certain time; the other refers to the shift of the production function in the course of time. In other words, increasing or diminishing returns relate to the production possibilities existing at a certain time; accelerating or decelerating rates of invention relate to changes in the production possibilities over time. In the former relationship the accomplishment per man is a function of the number of men employed while "time," with all environmental conditions, is unchanged; in the latter the accomplishment per man is a function of time while the number of men employed (in the invention industry) is unchanged (absolutely or relative to the labor force).

THE LAWS OF RETURNS AND THE TECHNOLOGY OF PRODUCING TECHNOLOGY

Increasing returns in the inventive work of a nation can prevail if the national scale of research is too small to permit sufficient division of labor among specialists and enough cross-fertilization between experts in different fields of knowledge. There may be such a thing as a balanced growth of knowledge that can be achieved only if the total amount of research is large enough for simultaneous work in many areas. If some of the frontiers of knowledge are not manned with sufficiently large forces, the progress of work along other sectors may be retarded. An increase in the total work force may then bring about a more than proportional increase in the rate of invention. This range of increasing returns is of course limited: as soon as the required minimum numbers of research workers are allocated to all areas of scientific and technological knowledge, further additions to the inventive work force can at best produce proportional increases in inventions.

As from time to time fundamental discoveries open up entirely new areas of research, development, and experimentation, the opportunities to produce new inventions may be radically improved and an inventive work force which had been large enough to extend far beyond the range of increasing returns may suddenly be too small to take advantage of the new opportunities. In other words, the new (or shifted) production function for inventions may be such that a given amount of inventive labor, previously operating under constant or diminishing returns, would be back in the range of increasing returns.

The possibility of diminishing returns in the invention industry may seem puzzling on first thought. The phenomenon of diminishing returns is always attributable to the presence of one or more fixed factors —factors necessary in production but not present in increased quantities when the input of variable factors is increased. The variable factors in the case before us are inventive labor plus the required facilities for research and experimentation (laboratory space, instruments and machines, materials, energy, administrative and clerical help). What are the fixed factors in the production of inventions?

In order to answer this question we must inquire a little into the technology of the production of technological inventions, which is a rather peculiar, bewildering business. In general, technology is the art of transforming certain materials into certain products, usually with the aid of certain kinds of equipment; in the production of inventions, however, technology is also the chief raw material and equipment, and it is the product, to boot. The inventor starts with technology, applies technology, and ends up with technology.

The process of inventing may be schematized as follows. First, the inventor is confronted with a problem, that is, with dissatisfaction about the ways certain things are done coupled with a feeling that there are better ways of doing them. Second, he tries to think of similar problems that have been solved before, which either are familiar to him or which he proceeds to study. This usually gives him clues for possible plans to be followed in the solution of his problem. Third, he carries out these plans, several of which may not work but may suggest other clues. Finally, he finds a solution.[11] If this scheme describes the technology of problem solving and inventing, it also makes clear that, in the earlier steps, technology, the existing stock of scientific knowledge and knowledge of the industrial arts, enters as raw material and equipment, while in the end technology, an advance in the technical arts, emerges as the product of the inventive process.

Once the multiple role of technology in the inventive process is understood, it will not appear paradoxical if the existing stock of scientific knowledge and the state of the industrial arts at any moment of time is named as a fixed factor in the process of producing new inventions. The number of problems to be solved (the stock of known problems) is another factor fixed at any moment of time. If increasing amounts of variable factors—inventive labor effort with all the required facilities—are applied to a given amount of known problems and a given equipment of known technology, the increase in the amount of product in the form of technological advances will, beyond a point, be less than proportional.

DIMINISHING RETURNS

Increased amounts of inventive talent devoted to the search for solutions to given problems, and further drawing on the given stock of knowledge, will bring forth novel solutions in increased numbers but after some point the increase in output, in terms of solutions or inventions, will not be in proportion to the increase in input. An expansion of the number of research men working on the production of new knowledge would of course always be technically possible (in contrast to those kinds of production where the fixed factor is a tangible thing, such as land or machinery, and where men, beyond some number, would get in one another's way or could physically not get near the fixed factor). But the addition of more researchers, beyond some number, would imply duplication of effort, resulting not in more new solutions to open problems but in more frequent instances of simultaneous or nearly simultaneous arrivals by several inventors at similar solutions

---

[11] Cf. G. Polya, *How to Solve It*, Princeton University Press, 1948, *passim*. From this schematic description it ought to become obvious that a separation of the cost of failures from the cost of successful tries cannot reasonably be attempted.

to identical problems. The output of new inventions might not be much increased.

Merely in order to guard against misunderstandings, it should be remembered (1) that diminishing returns in the production of inventions prevail not from the start, that is, not for small amounts of input of effort, but only after input has reached a certain point; and (2) that the point where diminishing returns set in is apt to be pushed up as the stock of existing knowledge grows, because the number of problems on which work may fruitfully be done is likely to increase with that growth.

Some economists with an exaggerated opinion of dynamic theory and an inadequate understanding of static reasoning might hold that the entire conception of diminishing returns is out of place in an area as intrinsically dynamic as the production of knowledge. Since any new discovery or invention changes the stock of knowledge as well as the stock of problems to be solved, what sense is there in assuming that knowledge and problems are fixed?

If some may have a hard time seeing the sense of such an assumption, an explanation must be provided even if it insults the intelligence of those to whom the point is obvious. The point is that an allocation of research personnel that will fit the research agenda of next year need not fit the agenda today. If the list of problems to be solved is apt to grow from today to next month, and still more to next year, this does not mean that it would serve any good purpose to employ a research staff too large for the present tasks. It may, of course, be wise to provide for a gradual increase in the research staff commensurate with the increase in the stock of problems to be solved. At any moment, however, the number of men used for inventive work may be such that the amount of duplication is moderate, substantial, or enormous. At any moment, in other words, the production of inventions may be pushed far into the range of diminishing returns, conceivably even into the range where marginal returns to inventive input are zero. If the manpower so lavishly employed is kept unchanged for some time, it is possible that the research agenda will grow to a point of parity with the oversized research outfit. This would not make the original over-allocation of resources any more justifiable than it would be in any other industry: the expectation of growth, and therefore of growing manpower needs, does not warrant the employment of more labor than can be efficiently used at the time being.

Comprehension of this point is perhaps made more difficult by the realization that the technological horizon may rather suddenly be expanded by a fundamental discovery which shifts the production function for technical inventions most drastically. In view of this peculiar way in which the dynamic aspects of the growth of knowledge impinge on the relevance of static theorizing, it may be desirable to deal once more with the effects which discoveries and inventions may have upon the production of inventions.

PROBLEM-RAISING SOLUTIONS

Invention is the solution of a technological problem; but it is possible that in the course of solving a problem or as a result of solving it new problems are raised. Thus, an invention may fulfill a task and at the same time create more tasks. To be sure, not all inventions are of this sort. The solution of an old problem may leave less to be done, one item of the agenda having been checked off as completed. We may call such a solution an agenda-reducing invention. If a solution by raising new problems leaves more to be done than there had been before, we may call it an agenda-increasing invention or discovery.

Fundamental discoveries and basic inventions, by definition, open up new vistas and create new opportunities for further invention. Thus, one might be tempted to generalize and state that basic research will yield agenda-increasing discoveries while applied research will yield agenda-reducing inventions. This would, however, be an exaggeration. Industrial research of a definitely applied kind may result in inventions of considerable complementarity with solutions to new technical problems. Indeed, a relatively narrow invention may point to some previously unnoticed gap in basic knowledge and thus raise problems for fundamental research. And, more often, an invention of the mere gadget type may unexpectedly create the opportunity—nay, the necessity—for scores of additional inventions.

Several writers have distinguished between two kinds of inventions: fundamental (basic, major, revolutionary, breakthrough, key) inventions and accessory (adaptive, minor, perfecting, improvement) inventions. Every fundamental invention creates an opportunity for many accessory inventions. Hence, the emergence of a fundamental invention is apt to change the input-output ratio of inventive effort, that is, the productivity of a given size of inventive labor force and the productivity of a given increase in the same. But the dichotomy is not the same as that between agenda-increasing and agenda-reducing inventions. Mere perfecting or improvement inventions may suggest possible combinations with other technological elements or possible applications to entirely different kinds of products, and thus be of the agenda-increasing type, leaving more, not less, to be done in times to come.

The predictions of acceleration or of retardation in the rate of invention, which we have mentioned above, reflect to some extent judgments about the relative frequencies of agenda-increasing and agenda-reducing inventions. But the conflict of recorded opinion is probably less serious than one may think. For it seems that several writers who assumed a prevalence of agenda-reducing inventions and predicted, therefore, a retardation in the rate of inventive achievements were thinking of particular industries or particular areas of technology. On the other hand, those who assumed a prevalence of agenda-increasing inventions and consequently predicted an acceleration of invention appear to have been thinking of the entire domain of technology. Retardation of invention in particular industries would be perfectly compatible with acceleration of invention in the economy as a whole.

For the economy as a whole, or for the entire domain of technology, the assumption of a prevalence of agenda-increasing inventions is probably more plausible. This does not, however, imply that the production function will necessarily shift upward in the sense that a given number of inventors will produce more inventions per unit of time. The continuing increase in the stock of technological problems to be solved, which is implied in the assumption of a prevalence of agenda-increasing inventions, will extend both the ranges of increasing and of diminishing returns to inventive personnel and, thus, allow a larger inventive work force to be employed without excessively wasteful duplication. But the enlargement of the agenda, the increase in the number of problems on which work can be done, need not increase productivity per research worker. Many of the new problems may be tougher than the older ones were. An increase in opportunities to invent need not mean that inventions become easier to make; on the contrary, they may become harder. In this case, there could be a retardation of invention despite the prevalence of agenda-increasing inventions and a continuing increase in inventive possibilities.

The hypothesis of the increasing difficulty of new technological problems would force abandonment of the homogenizing device proposed in the discussion of the quantification of invention. It may be permissible to speak of an output of inventions of average difficulty so long as one deals with the potential solutions of given technological problems worked upon by varying numbers of inventive personnel. But if one has to deal with the dynamic problem of changes, from period to period, in the state of knowledge and the stock of problems to be solved, then the homogenizing of the output of inventions becomes useless and even misleading.

If the separability of the static problem from the dynamic problem is conceded, if it is understood that the shift of the production function for inventions is one thing and its shape another, and if the implications of that shape for problems of resource allocation are realized, then the previously stated conclusion, that it is possible for society to devote such large amounts of productive resources to the production of inventions that additional inputs will lead to less than proportional increases in output, will no longer be questioned. Whether at any given moment the inventive labor force employed has actually reached the point of diminishing returns is a question for practical expert judgment.

In any event, even if we knew for certain that society had pushed its inventive efforts far into the phase of diminishing returns, we could not infer that it had gone too far. Similarly, the most certain knowledge that we were still far away from that phase would not provide sufficient reason for society to go more heavily into the business of inventing. After all, the evaluation of the physical cost of inventing is only a small part of the task of evaluating the economic or social net benefit of inventive work. But it is by no means irrelevant or unimportant to know that the cost of inventions in terms of physical inputs may be diminishing, constant, or increasing, depending on the circumstances, and also to know under what circumstances one might have to take account of the possibility that the cost is increasing at a forbidding rate.

INVENTIONS SELECTED OR REJECTED FOR USE

Not all new inventions turn out to be workable; not all that seem technically workable turn out to be commercially usable; and not all that might be commercially usable are actually used, many being rejected in favor of others that look more promising. As a matter of fact, the percentage of all new inventions actually put to practical use is very small indeed.[12]

---

[12] "Invention is necessarily wasteful. When everything feasible has been done to plan research coherently, the uncertainty of the outcome, even of the less revolutionary

Should only the inventions selected for use or the rejected as well be counted in the quantity of inventions produced? One may wish to follow the practice of other industries in reporting total output, and ask whether rejects—units or lots discarded as substandard—are commonly included in or excluded from total output. It happens that the conventions are not uniform. In a large number of industries anything that is rejected as inferior, defective, or below standard before it is shipped or sold is not regarded as produced, whereas waste or discard in processing plants or in distributing establishments is included in total output. (For example, in fruit crops the quantities not approved for sale are excluded but the quantities spoiled in transport or at the distributors are included; steel output excludes defective lots which the steel mill regards as scrap, but includes waste and scrap at the fabricators; total paper production excludes the so called broke in paper manufacturing mills but includes the waste in paper converting mills.) Thus, it usually depends on where the quality control takes place and who does the rejecting. But, no matter whether this or any other convention of terminology is followed, it should always be possible to distinguish gross and net production and to ascertain the net output—quantity produced net of all rejected or discarded portions —or the effective supply, the schedule of quantities supplied after deducting rejected quantities. If the ratio of rejects to gross output is in any way related to changes in the latter, it is highly important not to stop the analysis with gross output. This seems to be a significant

---

inventions, is bound to mean much failure and disappointment. Thus Carter and Williams report that: 'It is not possible to get useful statistics for the proportion of good ideas that are rejected after applied research—in industrial laboratories that we have visited it varies between 50 and 90 per cent—but certainly the proportion is high.' Even the ideas that pass this technical test may fail to pass the economic test and may very properly be rejected at this stage." Quoted from Thomas Wilson, "Science and Industry," *Lloyds Bank Review*, October 1957, p. 37. It has been estimated that between 80 and 90 per cent of all patented inventions remain unused for technical or economic reasons. Cf. Peter Meinhardt, *Inventions, Patents, and Monopoly*, 2nd ed., London, Stevens, 1950, p. 256. Other estimates are even more pessimistic: "Perhaps 95 per cent of all patents have no commercial value at all" (Jewkes *et al.*, *op. cit.*, p. 106). The failure of patentees to renew their patents, in countries charging renewal fees, throws some light on this question. In Germany before 1920, 80 per cent of all patents had been allowed to lapse after six years and more than 96 per cent had been allowed to lapse earlier than after fifteen years, their maximum duration. See Robolski and Lutter, "Patentrecht," *Handwörterbuch der Staatswissenschaften*, 4th ed., Jena, Fischer, 1920, Vol. VI, p. 826. On the other hand a recent study of "patent use" arrives at a surprisingly high ratio of patented inventions actually used by the patentee or his assignee; but it was based on a questionnaire method, which is not usually satisfactory evidence. See Barkev S. Sanders, Joseph Rossman, and L. James Harris, "The Non-Use of Patented Inventions," *Patent, Trademark, and Copyright Journal of Research and Education*, 1958, pp. 1–60.

consideration with regard to inventions for there are several strong reasons for expecting that the share of rejected inventions increases as the total output of inventions, selected plus rejected ones, increases.

The rejection of an invention may be either implicit in the failure to consider its application or explicit after hasty or thorough consideration. Such rejection may occur at many different points: the invention may not be accepted as a project for applied research and development;[13] it may be so accepted but dropped later at some stage during the development phase;[14] it may be fully developed but rejected because it requires large-scale testing in pioneer plants, regarded as too costly and too risky;[15] it may be technically ready for practical application but scrapped because it has yet to pass a market test judged to be too risky by the sales department; it may be given a market test, but fail; it may have passed all technical and market tests and still fail to be adopted in competition with other ventures that look more promising to a busy management, which cannot get around to doing all the things that might look good. At almost every one of these points in the career of an invention toward application the ratio of rejections is likely to increase as the flow of invention, in the sense of the gross total of inventions produced, is enlarged.

[13] There is not "any simple or uniform percentage of research results that go into development. That varies very largely from firm to firm with the origin of their research or development projects and with the ways in which potential projects are evaluated. Nevertheless many research results are not taken further, either because it seems fairly clear that it would be unprofitable to develop them, or because some must be excluded on cost grounds. The greater the cost of development, the greater the importance of exclusion. The less the attention of the research staff to the commercial significance of their projects, the greater the chance that research with great potentialities in industrial application will be excluded, if only because a man who is preoccupied with research as such will not be anxious to follow his idea on to the development staff." Carter and Williams, *op. cit.*, p. 58.

[14] "Development is a term which is loosely used in general discussion to cover a wide range of activities and purposes, but all these activities seem to satisfy three conditions. One, development is the stage at which known technical methods are applied to a new problem which, in wider or narrower terms, has been defined by the original invention. Of course, it may happen that in the course of development a blockage occurs, existing technology may provide no answers, and then, what is strictly another invention, is called for to set the ball rolling once more. Two, and consequentially, development is the stage at which the task to be performed is more precisely defined, the aim more exactly set, the search more specific, the chances of final success more susceptible to measurement than is true at the stage of invention. Invention is the stage at which the scent is first picked up, development the stage at which the hunt is in full cry. . . . Three, development is the phase in which commercial considerations can be, and indeed must be, more systematically examined, the limits of feasibility imposed by the market are narrowed down." Jewkes *et al.*, *op. cit.*, pp. 18–19.

[15] "Sometimes development consists of finding ways of producing on a large scale the same thing—or broadly the same thing—as has been produced already on a small scale. . . ." *Ibid.*, p. 199.

The Effective Supply and Cost of Inventions

We have now reached a convenient point to bring together the major results of our analyses of the supply of inventive labor, the production of inventions, and their selection for use.

First, we discussed the supply of inventive labor, regardless of quality, and found it to be subject to increasing supply prices. Second, we looked into the supply of inventive labor capacity and were impressed with the possibility that additions to the inventive personnel will be of inferior quality. Third, we analyzed the supply of new (raw) inventions and concluded that, beyond a point, the law of diminishing returns will be operative. And fourth, we inquired into the supply of inventions selected for actual use and discovered a tendency toward a diminishing ratio of exploitation.

These findings may be formulated in the following four propositions:

1. As the total amount of compensation for inventive work increases, the amount of inventive labor is likely to increase less than proportionately.

2. As the total amount of employment of inventive labor increases, the size of inventive labor capacity (the amount of inventive labor corrected for quality) is likely to increase less than proportionately.

3. As the total amount of inventive labor capacity (the input of inventive labor of standard quality) increases, the amount of new inventions made (the output in the form of workable technological ideas) may increase less than proportionately.

4. As the total amount of new inventions increases, the amount of "effective" new inventions (inventions developed and actually put to work) is likely to increase less than proportionately.

The cumulative loss in the efficiency of incremental compensation for inventive work may be very serious. We shall show elsewhere that the four transmission losses in the transformation of social energy need not exhaust the list of possible cost items in the accelerated procurement of workable inventions.

These relationships can be expressed in the form of four supply functions—the supply of (1) inventive personnel, (2) inventive capacity, (3) new "raw" inventions, and (4) effective (worked) inventions —in terms of the prices or compensations offered, that is, as functions of the compensation paid per inventive worker, per unit of inventive labor of standard quality, per invention of standard importance, and per utilized invention of standard importance. Put in this form, one may state that: (1) The supply of inventive labor is unlikely to be infinitely elastic and quite likely to be relatively inelastic; (2) The supply of inventive labor capacity is probably even less elastic than the supply of inventive labor; (3) The supply of new raw inventions may, in certain circumstances, be even less elastic than the supply of inventive labor capacity; and (4) The supply of effective (worked) inventions is likely to be even less elastic than the supply of raw inventions.

Of course, it is conceivable that all four supply functions are infinitely elastic: additional inventive labor may be available at the same rate of pay and in the same quality, and new raw inventions may be produceable under constant returns and found to be eligible for application at an undiminished rate. In this case a given percentage increase in the outlay for inventive work will yield an equal percentage increase in the number of inventions selected for application. But there are four potential shrinkages of the percentage increase in yield: higher rates of pay, lower quality of the personnel, smaller output of raw inventions per input of inventive capacity, and a higher rate of rejection in the selection of inventions for use. These shrinkages are independent of one another; but they may add up with a vengeance.

COMMENT

JACOB SCHMOOKLER, University of Minnesota

I find myself in substantial disagreement with Machlup on only one point. Rossman and Sanders report finding that between 40 and 50 per cent of the inventions patented by independents and between 50 and 60 per cent of those patented by captive inventors are used commercially. Machlup rejects these findings on two grounds: (1) they were achieved by questionnaire, and (2) they disagree with other estimates, as he interprets them.

Now, so far as I know, only two actual studies have been made of the commercial use of patents: the Rossman-Sanders study and a study of patent usage by large firms conducted at the Harvard Business School.[1] Both studies agree completely for firms of the same size class. Moreover, both studies are consistent with a reasonable interpretation of the record of tax payments by patentees in England and Germany where patentees must pay substantial taxes or forfeit

---

[1] Frederic M. Scherer *et al.*, *Patents and the Corporation*, Boston, 1958.

their patent rights. One cannot dismiss the results of a questionnaire study merely by saying questionnaires are unreliable. One has to show how the particular study was unreliable, and this Machlup has not done.

The other estimates with which the Rossman-Sanders results conflict were armchair estimates so far as I am aware. Further, they were mainly estimates not of the proportion of patented inventions used commercially, but rather of the proportion which yielded a profit to the inventor.[2]

Let me comment briefly on the lines of future research which are suggested by a reading of Machlup's paper. One is the development of quantitative estimates of Machlup's aggregate supply curves. Another is the development of similar estimates of the supply curves for specific fields of invention: there is no reason really to suppose that the women who invent waterproof mattress covers are part of the same labor supply as the men who invent artificial earth satellites.

Finally, and most important of all, we need an analysis of the factors that cause shifts in the Machlupian supply curves. So far as the supply of inventions is concerned, we need to know how scientific discoveries and inventions affect the efficiency with which inventive effort is converted into inventions.

So far as shifts in the supply of inventors are concerned, there are a whole host of familiar, unsolved problems: the effect of education on originality as well as on technical proficiency; the effect of ethnic and religious influences; the existence of secular changes in risk preferences and perhaps in the very recognition of risk; the effect of the shift

---

[2] Thus, Vaughan said, "It is estimated that nine-tenths of the patents issued by the United States do not bring *enough financial reward* to the inventors to cover the Patent Office fees, the charges of patent lawyers, and attendant expenses" (Floyd L. Vaughan, *Economics of Our Patent System*, New York, 1925, p. 169). C. F. Kettering testified that less than one per cent of General Motors' patents had proved *valuable* (T.N.E.C. *Hearings*, Part 2, p. 353). On the other hand, International Harvester Company stated that it *used* two-thirds of its patents (*Pooling of Patents*, H.R. 4523, 74th Cong., 1936, p. 3412, cited in W. B. Bennett, *The American Patent System, an Economic Interpretation*, Louisiana State University Press, p. 188). Kaempffert declared that less than five per cent of the patents issued have *paid* for their government fees (Waldemar Kaempffert, "Our Defective Patent System," *Outlook*, 1912, pp. 548–51). Warner held that not more than one per cent of the patents issued *repaid* all the inventors' expenses (E. P. Warner, "The Nature of Invention," *Harvard Graduates Magazine*, 1923, pp. 310–17). But Thomas contended that between ten and eighteen per cent of patents are "*more than reasonably profitable*" (Edward Thomas, "Are Patents Worth While?" *Journal of the Patent Office Society*, Vol. 13, pp. 232–35). With the possible exception of the estimates of company executives relating to patents held by their own companies, these are nothing more than conjectures, and most of them relate not to use but to return received. (Italics supplied in above quotations.)

from independent to hired invention, i.e. the effect of the organization of risk-bearing; and the effect of the different degrees of risk of failure for hired inventors as distinct from the risks of failure confronting, say, production engineers or college professors.

Does the Market Direct the Relative Factor-Saving Effects of Technological Progress?

WILLIAM FELLNER

YALE UNIVERSITY

IT IS well known that the forces of competition tend to direct individual firms toward adopting methods of production that are in accordance with relative resource scarcities. This proposition assumes a given level of technological knowledge, that is to say, it assumes production functions in which time does not figure as a variable.

The present paper examines the conditions under which inventive activity, resulting in industrial innovations, i.e. in changes in production functions, also becomes directed toward making this activity accord with relative scarcities in the available factors of production. But this theme will not be taken up immediately. First, I shall make a few introductory observations concerning the directing mechanism on a given level of technological-organizational knowledge, and then some of the imperfections of this mechanism will be discussed. This will clear the ground for an analysis of the problem of directed inventions and innovations.

In Figures 1 and 2 the individual firm is faced with average and marginal productivity functions for labor and for capital, respectively. The "factors" measured along the axes are to be interpreted as the current services of workers and of capital goods.

If $Ow \div Or$ expresses the ratio of the wage rate to the market rate of interest with which the firm is faced, the ratio of the labor input to the capital input in the firm will be OL_1/OK_1. The graphs do not in general answer the question of the absolute quantity of the labor input and of the capital input, since to assume one of the two inputs as given when we solve for the other input would beg the question.

In the event of linear homogeneous production functions, the total inputs in each firm are indeterminate unless a limitation is introduced from the outside. For example, if capital is rationed to the firm at the quantity OK_1, or labor at the quantity OL_1, then the graph indicates

NOTE: I am greatly indebted to Charles J. Hitch and Richard R. Nelson for a discussion of the first draft of this paper; to John H. Power, Arthur M. Okun and James Tobin for valuable suggestions; and to Robert M. Solow for an exchange of notes which was exceedingly illuminating to me. I made various revisions under the influence of the comments received from these colleagues.

FIGURE 1
Labor Input

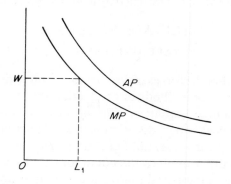

Quantity of capital constant at OK_1.

FIGURE 2
Capital Input

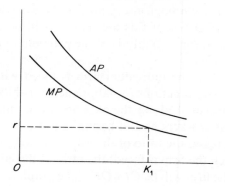

Quantity of labor constant at OL_1.

correctly the quantity of the nonrationed input. But even in these constant-cost situations where, aside from an outside limitational factor, the absolute size of the inputs is indeterminate, the graph will correctly indicate the input-ratio in the firm which corresponds to any given resource-price ratio (unless even with this input-ratio unit costs exceed the product price, in which case the firm would, of course, be out of business).

The directing mechanism in a competitive economy functions through the effect of a macro-economic excess supply of a factor of production, or of a macro-economic excess demand for a factor of production, on the relative factor prices with which the individual firms are faced. These factor-price ratios shift in such a way as to induce the firms to use input ratios consistent with the ratios of macro-economically available supplies. Furthermore, the product-mix also changes in the equilibrating direction. In the event that the production functions are not linear homogeneous but of the kind to which U-shaped average cost curves correspond, not only the input ratios but even the absolute quantities of input in the individual firms become determinate and this conclusion does not require introducing limitational circumstances from the outside. This is because the upward sloping range of the average cost curves always expresses the same sort of deviation from linear homogeneity as the presence behind the scenes of a hidden factor of production which is scarce and rationed to the firm. This hidden factor eliminates the indeterminateness of the absolute size of the labor and of the capital input. In the event of the linear homogeneity the indeterminateness is a consequence of the fact that if both the input of labor and that of capital are increased in the same proportion the higher inputs have the same marginal productivity as the smaller inputs had earlier.

As to the imperfections of the mechanism, in a sense, monopoly power and monopsony power may always be said to misdirect resources. However, not all deviations from perfect competition lead to an aggregative excess supply of factors of production, if by excess supply we mean resources which are idle when their owners would prefer to have them used at going prices. The deviations from perfect competition which can lead to this particular result may be listed in the following way.

1. The directing mechanism described earlier operates with lags. Indeed, even to show conclusively that factor markets will be cleared with a lag would necessitate spelling out dynamic sequences which incorporate assumptions concerning the precise effects of the excess demands and the excess supplies of a period on the price movements from period to period. This is in essence the stability problem. Even if one assigns high probabilities to the presumption that the directing mechanism comes through, i.e. that it is not obviated by events happening on the road toward market clearance, one should recognize that the mechanism does not complete its workings instantaneously. Lags may create underutilization.

2. Lasting rigidities of the money-wage and price level are quite

likely to put Say's Law out of commission. It is necessary to eliminate Say's Law from our analytical apparatus if imperfections of competition are recognized as causing downward rigidities in the money-wage and price level, because Say's Law can be based only on the real-balance effect, and this in turn presupposes perfect flexibility of the general price level. In a non-Sayian world, unemployment of labor at the existing level of money wages is a possibility even in the long run.

All that is required for such underutilization is that at the given price level the demand for goods out of a full-employment income should fall short of the full-employment supply of goods. If this situation arises the wage-price structure will fail to direct the entire labor force into one or another occupation, and this deficiency of the market process will be a consequence neither of a higher-than-equilibrium real wage level nor of a deficient relative price structure or wage structure. The deficiency will be a consequence of the fact that rates of return on investment have become too low to induce an amount of investment which would match the amount of savings at full employment. If now the general price level does not decline to the point where a plentiful supply of real balances would saturate the demand for liquidity, then the demand for goods does not rise to the level needed for full employment. This is a "Keynesian situation" stated in terms which take account of post-Keynesian contributions. A lowering of the money rate of interest could help, but if the money rate has already declined to a near-zero floor level, the system will necessarily tend to an underemployment level.

In such a Keynesian situation there is an excess supply of labor, even in the long run. An excess supply of capital does not persist in the long run because, while capital may be in excess when a Keynesian situation first develops, nonreplacement will gradually eliminate the excess capacity. Nevertheless, even in the long run the potential full-employment supply of savings and of capital does stay in excess relative to the full-employment demand for capital.

3. There may be underutilization of labor but not of capital also because real wage rates are rigid downward at a level exceeding the marginal productivity of the full labor force with the given capital stock. In situations of this sort an equiproportionate reduction of money wage rates and of prices would not help. An equiproportionate reduction would indeed raise the money demand for goods. But in the case we are now considering unemployment is not a consequence of any insufficiency of demand for an increased output. With a more

liberal credit policy (lower interest rates) the demand for goods would at any event be sufficient for taking up a bigger output. In the case at hand the potential full-employment supply of savings and of capital would be no greater than the full-employment demand for capital (at interest rates above the floor level). Such a potential excess supply at full employment is not the reason why full employment is out of reach.

If full employment is nevertheless not achieved (and if this is not simply a consequence of the lags in the adjustment process discussed under 1 above), then the reason must be that the actual supply of capital is insufficient to make the ruling real wage rate a full-employment equilibrium wage rate. Hence, the net capital formation which takes place under these conditions of underemployment wherever the propensity to save is positive, will automatically lead to full employment unless the actual real wage rate is gradually further raised or unless other forces tend to reduce that level of the real wage rate which is consistent with full-employment equilibrium. Such other forces may develop from rapid population growth, from the presence of a scarce hidden factor of production, and, as we shall see, from innovations whose relative labor-saving character is very pronounced. If no forces come into play which would reduce the real wage rate consistent with full employment, then gradual capital formation will automatically create full use, at any given real wage rate.

It is this last sentence which is not valid in the event that the under-utilization is of the Keynesian variety discussed under 2 above. That sentence draws the line between the two types of general unemployment. In the Keynesian case capital is too abundant relative to labor in an economy in which the levels of money wage rates and of prices are subject to a floor; in the other case labor is too abundant relative to capital in an economy in which the level of real wage rates is subject to a floor. A simpler but still adequate expression of this result is as follows: in the Keynesian case the rate of return on investment would have to be below a floor level in full employment, in the other case the real wage rate would have to be below a floor level in full employment.

A Mechanism Directing the Relative Factor-Saving Effects of Inventions

We now turn to the main theme of this paper which relates to the role of inventions in creating or preventing the two types of maladjustment described in the concluding paragraph of the preceding section. Any market mechanism which one would be willing to regard as directing inventive activity into the correct channels would have to have the property of guiding innovations (and thus the underlying inventions) in a labor-saving direction if an abundance of capital relative to labor is creating one of the two types of maladjustment, and of guiding innovations in a capital-saving direction if a relative abundance of labor is creating the other type of maladjustment.

At this point it is necessary to draw a distinction between the quantity of innovating activity and its character (i.e. its relatively labor-saving or relatively capital-saving character). Given all resource inputs, the output and hence also the average productivity of each factor input will be increased much or little depending upon the quantity of innovating activity. For given resource inputs, the average productivity of each resource (say, of labor and capital) is increased, of course, in precisely the identical proportion, namely, in the proportion in which total output increases. This is true regardless of how relatively labor-saving or capital-saving the innovation may be (regardless, say, of whether we are concerned with labor-saving automation devices or with a capital-saving move from cables to wireless telegraphy). The answer to the question by how much the average productivity of all resources increases depends for given inputs on the quantity of innovating activity, not on its character.

On the other hand, the answer to the question of how innovations influence trends in real wage rates relative to trends in rates of return on investment depends on the relative labor-saving or capital-saving character of innovations. This statement implies of course a macro-economic way of looking at the matter. To an individual firm possessing no monopsony power, factor prices are given. A relatively labor-saving innovation induces such a firm to use more capital per unit of labor, and a relatively capital-saving innovation induces it to use more labor per unit of capital. But if innovations are adopted on a macro-economic scale, then the factor-price ratios (and the relative factor shares) change for any given total input of the factors of production.

We shall use the following definition: innovation A is more relatively labor saving, and hence less relatively capital saving, than innovation B if, for macro-economically given resource inputs, innovation A reduces the relative share of labor more (or raises the relative share of labor less) than does innovation B.[1] However, the observable trends in distributive shares do not, of course, result exclusively from innova-

[1] This definition could, of course, be extended to a three-factor model.

tions. They result jointly from innovations, from movements along production functions, and from changes in the product-mix.

Both the quantity and the character of innovations were here defined for given resource inputs. For the present purpose it is convenient to use given inputs to mean the inputs actually undertaken.

If we further develop our definition of the character of innovations in terms of the marginal productivity theory of distribution (Figures 1 and 2), then it is an essential corollary that we regard an innovation as the less relatively labor saving (the more relatively capital saving), the more it shifts up the marginal productivity function of labor relative to that of capital. Since for given resource inputs the two average productivity functions are shifted up in the same proportion, the relative factor-saving effects are effects on the percentage gaps between average and marginal productivities. This is in accordance with the definition of "labor-saving" and "capital-saving" which was suggested by Hicks in his *Theory of Wages.*

A NEGATIVE PROPOSITION

Coming now to the problem of market incentives for the correct slanting of the relative factor-saving effects, we shall first formulate a negative proposition, and subsequently replace it by a positive one which rests on somewhat more complex but, we feel, also on more realistic assumptions.

The negative proposition is that in the event of purely competitive factor hiring, with no factor rationing to individual firms, the market provides no incentive to seek for any given factor inputs one rather than another distribution of the factor-saving effects. This proposition assumes that the individual firm knows for what factor inputs it would be using each available new technology, and that the firm has no objective other than to maximize its profits. We also assume that the cost of acquiring an invention which raises total output in a specific proportion for certain inputs does not depend on whether the marginal productivity of labor is increased in a higher proportion than that of capital or vice versa. In other words, we are concerned here with the question of economic bias, not with that of laboratory bias.

Assume that the firm has the conventional U-shaped cost curves which it can try to lower by seeking new technological knowledge either of a more relatively labor-saving kind or of a more relatively capital-saving kind. The firm expects to earn extra profits, at least temporarily, since the individual firm's ability to innovate does not alter prices, wage rates or rentals (say, the relatively high wage rates and low rentals of advanced economies). While the excess profit situation lasts, the following statements are valid, and they make up our negative proposition. One, if with no innovation the firm would have found it most profitable to produce a given output by using, say, 5 units of "cheap" capital for each unit of "expensive" labor, then raising the physical productivity of this specific combination by 10 per cent gives more extra profits than would a 10 per cent productivity increase for any other combination.[2] Two, if it so happens that with the same difficulty a greater product raising effect can be obtained for a combination other than 5:1, then the other combination may, of course, become superior, but there is no reason to assume that the firm would have a predilection for making some other combination superior to the combination 5:1. Therefore, the negative part of our conclusion stands. If there exists no laboratory bias, then there exists no systematic bias whatever (in other words, there is no reason to expect systematic economic bias). Even without innovations, increasing macro-economic labor scarcity leads, of course, to a movement toward points of higher capital intensity. But given these points, there is no further inducement to seek innovations of a more relatively labor saving character.[3]

---

[2] This proposition is strictly valid (valid in each individual case) only if the optimum factor ratio does not depend on the scale of operations. If the optimum ratio does change along the firm's cost curves, then the post-innovation output will be produced with a factor ratio which is usually not identical with the ratio with which the same output would have been produced earlier, nor with the ratio with which the actual pre-innovation output was produced. But this introduces merely a random deviation from the negative proposition of the text, since the optimum factor ratio may change either way along various stretches of the cost curves. The reasoning in the present footnote does not point to a systematic economic bias for the innovating process in general.

[3] Take for illustration the average capital-productivity function (AP_k) of a firm for a given labor input, and denote several points on the abscissa which are close to each other, as points K_1, K_2, K_3, etc. These points on the capital axis stand for increasing inputs of capital, and thus for rising capital intensity. Assume that the firm now operates in K_1, and that it anticipates a movement toward K_2, K_3, etc. This is the equivalent of the assumption that the firm expects a rise in real wage rates relative to rates of return on investment.

In these circumstances the firm does indeed have an interest in finding through innovation a higher AP_k curve which in the next period lies above the present curve mainly in the region around K_2; and subsequently the firm will have an interest in producing a further upward shift mainly in the region around K_3. But there exists no presumption that within these regions the firm would want to shift up the curve at one end in a higher proportion than at the other end. Hence there exists no presumption that in the region in which it will be operating the firm would want to make the elasticity of the higher AP_k curve different from that of the lower one, i.e. tha it would want to decrease the percentage gap between the average and the marginal productivity of capital, thus making the more efficient technology also more "relatively labor-saving." Alternatively expressed,

Figure 3 provides a further explanation of our negative proposition. OR is the aggregate revenue function of the firm, OC_1 its pre-innovation long run aggregate cost function, OC_2 its post-innovation long run aggregate cost function. Om_1 is the pre-innovation profit maximizing output, Om_2 the post-innovation profit maximizing output. If the

FIGURE 3
Graphic Illustration of the Negative Proposition

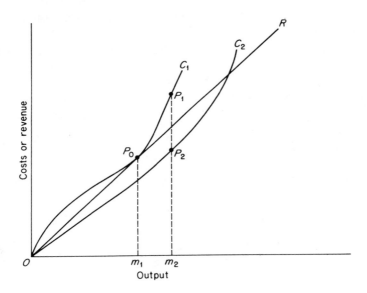

inventions are capable of yielding a 10 per cent increase in the total product for all conceivable factor mixes with which a given output can be produced, then the optimum factor mix will be the same in P_2 as it is in P_1, except for the random qualification expressed in footnote 3. Before the inventions all other factor mixes lay on higher cost functions than OC_1, hence the other factor mixes stay handicapped too under the improved circumstances. The argument applies also to monopolistic selling as long as the ruling factor prices are given to the

---

when the firm is in K_1 an effort is likely to be made to find for the next period a higher AP_k curve which is particularly high in K_2; this changes the arc-elasticity of the AP_k curve for the jump from K_1 to K_2 in one direction, but changes the arc-elasticity of the curve for the jump from K_2 to K_3 in the other direction, and there exists no presumption that the resulting higher technology is either more "relatively labor saving" or more "relatively capital saving."

individual firm while it is putting the innovation into effect. In the
event of monopolistic selling the *OR* line acquires a curvature.

The reader will remember that on the micro-economic level on
which we are analyzing the problem in Figure 3 (and Figure 4), the
test of the character of innovations is whether given all market prices
the individual firm is led to use more labor input per unit of capital (or
vice versa). But on a macro-economic level the test is whether the
factor-price ratios are changed in one direction or the other, for given
total macro-economic resource inputs. It is obvious that this is the
macro-economic equivalent of the foregoing micro-economic way of
looking at the matter.

Figure 4 provides an alternative illustration of the same negative

FIGURE 4
Alternative Illustration of the Negative Proposition and of a Qualification

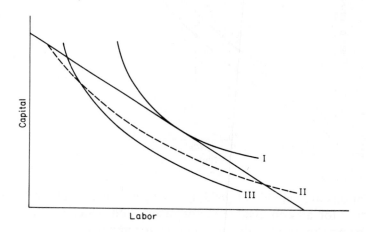

proposition. In this illustration all three isoquants relate to the
identical quantity of output. Isoquant I expresses the old technology,
while isoquants II and III express newly invented technologies. The
ruling factor-price ratio is expressed by the slope of the iso-cost line
connecting the axes. The conclusion here is that for the given output-
level technology III is optimal, although technology II is more
relatively labor saving. *However, a rise in the relative price of labor will
make technology II optimal at a later date, provided that no new invention is made between now and then.* This is because a steeper factor-
price ratio line would reach tangency with isoquant II below the point

at which it would reach tangency with isoquant III. We have here our first reason for qualifying our negative proposition, and we are on our way toward positive statements concerning a directing mechanism. It was just shown that the more labor saving isoquant—i.e., isoquant II—becomes superior for a steeper iso-cost line (or factor-price ratio line), and this qualifies our negative proposition for a reason that can be expressed as follows.

The significance of the negative proposition formulated above is at least somewhat reduced—and for some periods it may even be wiped out—by the fact that when the relative scarcity of, say, labor is increasing and factor prices shift correspondingly, certain new methods which were discovered earlier can automatically become economical even though previously they were uneconomical; and the new methods which may qualify with a lag under this heading are necessarily relatively labor saving. Through this mechanism growing relative labor scarcity may conceivably result in a labor saving bias, even if all factors are available to the individual firm in infinitely elastic supply.

Let us now go one step further. If the services of labor or of capital are *not* in infinitely elastic supply to the individual firm, then it is not enough to qualify our negative proposition concerning the existence of a directing mechanism. In this case, the negative proposition loses its validity completely.

Assume, for example, that the terms on which capital is available to the firm become increasingly unfavorable as the borrowings of the firm increase, while more labor of given quality is available on unchanging terms. In these circumstances the firm does have incentives to seek for the inputs of each period new technological knowledge of a relatively capital-saving kind. In other words, the firm does have incentives to seek improved methods which raise the marginal productivity of labor more than that of capital and thus raise the firm's demand for labor more than its demand for capital. The firm will have incentives to seek such relatively capital-saving innovations because a rise in the price of capital is an effect which the individual firm must take into account in its calculation. It is not *merely* a macro-economic phenomenon which happens if a great many firms increase their demand for capital, but a phenomenon taking place even if the individual firm alone acts to increase its input of capital. In contrast to this, the macro-economic wage-raising effect of relatively capital-saving innovations is a phenomenon which the individual firm has no reason to take into account in its calculations and hence does not "hold against" this type of innovation. The contrary incentives develop if labor is hired in monopsonistic circumstances while the supply of capital is infinitely elastic to the firm. Graphs of the type drawn in Figure 4 will show this up, provided the iso-cost lines are drawn with the appropriate monopsonistic curvature.

Further, it is important to realize that if the firm size becomes determinate not because of the U-shape of the cost curve but because of the rationing of one of the factors of production to the firm, this implies an infinitely inelastic supply of that factor at the pre-innovation input. Hence the incentive to raise the marginal productivity function of this factor is smaller than the incentive to raise the marginal productivity function of the other factor. In this case, too, our quasi-monopsonistic results become established.

A POSITIVE PROPOSITION

Our positive proposition then is that a directing mechanism does come into play as soon as factor scarcities are transmitted to the individual firm by monopsony, or in some quasi-monopsonistic fashion (as in the event of factor rationing which implies infinitely inelastic supply to the firm). From this we may infer that a directing mechanism is quite likely to come into play if the character of the innovations "overshoots" strongly enough in one direction or the other. For, if the innovating activity of a period is slanted strongly enough in a relatively labor-saving direction then the demand for capital is quite likely to rise fast enough to result in excess demand and thus, for the individual firms, in difficulties of financing. For a sustained period the market price of capital lags behind the price at which all the demand would be satisfied. This expresses itself in the fact that the terms of borrowing are made more onerous to the individual firm if it wishes to acquire appreciably more capital than it already has. A monopsonistic situation develops and innovating activity is guided in a more capital-saving direction (which then puts an end to the monopsonistic situation). The effect of the innovations on the marginal productivity of labor becomes more favorable.

On the other hand, if the innovations of a period overshoot far enough in a relatively capital-saving direction, i.e. if it is primarily the demand for labor which is increased, then the labor market is likely to show signs of excess demand. For a sustained period the market price of labor of various sorts lags behind the price at which all the demand would be satisfied. In a sufficiently tight labor market—which is consistent with a small degree of over-all unemployment—most individual firms are aware of the fact that increasing the work force in their own establishments requires hiring workers away from other employers on terms more onerous than those implied in the concept of going wage rates for given qualities of workers. This, too, creates temporarily quasi-monopsonistic conditions but in the labor market rather than in the capital market. Hence an incentive is created for seeking more relatively labor-saving improvements. Under the influence of these the marginal productivity of capital fares better, although it is conceivable that within certain limits the effect on the rate of return on capital is offset by a higher propensity to save and a higher rate of investment.

To put it briefly, monopsonistic awareness of factor scarcities is less rare than is commonly believed. Temporary monopsony does not even require "large" firms in any reasonable sense of this word. Such a condition merely requires firms that are large in relation to the markets in which they hire, and acute scarcities may narrow these markets very greatly. A rapidly rising macro-economic demand for a factor is likely to create for a while monopsonistic awareness of relative scarcities. Therefore a sufficient slanting ("overshooting") of innovating activity one way or another may very well lead to this same result. If this is so, incentives are created for seeking innovations whose character is more in accordance with the existing macro-economic resources position.

A word should be added here about the role of monetary fiscal policy. We said a moment ago that innovations which overshoot in a capital-saving direction create a monopsonistically observable labor scarcity, and that, therefore, such overshooting tends to be self-correcting. It is necessary, however, to add that if this kind of over-shooting lasts long enough, the labor scarcity disappears and the directing mechanism breaks down. The reason is that a sufficiently pronounced and sufficiently protracted weakness of the trend in rates of return on investment (coupled with rigidities in the money-wage and price level) leads to the Keynesian variety of unemployment. This type of unemployment expresses the paradox that a relative labor scarcity (insufficient marginal productivity of capital) may indirectly result in an excess supply of labor. Once the paradox has developed the directing mechanism is put out of commission. The mechanism can be called to life again by policies which raise the level of effective demand, i.e., eliminate the paradoxical excess supply of labor, and it is advisable to use such policies with moderation even at an early stage to prevent the Keynesian paradox from developing.

Earlier we also said that overshooting in a labor-saving direction tends to create a monopsonistically observable scarcity of capital which should guide innovating activity into more capital-saving channels. In such circumstances government policy can play a harmful role by making too ambitious efforts to eliminate the relative excess of labor, i.e. by creating a monopsonistically observable scarcity of labor as well as of capital. This last sentence involves, of course, a value judgment because, while a government policy of the sort which is here criticized would indeed weaken the directing mechanism, such a policy could be said to accomplish socially desirable results directly, without the guiding mechanism of the market. Nevertheless, the statement will probably be acceptable to those who wish to aim at reliance on market forces, coupled with corrective policies, rather than at a condition of overfull utilization of all resources coupled with rather comprehensive controls.

MACRO-ECONOMIC ELABORATION

The macro-economic elaboration on our theme will take its departure from a more flexible variant of the Harrod-Domar type of approach. This version which was used also in earlier writings of the present writer will here be formalized somewhat further.

The Harrod-Domar type of approach places in the foreground a macro-economic relationship expressed by the equation

$$\frac{dY}{dt} \cdot \frac{dK}{dY} = s\,Y \tag{1}$$

where Y is output or income, t is time, K is the capital stock, and s is the average propensity to save (so that $s = S/Y$, where S is the aggregate saving of a period).

This relationship is intended to be a condition of dynamic equilibrium (smooth or sustained growth), rather than merely an identity. To make the equation a condition of smooth growth, it is necessary to add

$$Y = F(L,K) \tag{2}$$

$$S = f(Y) \tag{3}$$

A more complete formulation would include further independent variables in the production function 2, and also in the saving function 3.

We now turn to an essential point which conventionally receives too little attention. The conventional, very rigid version of the Harrod-Domar approach implies the following constraint: ·

$$\frac{dY}{dK} = \frac{Y}{K} = \text{constant} \tag{4}$$

The only reasonable interpretation of this constraint is that smooth growth cannot continue in the event of a rising capital-output ratio, i.e. of a falling Y/K, and that the case of a rising Y/K ratio may be disregarded (perhaps because the equations are intended to formulate the minimum conditions of smooth growth). In other words, the only reasonable interpretation of (4) is to postulate, or to require for smooth growth, nondiminishing returns to capital, in the sense of a nondiminishing Y/K ratio. This point is rarely made clear in discussions based on equation (1) or on equivalents thereof.

What I consider to be a necessary (and for the present purpose, adequate) relaxation of this approach—a more flexible version which I have used in my earlier analysis of growth problems—has the following main characteristic. The constraint expressed in (4) is replaced by the constraint:

$$\frac{Y}{K} \cdot \frac{P}{Y} = \pi \geqslant \pi_0 \tag{4}$$

where P is the income going to the owners of capital (profit plus interest), π is the rate of return on capital, and π_0 is the minimum below which π cannot decline because of risk-premium requirements.

What I am suggesting here is that the constraint must be made to relate not to the capital-output ratio, or to the Y/K ratio, but to the algebraic product $Y/K \cdot P/Y$ which is the rate of return on capital. Furthermore, the constraint should not postulate that in the economy with which we are concerned, e.g., the American economy, $Y/K \cdot P/Y$, is at a floor level below which it cannot be reduced; the constraint should merely postulate that there exists a minimum requirement for $Y/K \cdot P/Y$, at some level.

The concepts developed earlier can now be applied to this macro-economic framework. We shall assume that in the kind of economy

which we are studying the capital stock is rising at a greater proportionate rate than the labor force, and that along given production
functions this would reduce Y/K.[4] Whether along given production
functions P/Y would rise, or fall, or stay unchanged depends on the
elasticity of substitution and is therefore not *entirely* certain.[5] But
$Y/K \cdot P/Y$ would be declining. As for the effect of innovations, a
sufficient quantity of innovating activity would always prevent the
Y/K ratio from declining; and a sufficiently pronounced relatively
labor-saving effect of the innovations would always prevent the P/Y
ratio from declining.

This last sentence concerning the effects of innovations has been
formulated in such a way as to take account of the fact that the
observable trends in Y/K, in P/Y, and in the algebraic product of
these (i.e. in π), depend not merely on innovations but on the joint
effect of innovations, movements along production functions, and
changes in the product mix.

As for the observable trends in these various ratios, the available
data for the United States show that in the long run the aggregative
Y/K ratio has not declined. Nor does this ratio show a falling trend in
some other countries for which we have data. This points to a sufficient
quantity of innovating activity to maintain, or even slightly to raise in
the long run, the average productivity of the factor of production
whose supply has been rising the most rapidly. Consequently, the
average productivity of the factors whose supply has been rising in
lesser proportion than that of capital shows a pronounced uptrend,
and innovating activity may be regarded as quantitatively sufficient
by reasonable standards.

The factor-saving effects have been distributed so that an appreciable
and consistent uptrend in real wage rates results, and at the same
time, that distribution probably results in a mild long-run lowering of
the rates of return on investment (although this lowering, or "down-
trend," does not show for all subperiods of reasonable duration which
can be distinguished in long-run materials). When allowance is made
for the labor income and profit income of the self-employed, the

---

[4] This assumes that on a given level of knowledge the economies of scale would have
been exploited long ago.

[5] It seems to me very likely that P/Y would decline. For example, if the American
capital stock were doubled with absolutely no technological progress and no growth of
employment, the rate of return on capital would hardly be higher than one-half of its
present value, and wages would no doubt rise.

relative share of labor has not changed much in the long run; it probably has increased to some extent.

It is possible to conclude that in the long run the distribution of the factor-saving effects has come out "just about right," in that rates of return on investment have not declined to a level which would have been too low for sustained investment activity. For the rest, the effect of innovations, along with that of capital formation, has been to raise real wages. In a sense, the innovations have been neither too capital-saving nor too labor-saving. But we must guard against accepting the (in this sense) correct results of innovating activity as a cogent proof of the existence of the previously discussed directing mechanism.

That directing mechanism should come into operation whenever the relative labor-saving effect of innovations overshoots to the point where there develops "monopsonistic" awareness of a capital short-age; and whenever the relative capital-saving effect of innovations overshoots to a point where there develops monopsonistic awareness of a labor shortage. While a directing mechanism of this sort is very likely to set limits to the overshooting in either direction, I am not familiar with observations which would establish the conclusion that a somewhat more pronounced capital-saving effect than that actually developed would have monopsonistically transmitted a chronic labor shortage to the individual firm. Neither am I familiar with observations which would establish the conclusion that a somewhat more pro-nounced labor-saving effect than that which has developed would have monopsonistically transmitted a chronic capital shortage to the individual firm. To me it seems tempting to suggest that the kind of directing mechanism outlined above has played a role in keeping the relative factor-saving effects of innovations within bounds. Much stronger claims could not be justified at present.

The alternative proposition which qualifies the negative proposition illustrated by Figure 4 may conceivably point to a nonmonopsonistic directing mechanism. One way of expressing this alternative proposition is to say that if, for the time being, a more capital-saving innovation is neither better nor worse than a more labor-saving one, then, in the absence of further inventions, the more labor-saving innovation will later become superior.

Whenever the monopsonistic mechanism previously discussed or this latter alternative adjustment process is at work, the characteristics of technological change contribute to the avoidance of underutiliza-tion. One disadvantage of basing economic development in primitive countries on Western knowledge is that Western technological progress seems to have adjusted to Western resource positions which, of course, are different from the resource positions of primitive countries. Thus, the present problem of primitive countries frequently is to choose between a backward capital-saving technology and an innovated Western labor-saving technology. A genuine adjustment process in primitive countries would, on the other hand, make innovated capital-saving technologies available to them.

COMMENT

EDWIN MANSFIELD, Carnegie Institute of Technology

In his present paper, William Fellner returns to a subject considered in his book on economic growth.[1] He asks the following question: What mechanisms exist in a capitalist economy to direct inventive activity into the correct channels? If capital—or labor—becomes relatively "abundant," are there market forces stimulating the search for labor-saving—or capital-saving—inventions?

First, he considers a perfectly competitive economy and concludes that no such forces exist. Next, he allows imperfections to be present in the factor markets and points out that if these imperfections reflect macro-economic scarcities, firms will have the incentive to seek out inventions of the proper type. Then he goes on to suggest that this sort of mechanism may have prevented innovations from becoming too "capital saving" or too "labor saving."

Fellner's two central propositions seem formally correct. In a perfectly competitive economy I can see no reason why a firm, in searching for new methods, should prefer ones that are relatively capital saving or relatively labor saving. What matters is the extent to which profits will increase. Moreover, if there are imperfections in the factor markets of the sort he assumes, it seems clear that firms will find innovations of the proper type more profitable to install.

However, I think he seriously understates the significance of a qualification he mentions. Although firms may have no preference for inventions of the proper type, a "sufficient" quantity of such inventions may be available as a by-product of past research efforts. In the course of project research and other inventive activities, many bits of

---

[1] *Trends and Cycles in Economic Activity*, New York, Holt, 1956, pp. 220–222.

technical knowledge are unearthed that can only be applied economically under subsequent factor prices. Presumably, the extent of past inventive efforts determines (at least in part) whether the supply of such innovations is "sufficient."

Turning from Fellner's paper, I would like to describe briefly some related work of my own. Part of a larger project on technical change that I have been conducting,[2] this work deals with the factors influencing a firm's spending on research and development. At this point, only the first parts of this study have been completed. But the results to date and the broad lines of the investigation may be worth presenting.

I shall begin by presenting a very simple model to help explain the short-term variation in a firm's expenditures on research and development. Then I shall describe the results of some preliminary tests to which it has been subjected. Finally, I shall outline how this simple model fits into the overall study of R and D expenditures. Note at the outset that the analysis applies only to industries whose R and D is mainly privately financed (chemicals, petroleum, etc.) and that the results so far are extremely tentative.

In its simplest form, the model assumes three things. First, it assumes that a firm's managers, when they determine how much to spend on R and D during the coming year, begin by taking this year's expenditure as a base from which to figure. Second, it assumes that they have some target percentage of sales in mind and that they apply this percentage to their sales forecast for the coming year to obtain a target figure for R and D expenditures. For the ith firm, let this percentage be α_{i1}. Third, it assumes that they set the R and D budget so as to move a certain fraction of the way toward this target. For the ith firm, let this fraction be α_{i2}. Thus, if $r_i(t)$ is the ith firm's R and D budget for year t, $R_i(t-1)$ is its actual expenditure in year $t-1$, and $s_i(t)$ is its sales forecast for year t,

$$ r_i(t) = R_i(t-1) + \alpha_{i2}[\alpha_{i1}s_i(t) - R_i(t-1)] . \qquad (1) $$

These assumptions seem to accord at least roughly with the results of various surveys. For example, the National Science Foundation, having interviewed officials of about 200 corporations, concludes that firms generally take existing expenditures as a base in formulating R

[2] This work has been financed principally by a contract with the Office of Special Studies of the National Science Foundation.

and D budgets.[3] It also finds that the most prevalent way in which firms determine the "optimal" level of R and D expenditures is by taking some percentage of sales.[4] And it points out the value placed by firms on the stability of their research organizations.[5] Because of the long-term nature of research projects and because changes in sales may only be temporary, one would expect α_{i2} to be considerably less than unity.

If we go on to assume that the forecast sales equal the actual sales and that the actual R and D expenditures equal the budgeted amount in equation 1 plus a random error term,[6] we have

$$R_i(t) = R_i(t-1) + \alpha_{i2}[\alpha_{i1}S_i(t) - R_i(t-1)] + z_i(t), \qquad (2)$$

where $S_i(t)$ is the firm's actual sales in year t and $z_i(t)$ is a random variable with zero expected value. Letting $\beta_{i1} = 1 - \alpha_{i2}$ and $\beta_{i2} = \alpha_{i1}\alpha_{i2}$, we have

$$R_i(t) = \beta_{i1}R_i(t-1) + \beta_{i2}S_i(t) + z_i(t), \qquad (3)$$

and according to the model,

$$O \leq \beta_{i1} \leq 1 \quad ; \quad O \leq \beta_{i2} \leq 1. \qquad (4)$$

Turning now to the matter of empirical testing, how well does equation 3 fit the past behavior of various firms? Using pre-1957 data for ten major chemical companies,[7] I obtained least-squares estimates of β_{i1} and β_{i2}. The results—presented in Table 1—indicate that equation 3 represents these data extremely well. The correlation coefficients are generally 0.99 or higher. The estimates of β_{i1} and β_{i2} generally have the correct signs, they are generally of the expected

---

[3] See *Science and Engineering in American Industry, Final Report on a 1953–1954 Survey*, National Science Foundation, 56–16, Washington, 1956, p. 46. My colleague, Norton Seeber, is currently involved in a similar but more intensive sort of interview study.

[4] *Ibid.*, p. 41.

[5] *Ibid.*, p. 46.

[6] The assumption that sales forecasts are perfect is clearly only a convenient first approximation. Its effect is probably to bias the estimate of β_{i2} toward zero.

[7] The data come from Charles Langenhagen, "An Evaluation of Research and Development in the Chemical Industry," (unpublished M.S. thesis, Massachusetts Institute of Technology, 1958). Included were all firms for which he presented exact figures for twelve or more years, and for which corresponding sales figures could be obtained. He obtained the figures through correspondence with the firms and through annual reports and similar documents. Only the exact figures (not his estimates) are included. Of course, there may be interfirm differences in the definition of research and development.

TABLE 1

ESTIMATES OF β_{i1} AND β_{i2}, TEN MAJOR CHEMICAL COMPANIES

Company	Number of years[a]	Estimates[b]			Standard Errors		Coefficient of Determination[c]
		β_{i0}	β_{i1}	β_{i2}	β_{i1}	β_{i2}	
Allied Chemical	11	−.55	.74	.0093	.15	.0053	.98
American Cyanamid	20	−.41	.70	.0177	.12	.0059	.98
Atlas Powder	20	−.14	1.02	.0053	.15	.0039	.94
Diamond Alkali	15	−.36	.81	.0141	.12	.0039	.98
General Analine	11	1.66	.75	−.0027	.28	.0146	.75
Hercules Powder	25	−.27	.88	.0095	.11	.0040	.97
Hooker Electrochemical	19	−.02	.48	.0139	.13	.0019	.99
Minnesota Mining	19	−.23	.77	.0131	.22	.0069	.99
Monsanto Chemical	24	−.35	.65	.0158	.14	.0036	.99
Union Carbide	12	−.92	1.10	.0029	.11	.0045	.99

SOURCE: Charles Langenhagen, "An Evaluation of Research and Development in the Chemical Industry," Unpublished M.S. thesis, Massachusetts Institute of Technology, 1958, and *Moody's Industrials*.

[a] The number of years for which data could be obtained for $R_i(t)$, $R_i(t-1)$, and $S(t)$. The years are consecutive and end with 1956 in all cases but Diamond Alkali and Union Carbide where the last year is 1955.

[b] In computing the regression, all variables were measured in units of millions of dollars. β_{i0} is the intercept of the regression—which according to the model should be zero. Although no formal tests were carried out, it seems unlikely that many of these estimates would be statistically significant. However, it is noteworthy that in almost every case the estimate is negative.

[c] The square of the coefficient of correlation.

order of magnitude, and despite relatively few degrees of freedom, they are generally statistically significant.[8]

How well does equation 3 forecast the expenditures on R and D of these firms? Taking each firm's sales in 1957 as given and using the estimates of β_{i1} and β_{i2} in Table 1, I used equation 3 to forecast each firm's 1957 R and D expenditures. (I did not have data on their R and D expenditures in later years.) The results—shown in Table 2— indicate that the forecasting errors for individual firms are generally from 5 to 10 per cent and that for the group as a whole the error is only about 2 per cent. This is considerably better than the performance of three standard naive models.[9]

[8] In three cases, the estimates violate the inequalities in equation (4) but in every case the standard errors are so large that this could well be due merely to sampling fluctuations.

[9] The three naive forecasts are (1) that expenditures next year will equal those this year [i.e. that $R_i(t) = R_i(t-1)$], (2) that expenditures next year will differ from those this year by the same amount that expenditures this year differed from those last year [i.e. that $R_i(t) = 2R_i(t-1) - R_i(t-2)$], and (3) that expenditures next year will differ by the same per cent from those this year as this year's expenditures differed from those last

TABLE 2

COMPARISON OF ACTUAL AND FORECAST R AND D EXPENDITURES
TEN MAJOR CHEMICAL COMPANIES
(millions of dollars)

Company	Actual	Forecast
Allied Chemical	17.5	18.7
American Cyanamid	22.7	24.7
Atlas Powder	2.8	2.4
Diamond Alkali	3.9	4.2
General Analine	5.8	5.1
Hercules Powder	10.2	11.3
Hooker Electrochemical	2.8	2.6
Minnesota Mining	16.4	14.1
Monsanto Chemical	22.7	21.1
Union Carbide	55.0	52.4
Total	159.8	156.6

SOURCE: see Table 1. For each firm, the actual and forecast expenditures refer to the last year for which Langenhagen gives exact figures. For Diamond Alkali and Union Carbide, this is 1956. For the others it is 1957.

Thus, on the basis of the little evidence available so far, this model—highly simplified though it is—seems to fit past data quite well and to be a promising device for short term forecasting (at least in the chemical industry).[10] However, this result is still only a first step toward an understanding of the basic mechanisms governing the level of R and D expenditures. Hopefully, it will be a useful first step.

This result suggests that to structure the problem and simplify it somewhat, it may be a fruitful strategy to regard α_{i1} and α_{i2} as the key variables to be explained in a broader model. The problem then is to investigate the factors that influence these two parameters. In the months ahead I shall try to do just that.

By taking each of several industries and making interfirm comparisons at various points in time, I shall try to measure the effects of various factors on α_{i1} and α_{i2}. For example, α_{i2} may depend on a firm's profitability and size. Naturally, the extent to which data are available

year [i.e. that $R_i(t) = R_i(t-1)^2/R_i(t-2)$]. The root-mean-square error for the forecasts in Table 2 is 1.48. It is 3.61 for the first type of naive forecast, 2.24 for the second type, and 2.2 for the third type.

[10] Of course, one would need a forecast of next year's sales for the firm or the industry. But such forecasts are now collected in various surveys. Moreover, it may be that $S_i(t-1)$ provides almost as good an approximation to the forecast as $S_i(t)$. There are also the usual problems of aggregation if one is interested in using a single equation to forecast for the entire industry. But these problems may not be so very troublesome here.

will determine how thoroughly some of the relevant hypotheses can be tested.

Moreover, I will try to measure the effects of certain variables that might cause differences over time in the parameters for a given firm. Although equation 3 may be useful for short term forecasting, it is unlikely to be of value over longer periods because α_{i1} and α_{i2} are likely to change with time. For example, α_{i2} may depend on factors such as the tightness of the market for research personnel, and α_{i1} may depend on tax rates and the anticipated profitability of research.

To sum up, this model provides a good representation of the data available thus far. If further work shows it fits data for other firms (and other industries) equally well, it may be quite useful for short term forecasting. Moreover, it may also be a worthwhile first step toward the construction of a more fundamental model explaining the level of R and D expenditures in a firm or industry. The investigation that will soon be under way of inter-firm and temporal differences in the parameters should bring us closer to this goal.

COMMENT

CHARLES J. HITCH, The RAND Corporation

The papers and the discussants have expressed many views on the productivity of research and development. As we all know, Griliches has measured it in one instance and come up with a formidable number (but he does not include the cost of unsuccessful research in his denominator). Minasian succeeds in "explaining" interfirm differences in profits in one industry by differential research activity; others have made similar attempts in other industries with negative results. Arrow has given us reasons for believing that the social productivity of development (and especially of research) is higher than the appropriable private productivity, but he makes no attempt to estimate either quantity. At one extreme, several discussants have referred to industrial research and development as a "fashion" whose main purpose is to impress the stock buying public, and wondered out loud whether, in the aggregate, it is worth the cost. Machlup, in particular, wonders whether more of it is worth the marginal cost, which is a great deal higher than the average cost.

I can present no numbers to reconcile these divergent views but there is, I think, some relevant empirical evidence from an industry that has spent and is spending very heavily on research and development; namely, the military industry. By whatever arbitrary index of military power one measures the productivity of this industry, it has increased since World War II not by a few percentage points per annum but by many orders of magnitude. And it has increased not because of a larger allocation of resources or their more efficient use within given technological state-of-the-art constraint, but because of technological progress stemming from a very large, deliberate, and expensive research and development program. By far the most important factor has been the successful development and later improvement of, first, fission and then fusion bombs. But many other developments have also contributed in a major way; for example, those in delivery vehicles, guidance techniques, and radar. To mention just one example which does not depend on nuclear energy, we have developed antiaircraft missiles which could annihilate a World War II style bomber raid.

This tremendous increase in our military power, measured in an absolute sense, has been obscured by the fact that the Russians, with a similar reliance on research and development, have increased their power to perhaps a greater extent, so that during part of this period our relative power has been declining. We are pessimistic about air defenses in spite of our great progress because qualitative improvements in air offense have proceeded even more rapidly.

Nevertheless, if we had not spent lavishly on military research and development, if we had used the same funds to acquire additional World War II type forces, our relative power would have declined much more precipitously. In fact, we should scarcely be participating in the race.

I have tried to think of some reason why the military industry should be unique in this respect but I cannot. Throughout most of history military technology has advanced very slowly, as in most other industries, sparked by more or less chance inventions at widely separated intervals. What has been new since 1940 has been the deliberate. seeking of inventions within the framework of billion dollar research and development programs. Perhaps somewhat similar measures would produce similar results in some other industries. Perhaps the divergence between social productivity and private productivity in research and development is a matter of great and general practical significance.

Changes in Industry and in the State of Knowledge as Determinants of Industrial Invention

JACOB SCHMOOKLER

UNIVERSITY OF MINNESOTA

THIS is a progress report on a larger study of the growth of technical knowledge. The study as a whole centers on the course of patented inventions in many American industries from 1836 to 1957. This paper, however, will deal with only four of the most important industries—railroading, farming, paper making, and petroleum refining, with primary emphasis on the railroad industry, the industry for which our data are most complete.

Before our preliminary findings are described, it seems worth while to say a few words about the conceptual framework of the project as a whole. We assume that the growth of modern western industrial technology has been primarily the result of the interplay of (1) changes in the state of knowledge and (2) changes in industry. The "state of knowledge" includes not only science and technology but also any other aspects of thought, e.g., art and religion, which affect man's perception of the material universe. "Changes in industry" presumably change, among other things, the benefits expected from a potential change in technical knowledge. The "benefits expected" from changing the stock of technical knowledge are those anticipated and valued by the unit seeking to make the change. Presumably, in a private enterprise economy these benefits usually take the form of profit to the inventor or his backer.[1]

Changes in the state of knowledge can influence inventive activity by affecting either (1) the prospective cost of making an invention and

NOTE: The author wishes to acknowledge the helpful criticisms of Leonid Hurwicz, Simon Kuznets, Fritz Machlup, Robert S. Merrill, and Sidney Winter of an earlier draft of this paper; the financial support of the John Simon Guggenheim Foundation, the National Science Foundation, the Ford Foundation, the University of Minnesota, and Michigan State University; the indispensable work of his research assistants who prepared the chronologies of important inventions—Heinrich H. Bruschke in railroading, A. Luis Darzins in paper making, Sushila Gidwani in petroleum refining, and Allan L. Olson in farming; the general assistance of Irwin Feller; and the advice of a number of employees of the U.S. Patent Office.

[1] Cf. Jacob Schmookler, "The Level of Inventive Activity," *Review of Economics and Statistics*, May 1954.

thereby the *net* profit anticipated from it; or (2) the intrinsic interest of explorations in different fields of technology. While analytically distinct, (1) and (2) are probably often impossible to differentiate in practice: though an employer may finance the pursuit of an idea because new knowledge reduces its prospective cost, his hired inventors may pursue the idea mainly because they find it interesting.

The conceptual framework of the project, which is naturally subject to change as our work progresses, is summarized in the following diagram, in which the arrows signify "determines".

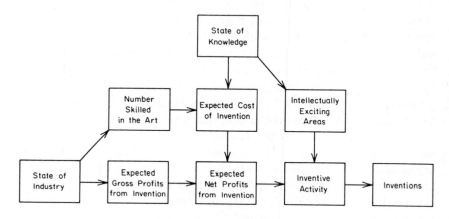

At any moment the existing state of knowledge wholly determines the set of all conceivable inventions by definition of the latter. Since increases in technical knowledge change the state of knowledge always, and the state of industry often, the process described in the diagram is continuous. It is not a closed process because other factors affect both industry and the state of knowledge. Because it is so difficult to get data on the variables in the interior of the diagram, we concentrate our analysis on those on or near the boundaries—the state of knowledge, the state of industry, inventions and inventive activity.[2]

In emphasizing the role of expected benefits, changes in which are assumed to arise from economic change, this conception of events stands in marked contrast to that which views technological progress exclusively as an automatic outgrowth of the state of knowledge itself. In the latter view, the growth of technology takes on the character of a

[2] We hope to give special attention, in our project but not in this paper, to the number skilled in the art.

process which, given some indispensable minimum institutional framework, is largely independent of economic life.

Two variants of the latter interpretation may be distinguished. According to the more sophisticated version, which seems implicit in many sociological and anthropological analyses, new inventions can be adequately explained by reference to the state of prior knowledge, because every new invention grows out of existing knowledge, whether that knowledge be scientific, technological, or otherwise. The more popular version, the application of which is usually limited to recent times, differs from the sophisticated only in that the relevant knowledge base consists wholly of science. In this variant, therefore, new inventions are considered adequately explained by reference to the scientific discoveries from which they allegedly grow.

The persuasiveness of both variants derives from the genetic logic evident in the history of ideas, for each new idea does build on earlier ideas. Yet neither variant can answer two crucial questions: (1) What determines the lag between the formation of the indispensable prior knowledge and the emergence of the new ideas based on it? (2) Since, one must suppose, only some of the useful ideas which could evolve from a given knowledge base actually appear, what is the nature of the selection process?[3]

Our central hypothesis assumes that the answers to these two questions will be found primarily in the anticipated costs and benefits —with risk preferences, intellectual curiosity, and purely random factors undoubtedly also playing a part. The problem may be stated in the parlance of traditional economics. The supply of inventions is in a sense determined by the number of creative individuals skilled in the technical arts, and by the state of knowledge which affects the conversion of inventive effort into inventive output. The demand for inventions, in turn, is presumably determined by economic conditions.

Those who, like Ogburn and his followers, have emphasized the dependence of new inventions on the prior art to the point where the whole process takes on an inevitable character, appear to believe that the supply of new inventions at any moment is completely inelastic, and that the new knowledge gained from one moment to the next

---

[3] The popular variant is not only unable to answer these questions but ignores the frequent instances in which inventive activity either flows into channels unaffected by scientific discovery, or fails to flow into channels which have been so affected. Likewise, it overlooks the influence of industrial technique on scientific inquiry and, like the sophisticated variant, has no apparent regard for the effect of instrumental considerations on the direction and level of scientific work.

causes the supply curve to shift (exponentially) rightward. By contrast, Gilfillan[4] and the present writer[5] have stressed factors on the demand side.[6]

In a sense, therefore, the problem before us is the relative influence of changes in (1) demand conditions and (2) supply conditions on the production of inventions.

Of the variables noted affecting the supply of inventions in a field—the number of workers skilled in the art and the state of knowledge—we shall consider in this paper only the latter, and of the many factors which might affect the demand for inventions we shall consider only investment here. Obviously, any statements to be made about the relative influence of investment and the state of knowledge apply only to the four industries covered. Even for these industries any statements made must be regarded as tentative.

The study of our four industries is continuing, we are studying other industries as well, and the underlying data are not in final form. While the patent statistics presented here are for patents counted at the time of granting, our study will ultimately be based on patents counted at the time of application for the patent right. Such data are superior to those used here, which are affected by significant variations between fields and over time in the interval between the date of application and the date of granting. Such variations inevitably obscure the inventive process which it is our purpose to study. Yet, the data presented below do provide indications of the long-term trends and long swings[7] (if any) in invention in the industries covered. The highly interesting results reported justify their use.

The findings are tentative for still another reason, however: they traverse territory so novel that important features of the landscape may easily escape notice. The data have been available only briefly,

---

[4] S. Colum Gilfillan, *The Sociology of Invention*, Chicago, 1935.

[5] Schmookler, *op. cit.*

[6] For a more extensive discussion of the literature in this context, cf. Richard R. Nelson, "A Survey of the Literature on Invention," *Journal of Business*, April 1959.

[7] Long swings are alternating phases of expansion and contraction, either in absolute terms or relative to trend, whose combined duration exceeds that of business cycles, i.e. four to eleven years. Their maximum duration is shorter than that of the trends about which they move. They, thus, characteristically exceed a decade and may last over half a century. Cf. Simon Kuznets, "Long Swings in the Growth of Population and in Related Economic Variables," *Proceedings of the American Philosophical Society*, Vol. 102, No. 1, pp. 25–52; Moses Abramovitz, "Long Swings in U.S. Economic Growth," and Richard A. Easterlin, "Long Swings in the Growth of Population and Labor Force," in *The Study of Economic Growth*, National Bureau of Economic Research, Thirty-ninth Annual Report, New York, 1959, pp. 23–27 and 27–30, respectively.

and further study and the consideration of other variables may well reveal significant characteristics as yet unobserved.

Subject to the foregoing qualifications the evidence presented below suggests the following: (1) The trends and long swings in patented invention tend to match those in investment. (2) Both investment and invention quite clearly move together with prospective profits in railroading, the only industry for which we have an index of the latter. (3) There is some tendency for important inventions to lead run-of-the-mill inventions, but this tendency is slight and its significance is unclear. (4) Scientific discoveries played no appreciable and obvious role in triggering important inventions in our four industries. However, scientific discoveries undoubtedly sometimes played a permissive role, particularly in the case of petroleum refining and papermaking inventions, many of which necessarily depended on the growth of chemical science. Moreover, if plant improvements, e.g., hybrid corn, were included in our list of important agricultural inventions, the triggering effect of scientific discoveries might seem greater than our present evidence suggests.

Important Inventions, Run-of-the-Mill Inventions, and Investment in the Railroad Industry

Because our economic data are most complete and the case seems clearest for railroading, we consider it first. Chart 1 shows the course of railroad stock prices, capital formation, and patents. The patents cover equipment and structures. The stock prices have been adjusted for changes in the general level of wholesale prices.[8] Net additions to road are taken as representative of capital formation during the early years when a more suitable index is not available.[9] These three variables are shown as seven-year moving averages. Gross capital formation is presented in the same form as in the source, i.e., as a five-year moving average.

The general impression conveyed by Chart 1 is unmistakable. The trends and long swings in railroad stock prices, capital formation, and patenting are very similar. Net additions to miles of road decline from

---

[8] If railroad stock prices were adjusted for changes in the general level of stock prices, or not adjusted at all, the net impression created would be much the same.

[9] Cf. Melville J. Ulmer, *Trends and Cycles in Capital Formation by United States Railroads, 1870–1950*, Occasional Paper 43, New York, NBER, 1954, p. 54, which suggests, by implication at least, that this series is a tolerable indicator of capital formation in this period.

CHART 1

Railroad Stock Prices, Capital Formation, and Patents

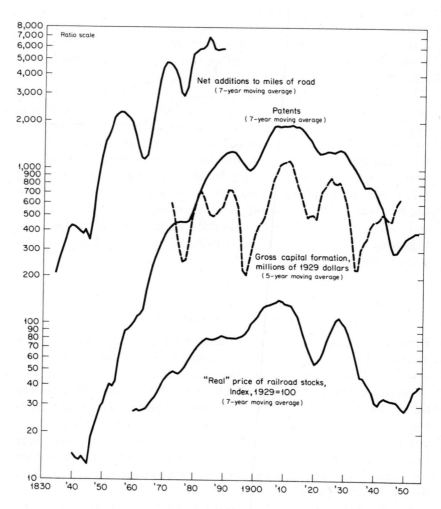

SOURCE: Gross railroad capital formation in 1929 prices: Melville J. Ulmer, *Trends and Cycles in Capital Formation by United States Railroads, 1870–1950,* Occasional Paper 43, New York, National Bureau of Economic Research, 1954, Table A-1. Net additions to miles of road: calculated from *Historial Statistics of the United States,* Series K-1. The "real" price of railroad stocks: calculated by taking stock prices from F. R. Macauley, *Some Theoretical Problems Suggested by Interest Rates, Bond Yields, and Stock Prices in the United States Since 1856,* New York, NBER, 1938, App. Table 10; and from *Moody's Transportation Manual,* 1959, p. a3; and adjusting for changes in the BLS index of whole-sale prices, *Historical Statistics,* Series L-15, and *Statistical Abstract of the United States,* 1959.

1839 to 1845. Patents granted decline from the start in 1840 to 1845. Both series then rise rapidly after 1845, with additions to road suffering a check in the rate of climb from 1850 to 1851 and patents declining absolutely in 1852–53. After a further rise additions to road decline absolutely from 1855 through 1863, while patents undergo marked retardation in the rate of climb from 1857 to 1863.

Rail stock prices begin rising in 1862, additions to road and patents, in 1863. Additions to road reach a peak in 1870, stock prices in 1873, and patents in about 1875. Stock prices start rising again in 1875, capital formation in 1876, and patents in 1877. The next set of peaks are difficult to locate. In investment, in fact, there are two peaks. Stock prices appear to reach their high in 1889, capital formation in 1891, and patents in 1892. Stock prices then reach a trough between 1891 and 1893, capital formation in 1897, and patents in 1898. The next series of peaks, which happen also to constitute all-time highs, occur in 1908 in stock prices, 1911 in capital formation, and 1912 in patents.

Stock prices, which generally led during the trend expansion, move into second place or tie for third during the trend contraction. Capital formation reaches a low in 1917–20, stocks in 1920, and patents in 1921. Capital formation then moves to a high in 1925, with stock prices and patents reaching their highs in 1928. Capital formation then falls to a low in 1933–34, stocks in 1935, and patents in 1936, with both of the latter falling thereafter but at a slower rate. The subsequent timing relations are not clear, perhaps because the recent swings are incomplete.[10]

One of the striking features of the relation between railroad patents and the other variables shown in Chart 1 is its substantial invariance over the whole period. *During a century in which inventive activity itself changed drastically, and in which the railroad industry moved from an unregulated to a regulated status and from growth to decline, patents continued to rise and fall with the level of railroad investment and expected profit as represented by stock prices.*

What is the explanation of this striking phenomenon, this covariation of patents, investment, and expected profits? Clearly, the rise of highway transportation explains the long-term decline which began around 1910 in all three railroad variables. With the growth of rival forms of transportation, investors and inventors simply turned to more remunerative fields. Thus, in a sense, one might argue, a major

---

[10] Obviously, if trends were eliminated the timing estimates might change somewhat, but not enough to affect the general picture of synchronization of movement.

invention, the automobile with its variants—the truck and bus—was responsible for the secular decline of railroad investment, invention, and stock prices. (We shall discuss this argument later.) This argument provides us with a clue to a possible and obvious line of further inquiry: Can it be that the long swings in railroad stock prices and investment also reflect the implementation of railroad inventions, just as the secular decline in railroad investment reflects the implementation of a major rival invention? In short, are the waves of railroad investment generated by the waves of railroad invention? This is a natural question, and we shall consider it first.

The first point to note is that the long swing turning points in patents generally lagged from one to three years behind the turning points in the two capital formation series. Only at the two earliest troughs, 1845 and 1863, did patents manage to turn as early as investment. Since the interval between application and granting of patents was generally about a year or less before World War I, and about two years in the interwar period, and since our investment data pertain to installations, not decisions, the most that can be plausibly inferred from the data is that the long swings in railroad inventing and patenting coincided with those in railroad investing. This suggests that whatever effect the waves of potentially useful invention had on the concurrent waves of investment was probably superimposed on the latter and not a cause of them.

Conceivably, however, a given swing in invention could cause the next swing in investment. Yet, if this is the case, why do the trend peaks in both variables occur practically simultaneously? If a given swing in invention causes the next swing in investment, the all-time high in investment should have come in the 1920's, not around 1910. Secondly, according to this hypothesis one would expect variations in the duration of the swings in invention to reappear, with a lag of one cycle, in the swings of investment. Yet, Table 1 shows duration of a swing in invention is usually more like that of its companion swing in investment than like that of the next swing in investment.

Inspection of the table reveals that in only one case, Cycle III in patents, is a given patent cycle matched as well by the next investment cycle as by its companion investment cycle. Thus Cycle III lasts 21 years in patents and 23 years in investment, compared to 19 years in Cycle IV in investment. In the other four cases, the duration of each patent cycle is much closer to that of the concurrent cycle in investment than to the succeeding cycle of the latter.

TABLE 1

DURATION OF LONG SWINGS IN RAILROAD PATENTS AND CAPITAL FORMATION

Cycle	Date of Initial Trough		Cycle Duration	
	Patents	Capital Formation	Patents	Capital Formation
I	1845	1845	18	18
II	1863	1863	14	13
III	1877	1876	21	23
IV	1898	1899	23	19
V	1921	1918	15	17
VI	1936	1935		

SOURCE: Patents: Chart 2. Cycles I and II in capital formation: from net additions to miles of road in Chart 2. The timing of subsequent cycles in capital formation is for nine-year moving averages of the same presented in Melville J. Ulmer, *Capital in Transportation, Communications, and Public Utilities* (Princeton University Press for National Bureau of Economic Research, 1960), p. 120. Using the timing indicated by Chart 2 for all the cycles would not affect the results.

Given the simultaneous trend peaks and the good matching of durations of simultaneously matched long swings, the evidential basis for the hypothesis that a given swing in invention causes the next swing in investment does not seem strong. Moreover, since the waves in patents either coincide with, or lag behind, the waves in investment, the notion that a given wave in invention causes the companion wave in investment likewise seems rather improbable.

The next point along this line of inquiry is plain. Inventions, obviously, are not all the same. While the swings in investment were apparently not responsive to the swings in invention generally, were they generated by waves of *important* inventions?

Chart 2 provides us with a basis for answering this question tentatively. As part of our project we compiled a chronology of about 250 of the most important railroad inventions made since 1800. Unlike the inventions covered by our patents, these are dated, so far as possible, at the time the inventions were actually made. They are shown in the Chart, starting with 1826, in the form of nine-year moving *totals*. The heroic, if not foolish, act of marking off long swings in this series, which from 1870 to 1938 fluctuates between 10 and 19, was performed in order to, and in such a fashion as to, give the hypothesis the most favorable "test" within the stringent limitations imposed by this whole approach. The long swings in the two capital formation series were used as a guide in determining the swings in important inventions, and whenever a choice existed in selecting turning points, doubts were resolved so as to give the important invention series the lead. For

CHART 2
Important Inventions and Investment in Railroading

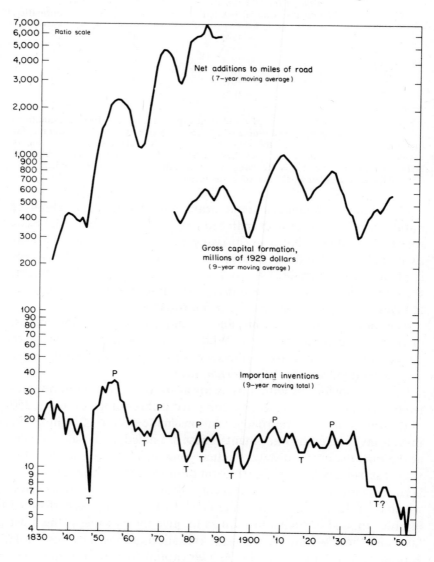

SOURCE: Gross railroad capital formation in 1929 prices: Ulmer, *Capital in Transportation, Communications, and Public Utilities: Its Formation and Financing,* Princeton for NBER, 1960, Table K-2. Net additions to miles of road: same as for Chart 1.

example, a trough in important inventions was dated in 1894 instead of 1898, and a peak dated in 1927 instead of 1934, though the later dates would have been perhaps more defensible. Again, by dividing in two the major swing in capital formation from the middle 1870's to the late 1890's and recognizing thereby the small decline from 1884 to 1887 in that series, two instances were created in which the important invention series lead.

Given the limitations imposed by our data and general approach, the hypothesis that long swings in important inventions generate similar movements in capital formation could hardly receive more advantageous treatment. The results are summarized in Table 2. At

TABLE 2

LONG SWINGS IN IMPORTANT RAILROAD INVENTIONS AND CAPITAL FORMATION

| | IMPORTANT INVENTIONS | | CAPITAL FORMATION[a] | | SEQUENCE AT TURNING POINTS | | | |
| | | | | | *Important Inventions* | | *Capital Formation* | |
CYCLE	*Trough*	*Peak*	*Trough*	*Peak*	Trough	Peak	Trough	Peak
I	1847	1855	1845	1855	2	1.5	1	1.5
II	1865	1870	1863	1870	2	1.5	1	1.5
IIIA	1879	1883	1876	1884	2	1	1	2
IIIB	1884	1889	1887	1890	1	1	2	2
IV	1894	1908	1899	1910	1	1	2	2
V	1917	1927	1918	1926	1	2	2	1
VI	1942+	?	1935	1949[b]	2	2	1	1
MEAN RANK AT TURNING POINTS					1.6	1.4	1.4	1.6

SOURCE: see Chart 3.

[a] The timing through 1870 is derived from seven-year moving averages of net additions to miles of road. After 1870 it is derived from 9-year moving averages of gross capital formation in 1929 dollars.

[b] Estimate of Ulmer based on annual data (Melville J. Ulmer, *Capital in Transportation, Communications, and Public Utilities,* Princeton University Press for National Bureau of Economic Research, 1960, Table 39, p. 125).

the troughs, the important invention series lags four times and leads three times. At the peaks, the important invention series lags twice, leads three times, and ties for the lead twice. The mean rank at the troughs is 1.6 for the important inventions, compared with 1.4 for capital formation. At the peaks, these mean ranks are reversed. Even if we ignore the fact that the test was rigged in its favor, the hypothesis receives little support from this evidence. On the contrary, to the degree that the swings in the important invention series are bona fide, they seem to be synchronized with those in investment as much as are those in railroad invention generally. (We recognize, of course, that the fundamental inventions which establish an industry—in this case made almost entirely abroad—must come first. Our discussion here is limited to the later important inventions.)

A legitimate objection to this conclusion is that our analysis, while taking into account important inventions, has failed to differentiate among them. Conceivably, when properly weighted in terms of economic potential, the important inventions would be found to lead the investment swings. This possibility is given consideration next, although obviously full consideration could be given to it only by a much more extensive investigation.

Bruschke, who prepared the chronology of important railroad inventions, undertook to determine the 100 most important among them. He then ranked this more select group according to two criteria: economic importance and technological importance.[11] (The distinction between the two arises from the fact that an invention, whether or not it has an appreciable economic impact, may lead to other economically important inventions. Inventions possessing this seminal quality were designated as technologically important.) Thus, each invention was assigned a rank running from 1 to 100 under each standard, the more important inventions under each standard being assigned the higher numbers.

The ranks under each criterion were summed for overlapping decades with results as shown in Chart 3. Given the lack of anything like adequate data for fixing a firm value for each invention in each category, the results are, of course, based only on impressions from the literature and are only suggestive. The general impression conveyed by the chart is that, on the whole, it makes little difference whether the inventions are weighted or unweighted, or whether they are weighted according to their economic or technological importance.[12] Moreover, when weighting does make a difference, it postpones turning points by about five years. Possibly a weighting scheme which ran from 1 to 1,000 or 1 to 1,000,000 would have altered the picture but Bruschke did not think so. Finally, as with the patent series, the duration of a given swing in the important invention series bears no special relation to the duration of the next swing in investment.

[11] These correspond to two of the dimensions of an invention discussed in Kuznets' paper in this volume.

[12] These conclusions are confirmed by similar operations performed on the 100 most important inventions in petroleum refining and papermaking, respectively. We have not attempted to weight the important farm inventions.

CHART 3

The One Hundred "Most Important" Railroad Inventions, Overlapping
Decade Totals, 1803–1957

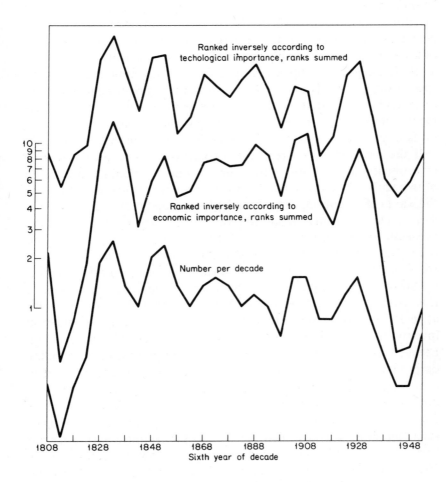

In short, there is little present basis for assuming that the waves of
minor or major inventions, once the industry is established, cause the
swings in railroad investment, either immediately or with a lag. Of
course, this does not mean that the major and minor railroad inventions had no effect on railroad investment. Presumably, really useful
inventions go through, first, a period of increasing use as their value
becomes known, initial defects are eliminated, and occasions for

207

adoption arise; and then, a period of declining use as superior inventions or changed economic conditions make them obsolete. If this "life cycle" of an invention is approximately correct, then investments embodying the inventions probably follow a similar pattern. Other inventions may, of course, never be used, or used only until fatal defects are revealed in practice. The pattern of investment in inventions of the latter sort presumably is one of swift decline from a low initial level. These patterns, however, apply only to investment embodying specific inventions. The effect of these inventions on the aggregate level of investment is indeterminate a priori, for the expansion of investment embodying a given invention obviously may depress total investment in the industry below what it would otherwise have been.

If the foregoing is correct, the association between the waves of investment and invention in the railroad industry would appear to be of two sorts. On the one hand, either the waves of investment induce the waves of invention, or both variables respond to the same external forces. On the other hand, the waves of investment provide the occasion for the introduction and diffusion of inventions, new and old.[13] But *the introduction and diffusion of inventions in the industry seem merely to accompany but not to cause the waves of investment.*

One important implication of the failure of important inventions to lead investment is that, once past the fundamental pioneer inventions, at least, important inventions also fail to lead the run-of-the-mill inventions which dominate the patent statistics. Indeed, a comparison between the trough dates of patents in Table 1 and the corresponding dates of important inventions in Table 2 shows that patents lead in four long swings while important inventions lead only in two. This does not mean that the minor inventions did not build on the major ones—or vice versa, for that matter. It does suggest that the timing of such "building" was governed by the factors that controlled the general level of inventive activity in the industry, and not by factors arising directly out of the growth of knowledge. In short, the role of changes in the state of knowledge as a determinant of inventive activity in this industry does not seem overwhelming, if the number of either major or minor inventions or both are taken as representing changes in the state of knowledge.

The proposition that the swings in railroad investment are not

[13] That investment constitutes either innovation or diffusion of new or old inventions is, obviously, little more than a truism. Each kind of equipment must have been invented sometime. (Only when a worn-out machine is replaced by an identical one can we say that neither innovation nor diffusion has occurred.)

CHART 4

Net Changes in Railroad Output and Labor Force

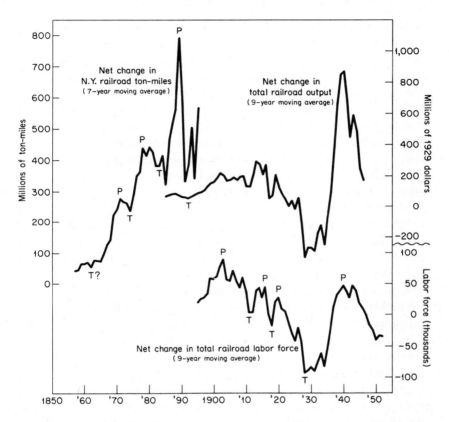

SOURCE: Net change in New York railroad ton-miles: calculated from *Historial Statistics of the United States*, Series K-169. Net change in railroad labor force: calculated from Harold Barger, *The Transportation Industries, 1889–1946: Output, Employment, and Productivity*, New York, NBER, 1951, Table B-1; and from *Statistical Abstract of the United States*. Net changes in output: calculated from Ulmer, *Capital in Transportation, Communications, and Public Utilities . . .*, Table 1-13.

caused by invention and innovation is supported by careful students of the phenomenon. Thus, Ulmer writes, "Second—and more important—it seems impossible to provide an explanation for each of the three and one-half swings during the 1870–1950 period in terms of specific transportation innovations."[14]

[14] Ulmer, *op. cit.*, p. 137. Ulmer treats the period from 1876 to 1899 as one long swing in this quotation, which is based on his data in the form of nine-year moving averages. However, he identifies two long swings for this period when he uses annual data (*Ibid.*, Table 39, p. 125).

Similarly, Cootner writes, "The key railroad innovations were adopted in response to explicit economic demands. The railroad investment . . . was specifically motivated by the growth of industrial requirements, and that motivation was repeated in the early sixties and eighties, while building in the fifties and in the post-Civil War period was induced by the need for the expansion of primary production."[15] Cootner's suggestion that the long swings in railroad investment arose from the ebb and flow of pressure on railroad capacity is borne out by the fact that long swings in the rate of growth of gross national product precede by a few years those in railroad investment.[16] It is further supported by the fact that major peaks and troughs in net additions to railroad output and to railroad labor force generally occur one to seven years before the long-swing peaks and troughs, respectively, in railroad investment, as shown in Chart 4.

While changes in output and labor force are not nearly as smooth as are those in investment, and the existence of long swings in the former two variables is debatable, the evidence that changes in output and labor force lead changes in capital stock nonetheless seems clear. The long-swing peaks and troughs marked off in these two series are compared in Table 3 with the related dates in capital formation.

Whether or not long swings exist in changes in railroad labor force and output is probably not important. That these variables exhibit major peaks and troughs well ahead of the long-swing peaks and troughs in railroad investment probably is important, however. A major peak in additions to output implies impending or actual pressure on capacity and therefore a rising incentive to invest. By the same token, a major trough in additions to output is a signal to reduce the rate of investment. That the waves in investment are not nearly as choppy as are those in increments to output and employment probably results from the character of the investment process in the industry.[17]

The trend and long swings in railroad investment are, therefore, probably not caused by the trend and long swings in railroad invention. If this is correct, then the similarity between the two variables must be explained either by (1) a highly improbable degree of coincidence, (2) a tendency for variations in investment in the industry to induce corresponding variations in invention, or (3) a tendency for inventors

[15] Paul H. Cootner, "Transport Innovation and Economic Development," Unpublished Ph.D. Thesis, Massachusetts Institute of Technology, 1953, Ch. IX, p. 4 of azograph copy kindly supplied by Mr. Cootner.

[16] Cf. Ulmer, *op. cit.*, Table 44, p. 133.

[17] Cf. Ulmer, *op. cit.*, p. 140.

TABLE 3

MAJOR PEAKS AND TROUGHS IN CHANGES IN RAILROAD OUTPUT
(OR LABOR FORCE) AND CAPITAL FORMATION

Cycle	Changes in Output (or Labor Force) Trough	Peak	Capital Formation Trough	Peak	Lag of Capital Formation Behind Changes in Output (or Labor Force) (years) Trough	Peak
	(1)	(2)	(3)	(4)	(5)	(6)
II	1862 or earlier	1871	1863	1870	1 or more	−1
IIIA	1874	1878	1876	1884	2	6
IIIB	1883	1889	1887	1890	4	1
IV	1892	1903	1899	1910	7	7
VA	1911	1916				
VB	1918	1920				
V			1918	1926	0–7[a]	6–10[a]
VI	1928	1940	1935	1949	7	9

SOURCE: Cols. (1) and (2): Chart 5. Dates shown are from output through 1892, from labor force thereafter. Cols. (3) and (4): Table 2.

[a] The first figure is the interval between the date for capital formation and that for Cycle VIB in labor force. The second figure is for the interval between the former and that for Cycle VIA in the labor force.

to respond similarly to the conditions which govern investment. The first explanation can be rejected not only on the basis of the evidence presented for this industry but also in the light of the evidence to follow for other industries.

Whether invention responds primarily to investment or to the conditions which govern the latter cannot be determined yet for lack of evidence. Whichever explanation is ultimately accepted will have to apply to the activities of independent and captive inventors alike, for the association between investment and invention is observable when first one and then the other was predominant.

Perhaps clues to the nature of the association can be found in two elementary facts. First, investment in the railroad industry consists of sales—by the railroad equipment makers and the construction industry. Second, independent inventors, for whom invention is generally an avocation rather than a vocation, do their inventing when they encounter, or hear of, a technical condition which dissatisfies them and which they think they can remedy. (These two properties identify the potential inventor.) We may, therefore, surmise that the timing relations between invention and investment arise from circumstances connected with either (1) the identification of a technical problem, or (2) the activity of remedying the problem, or both.

The identification of a problem can occur at any time during the use, or observation of the use, of an article or piece of equipment. And the man with an irrepressible urge to improve things may, without any special economic motivation, begin inventing as soon as he "recognizes" the problem. The problem may be solved in minutes. In this case—except for the circumstances to be noted later—there need be no association between the given act of invention and the level of investment. On the other hand, as often happens, the solution may take years. In the latter case, the internal drive is likely to slacken and the work put aside and taken up time and again. Under these circumstances, economic motives (or the desire for the recognition which economic success brings) are likely to become relatively more powerful as the first surge of enthusiasm wanes. Now, if sales of the product the inventor wishes to improve are high, he is likely to push harder to finish his improvement and make money from it, while if sales are low, his efforts may subside. Thus, there will tend to be some positive correlation between the sales of a product and the timing of difficult improvements, even when the initial stimulus to the inventor was noneconomic.

Moreover, prolific but equally irrepressible inventors may have several problems with half-finished solutions in their minds. And while their underlying drives may also be noneconomic, it seems reasonable to suppose that the economic prospects of the different incomplete inventions will affect the direction of their efforts, other things being equal.[18]

In addition to this tendency for the solution of technical problems to be stimulated or inhibited by the level of sales of the products involved, there is the possibility that the very recognition of a problem —the initial stimulus to invention—may come when the inventor or an acquaintance of his is shopping for the article which later becomes the object of the inventor's efforts. This may happen particularly if the article turns out to be (1) more costly than anticipated or (2) lacking in

[18] Following the same line of reasoning, there will be tendencies for (1) the proportion of inventions patented to rise and fall with the industry's sales, and (2) inventors to try to juggle the issue dates of their patents in accord with the state of business. Of course, these tendencies cannot account for the marked trend of the railroad patents. The possible effect of (2) will be eliminated from our data for the period beginning with 1874 when application dates rather than granting dates will provide the basis of the time series. (1) creates the real possibility that minor deviations about the trend reflect changes in patenting rates and not changes in inventing. However, since the economic incentives to invent are the same as the incentives to patent, appreciable movements in patenting— including appreciable deviations about trend—should ordinarily be construed as reflecting movements of invention in the same direction.

performance requirements of the customer. If the article is too expensive, the price itself may make the inventor feel he can design a cheaper one. If his requirements are more exacting than can be met by the product already on the market, he may feel he can design a better one.[19] If these surmises are correct, the number of dissatisfied customers may tend to vary directly with the volume of an industry's sales—with the result that the amount of inventing may rise and fall with sales.

The foregoing conjectures are transferable to the activities of captive inventors. The economic considerations which are perhaps marginal with independent inventors become central in the calculations of businessmen. The common corporate practice of setting research and development budgets at a fixed percentage of sales practically assures a high correlation between invention and sales. Far from being a mere convention, this practice has an intelligent rationale, part of which is that inventing a given improvement in the firm's product will entail a certain expected cost which is unrelated to the product's sales volume, and will probably increase the firm's market share by a given percentage. Hence, if the industry's sales are high, the absolute amount resulting from an enlarged market may be great enough to warrant the cost of the invention, and the project will be pursued. But if the industry's sales are low, the increase in the relative market share may promise a revenue from the invention that is too small to justify the project. In addition to these considerations, the higher the firm's sales, other things being equal, the more it can afford research and the farther ahead it can plan, by means of research and other activities.

The general relation of the foregoing to the association between investment and invention in railroading seems clear, but how much is fancy and how much fact remains to be determined. As indicated above, investment in the railroad industry consists primarily of sales to it by the equipment and construction industries. The independent inventors presumably are both railroad employees and outsiders; the captive inventors, the engineers and research men of the locomotive and car companies, rail manufacturers, etc. Some technical problems arose or were recognized in the daily operation of the business, and independents or representatives of suppliers tried to solve them. When equipment purchases were high these efforts were increased—partly

---

[19] Alternatively, recognition of the problem may come before shopping begins, but the decision to solve it inventively may not be made until the inventor discovers that none of the goods on the market constitute a solution.

because, from the buyer's standpoint, the problems would be longer-lived if incorporated in brand-new equipment, partly because the problems may have been recognized for the first time when the very expensive purchases were being considered, and partly because it would be most profitable for the seller to solve the problems then.

Two other considerations may be mentioned relating to the possible timing of the inventor's recognition of the problem to be solved. We noted earlier that increments to output and labor force tended to lead increments to plant by several years. Conceivably, technical problems may be created by the changing capital-output and capital-labor ratios which result. Particularly, a fall in either or both of these ratios below a certain minimum (which, of course, changes with changes in the technique of production) would indicate a strain on plant capacity, a condition which might stimulate some to invent improvements to relieve the pressure on capacity. This would assume a lag of several years between the recognition of the problem and the completion of the invention—a lag as long as that between the pressure on capacity and the consequent increase in capacity represented by the upturn in investment which coincides with the upturn in patenting.

A somewhat different timing in recognizing the problem to be solved is suggested by the presumption, suggested previously, that the waves of investment in the industry determine the timing of waves of innovation and diffusion. If this is correct, one would expect that the new equipment introduced during expansion will exhibit defects under special, local circumstances, or otherwise evoke dissatisfaction in the breasts of inventive men. Thus, the hypothesized environment of relatively rapid technical change may stimulate invention among those who make, sell, use, or service the new equipment. The disproportionately large contribution of "new men" or outsiders—Quakers, Huguenots, etc.—to invention and innovation has been noted by scholars in the past. The proposition here is the other side of the coin—a changing environment can make new men out of old ones. In this case, inventing and patenting these inventions takes little time, given the similarity of timing between the swings in investment and those in patenting.

In both cases supposed in the preceding two paragraphs, recognition of the problem to be solved is associated with the level of investment in some way. In the first case, it is the low level of the latter relative to increments in output or labor. In the second case, it is the high level of investment with the high rate of technical change assumed to be associated with it. How serious these possibilities or the alternative possibility that the problem tends to be identified when the purchase is under consideration may be, we do not know. Moreover, in an industry as large as railroading inventors probably are continually recognizing problems. The question then is presumably one of the relative frequency of each kind of timing and not whether one kind exists and the others do not.

The one argument which seems persuasive, at present, is that the prospective profit from invention tends to vary with equipment purchases and construction, i.e. with the sales of the product being improved, so that regardless of when the idea was conceived, an inventor—or the firm employing him—will tend to press for a solution when sales are high and slacken his efforts when sales are low. (While an inventor could still profit, even if the industry planned to invest nothing, by making such a drastic improvement that, for a given level of output, the total cost with his invention would be lower than the total variable cost with existing installations, this is stacking the cards against himself. His task is much less demanding, especially in a high fixed-cost industry like railroading, when the industry is buying equipment anyway. In this case, total production costs with his invention need only be less than total costs with other new equipment.)

Let us now try to summarize what can be said at present about the relation of invention and investment in the railroad industry. (1) The trend and swings in invention probably do not cause the trend and concurrent swings in investment. (2) A given swing in invention does not constitute the cause of the next swing in investment. These tentative judgments seem as valid for major railroad inventions as for run-of-the-mill inventions. (3) Rather, the trend and swings in railroad investment appear to reflect, fundamentally, the industry's response to changes in the demand for railroad service. This statement, of course, applies to the industry only after the pioneer inventions essential to its establishment have been made. (4) The trend and swings of invention are probably caused in some fashion by those in investment or by the same forces which dominate the latter.

The next question we may ask is whether the concordance between invention and investment found in the railroad industry exists in other industries as well. The other industries for which we have data are petroleum refining, papermaking, and farming, and we turn to them next.

Investment, and Important and Run-of-the-Mill Inventions in Petroleum Refining, Papermaking, and Farming

Comparisons of the sort presented for the railroad industry are, for the present at least, impossible for the other three industries because the necessary data on investment are lacking. What we have instead are estimates of annual rates of net investment between several dates. Given the kind of reasoning developed in the preceding section, gross investment seems by far the more relevant variable. However, since the direction of change is likely to be the same for net as for gross investment, we can still gain some impression of whether or not gross investment and invention rise and fall together in these industries as in railroading.

A more serious difficulty is that our estimates of annual net investment cover only nine time intervals in petroleum refining and papermaking, and only eleven intervals in farming. Moreover, five of the intervals in the two manufacturing industries are approximately decades, and only four are for quinquennia. Hence, impressions as to long swings generally cannot be formed. In farming, five are for decades, and six are for quinquennia, which is a little better. Another consequence of this type of data is that the resulting values naturally must be plotted at the mid-points of the intervals to which they relate and this creates at least one serious distortion for petroleum refining and papermaking. Specifically, the annual rate of investment from 1919 to 1929 is plotted at 1924, and the rate from 1929 to 1937 is plotted at 1933–34. As might be expected, an impression of a great decline in investment from 1924 to 1933–34 is conveyed. Yet the true peak in investment even for, say, a seven-year moving average, probably occurred in these industries sometime around 1927–29.

The comparison between invention and investment for these industries is further distorted by the increased lag between application for and granting of patents which occurred after World War I, at least in rapidly growing fields like petroleum refining and papermaking. Preliminary studies show that in the early 1930's, the average lag was about four and one-half years in petroleum refining. The lag in papermaking patents, at least for chemical inventions, was probably comparable. When our data have been converted to an application date basis, this difficulty will be eliminated.

With these precautionary statements in mind, we turn to Chart 5 which shows the course of patents, net investment, and important

CHART 5

Important Inventions, Patents, and Capital Formation in Petroleum Refining

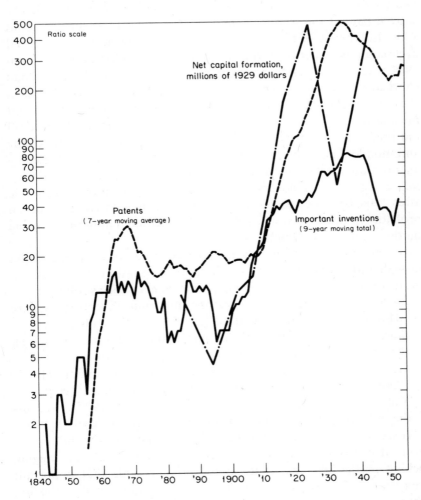

SOURCE: Net capital formation: calculated from Daniel Creamer, Sergei Dobrovolsky, and Israel Borenstein, with the assistance of Martin Bernstein, *Capital Formation in Manufacturing and Mining: Its Formation and Financing*, Princeton for NBER, 1960, Table A-1.

inventions in petroleum refining. The two invention series apply almost entirely to process and equipment inventions. The number of product inventions covered is trivial. The most important single impression from the chart is that all three variables show two distinct growth cycles—the first associated with the kerosene stage of the industry and the second, with the gasoline stage. The presence of these two growth cycles is clearly indicated in both invention series. In the case of patents the second cycle of growth appears to start at about 1908. In the case of the important inventions, the start of the second cycle could be either 1895 when the series reaches a low point, or about 1904 when it returns to approximately the same trend level as had characterized it earlier. The existence of two distinct growth phases in the investment series can reasonably be inferred, since investment must have risen rapidly after Drake's well in 1859 and then levelled off until the demand for gasoline began to swell with the coming of the automobile. The assumption of a second growth cycle is supported by an absolute decline in investment from the 1880's to the 1890's, followed first by a recovery to the old level, and then by a sharp rise after 1906–07. The second growth phase in investment thus began probably in the 1900's, when the gasoline powered automobile came on the scene in large numbers.

If we divide the secular movements in the three variables into rapid growth and retardation (flat or falling trend) phases for each growth cycle, the order of secular turning points seems to be as follows:

Start of first phase of rapid growth: important inventions (before 1840), run-of-the-mill inventions (c. 1850), investment (1859)

Start of first retardation phase: important inventions (1864–71), run-of-the-mill inventions (1868), investment (unknown)

Start of second phase of rapid growth: important inventions (1895–1904), investment (1900's), run-of-the-mill inventions (1908)

Start of second retardation phase: investment (late 1920's), run-of-the-mill inventions (late 1920's), important inventions (late 1930's)[20]

It seems clear that important inventions led run-of-the-mill inventions at two out of four of the secular turning points, while lagging behind at the last one. It is, moreover, inevitable that important inventions led investment during the phase of rapid growth in the first growth cycle. On the other hand, at the start of the second retardation phase, investment led at least the important invention series, and it is not clear whether investment led or lagged behind the important invention series at the start of the second phase of rapid growth. In any case, the important invention which "caused" the second phase of rapid growth in refining investment was obviously the internal-

---

[20] The timing indicated for investment and run-of-the-mill inventions reflects consideration of the factors discussed earlier in this section.

combustion engine (and its diffusion), and not the refining inventions per se.

Given the nature of our data, no possibility exists for detecting long swings, if such exist, in investment. However, the 1890's and the 1930's were periods of subnormal investment, and there seem to have been more or less matching declines in both invention series. Marking off long swings in the invention series is neither easy nor necessarily warranted. Neither invention series exhibits the smooth variation characteristic of the railroad patents. Hence, such variation about the trend as exists may be largely random or a reflection of changed patenting propensities. In the first growth cycle there is, however, some suggestion that fluctuations in important inventions led those in run-of-the-mill inventions, and this impression tends to carry over until, but not including, the second retardation phase in the 1930's. Yet, given the low amplitude of most of these fluctuations about trend, attributing any statistical significance, let alone causal association, to this weak pattern seems hazardous at this stage.

In brief, in petroleum refining two successive growth cycles probably occurred in each variable. As might be expected, important inventions led the other two variables during the first phase of rapid growth, but they lagged in the last phase of retardation. These are the only timing relations we can be sure of at present. Since the entire first growth cycle in each variable was induced by the rising demand for illuminants[21] and kerosene in particular, and the second, by the rising demand for gasoline, the pattern of responsiveness of investment and invention to underlying demand conditions suggested in the preceding section on the railroad industry appears to have been repeated here.

The situation in farming is shown in Chart 6 where, because during two quinquennia net disinvestment occurred, it has been necessary to use an arithmetic scale. The important inventions[22] presented are restricted to mechanical equipment in order to make them comparable with the inventions represented by the patent statistics. Thus, important agricultural advances like hybrid corn are left out. For the same reason, the investment data pertain only to implements and machinery and not to farm real estate, livestock, or inventories.

The free wheeling, not overly critical imagination can find many

---

[21] Cf. H. R. Williamson and A. R. Daum, *The American Petroleum Industry*, Evanston, 1959, Chaps. 2–5.

[22] Makers of important farm inventions, unlike inventors in the other industries, were primarily American from the start. In the other industries Americans dominated after the first few decades.

CHART 6

Important Inventions, Patents, and Capital Formation in Farm Implements and Machinery

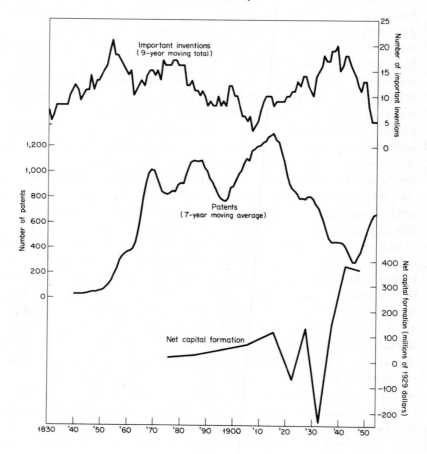

SOURCE: Net capital formation calculated from Alvin S. Tostlebe, *Capital in Agriculture: Its Formation and Financing Since* 1900, Princeton for NBER, 1957, Table G-1.

suggestive phenomena in Chart 6. Two long-term growth cycles in important inventions, the first ending and the second beginning in 1907, seem fairly clear. The first of these could be the cause of the entire movement in the run-of-the-mill inventions reflected in the patent statistics. This is, in one sense, not a very remote possibility since many of the latter are made by farmers who may not be abreast of the industry's needs and technology, as well as by equipment makers who presumably are more up-to-date. On the other hand, the deep decline of agricultural patenting in the 1890's suggests that perhaps there were two long-term growth cycles in this series, too. If so, while important inventions led run-of-the-mill inventions in the first growth cycle, run-of-the-mill inventions led the important ones in the second cycle. The long swings in the patent series seem quite pronounced, and while this seems also to be the case with the important invention series, the fact that only about 150 items appear in the latter (far fewer than in the comparable series for our other three industries), or slightly less than one per year, should make us treat the minor fluctuations in this variable with considerable skepticism. Be that as it may, except for the obvious lead of important over run-of-the-mill inventions at the outset, the timing relations between the two are not constant. Only some kind of content analysis of the inventions involved seems likely to disclose the kind and degree of interdependence of the two series.

The investment-invention relationship, however, seems more stable in some respects, and indeed is like that found earlier in railroading. Until 1920 the investment data are only for decade intervals, but the trend is upward like that in patents.[23] After 1915, however, the trend of patents is downward, while that of investment is generally rising, despite big drops. On the other hand, with quinquennial average rates of investment available after 1920 we can compare the long swings in the variables, and these are similar. Starting with a peak in 1915 in patents and in 1910–20 in investment, we have next a trough in investment in 1920–25 and in patents in 1925; a peak in investment in 1925–30 and in patents in 1929; a trough in investment in 1930–35 and in patents in 1937; and finally, a peak in investment in 1940–45 and in patents around 1941. Interestingly enough, at the last three turning points the important invention series seems to lead, with dates at 1926, 1930, and 1939. However, the low level of farm investment in the early 1930's certainly reflected the depression, and the high level in the early 1940's, war-time demand and labor shortage, and not the changing rate of important inventions.

The same variables in papermaking are shown in Chart 7. Equipment, processes, and products are all reflected in the two invention series. When the data are decomposed, this combination may prove

---

[23] This remark applies only to the trend in investment in implements and machinery. The trend for total farm investment was down during the period, and the fluctuations in it run directly counter to those in farm patents. Starting with 1910–20, investment in implements and machinery and total farm investment move together.

CHART 7

Important Inventions, Patents, and Capital Formation in Papermaking

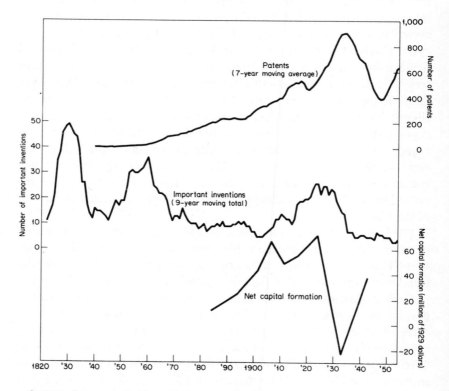

SOURCE: For net capital formation, same as for Chart 6.

to have been a mistake. In particular, we do not yet know what the timing pattern is between improvements on products and improvements on the machines that make them. Since the investment series pertains by definition to plant and equipment, it would have been preferable, in the light of the discussion in the previous section, to have had a separate series on equipment inventions.

The over-all impression conveyed by Chart 7 is that the trends in investing and general inventing were similar in timing and direction. This statement is made on the basis of the contentions advanced earlier in this section that the all-time peak in investment occurred not in the early but in the late 1920's, and that the all-time peak in run-of-the-mill inventions occurred not in the early 1930's but in the late

1920's. If these arguments are correct, then on the whole patents rose when investment rose and declined when investment declined. On the other hand, it is doubtful that the bulge in patenting from about 1910 to 1920 is tied to the earlier bulge in investment from 1899–1904 to 1909–14, for the average lag between application for and granting of patents then could hardly have been ten or eleven years.

In addition, the long swings in important papermaking inventions seem similar to later movements in the patent series. Conceivably, the first phase in patenting ending in 1895 was associated with the rise and fall in important inventions from 1845 to about 1869; the period of steady rise in patenting from 1895 to about 1910 with the nearly stationary level of important inventions between 1870 and 1903; the patent swing from 1910 to 1920 with the swing in important inventions from 1903 to 1915; and the patent swing from 1920 to 1947 with the swing in important inventions from 1915 to the close. Obviously, however, whether the temporal association between the run-of-the-mill inventions and the important ones is that suggested by the graph could be ascertained only by means of a content analysis of both.

Without wishing to spin out still another speculative thread, one may suggest that this industry may be one in which the chain of direct causality runs mainly from major inventions to the level of investment and from the latter or both to run-of-the-mill inventions. That is, important inventions in this industry may conceivably dominate the level of investment, and inventing generally may respond to investment in this industry in the ways suggested earlier for the railroad industry. The hypothesis that important inventions dominate investment would become tenable if it could be shown that the paper industry—perhaps because its products on the average occupied a smaller share of their respective markets than was the case with the products of the other three industries—faced a product demand that was more responsive to cuts in price and to new and improved products than the demand confronting the other three industries was. In that event, innovations would tend to stimulate aggregate investment in the industry. When such conditions do not exist, the level of investment in an industry is likely to be dominated by the external factors that govern demand.

In brief, the trend movements of patents and investment run roughly parallel in railroading, petroleum refining, and papermaking. In farming, however, these variables rise together until the mid-1910's but then patents decline while investment in implements and machinery pursues a choppy but slightly rising course. The long swings in patents and investment seem approximately synchronized in both railroading and farming. In petroleum refining and papermaking, however, long swings in investment, if they exist, are not observable in our data. Nor is the existence of long swings in patenting in petroleum refining at all certain.

Important inventions lead at the outset in all four industries, but their subsequent relation to the other two variables seems unclear. In petroleum's second growth cycle, they lead patents and may lead investment at the start but in the same growth cycle they later decline absolutely after both investment and patents. In railroading, the later long swings in important inventions are approximately concurrent with those in patents and investment. In farming, where the number of important inventions in our chronology is relatively small, no obvious relation between these inventions and the other two variables appears. In papermaking, however, the graph suggests the possible existence of three or four long swings in important inventions which lead somewhat similar movements in patents.

The variety of the relations thus far observed indicates the desirability of decomposing some of our variables in an effort to determine whether the differences actually exist or merely result from incomparabilities in the underlying data, e.g. the inclusion of product and process patents in papermaking, and process patents in petroleum refining.

For the present, at least, the evidence and the reasoning developed earlier suggest that inventive activity tends to rise and fall with the sales of the product which the inventions improve, although other factors undoubtedly also play a role. In industries like railroading where investment lags behind sales, one would therefore anticipate a tendency for product inventions to lead equipment inventions. While the bearing of this line of reasoning on process inventions is not clear, where process inventions entail equipment changes, one may conjecture that their timing will tend to be the same as that of equipment sales.

Note on the Role of Science in the Four Industries

In light of the common belief that modern inventions represent the industrial application of prior scientific discoveries, a belief reflected in some of the other conference papers and partially justified by examples too well known to warrant repeating, the four researchers who compiled the chronologies of important inventions were instructed to note any suggestion in the literature that a particular scientific discovery or any other factor prompted a particular invention included in their chronologies.

For most of the roughly 1,000 inventions in our four chronologies, the records unfortunately omit mention of stimulating factors, but the subject is mentioned in a number of cases, almost always referring to industrial problems the inventors sought to solve. In only one or two cases in petroleum refining and papermaking did prior scientific discoveries appear to constitute a direct stimulus. At present, therefore, the direct influence of individual scientific discoveries, even in industries like petroleum refining and paper with their strong dependence on chemistry, seems to have been nominal. Possibly careful research into unpublished materials would raise this estimate.

This, however, should not be interpreted as meaning that scientific discoveries may not have played a crucial role in many of the major and perhaps minor inventions in these four industries. It merely means that in our industries science has been like a book on a reference shelf— taken down when needed and enriching and perhaps even making possible what is accomplished. The point is only that scientific discoveries per se have apparently seldom constituted a direct stimulus to the making of important (and presumably unimportant) inventions in these four industries.

Finally, it may be suggested that more powerful than individual scientific discoveries as a general precondition for invention in these industries has been the pervasiveness of an empirical, experimental attitude, an attitude characteristic of modern society and reflecting a popular belief in the efficacy of experimental science. But, of course, this general and indispensable precondition can hardly explain the temporal variations in invention in these or other industries.

Concluding Remarks

Why should economists be interested in patent statistics since unpublished attempts by Sanders, Griliches, and the present author to compare these data for individual industries with data on output per unit of input in the same industries reveal no consistent relationships? This is a fair question and one which was raised at the Conference in connection with the first draft of this paper.

Two answers, at different levels, can be given to the question. The most important in the present context is the light which a study of the data has already cast on fundamental questions of social theory and the theory of economic development. Many, if not most, economists, historians, sociologists, and anthropologists find in scientific discovery and invention a pair of exogenous variables which together or separately largely explain long-term social change and economic growth. A whole theoretical superstructure has been built around this postulate by one school of sociologists. In economics, anthropology, and history, system building is uncommon, but it would be easy to cite authors in these fields who make the same facile technologically deterministic assumption. Much more important, the same assumption seems to serve as a tacit article of faith and point of departure for both laymen and many social scientists.

In public and in the universities, we are constantly told that science shapes our lives, and that the rest of culture lags behind changing technology. In economics, waves of investment are often, if not usually, in certain contexts construed as waves of innovation and imitation *a la* Schumpeter. The half-truth of these statements is hardly ever made whole by correlated statements showing how our lives shape science, how technology lags behind the rest of culture, and how economic change induces waves of innovation. The atomic bomb and advances in nuclear science are imputed to non-Euclidean geometry, Einstein ($e = mc^2$), and a few foreign born physicists. The obvious role of World War II and its aftermath, of a system of dangerously entangled rival nation-states, and of the expenditure of several billion dollars a year on research is hardly mentioned. High farm surpluses are accounted a consequence of the lag of culture behind technological change, because the farm population has failed to adjust to higher productivity. Yet, the lag is just as much in the opposite direction. Farm technology, after all, has failed to develop new uses for farm products which would eliminate the surpluses.

Finally, let me cite just one example of a wave of innovation induced by economic change. While Schumpeter is correct in assigning a large role to the automobile industry in the so-called Kondratieff which began around the turn of the century, it seems almost obvious, to this writer at least, that the automobile came when it did more because of economic and social changes than because of technological change as such. In the first place, in the automobile, prestige, flexibility, privacy, recreation, and utility are combined in ways which only an individual-istic high-per-capita-income society could afford or develop. (The so-called bicycle craze of the 1890's was part of the same phenomenon.) The automobile, after all, did not and has not revolutionized life in low-income India or China. Its effects have been confined primarily to the United States and other industrialized countries, roughly in proportion to income. A good case can be made for the contention that among the indispensable conditions for the coming of the automobile age were relatively high levels of income, at least for the middle-income classes, and an individualistic society.[24]

Secondly, there is no warrant for supposing that the advent of the automobile depended on the development of the internal combustion engine. At the turn of the century, after the industry was thoroughly launched, experts were still divided over whether the automobile of the future would be driven by steam, electricity, or gasoline. Each type was heavily represented in the market. Even more important, the first "locomotives" over a century and a half ago were not locomotives at all but automobiles—engine-driven road vehicles. Had the wealthy of that day wanted mechanical playtoys as did those of a century later, the automobile industry could have come nearly a hundred years before it did. Even so, steam-powered buses operated for a few years in the first half of the nineteenth century on some of the highways of England, until driven from them by vested interests. Putting the vehicle on rails, hitching cars behind it, and converting the whole into a means of public transportation was as much a reflection of the political and socio-economic elements of the situation as of the technological characteristics of the machine. (One implication of this analysis is that our earlier imputation of the decline in railroad investment and invention after about 1910 to the invention of the automobile was a conventional over-simplification.)

The antidote urged here for the popular conception of the role of science and technology is far from new. Bagehot said long ago, "Most men of genius are susceptible and versatile, and fall into the style of their age." The same view has been cogently argued by Gilfillan,[25] and by others. It has been overdone by those Marxists who seek to substitute economic determinism for the currently more popular scientific and technological determinism. The antidote merely recognizes the wholesale interdependence of changes in society and changes in the state of knowledge. It regards the two somewhat like blades of a

---

[24] Khrushchev's statement on looking at our west coast's jammed freeways comes to mind.

[25] *Op. cit.*

scissors. One is not an inert material on which the other operates ad libitum.

The lack of currency of this alternative and more appropriate construction of events is explained primarily by the absence of substantial objective evidence of a two-way flow between the variables. Such evidence has already begun to come from the study of patent statistics, as this paper indicates. If the study of the data accomplishes no more than a righting of the balance and an elimination of the present serious distortion in social theory; if it does no more than persuade social scientists and through them the public that men shape science and technology as much as these forces shape men, that the production of knowledge, though doubtless in lesser measure than the production of goods, responds to social pressures including those of the market, as well as to the exigencies of genius; then the study of patent statistics will have contributed its fair share to the advancement of social science.

These considerations pave the way for the second answer to the question with which this section began. After socioeconomic forces have directed the activities of inventors, similar though even greater forces affect the fate of their brain children. Between the discovery of new knowledge and its filtration through industry lie the processes of innovation and diffusion. These processes in turn are drastically altered by depression and prosperity, war and peace, the advent of rival and complementary inventions, and the secular rise and fall of the industries concerned. Hence, there is little reason to suppose that the economic impact of the average invention in an industry will be the same over time. The invention of a new product or process is but the first link in a long, poorly-understood chain of events.

The study of patent statistics is consequently but one stage in the study of that chain.[26]

---

[26] A further point in answer to the question which opened this section of the paper may be mentioned here. It is not logical to assume that the average invention of a given period should yield the same increase in output per unit of input as does the average invention of some other period. If we suppose as a first approximation that the cost of making the average invention is constant over time, then as an industry (or firm) grows, it will pay it to seek inventions which yield increasingly smaller increases in output per unit of input. Similiarly, as an industry declines, inventions which yield increasingly large increases in output per unit of input will be sought. In brief, it is the saving in total cost, or the increase in total output, that is likely to provide the incentive for invention, and not the increase in output per unit of input.

It was this line of reasoning, following his failure to find any clear relation between patenting and later changes in output per unit of input, which led the author to seek and find a positive association between the volume of patent applications and the volume of employment of all resources in the United States from 1869 to 1938 (Cf., Schmookler, "The Level of Inventive Activity"). Whether the association observed is to be explained

APPENDIX

Note on Statistics of Patents Granted by Industry

Anyone wishing to use statistics of patents classified by industry must recognize that he will be able to find out little concerning temporal changes in (1) the propensity to patent in each industry, (2) the quality of the average patented invention, or (3) the quantity of inventive inputs actually employed per patented invention. About all that can be said with confidence at present is that, roughly since 1940, there has apparently been a decline in the ratio of patents granted to corporations to inventions made by corporations. The economic input per patented corporate invention may also have increased since 1940. The reasons for suspecting that these changes have occurred are mentioned in the author's comment on Sanders' paper in this volume and will be discussed by him in a forthcoming critique and review of the literature on patent statistics. Simon Kuznets and Barkev Sanders discuss some of the possible difficulties in interpreting patent statistics in their papers in this volume.

Yet, despite these largely insoluble difficulties, it seems very reasonable to believe that far more railroad inventions were made around 1910 than in the decades before or after, that far more petroleum refining inventions were made in the 1920's than in earlier years, and that the number of papermaking inventions grew fairly continuously until the depressed 1930's. Given common knowledge about the economic growth patterns of the industries concerned, acceptance of the data as indicative of the trends and long swings in inventive output places no strain on one's credulity. (On the other hand, the author's very limited knowledge about the growth of agriculture provides him with no similar assurance in the case of farm patents.) By the same token, declines in patenting in wars and deep depressions and increases in patenting with the return of peace or prosperity can be readily accepted as indicative of the behavior of the output of inventions and the input of inventive effort (except, of course, for war-associated industries).

---

by this reasoning is not clear. However, this finding, in conjunction with a recognition that the processes of innovation and diffusion occur in a changing environment, suggests that the lack of correspondence between inventions patented and later changes in output per unit of input does not diminish the utility of patent statistics in the study of economic growth.

PREPARATION OF THE SPECIFIC SERIES USED

The conceptual and operational difficulties associated with the compilation of statistics of patents issued by industry deserve more attention than can be afforded here. On the conceptual side lies the problem of choosing the criteria for assigning a given invention to one industry instead of to another. This choice is naturally affected by the purpose at hand: one industry may inspire the invention, another manufacture it, and a third use it.

In each case the assignment might differ depending on whether the interest is in the industry immediately, or the industry ultimately inspiring, producing, or using the invention. Whatever the purpose, the implementation of the criteria chosen is impeded by the host of inventions that cut across many industries (whether the latter be inspirers, makers, or users), and which therefore cannot be properly assigned to a single industry.

In the present study the investigator assigned inventions to the current main producing or using industry. If, in the case of a given invention, both the producing and using industries were to be included in the project, the invention was assigned to both. Silos, for example, were assigned to both construction and agriculture. Inventions with significant multiple industry application, such as bearings, motors, engines, etc. were simply excluded. Any alternative treatment of this significant group of inventions requires more knowledge than the author has.

In practice these criteria had to be compromised. For any individual or small group to assign to specific industries each of the nearly 3 million patents issued by the United States Patent Office since 1836 (or, for that matter, any sample large enough to be useful for our purpose) would be impractical. Instead the author assigned whole Patent Office subclasses to specific industries. The subclass is the elementary unit of the classification system designed by the Patent Office to facilitate the search of the prior art. Nearly 50,000 such subclasses exist, each a member of one or another of more than 300 main classes. The average subclass has slightly more than 50 patents in it.

Each subclass has its own definition, typically of a technological-functional character. When the definition clearly implied that nearly all the inventions in a given subclass would be made or used, if at all, by a single industry the whole subclass was allocated to that industry. When, as often, the definition provided an insufficient basis for such a decision but implied a reasonable possibility that at least two-thirds of the patents might be assignable to a given industry, the investigator sampled the patents included in the subclass in the files of the Patent Office search room. If, on the basis of this sampling, at least two-thirds of the patents seemed to apply to the industry, the whole subclass was so assigned. The 10,000 subclasses ultimately assigned to 88 four-digit industries were then reviewed by a group of principal examiners in the Patent Office, and corrections in our industrial classification were made in accordance with their suggestions.

The resulting statistics of patents issued classified by industry thus necessarily include some inventions that do not belong to the industry to which they have been credited and exclude some that do. As is common in life, however, the signs of omission probably outweigh those of commission. In all likelihood, at least 95 per cent of the inventions covered by the series for our four industries belong to the industries to which they have been assigned. On the other hand, an indeterminate number of equally pertinent inventions have been omitted because they were in highly heterogeneous subclasses. But perhaps even more serious than the omission of inventions with primary applicability to a given industry is the absence of inventions with substantial multiindustry application. Whether our concern is with the causes or with the effects of invention in an industry, such lacunae are troublesome. Inventors traditionally seek to maximize the generality of their inventions, and patent applicants, the generality of their patents. A man who starts by trying to improve the woodsawing art may end by improving the sawing art generally. Such examples could be multiplied easily. Ideally, to study the inventions affecting or affected by an industry one would want to know not only those inventions pertinent to that industry alone, but also those inventions which relate to the given industry and others as well. Unfortunately, to determine which electric motor, for example, belongs to which industry or group of industries was simply not feasible.

Because of the exclusion of inventions which, though primarily applicable to a given industry, are classified in excessively mixed subclasses, and because of the exclusion of inventions with a substantial multiindustry application, the resulting time series of patents by industry provide an incomplete record of the patented inventions arising from or affecting the industries in our project. Perhaps by sampling all the patents issued in some years we may later be able to measure and correct some of the bias present because of the first deficiency. The task of remedying the second deficiency seems hopeless.

FIELDS COVERED IN THE FOUR INDUSTRIES

The farm patents are primarily for inventions pertaining to plows, harvesters, harrows, manure spreaders, cultivators, threshers, etc.— bins and silos, tools, and plant husbandry. Farm tractors are omitted because inventions relating to them are mixed in many subclasses with technologically related nonfarm inventions. However, inventions induced by the tractor in the fields covered are naturally included. Little government agricultural research is reflected since patents seldom result from it. The aggregate farm series presented is a summation of dozens of separate time series, each series pertaining to a specific phase of farm technology and covering at least six Patent Office subclasses. The patents number 83,000.

The railroad patents cover locomotives, passenger and freight cars, draft appliances, brakes, wheels and axles, rail cleaning and snow removing, track laying, ties, rails, switches, signals, crossing gates, and railway mail delivery. Altogether the data reflect over 90 individual time series and 90,000 patents. Those power plant inventions are included which apply only to railroading and which were, in consequence, classified in one of the subclasses covered. The development of steam and diesel engines per se is not directly represented, although some of their indirect effects undoubtedly are.

The papermaking inventions, which number 38,000, relate to the disintegrating and grinding of wood; bleaching, preparing, and working pulp; forming and delivering the web; coating, finishing, and drying paper; and special products such as boxes and envelopes, and machines for making them. Twenty-seven individual series underlie the aggregate for this industry.

The petroleum refining patents, 12,000 in number, pertain to bubble towers, refining with paraffin, refining with solvents, refining with chemicals, distillation, cracking, and petroleum products. This aggregate is a summation of twelve separate time series.

The four industries collectively represent roughly 3,500 subclasses, over a third of those included in the major study.

The Changing Direction of Research and Development Employment Among Firms

JAMES S. WORLEY

VANDERBILT UNIVERSITY

Introduction

THIS paper examines the participation of certain firms in the nation's research and development effort. More specifically, it focuses upon the 100 firms reported as employing the largest number of research and development personnel in 1927, 1938, 1950, and 1955.[1] Selection of 100 firms for analysis in each year is, of course, arbitrary. However, the inclusion of firms with a relatively small volume of research and development employment assures us that, insofar as data are available, all of the very large employers have been included. With this goal fulfilled there is little need to undertake the considerably greater task of identifying a larger number of firms.

The nation's industrial research and development effort was relatively small in the beginning of the period under review. But a substantial increase in both the size of the effort and in the number of participating firms is evident in prewar data, and the growth has been even more pronounced in recent years, in good part because of government support to meet the demands of the cold war. Against that background this paper analyzes the changes in leadership in research and development that have occurred. So far as possible we shall ascertain the impact of the higher postwar level of government support upon the

NOTE: Most of the material upon which this paper is based is presented in the writer's doctoral dissertation, "Industrial Research and Development and the New Competition —A Study of the Leading Employers of Research and Development Personnel by Industry Group and by Size of Firm," submitted to Princeton University in 1958. The writer wishes to acknowledge financial assistance from the Institute of Research and Training in the Social Sciences of Vanderbilt University, made possible by a grant from the Rockefeller Foundation, which provided time to extend the dissertation material.

[1] These firms were identified by tabulating data contained in the National Research Council surveys of industrial research laboratories conducted on these dates. For a discussion of the adequacy of these surveys and of the procedure involved in tabulating the data, and for the identification of the leading firms, the reader is referred to the writer's dissertation.

The lists of the 100 largest exclude commercial and nonprofit research organizations because we wish to concentrate on those firms whose principal line of activity consists of the manufacture and sale of commodities or the sale of services other than research and development service.

composition of the 100 leading firms. Following this we shall examine the influence of two factors that are widely believed to play an important part in determining the distribution of research and development activity and that may consequently help explain the pattern of leadership. These factors are the size of the leading firms and the variability in intensity of research effort among industries.

Before proceeding a note of caution must be issued. The study concentrates upon employment of research and development personnel—the principal input in research and development—and the findings are not intended to have output significance. Scattered evidence points to considerable variation among firms in the proportion of research and development projects that are successful as well as in the quantity of inputs per successful project. Extent of employment of research and development personnel is, therefore, not an accurate index of the rate of innovation.

We begin by briefly discussing the relative importance of the leaders, hoping to demonstrate that they have accounted for a sizeable share of industrial research and development and that their importance in this respect measures only partially their sphere of influence in the economy.

Importance of the 100 Largest Employers of Research and Development Personnel

It is well known that research and development activity today is highly concentrated in the largest firms in the economy. A high degree of concentration is also visible in earlier data, although the extent to which the largest firms were involved is revealed less clearly.[2] Examination of the proportion of industrial research and development employment accounted for by the 100 largest employers and of the interrelationship between these firms and the largest firms indicates that very considerable concentration in the largest firms has typified the period since 1927.

The writer estimates that the 168,808 persons in the laboratories of the 100 largest employers in early 1955 amounted to about 40 per cent of all such personnel employed in the industrial sector at that time. The significance of this figure is apparent if we note that in 1950 the 100 largest manufacturing firms accounted for 33.3 per cent of the total

[2] The National Research Council data for 1920–38 have been tabulated and analyzed by George Perazich and Phillip M. Field in *Industrial Research and Changing Technology* (Works Progress Administration, National Research Project Number M-4, Philadelphia, 1940).

value of product of all manufacturing industries and that the 200 largest accounted for 40.5 per cent.[3] Although we are unable to estimate the share of the 100 largest before World War II with accuracy, the available evidence indicates that it was higher than it is now.[4]

Not only has the share of the 100 largest been substantial but also there has existed considerable inequality in the distribution of research and development employment among the leaders themselves. This is shown in Table 1. It is evident, however, that the inequality is now less marked than previously, although some ambiguity surrounds the 1955 data. Lorenz curves constructed for 1927, 1938, and 1950 lie successively closer to the diagonal line of equal distribution, but those for 1950 and 1955 intersect at a point corresponding to the twentieth largest employer, displaying (when compared to the 1950 data) greater equality among the first 20 firms in 1955 and less equality among the remaining 80 firms. By inspection it appears that the Gini coefficients for 1950 and 1955 are roughly equal, signifying no change in the overall degree of inequality within the 100 largest. Therefore it is probably more accurate to conclude that, while inequality in the distribution of employment within the 100 largest decreased substantially from 1927 to 1938 and slightly from 1938 to 1950, no marked overall change occurred between 1950 and 1955.

To study the extent to which the leading research and development employers have also been among the largest firms we may compare the leaders with Kaplan's lists of the 100 largest industrial companies for 1929, 1935, and 1948,[5] the Federal Trade Commission list of the 1,000 largest in 1948,[6] and *Fortune's* list of the 500 largest for 1955.[7] We must use assets to measure size in order to maintain consistency between the lists. In addition to the fact that only the *Fortune* list coincides in time with our data, the lists are not strictly comparable among themselves because of differences in the details of their

---

[3] *Changes in Concentration in Manufacturing, 1935 to 1947 and 1950*, Federal Trade Commission, 1954, pp. 17–18.

[4] It must be noted that there is a downward bias to the estimates over time. While all measures involving an absolute number of firms in the numerator are subject to some bias if the total population of firms under analysis is changing, the problem may be more acute in our case because of the sizeable growth in the number of companies conducting research and development.

[5] A. D. H. Kaplan, *Big Enterprise in a Competitive System*, Washington, The Brookings Institution, 1954, pp. 145–154.

[6] *A List of 1,000 Large Manufacturing Companies, Their Subsidiaries and Affiliates, 1948*, Federal Trade Commission, 1951.

[7] *The Fortune Directory of the 500 Largest U.S. Industrial Corporations*, supplement to the July 1956 issue.

TABLE 1

DISTRIBUTION OF RESEARCH AND DEVELOPMENT PERSONNEL WITHIN
THE 100 LARGEST EMPLOYERS

Number of Firms[a]	1927		1938		1950		1955	
	R and D Employment	Per Cent of Share of 100 Largest	R and D Employment	Per Cent of Share of 100 Largest	R and D Employment	Per Cent of Share of 100 Largest	R and D Employment	Per Cent of Share of 100 Largest
2	2,973	28.35	6,732	22.38	16,406	15.72	22,920	13.58
4	4,351	41.49	9,409	31.28	27,907	26.74	37,342	22.12
6	5,454	52.01	11,475	38.14	36,160	34.64	48,855	28.94
8	6,125	58.41	12,842	42.69	41,518	39.78	58,679	34.76
10	6,686	63.76	14,043	46.68	46,249	44.31	67,704	40.11
20	7,896	75.29	18,839	62.62	62,941	60.30	102,765	60.88
30	8,509	81.14	22,270	74.03	72,961	69.90	120,299	71.26
40	8,965	85.49	24,438	81.24	80,487	77.11	132,156	78.29
50	9,315	88.84	26,148	86.92	86,137	82.52	141,066	83.57
60	9,610	91.64	27,279	90.68	90,889	87.08	148,139	87.76
70	9,868	94.10	28,146	93.56	95,064	91.08	154,256	91.38
80	10,111	96.41	28,880	96.00	98,621	94.48	159,689	94.60
90	10,316	98.37	29,518	98.12	101,727	97.46	164,507	97.45
100	10,487	100.00	30,083	100.00	104,379	100.00	168,808	100.00

[a] In order of number of research and development personnel employed.

construction. Nevertheless the comparisons, though presented more precisely than the data warrant, are generally valid. They show that 36 of the research and development leaders in 1927 appeared among the 100 largest firms in 1929, 45 of the 1938 leaders were among the 100 largest firms in 1935, 45 of the 1950 leaders appeared in the 1948 list of the 100 largest, and 51 leaders were in the top 100 firms in 1955.

Most of the research and development leaders that did not rank among the 100 largest firms were, nevertheless, among the larger firms in the economy—86 of them among *Fortune's* 500 in 1955. We may account for the failure of 5 others to appear in that list—3 because they did not disclose financial data, 1 because it was not primarily a manufacturing firm, and another probably because *Fortune's* decision to employ sales as the primary basis of selection excluded its revenue derived from leases. Similarly, 89 of the leading research and development employers in 1950 appeared among the 1,000 largest firms in 1948, and at least 6 others were absent only because they did not publish financial information or because they were not engaged in manufacturing. Inspection of the relative asset size of the research and development leaders in 1927 and 1938 suggests that many of them were among the larger firms in those years, although the relationship may have been less strong in 1927.

Thus it seems clear that there has existed a substantial overlap between the firms accounting for the concentration of research and development and those responsible for asset concentration and that the interrelationship now is probably even more pronounced than formerly.

Changes in Firm and Industry Distribution of the 100 Largest

We turn now to an examination of changes in research and development leadership. First we analyze changes in the 100 largest by industry group, and then calculate the turnover of firms among the leaders and evaluate the significance of the turnover that has occurred.

DISTRIBUTION BY INDUSTRY GROUP[8]

Table 2 shows the distribution of the 100 largest R and D employers by industry classification.[8] If we treat the nonmanufacturing sector as

[8] We are forced to employ a broad industry classification because the firms under analysis are among these most highly diversified. Furthermore, since research is held to be a major means of diversification, division of the firms into their constituent markets might not be an appropriate guide to allocation of their research and development programs. Unfortunately the data are not sufficient to allow us to allocate research and development activity more directly.

TABLE 2

DISTRIBUTION OF THE 100 LARGEST EMPLOYERS OF RESEARCH AND DEVELOPMENT PERSONNEL, BY INDUSTRY GROUP

Industry Group	1927			1938			1950			1955		
	Number of Firms	R and D Personnel	Per Cent Share of 100 Largest	Number of Firms	R and D Personnel	Per Cent Share of 100 Largest	Number of Firms	R and D Personnel	Per Cent Share of 100 Largest	Number of Firms	R and D Personnel	Per Cent Share of 100 Largest
Food and kindred products	3	78	0.74	6	566	1.88	6	2,279	2.18	3	1,749	1.04
Textile mill products	1	39	0.37	1	95	0.32	1	425	0.41	1	601	0.36
Paper and allied products	2	91	0.87	2	130	0.43	0	0	0.00	0	0	0.00
Chemicals and allied products	20	2,086	19.89	23	6,500	21.61	23	19,692	18.87	20	25,067	14.85
Petroleum and coal products	11	1,217	11.60	13	4,915	16.34	12	15,353	14.71	13	17,404	10.31
Rubber products	7	941	8.97	5	2,116	7.03	4	4,108	3.94	5	11,302	6.70
Stone, clay, and glass products	7	223	2.13	8	863	2.87	5	2,596	2.49	3	1,563	0.93
Primary metal products	12	441	4.21	11	1,956	6.50	4	2,144	2.05	3	2,259	1.34
Fabricated metal products	2	60	0.57	2	252	0.84	4	1,801	1.73	3	1,732	1.03
Machinery (except electrical)	11	900	8.58	6	1,211	4.03	5	2,660	2.55	7	10,774	6.38
Electrical machinery	9	1,413	13.47	9	3,421	11.37	12	16,520	15.83	16	32,175	19.06
Transportation equipment	7	619	5.90	5	2,233	7.42	17	23,553	22.56	19	47,260	28.00
Instruments and related products	3	191	1.82	2	466	1.55	4	3,092	2.96	4	4,077	2.42
Nonmanufacturing	5	2,188	20.86	7	5,359	17.81	3	10,156	9.73	3	12,845	7.61
Totals	100	10,487	99.98	100	30,083	100.00	100	104,379	100.01	100	168,808	100.03

a single industry group (with reason, because electrical communication is the principal contributor to this sector's prominence), 14 industry groups were represented in 1927 and 1938 and 13 appeared in 1950 and 1955. The contribution of many of these industry groups was almost negligible, however, and the 7 leading groups in each year dominated the distribution, accounting for from 88 to 93 per cent of the total employment of the 100 leaders. Indeed, as the following tabulation shows, the 4 leading groups accounted for almost two-thirds of the total in 1927, and their share persistently increased thereafter.

1927	*Per Cent*
Nonmanufacturing (primarily electrical communication)	20.86
Chemicals and allied products	19.89
Electrical machinery	13.47
Petroleum and petroleum products	11.60
	65.82

1938	
Chemicals and allied products	21.61
Nonmanufacturing (primarily electrical communication)	17.81
Petroleum and petroleum products	16.34
Electrical machinery	11.37
	67.13

1950	
Transportation equipment	22.56
Chemicals and allied products	18.87
Electrical machinery	15.83
Petroleum and petroleum products	14.71
	71.97

1955	
Transportation equipment	28.00
Electrical machinery	19.06
Chemicals and allied products	14.85
Petroleum and petroleum products	10.31
	72.22

Note also that only 5 industry groups appeared among the 4 leaders, transportation equipment replacing electrical communication in the postwar years and assuming a dominant position. Further inspection of Table 2 shows that between 1927 and 1955 the changes associated with these industry groups were the most marked, that the share of electrical machinery rose moderately and that of chemicals fell by roughly the same amount, and that all other changes were relatively small. Thus we are presented essentially with a picture of stability in the combined influence of certain industry groups but with important changes in leadership taking place among those groups.

The changes in the industrial composition of the leaders reflect those pertaining to all firms, although the order of leadership differs slightly. They appear to be associated primarily with the distribution of the higher postwar level of government support of research and development. According to the 1953–54 National Science Foundation survey, the federal government paid for 84.4 per cent of all research and development conducted by the aircraft industry—a major component of transportation equipment—and for 54.5 per cent of that conducted by the electrical machinery industry. On the other hand, only 2.5 per cent of all research and development expenditures in the chemical industry and 5.6 per cent of those in petroleum were financed by the government. The government's support in aircraft and electrical machinery amounted to almost $1,044 million, about 77 per cent of its total support for all industries.[9]

The level of government support does not adequately explain the increased activity in motor vehicles, however, inasmuch as government financed research and development amounted to only about 10 per cent of that industry's expenditures in 1951[10] and it does not seem likely that this ratio would be substantially different in other postwar years. The appearance of motor vehicles as an important spender on research and development is probably associated with the industry's rapid expansion since the 1920's and may illustrate Blank and Stigler's discovery that a substantial part (about 40 per cent) of the increase in the ratio of engineers and chemists to total employment is attributable to the faster growth of industries employing relatively more persons trained in the technological professions.[11]

[9] *Science and Engineering in American Industry, Final Report on a 1953–1954 Survey,* National Science Foundation 56–16, Washington, 1956, p. 17. The report points out, however, that the low figures for chemicals and petroleum are misleading because the cost of some privately-financed research and development appears in the price of finished products sold under procurement contracts to the government (p. 16).

[10] *Scientific Research and Development in American Industry,* Bureau of Labor Statistics, 1953, p. 76. But the comment in the preceding footnote may apply here as well.

[11] David M. Blank and George J. Stigler, *The Demand and Supply of Scientific Personnel,* Princeton University Press for National Bureau of Economic Research, 1957, pp. 48–57.

TURNOVER OF LEADERSHIP IN RESEARCH AND DEVELOPMENT EMPLOYMENT

Forty-eight of the 100 leaders in 1927 reappeared in the 1938 list, and of the 52 firms that dropped out 8 had merged or consolidated with companies that remained among the leaders. Therefore only 44 firms failed to reappear because their employment of research and development personnel did not grow in pace with that of the other leaders. Sixty-one of the 100 largest employers of R and D personnel in 1938 reappeared in 1950 and another which had merged during the period appeared under the name of its parent, leaving a total of 38 drop-outs between 1938 and 1950. Seventy-four firms in the 1950 list reappeared in 1955. Two were excluded because of incomplete data (although the writer believes that they would have otherwise remained in the 100 largest) and mergers accounted for 4 additional disappearances. Therefore, only 20 firms dropped out because of insufficient growth in their employment of research and development personnel.

The rates of turnover from list to list—expressed on an average annual basis as the percentage of actual drop-outs to the maximum possible number of 100—were 4 per cent from 1927 to 1938, 3.2 per cent between 1938 and 1950, and 4 per cent between 1950 and 1955. Over the entire period the average annual rate of turnover was 3.64 per cent. We cannot deduce whether this rate is high or low, since neither empirical nor theoretical grounds exist for the construction of reference data against which to judge it. However, it is substantially higher than the 2.05 per cent annual rate of turnover among the 100 largest firms in Kaplan's lists from 1929 to 1948,[12] indicating that there has been greater opportunity for firms to achieve prominence in research and development than for them to push into the largest size class.

The numerical rates of turnover exaggerate the importance of changes in leadership, however, since firms dropping from the lists accounted for a relatively small part of the research and development

[12] Calculated by the writer. Kaplan draws the conclusion that "industrial leadership at the big business level is precarious" (*op. cit.*, p. 141). This is largely a matter of judgment, since reference data are also not available here to give an objective answer. Moreover, there is conflicting evidence. Seymour Friedland has shown that, apart from however high or low the rate of turnover may be, the composition of the 50 largest firms demonstrates increasing stability over time ("The Fifty Largest Industrial Corporations—A Study of Growth and Turnover," doctoral dissertation submitted to Harvard University, 1955).

employment of the 100 largest in each year. Indeed, given the substantial inequality in the distribution of employment among the leaders, this is what one might well expect. The 44 firms that dropped out after 1927 accounted for only 13 per cent of the research and development personnel in the 1927 list. The 38 drop-outs between 1938 and 1950 accounted for 14 per cent of the total in 1938, and the 20 firms that dropped out after 1950 accounted for 8 per cent of the 1950 total. Firms that replaced the drop-outs accounted for 28 per cent, 25 per cent, and 11 per cent, respectively, of the total research and development employment in subsequent lists. Although they were relatively more important than the firms they replaced, they nevertheless accounted for less than the average number of personnel employed by each of the 100 largest.

The following tabulation shows the relative importance of the leaders in terms of the frequency of their appearance in the four lists.

Number of Companies	*Number of Appearances*	*Per Cent of Employment in All Lists*
104	1	10
45	2	20
30	3	18
29	4	52
208		100

Whereas a total of 400 companies could have appeared if there had been a complete turnover from list to list, only 208 companies were actually involved.[13] Of this number, 149 (over 70 per cent of the 208) accounted for only 30 per cent of the combined research and development employment of the four lists. These firms therefore affected the rate of turnover to an extent that was considerably greater than their quantitative significance among the leaders. On the other hand, the 29 firms that appeared in all lists and the 30 firms that appeared in at least three lists accounted for 70 per cent of the total employment. It seems clear that a good part of the turnover consisted of what might be described as fringe movement.

[13] If we take account of those cases where a firm merged with another during the period and later appeared as part of the parent company, and if we recognize the exclusion of 3 firms from one or more lists because of the absence of data, the number of companies appearing in the lists is reduced to 182.

The role of the 59 firms that appeared three or more times deserves further attention, for the influence of this group among the 100 leaders signifies that the concentration of research and development employment has in large part been vested in the same firms throughout the period. We may call these firms consistent members of the 100 largest, since inclusion in at least three lists means that, regardless of industry classification, they survived the shift in the industry locus of research and development that took place during and after World War II. The consistent members accounted for a substantial share of each list, although their importance in recent years has declined. Those that appeared four times accounted for 70 per cent of the research and development employment in the 1927 list, for 61 per cent in 1938, 54 per cent in 1950, and 48 per cent in 1955. Inclusion of the 30 firms listed three times raises these figures to 79 per cent, 82 per cent, 74 per cent, and 64 per cent, respectively.[14]

The declining share of the consistent members in the postwar period appears to be largely attributable to the expanded role of the federal government in sponsoring industrial research and development, and especially to the unequal distribution of government support among firms in various industries. Twenty-one of the 50 largest employers of research and development personnel in 1955 were not among the leaders in 1938, and an examination of their activities, as described in Moody's *Industrials*, shows that 19 devoted a substantial portion of their research and development effort to national defense. Eleven of these firms were in aircraft or electrical machinery where the level of government support has been very high,[15] and a substantial share of the activities of the other 8 firms probably was financed by the government. If the influence of government financing of research and development were removed, it is likely that many of the 26 consistent leaders appearing in the lower half of the 1955 list, receiving only small assistance from the government, would have appeared in the first 50, replacing firms benefiting heavily from government support.[16]

---

[14] Recognizing mergers and treating the parent and merged firm as one firm throughout the period changes the figures to 82 per cent in 1927, 84 per cent in 1938, 78 per cent in 1950, and 68 per cent in 1955.

[15] *Scientific Research and Development in American Industry*, Table C-17, pp. 76–77.

[16] Blank and Stigler claim to have discovered a moderately strong substitution effect of government-financed for privately-financed research in the postwar data (*op. cit.*, pp. 57–62). Given sufficient strength, this effect could modify our conclusion. However, the writer believes that the importance of a substitution effect can be overstated, especially as applied to the aircraft industry, whose overall condition varies with the level of government support.

Factors Affecting Leadership in Research and Development

Although we have indicated that the postwar expansion of government support was responsible for some changes in the firm and industry distribution of the 100 largest, we have not assessed the role of other factors enabling firms to appear among the leaders. With our present restricted knowledge of forces determining the extent to which firms choose to engage in research and development, and with the limitations of our statistical data, we cannot hope to explore the determinants of leadership adequately. Nevertheless, modest progress may be made by examining the influence of size of firm and of industry orientation and by seeking to make some judgment about the relative strength of each influence. This is the task of this section.

SIZE OF FIRM

Our earlier examination of the size distribution of the leaders suggests that, with few exceptions (some of which are probably explained by government support), moderately large to large size appears to have been a necessary qualification for leadership. This is not surprising for, apart from any question of willingness to spend heavily on research and development, the larger size of these firms measures their ability to devote resources to this activity. Indeed we must recognize that, though most of the research and development leaders were among the largest firms, there exists considerable room for other influences to have been exerted and for the association between size of firm and employment of research and development personnel itself to vary. Consequently we must look further to discover any more fundamental effect of size.

Rank order correlations between asset size and employment of research and development personnel for those leaders for which assets data are available are given in the next tabulation.[17]

Year	Number of Firms	Correlation Coefficients
1927	79	+0.32
1938	86	+0.59
1950	95	+0.45
1955	96	+0.47

The correlations suffer from the use of assets to measure the size of

---

[17] We use rank order correlations to avoid spurious values that might otherwise occur because of great differences in asset size among firms.

firms in diverse lines of activity. Also, variations in the level of government support may have depressed the postwar values if, as seems likely, they had the effect of raising the research and development rank of smaller companies in heavily supported industries, thereby lowering the rank of larger companies not so dependent upon government support. However, to the extent that they are valid, the coefficients indicate an association between the rank order of assets and of research and development employment which is positive but not particularly strong. If we confine our calculations to the consistent members we obtain the results below.[18]

Year	Number of Firms	Correlation Coefficients
1927	31	+0.44
1938	52	+0.57
1950	57	+0.56
1955	55	+0.68

They suggest a stronger relationship between size and research and development employment for the consistent leaders than for all leaders, as might be expected. Still a large portion of the variance in research and development employment is left unexplained (although the increased strength of the association in later years should be noted).

Our final set of correlations, below, is based upon firms ranking highest in asset value, in eight industry groups,[19] for which research and development data are also available. Except for transportation equipment in 1950, the correlations are significant at the 5 per cent level.

Industry Group	Number of Firms		Correlation Coefficients	
	1950	1955	1950	1955
Food and kindred products	25	25	+0.57	+0.50
Chemicals and allied products	29	29	+0.57	+0.66
Petroleum and petroleum products	30	25	+0.90	+0.92
Stone, clay, and glass products	18	17	+0.63	+0.57
Primary metals	25	24	+0.65	+0.57
Machinery (except electrical)	25	26	+0.40	+0.58
Electrical machinery	25	25	+0.59	+0.50
Transportation equipment	25	29	+0.36	+0.54

[18] Here the effects of government support may be less important, since firms that appeared for the first time in the postwar period are excluded.

[19] Other industry groups were excluded either because of an insufficient number of large firms or because research and development data were not available for a sufficient number of firms.

Most prominent is the strong association in the petroleum industry, where more than 80 per cent of the variance is explained by rank order of asset size. Size is less important in other industry groups, however, accounting for from 16 to 44 per cent of the variance.

We may infer from the foregoing evidence that, among the largest firms in an industry group, there exists a tendency for research and development employment to increase with size, but that the strength of the association varies among industries and is not particularly strong except in petroleum. There also exists a tendency for the 100 research and development leaders, and for the consistent leaders, to be ranked according to their size, but again the relationship is not overly strong. Thus, while size of firm apparently has contributed to the determination of the leading employers of research and development personnel it is by no means a complete explanation.

RESEARCH INTENSITY

We have observed that several industry groups played a dominant role in the nation's research and development effort from 1927 to 1955. This reflects the fact that these groups were more research-intensive than others. The research intensity of each industry group is revealed by weighting its research and development data by the value added by manufacture, thereby removing effects of differences in industry size.[20] Four industry groups—chemicals, rubber, petroleum, and machinery (which, according to the census classification employed at that time, also included electrical machinery)—far exceeded others in the relative number of personnel devoted to research in 1927. These groups— together with stone, clay, and glass products, and professional and scientific instruments (included in the miscellaneous census category) —led in 1938. Transportation equipment, electrical machinery, professional and scientific instruments, petroleum, and chemicals led in 1953.

Industry differences in research intensity are further substantiated by an analysis of the variance ratio F—which compares the variances in intensity between firms in different industries and those in the same industry—for 94 medium-sized firms in the eight industry groups for

[20] For 1927 and 1938 we used Perazich and Field's data on research and development employment by industry group (*op. cit.*), dividing this by value-added data for 1927 and 1937 obtained from the Census Bureau's *Biennial Census of Manufactures*. For 1953 we used the expenditures data in the National Science Foundation survey (*op. cit.*) and the value added data in the *1954 Census of Manufactures*.

which previous calculations were made.[21] The F value obtained from data for 1955 is sufficiently high to warrant rejecting the null hypothesis that the true F value is one at the 1 per cent level of significance. Thus we may infer that there is an industry effect upon the intensity of research effort.

SIZE VERSUS INDUSTRY ORIENTATION

Since both size of firm and industry research intensity have helped to determine the leaders it is interesting to speculate about which effect has displayed the greater relative strength. We may gain some perspective on this point by extending our earlier comparison of the 100 research and development leaders and the 100 largest firms. Table 3 shows the industry distribution of firms in both sets of lists. It is immediately clear that the relative contributions of various industry groups to each list varied widely and that firms in the more research-intensive industry groups appeared among the leading employers of research and development personnel in considerably greater frequency, and with greater weight, than their asset size might justify. The petroleum industry is the only exception in that, although it was one of the leaders in research and development in all years, it was relatively less significant in the lists of the research and development leaders than it was in the lists of the largest firms. Although this may have occurred in part because the industry is capital intensive and thereby acquires an exaggerated influence when assets are chosen to measure size, its research and development significance in 1955 is only slightly greater than its size significance if we determine the 100 largest firms on the basis of their total employment.[22]

Antithetical situations—cases where firms and industries occupied a more important place in the lists of the largest firms than in the lists of the research and development leaders—are equally important. Primary metals is the leading example. While a number of firms in this industry group were among the leaders at various times, they were never very important. Indeed, by 1955 only 3 firms from this group— each in a different subgroup—appeared, and they accounted collectively for only 1.34 per cent of the total research and development

[21] Medium-sized firms were chosen for analysis because differences in firm sizes between industries are much more marked in the larger size range. Therefore intensity differences would be clouded by the effects of size if calculations were based upon the largest firms. Size differences still remain but they have been minimized as much as possible.

The writer is indebted to Mamoru Ishikawa for suggesting and conducting the F test.

[22] The reverse is true for transportation equipment, mainly because firms in the aircraft industry rank higher when measured by employment than when measured by assets.

TABLE 3

COMPARISON OF THE 100 LARGEST EMPLOYERS OF RESEARCH AND DEVELOPMENT PERSONNEL WITH THE 100 LARGEST FIRMS (ON AN ASSET BASIS), BY INDUSTRY GROUP

| | 100 LARGEST FIRMS | | | | | | | |
| | 1929 | | 1935 | | 1948 | | 1955 | |
INDUSTRY GROUP	Number of Firms	Per Cent of Assets of 100 Largest	Number of Firms	Per Cent of Assets of 100 Largest	Number of Firms	Per Cent of Assets of 100 Largest	Number of Firms	Per Cent of Assets of 100 Largest
Food and kindred products	10	7.17	10	6.63	11	6.81	9	4.19
Tobacco manufactures	4	2.42	3	2.36	3	3.35	4	2.48
Textile mill products	1	0.40	0	0.00	3	1.21	3	1.38
Lumber and lumber products (except furniture)	1	0.41	0	0.00	1	0.43	0	0.00
Paper and allied products	2	1.40	5	2.32	2	0.98	3	1.52
Printing and publishing industries	0	0.00	1	0.52	1	0.33	0	0.00
Chemicals and allied products	5	4.71	4	4.94	8	7.07	10	10.10
Petroleum and coal products	20	28.36	17	28.23	17	28.78	21	32.15
Rubber products	4	3.07	4	2.47	4	2.81	4	2.91
Leather and leather products	1	0.39	1	0.33	0	0.00	0	0.00
Stone, clay, and glass products	1	0.36	1	0.44	2	0.83	2	0.99
Primary metal products	17	22.32	19	23.15	16	17.65	18	16.94
Fabricated metal products	1	0.67	2	1.22	2	1.01	2	1.00
Machinery (except electrical)	4	3.20	7	4.18	6	3.66	7	4.39
Electrical machinery	3	3.26	3	2.78	3	4.32	3	4.29
Transportation equipment	8	10.77	6	11.27	6	10.57	11	14.64
Instruments and related products	1	0.57	1	0.67	1	0.84	1	0.71
Miscellaneous manufactures	1	0.76	0	0.00	0	0.00	0	0.00
Nonmanufacturing	16	9.77	16	8.54	14	9.33	2	2.26

employment of the 100 largest. We may speculate that the sheer size of these firms was sufficient to insure a place for them among the research and development leaders despite the fact that they were not heavily research intensive. There are a number of other cases—e.g., food and kindred products, tobacco, textiles, paper—less marked than that of primary metals, where size of firm was not matched by

TABLE 3 (concluded)

100 LARGEST R AND D EMPLOYERS							
1927		*1938*		*1950*		*1955*	
Number of Firms	Per Cent of RD Personnel of 100 Largest	Number of Firms	Per Cent of RD Personnel of 100 Largest	Number of Firms	Per Cent of RD Personnel of 100 Largest	Number of Firms	Per Cent of RD Personnel of 100 Largest
3	0.74	6	1.88	6	2.18	3	1.04
0	0.00	0	0.00	0	0.00	0	0.00
1	0.37	1	0.32	1	0.41	1	0.36
0	0.00	0	0.00	0	0.00	0	0.00
2	0.87	2	0.43	0	0.00	0	0.00
0	0.00	0	0.00	0	0.00	0	0.00
20	19.89	23	21.61	23	18.87	20	14.85
11	11.60	13	16.34	12	14.71	13	10.31
7	8.97	5	7.03	4	3.94	5	6.70
0	0.00	0	0.00	0	0.00	0	0.00
7	2.13	8	2.87	5	2.49	3	0.93
12	4.21	11	6.50	4	2.05	3	1.34
2	0.57	2	0.84	4	1.73	3	1.03
11	8.58	6	4.03	5	2.55	7	6.38
9	13.47	9	11.37	12	15.83	16	19.06
7	5.90	5	7.42	17	22.56	19	28.00
3	1.82	2	1.55	4	2.96	4	2.42
0	0.00	0	0.00	0	0.00	0	0.00
5	20.86	7	17.81	3	9.73	3	7.61

proportionate representation in the research and development lists.

Industry influences (especially the heavy representation of firms in chemicals and petroleum) are also evident in the distribution of the consistent leaders in research and development, as the next tabulation shows.

| | Number of Firms Appearing in: | | |
Industry Group	Four Lists	Three Lists	Total
Food and kindred products	1	2	3
Chemicals and allied products	7	7	14
Petroleum and petroleum products	5	7	12
Rubber products	4	0	4
Stone, clay, and glass products	2	2	4
Primary metals	3	1	4
Fabricated metal products	1	1	2
Machinery (except electrical)	0	3	3
Electrical machinery	2	4	6
Transportation equipment	2	3	5
Instruments and related products	1	0	1
Nonmanufacturing (electrical communication)	1	0	1

We see also that firms in industry groups not heavily characterized by research and development activity were present. Here again sheer size may have been an important determinant, although it is also possible that a factor which we cannot hope to measure may have been operative—i.e., that there have been important differences in the extent to which entrepreneurs perceived the wisdom of creating and exploiting research and development opportunities.

Which effect has been relatively more important? The writer believes that the evidence supports the judgment that the industry in which firms were located has been the dominant factor determining the extent to which they engaged in research and development and that, subject to this overriding influence, their size played a secondary role. As to the underlying reasons for differences in research intensity among industries, we may observe that our findings are generally consistent with those in the studies of patent statistics by Stafford and Schmookler; namely, that the portion of inventive activity that is patentable is concentrated in areas directly related to chemistry and physics and that a large part of inventive activity is generated by a "technological elite."[23]

[23] Alfred B. Stafford, "An Appraisal of Patent Statistics;" Jacob Schmookler, "Technical Change and Patent Statistics." These monographs were presented to the Conference on Quantitative Description of Technological Change, sponsored by the Committees on Economic Growth and on Social Implications of Atomic Energy and Technological Change of the Social Science Research Council, 1951.

Conclusion

Our purpose has been to analyze the changing direction of research and development employment among firms, concentrating upon the composition of the 100 leading employers in selected years from 1927 to 1955. We have shown that the leaders accounted for a substantial share of industrial research and development employment and that the 59 firms that led most frequently have been responsible for most of this share. We have also shown that the leaders have been concentrated in a few industry groups. In view of the sizeable growth in research and development that has taken place during the period under examination, one can only conclude that the pattern of leadership has displayed considerable stability.

Changes have, of course, occurred. The firms that have consistently appeared among the leaders now account for a smaller share of the total than in the past. The transportation equipment industry now occupies a dominant position in the industry-group distribution of the leaders, having replaced electrical communication among the four leading groups in the prewar lists. But these changes are largely attributable to heavy postwar government support of firms in a few industry groups and our conclusion still remains applicable as far as private forces generating research and development activity are concerned.

Of the two possible determinants of leadership examined in the paper, variations in research intensity among industries appears to have been dominant. But, since most of the leaders have come from among the larger firms in the economy and since there is some positive association between rank order of research and development employment and rank order of assets, size of firm has exercised an influence. Also, one cannot escape the feeling that entrepreneurial vision played a part.

Locational Differences in Inventive Effort and Their Determinants

WILBUR R. THOMPSON

WAYNE STATE UNIVERSITY

THIS is an empirical study with selected patent grants as the measure of inventive activity. The logic of an empirical approach here might be set forth as follows: lacking a ready-made stock of *directly relevant* conceptual work on which to draw and build, and lacking a long-standing familiarity with the general literature on the economics of technology on which pioneering deduction could be based, I selected the pedestrian task of assembling and editing some rough measures of the locational pattern of inventive activity. The job seemed to need doing; they also serve who only stack and weight.

While this rationale embodies the spirit of the effort, a more chronologically accurate description of the origin of this paper is that for some time now I have had in hand the grist to be milled. Specifically, an earlier piece of work left me in possession of a large number of worksheets on which were recorded the residences of persons who had received patent grants (primarily) during the years 1947 and 1948, tabulated by selected patent classes.[1] It would have been criminal, it seemed, to let that data gather dust when with—what seemed at the time—only minor marginal costs the data could be rearranged to shed light on some of the questions at issue in this Conference. Naturally, the additional investment mounted and the light generated was not quite so bright as had been hoped.

Identification of the Inventing Population

A sensible way to begin a locational analysis of invention would be to attempt to identify "inventors"—at least in broad terms. What population group best characterizes those who invent: male adults or the

---

[1] See Wilbur R. Thompson and John M. Mattila, *An Econometric Model of Postwar State Industrial Development*, Detroit, Wayne State University Press, 1959. The reason why the data on patent grants dates back to the 1947–48 period is that the econometric model was essentially a compilation of equations for estimating the growth of manufacturing employment, by industry, for the period 1947–54. Patent grants were, therefore, incorporated into the work as a leading series, applying to the origin year of the growth period. Ordinarily, the fact that the data is a decade old would not be too disturbing, but 1947–48 patent grants relate to patent applications of about three years earlier and this places the more critical date in the latter part of the war. I cannot say with assurance that this does or does not affect, significantly, my conclusions.

college bred or city dwellers or the professionally trained or craftsmen? Nine separate populations were defined—lifted from the *Census of Population* would be more accurate—and the number of persons in each state in each of these groups (1950) was correlated with the average annual number of patent grants issued to residents of that state (1952–54).[2] The simple, linear coefficients of correlation are presented in Table 1.

TABLE 1

COEFFICIENTS OF CORRELATION OF AVERAGE ANNUAL NUMBER OF PATENTS
ISSUED TO STATE RESIDENTS, 1952–54, WITH VARIOUS
POPULATION CLASSES, BY STATES, 1950[a]

Population Group	Coefficient	Per Cent Explained Variance
Number of persons 21 years old and over	.930	86.5
Number of persons 25 years old and over who have completed 4 or more years of college	.937	87.8
Number of persons residing in the urbanized part of a standard metropolitan area	.964	92.9
Number of professional, technical, and kindred workers	.952	90.6
Number of craftsmen, foremen, and kindred workers	.950	90.2
Number of professional, technical, and kindred workers plus craftsmen, foremen, and kindred workers	.955	91.2
Number of chemists, designers, draftsmen, engineers, natural scientists, and testing technicians[b]	.981	96.2
Total manufacturing employment	.928	86.1
Total labor force	.940	88.4

SOURCE: Derived from *1950 Census of Population*, Vol. II, Parts 1–49 and *Statistical Abstract of the United States*, 1955, Table 604, p. 500.

[a] The years 1952–54 for patent grants were used with 1950 population data because the typical (median) time lag between a patent application and a patent grant is about three years.

[b] An indication of the relative weights of these six occupational classes in the experienced civilian labor force can be gained by comparing their U.S. totals in thousands: chemists, 75.7; designers, 40.1; draftsmen, 124.7; engineers, 534.4; natural scientists, 40.7; and testing technicians, 77.0.

[2] The choice of the year 1950 with which to date the population characteristics was, of course, dictated by the availability of data from the Decennial Census; the choice of a later period, 1952–54, for the index of invention reflects the fact that (on the basis of a rough guess from a small sample) the typical (median) lag between the application for and receipt of a patent grant is about three years. The correlation is, then, chronologically synchronized on the year 1950.

With a simple correlation coefficient of 0.93, the distribution of adult population among the states accounts for over 86 per cent (0.93^2) of the interstate variation in the number of patent grants. Against this benchmark of inventors as "just folks," we can assess the relevance of more refined expressions of the inventing population. Some of the more interesting inferences that may be drawn from Table 1 are:

1. Substitution of either the labor force (0.94) or manufacturing employment (0.93) for the adult population does not raise the correlation coefficient.

2. Recourse to a very select population group, the college-educated (0.94), accomplishes no notable improvement in the statistical fit.

3. A significant improvement in the correlation does occur when the "urbanized population" is correlated with patents (0.96); explained variance increases from 86 to 93 per cent.

4. The best association is achieved by breaking through the professional and skilled worker occupational aggregates (the two correlations are on a par at 0.95) to the narrower amalgam of six selected occupational classes: chemists, designers, draftsmen, engineers, natural scientists and testing technicians (0.98). With this occupational mix, explained variance reaches a peak of 96 per cent.

If the charge be leveled that the most distilled product, 4, above, has become the bland correlation of invention with inventors, the defense is that this exercise was designed to name the population class from which inventors arise and not to quantify the inventing function. Thus, the early returns suggest that an identifiable occupational class of "inventors" does exist and can be roughly described. And that the next best characterization of the inventor is that of city-dweller.[3] So, while we may have but linked invention with inventors and not yet placed the latter in space, we have at least come to know better those whom we seek. (Although, admittedly, 4 might be merely an index of the inventive culture.)

An aggregate of all patents, when compared to the alternatives, is not without virtue in the difficult business of assessing the locational pattern of inventive activity, but this gross conglomerate will now be abandoned in favor of narrower and more internally homogeneous

---

[3] However, the inter-correlation between the number of persons in the six selected occupations and "urbanized-area" population is so high (.98) that the combination of these two factors (or any other two) in multiple correlation does not appreciably raise the level of explained variance.

classes of patents. The shoal on which the all-patent index runs aground is the familiar one of "industry-mix." The frequency with which patents are granted varies greatly between the many patent classes. Every new variation of a chemical compound becomes a potential patent grant; patent grants in the class "chemistry, carbon compounds" ran along at the rate of about 25 per week in 1947, as against a weekly rate of about 4 in "internal combustion engines" and less than one per week in "metallurgy."

An appreciation of the large variations in patent frequencies between classes quickly dispels any mystery that might be generated by the revelation that Delaware residents have received more patents per capita than the inhabitants of any other state in every year from 1936 to 1954, the full period for which data has been tabulated and presented in the *Statistical Abstract*.[4] Moreover, New Jersey, another chemical-industry state, took second place honors three-quarters of the time during this 19-year period. Thus, if the research orientation of a state reflects its industrial structure, any index which purports to measure the inventiveness of the residents of a state must be deflated for the industry-mix of that state.

The construction of a satisfactory overall state index of inventiveness was not stymied by lack of applicable index number technique, but rather by lack of appropriate data. Unfortunately, the Patent Office does not report the distribution of patent grants by states for the various patent classes, and without this information we can not even begin to construct a comprehensive set of "patent relatives." (What constitutes a "high" or "low" rate of patenting in engines? in plastics?) What is more important, our way is barred by the heroic task of linking patent classes to Census-defined industry groups, a clear prerequisite to the derivative job of compiling a set of industry weights to apply to the patent relatives. The industry weights would, of course, match the industry-mix of the local economy. The dilemma to be resolved is that patents are classified by process and industries by product, and processes often criss-cross product lines in bewildering fashion. "Abrading" (patent class number 51) includes technical advances in grinding wheels (a subgroup of the stone, clay and glass industry group) and drill presses (nonelectrical machinery) and certainly is related to fabricated metal products and (optical) instrument manufacturing. "Chemistry, electrical and wave energy" (patent class number 204) includes electrolysis (chemicals and allied industries)

---

[4] Derived from the 1946 issue, Table 986, p. 880 and the 1955 issue, Table 604, p. 506.

and electroplating (fabricated metal products). The task of aligning patent class with industry group is a formidable one and deserves a more skilled and sustained effort than can be rendered here and now, although some tentative probings will be attempted below.

Inventors as City Dwellers

The first tentative conclusion offered was that inventive activity is more a matter of occupation than of residence, but the correlation between the number of persons residing in "urbanized areas" of a state and the number of patents going to that state was much too close to deny the urge to investigate a bit further. Surely, we would all guess that inventing is more a pursuit of city than of town or rural inhabitants and that the Census standard metropolitan areas would encompass substantially more than their pro rata share of inventors. We might make this guess with some vague feeling of uneasiness, probably traceable to our heritage (mythology?) of Connecticut Yankees and basement workshops, but the image of the Du Pont laboratories would surely prevail. For all the merit of intuition and deduction, however, some rough quantification of the "urban-ness" of invention would help fix this impression and set the stage for more certain and sophisticated conceptualizing.

Our approximation of the urban-ness of invention is derived from data prepared for an earlier study, alluded to above. Lists of the places of residence of patentees were drawn from chronological entries in the weekly *Official Gazette of the Patent Office* and grouped by patent class (Class 123, internal-combustion engines, Class 18, plastics, for example). A dichotomy of patentees' residences was set up: metropolitan area residents and nonmetropolitan area residents, with the latter group classified by distance of residence from the central business district of the central city of the nearest standard metropolitan area—that is to say, by how far removed these places are from (industrial) "civilization." (The metropolitan area residents were, of course, tabulated by area and this data will become the focus of our inquiry below.)

The pattern of Table 2 is clear: the approximately one-half (54.6 per cent) of the total U.S. population residing in (168) standard metropolitan areas in 1945 received over four-fifths of the patents granted in the years 1947 and 1948 in fourteen out of sixteen of the selected processes associated with the metal, machinery, vehicle, and chemical industries. Ignoring the widest variations (particularly characteristic

TABLE 2

DISTRIBUTION OF PATENT GRANTS BETWEEN METROPOLITAN AND
NONMETROPOLITAN AREAS FOR SELECTED PATENT CLASSES, 1947–48

		PATENTS GRANTED (1947–48) TO RESIDENTS OF:			
PATENT CLASS		Standard Metropolitan Areas		Other Areas	
Number	Title	Number	Per Cent	Number	Per Cent
123	Internal-combustion engines	312	81.2	72	18.8
75	Metallurgy	106	80.9	25	19.1
266	Metallurgical apparatus	62	80.5	15	19.5
78	Metal forging and welding	33	78.6	9	21.4
148	Metal treatment	72	92.3	6	7.7
80	Metal rolling	11	84.6	2	15.4
205	Metal drawing	5	83.3	1	16.7
22	Metal founding	96	89.7	11	10.3
	Total of 7 basic metal processes	385	84.6	70	15.4
29	Metal working	282	86.0	46	14.0
82	Turning	42	75.0	14	25.0
90	Gear cutting, milling, and planing	98	83.8	19	16.2
	Total of 2 machining processes	140	80.9	33	19.1
51	Abrading[a]	216	83.4	43	16.6
23	Chemistry[a]	184	84.4	34	15.6
260	Chemistry, carbon compounds[b]	309	87.0	46	13.0
18	Plastics	393	85.2	68	14.8
204	Chemistry, electrical and wave energy[a]	96	93.2	7	6.8
	Total of 4 chemistry processes	982	86.4	155	13.6
	Total of 16 selected patent classes	2,317	84.7	419	25.3

SOURCE: Derived from *Official Gazette of the Patent Office*, Dept. of Commerce, Weekly issues 1947-48.

[a] Data is for one year only, 1947.

[b] Figures are for a twelve week sample from the year 1947. Patent grants in this class were so numerous that data was tabulated for only the first week of each month.

of the smaller-frequency patent classes wherein the sample was too small to be a reliable index), the proportion of patent grants issued to metropolitan area residents is remarkably similar for the chemistry, basic metal, and metal working processes, 86.4, 84.6, and 86.0 per cent, respectively. Patents covering machining operations and internal-combustion engines stand close by at 80.9 and 81.2 per cent, respectively. Abrading, a patent class built on a process which cuts across most of the product lines (industries) associated with the other patent classes, and more besides (instruments and stone, clay and glass, for example), lies, appropriately, between these two groups with 83.4 per cent of its patentees residents of metropolitan areas.

By introducing a little judgment and pressing inference a bit harder, an even closer approximation to the urban-ness of invention can, I think, be sensibly made. The standard metropolitan areas, for reasons of efficacy in data collection, are delineated along county lines and their central cities often lie well off-center in their counties, causing the influence of the city to spill over county lines, asymmetrically. Clearly, persons may live across a county line but still be within easy commuting radius of a central city. If we add, therefore, to the 2,317 patents granted to metropolitan area residents, the 116 granted to persons who lived outside of these metropolitan areas but less than twenty-five miles from the center of the central city of the nearest metropolitan area, then the metro-nonmetro division of all patents classified in Table 2 becomes 2,433 to 303. (A less than twenty-five-mile commuting radius would seem to be reasonable, especially in view of the fact that many industrial firms are located on the periphery of central cities.) The best estimate is now this: the approximately 57 per cent of the population who resided in standard metropolitan areas (in 1945) or within twenty-five miles of the central city of such an area[5] received (in 1947–48) approximately 90 per cent of the patents granted in sixteen selected patent classes covering chemistry, metal, machinery and engine products and processes.

Invention as a By-Product of Employment

The derivation of a measure of the urban-ness of invention was but a by-product of the process of classifying the patents by region, preparatory to a comparative analysis of inventive activity at the metropolitan area level. Closer analysis of the patent data might have been pursued at the state level of areal subdivision, as was done in the earlier

[5] The estimate of population residing outside of standard metropolitan areas but within twenty-five miles of the center of a central city of such an area was derived by multiplying the total population of all standard metropolitan areas by the ratio of the number of patents received by these persons to the number received by the metropolitan area residents. ($116/2,317 = .05$). That is, the assumption was made that the number of patent grants per capita was the same inside and immediately outside of the metropolitan area and, by implication, that the central city and suburban populations have the same relevant characteristics.

study. But to stand pat at the state level has a number of disadvantages: (1) Since there are barely a dozen states which have industrialized to the stage where inventive activity in manufacturing is significant and measurable, the statistical analyst is forced to work with a very small sample; (2) a state is usually composed of a number of separate, usually diverse subeconomies (the specialized steel making Pittsburgh economy and the highly diversified Philadelphia economy and other Pennsylvania regions are rolled out into one statewide economic conglomerate); and (3) the city region (standard metropolitan area) is roughly coincident with the local labor market and is the maximum radius within which personal contacts can be conveniently maintained. Thus, the city region would seem to represent, in rough measure, the community of intellectual intercourse; industrial and cultural, vocational and avocational. The manipulation above of the all-patents data has, moreover, established the city as the hothouse of technology. Accordingly, the remainder of the paper will focus on the metropolitan community.

The first hypothesis to be tested with patent grant data, spatially distributed by standard metropolitan area of the patentees' residence, is that inventive activity (as measured by patents) of a given kind is highly correlated (positively) with the current regional distribution of employment in the industry (or industries) most closely associated with that kind of inventive activity. Specifically, we assume that the number of patent grants covering "turning and gear cutting" is determined by the number employed in the Census major industry group, machinery, except electrical, region by region. The proposition that the production centers of an industry are also its research centers seems plausible, at least on first blush. The reasoning here is that new products and techniques are largely spawned by persons who work for or are otherwise closely associated with the industry most closely linked with the particular idea or device. To the extent that this is so, a substantial, persistent, and even cumulative advantage would accrue to any region which gained a head start in a particular industry; perhaps technological differentials tend to widen—the rich to grow richer.

The hypothesis that invention is an avocation related to one's vocation in kind will be tested by simple linear correlations between the (absolute) number of patent grants and related employment (all employees, rather than production workers), for a number of industry groups. But the act of correlating the two variables in absolute terms leads to an inherent and strong inclination toward positive correlation. A size-with-size bias occurs because, even if patents and related employment were randomly distributed throughout the population, the population is not evenly distributed, spatially, throughout the country. Consequently, the New York–Northeastern New Jersey metropolitan area residents will normally possess more of almost every kind of patent grant and employment than will the residents of the Indianapolis metropolitan area, effecting thereby this inherent tendency toward positive correlation. We might try to hurdle this obstacle by jumping to something like patents per capita as an index, but why population as a deflator? What evidence do we have to support population as the relevant potential-inventor group? Nothing from the work above. Besides our purpose should be to discover the functional relationship between the potential-inventor group and the rate of patenting, and a deflating ratio would tend to obscure this relationship if it is curvilinear—that is, if there are economies of diseconomies of scale.

The technique adopted to separate the associated-employment effect from the population effect is a simple one, as befits the exploratory character of this study. Patent grants in a given patent class will be correlated with employment in a specific (the associated) industry, all manufacturing industry and total population. The latter two measures will provide norms with which the associated-employment correlations may be compared, bench marks well above sea level from which we may measure the altitude of the associated-employment coefficients.

The coefficients of correlation linking selected patent grants with employment in the associated industries for the seventy-four standard metropolitan areas for which employment data are available are presented in Table 3. The pattern, if one exists, is not a simple one or, if it is simple, our data or devices have not captured it. We can begin well. The hypothesis that the employees of an industry—and their neighbors—are the population from which the inventors of products and processes related to that industry are drawn is firmly supported by the internal combustion engine–transportation equipment industry correlations. Related employment exhibits a correlation coefficient of 0.90, well above the coefficients for all manufacturing employment (0.61) or total population (0.55). With an "explained variance" of 81 per cent (0.90^2), the evidence is impressive that automobile, aircraft, and shipbuilders are the principal contributors to engine technology.

TABLE 3

COEFFICIENTS OF CORRELATION OF PATENT GRANTS IN SELECTED PATENT CLASSES WITH
EMPLOYMENT IN ASSOCIATED INDUSTRIES, ALL MANUFACTURING
EMPLOYMENT AND TOTAL POPULATION, BY STANDARD
METROPOLITAN AREAS, 1947

| | | COEFFICIENTS OF CORRELATION OF PATENTS WITH: | | |
| | | Employment in: | | Total Population |
PATENT CLASS	ASSOCIATED CENSUS MAJOR INDUSTRY GROUP	Assoc. Indus.	All Mfg.	
Internal-combustion engines	Transportation equipment	.90	.61	.55
Metallurgy; metallurgical apparatus; metal forging and welding; metal treatment; metal rolling; metal drawing; and metal founding	Primary metal industries	.64	.94	.92
Metal working	Fabricated metal products	.85	.86	.83
Turning; Gear cutting, milling and planing	Machinery, exc. electrical	.80	.74	.68
Aggregate of the 10 metal-making, working and machining processes (metallurgy through gear cutting) in the three preceding groups	Aggregate of: Primary metal industries Fabricated metal products Machinery, exc. electrical	.83	.93	.89
Chemistry[a]	Chemicals and allied ind.	.95	.92	.94
Chemistry, carbon compounds[b]	Chemicals and allied prod. Chemical plus Petroleum and coal products	.94 .95	.92	.92
Plastics	Chemicals and allied prod. Chemicals plus Rubber prod.	.91 .95	.90	.92

SOURCE: Derived from *Official Gazette of the Patent Office*, Dept. of Commerce, weekly issues 1947–48 and *Census of Manufactures*, 1947 and 1954.

[a] Data is for one year only, 1947.

[b] Figures are for a twelve week sample from the year 1947. Patent grants in this class were so numerous that data was tabulated for only the first week of each month.

But the primary metal production centers do not seem to be the source of the patents covering the basic metal processes to anywhere near the same degree. In fact, employment in the primary metal industries statistically explains only about 41 per cent (0.64^2) of the technically related patent grants, while population displays an 85 per cent association and total manufacturing employment reaches explained variance of 88 per cent. Why metalmaking, metal treating, and founding technology should be less indigenous to its production centers than engine technology is not readily apparent—to this layman. Are the skills less esoteric or has the linking of patent class to industry group been inept? Or is it simply that progress in primary metal technology originates in the shop of the metal user more often than in the workplace of the metalmaker?

There is little to choose from as between population, all manufacturing employment and employment in fabricated metal products in the attempt to account for metropolitan area variations in metal working patent grants, with explained variance clustered around 69 to 74 per cent. The principal explanation for the close correspondence of the three coefficients is that fabricated metals is perhaps the most ubiquitous manufacturing industry and employment in it is, therefore, highly correlated with both total manufacturing employment (0.93) and even population (0.86). (This may be compared with corresponding correlation coefficients of between 0.47 and 0.56 for the more spatially concentrated production of primary metals and transportation equipment.) Our statistical technique fails us here; we cannot isolate the specific from the general population.

But the nonelectrical machinery industry group comes to the rescue of our hypothesis; an aggregate of turning and gear cutting patents displays correlations which rise from a bench mark of 46 per cent explained variance for population, through 55 per cent for all manufacturing employment, up to the respectable height of 64 per cent for its parent industry. Apparently, inferentially and not surprisingly, the employees of machinery making firms—and not the population at large—devise the new machining tools and techniques. This last bit of evidence, a step toward the restoration of our hypothesis linking employees and their technology, however, leaves us unprepared for the next blow to fall. An aggregate of all metalmaking, metal working, and machining patents (ten classes) was correlated with the sum of the employments in the primary metal, fabricated metal, and nonelectrical machinery industries with the rationale that, if these various patent classes do in fact cut across industry boundaries to a serious degree, the ambiguity of the classifications and associations would be lessened. But the evidence is that all manufacturing employment (0.93) and total population (0.89) are more closely correlated with the ten-class aggregate than is true of an aggregate of direct employment in the three presumably related industry groups (0.83).

As some comfort, the advantage held by the two grosser measures is much less than an average (simple or weighted by patent or employment frequencies) of the coefficients of the component (three) sets of correlations. Still, the influence of the basic metal–primary metal industries relationship, wherein associated employment performed most poorly, was too strong to be fully offset by such improvements in process-product alignment as might have been achieved by using broader patent and industry classes. It seems that we must leave the metalmaking, metal working and machining patents with whatever consolation can be derived from the machining-machinery associations.

The attempt to link chemistry patents with related employment runs afoul of the same problem encountered in the metal working patents-fabricated metal industry correlation. Chemical employment is very highly correlated with manufacturing employment (0.96) and population (0.97), making it difficult to separate the three potential determinants of chemistry patenting. Still, while chemical employment plays nip and tuck with population in the correlations with chemistry and plastics patents, maintaining only a slight edge over the latter, by judicious combination of chemical employment with employment in petroleum and coal products in one case (carbon compounds) and with rubber products employment in another case (plastics), parent industry employment achieves a narrow but recognizable margin of superiority over total population as the probable inventing population. Certainly, much more work must be done before any neat technical linkage of process and product can be expected in any of these patent class–industry group associations.

This attempt to establish close correspondence between patent classes and Census industry groups is not a pure mental exercise. If the employees of a given industry are the primary, or even a significant, source of that industry's technological change, then the construction of a satisfactory over-all index of local inventiveness must await the tabulation of patent frequencies by patent class and the classification of patent classes by industry group. The former is a routine job; the latter will surely prove to be a very difficult task. Of course, if invention is substantially independent of an individual's vocation or industry association, an industry-mix deflator is superfluous. But modest as the results have been, it would be hazardous to assume that research and invention is not importantly job oriented. And some index of the propensity to invent would seem to be a prerequisite to any incisive analysis of the locational pattern of inventive activity, or at least a prerequisite to empirical analysis of a high order.

Technological and Industrial Complexes

Correlation programs for automatic data processing equipment yield the coefficients for each variable with every other variable, indiscriminately. While often the extra coefficients are meaningless, occasionally valuable by-products are formed. In the course of correlating patent grants in various patent classes with employment in related industry groups, the correlation coefficients of the various patent frequencies with each other and employments with each other were automatically generated. These separate patent and employment matrices are reported in Table 4 in the hope that they may suggest additional avenues of inquiry.

TABLE 4

Coefficients of Correlation Between Patent Grants in Selected Patent Classes and Between Employments in the Industries Associated with the Patent Processes, by Standard Metropolitan Areas, 1947

The Patent Matrix: The Technological Complex

Patent Class	Basic Metal	Metal Working	Turning & Cutting	Engines	Chemistry
7 basic metal processes	1				
Metal working	.89	1			
Turning and gear cutting	.72	.82	1		
Internal-combustion engines	.58	.74	.64	1	
Chemistry	.90	.72	.58	.41	1

The Employment Matrix: The Industrial Complex

Census Major Industry Group	Prim. Metal	Fab. Metal	Machinery	Trans. Equip.	Chemicals
Primary metal industries	1				
Fabricated metal products	.71	1			
Machinery, exc. electrical	.60	.90	1		
Transportation equipment	.36	.61	.59	1	
Chemicals and allied prod.	.40	.83	.71	.45	1

Source: see Table 3.

The first thought that comes to mind is that perhaps we may compare the general level of coefficients in the two matrices to determine whether the technological or the industrial complexes are tighter knit. That is to say, are the interindustry or the interprocess spatial ties the stronger? If our Table 4 does indeed accurately reflect agglomerative forces, inventive activity evidences the greater spatial cohesion with a median correlation coefficient of 0.72, as compared to a median of only 0.60 for employment. This is not to say that the various classes of inventive activity are more spatially concentrated than the various groups of industrial employment, only that geographic centers of one kind of inventive activity tend to a greater degree to be the centers of other kinds of inventiveness, than do production centers of one industry tend to be production centers of another industry. If this chain of thought has not yet strained fact or logic, these tentative conclusions suggest that inventive activity may be subject to external economies of scale (really economies of spatial agglomeration) that are more independent of a particular kind of process or product line than is true of production. (Or it may be that production entities more commonly repel each other, through labor market competition, for example.) But the base here is much too slim to support any more —perhaps even this much—deductive superstructure.

Attention is called to the fact that the two matrices present very similar patterns. Internal combustion engine patents as a class and its counterpart, transportation equipment employment, seem to stand aloof in technology and production with consistently low coefficients, whereas the class of metal working patents and its counterpart, fabricated metal products employment, seem to stand in the center of all activity with consistently high coefficients. Further, two of the tightest sets of spatial linkage are metalmaking patents with metal working patents with turning and gear cutting patents and their counterparts, primary metal employment with fabricated metal employment with nonelectrical machinery employment. These comprise very believable technological and industrial complexes.

One interesting divergence between the two matrices is the very high correlation (0.90) between chemistry patents and the seven selected basic metal patents, in contrast to the very low correlation (0.40) between chemical and primary metal employment. In fact, further study of the first column of the two matrices reveals that it is here that the patent matrix piles up its lead in spatial linkage over the employment matrix. If the first column were removed there would be little to choose between the two complexes—almost identical medians for the remaining six coefficients. The substance of this statement is that the primary metal industries have relatively isolated centers of production, while research and development in the basic metalmaking processes seems to be an integral part of industrial research in general.

The Scale Effect in Inventiveness

I have been playing the part of a host who has dallied through the hors d'oeuvres because the entree is not ready to be served. Certainly, the *piece de resistance* of this study should be a determination of the extent and character of any economies or diseconomies of spatial agglomeration in invention that may exist. Simple, linear correlations do not, of course, shed much light on this matter; a linear correlation, in fact, presumes that scale effects do not exist in significant measure. But recourse to the underlying scatter diagrams may disclose nonlinearities in the patent-employment-population relationships.

Careful examination of the scatter diagrams, however, failed to reveal any impressive evidence of curvilinear relationships. Occasionally, by squinting and frowning heavily, a slight suggestion of concavity or convexity was apparent—more apparent than real, no doubt. The pattern of scatter was never so suggestive as to warrant the minor inconvenience to trying to fit some simple second degree function to the data. Nor were the "y" axis (patent grants) intercepts of the simple regression lines significantly enough different from zero to indicate (linear) economies or diseconomies of very small size.

A priori, patent grants of any particular kind would seem to be a function of associated employment and of some more general population, with the former exhibiting a regression coefficient two or three or more times that of the latter. (That is, the expectation is that chemical workers contribute to chemical technology at a rate a couple of times as great as that which applies to other persons.) Some limited experiments with multivariate analysis were conducted but a much more comprehensive and sophisticated statistical treatment is indicated, bringing in population size, industrial structure, educational level and facilities, industrial maturity and other socioeconomic facets of the city region. In any event, multiple correlation and regression analysis seems to be a much more promising approach to the analysis of the location of inventiveness than further experimentation with indexes of local inventiveness. A prey as elusive as "inventiveness" calls for a very fine net.

APPENDIX TABLE

PATENT GRANTS, BY PATENT CLASS, AND MANUFACTURING EMPLOYMENT, BY CENSUS MAJOR INDUSTRY GROUP, FOR ALL STANDARD METROPOLITAN AREAS FOR WHICH EMPLOYMENT DATA IS AVAILABLE, 1947-48

Standard Metropolitan Area	Number of patents issued (1947–48) in patent class number.[a]								Number (in thousands) of employees (1947) in Census major industry group number.[b]									
	123	M	29	82 90	M 29 82 90	23[c]	260[d]	18	37	33	34	35	33 34 35	28	28 29	28 30	All Mfg. Empl.	Total Population
Akron, Ohio	0	2	1	1	4	2	6	32	3	1	9	5	15	4	4	65	9	4
Albany-Schenectady-Troy, N.Y.	0	3	2	1	6	0	4	3	8	3	1	7	11	4	4	4	7	5
Allentown-Bethlehem-Easton, Pa.	0	0	0	1	1	6	2	2	5	20	5	6	31	2	2	2	9	4
Atlanta, Ga.	0	0	1	0	1	1	0	2	2	2	2	3	7	2	2	2	5	6
Baltimore, Md.	3	17	9	1	27	6	1	7	28	30	16	8	55	9	12	11	17	12
Beaumont-Port Arthur, Tex.	1	0	0	0	0	0	0	0	1	0	1	0	2	1	1	1	2	2
Binghamton, N.Y.	0	0	2	1	3	0	2	0	1	1	1	8	9	0	18	1	4	2
Birmingham, Ala.	0	1	0	0	1	2	0	2	2	24	5	4	33	1	3	1	5	5
Boston, Mass.	6	12	4	3	19	24	6	18	13	4	17	26	47	11	14	26	27	23
Bridgeport, Conn.	0	3	8	4	15	0	2	2	10	8	8	12	28	1	1	2	7	2
Buffalo, N.Y.	4	18	1	1	20	27	14	4	24	38	12	15	66	17	20	21	18	10
Canton, Ohio	1	4	0	0	4	0	0	0	0	20	7	17	43	0	1	1	6	3
Chicago, Ill.	12	36	18	14	68	36	32	24	42	118	89	134	341	39	62	42	95	52
Cincinatti, Ohio	1	1	2	18	21	1	1	2	5	6	13	22	42	10	11	10	13	8
Cleveland, Ohio	16	30	29	17	76	15	2	19	35	43	33	54	130	14	17	16	27	14
Columbus, Ohio	1	6	0	1	7	2	5	3	5	4	8	12	24	2	2	2	5	4
Dallas, Tex.	0	0	1	0	1	6	2	0	3	0	4	3	7	2	2	2	4	5
Dayton, Ohio	1	4	2	3	9	0	5	5	9	3	3	42	48	1	1	4	10	4
Detroit, Mich.	63	26	30	18	74	2	8	14	254	57	56	85	198	19	21	30	56	27
Erie, Pa.	1	0	5	0	5	0	0	0	0	5	4	14	23	0	1	1	5	2

(continued)

APPENDIX TABLE

PATENT GRANTS, BY PATENT CLASS, AND MANUFACTURING EMPLOYMENT, BY CENSUS MAJOR INDUSTRY GROUP, FOR ALL STANDARD METROPOLITAN AREAS FOR WHICH EMPLOYMENT DATA IS AVAILABLE, 1947–48

	Number of patents issued (1947–48) in patent class number.[a]							Number (in thousands) of employees (1947) in Census major industry group number.[b]										
Standard Metropolitan Area	123	M	29	82 90	M 29 82 90	23[c]	260[d]	18	37	33	34	35	33 34 35	28	28 29	28 30	All Mfg. Empl.	Total Population
Evansville, Ind.	0	0	0	0	0	0	0	0	2	0	3	14	17	1	1	1	3	1
Flint, Mich.	4	0	1	1	2	0	0	0	50	3	0	1	2	1	1	1	5	2
Fort Wayne, Ind.	0	0	0	0	0	0	0	0	7	3	1	8	11	1	0	0	4	2
Fort Worth, Tex.	1	0	1	1	2	0	0	0	12	1	0	1	2	1	2	1	3	3
Grand Rapids, Mich.	3	0	0	1	1	0	0	0	7	1	9	9	20	0	0	1	5	3
Greensboro High Point, N.C.	0	0	0	0	0	0	0	0	0	0	1	1	1	1	1	1	3	2
Greenville, S.C.	0	0	0	0	0	0	0	0	0	0	0	1	1	0	0	0	3	2
Hamilton-Middletown, Ohio	4	1	1	1	3	0	0	0	2	5	5	5	15	0	0	1	3	1
Hartford, Conn.	24	0	0	1	2	2	0	9	16	1	5	21	27	1	1	1	6	3
Houston, Tex.	1	1	0	0	1	2	0	0	1	4	5	12	21	4	15	5	6	7
Indianapolis, Ind.	6	6	3	1	10	2	4	2	18	4	9	13	26	9	10	12	9	5
Kalamazoo, Mich.	0	0	0	0	0	0	0	0	2	1	3	2	5	2	2	2	2	1
Kansas City, Mo.	1	0	1	1	2	2	0	1	7	6	7	4	16	5	8	5	8	8
Lancaster, Pa.	0	1	0	0	1	0	0	4	0	1	4	4	9	0	0	0	4	2
Lansing, Mich.	1	0	1	0	1	0	0	0	17	2	2	2	6	0	0	0	3	2
Lorain-Elyria, Ohio	0	1	0	2	3	0	0	0	3	13	5	3	21	0	0	0	3	1
Los Angeles, Calif.	20	14	22	8	44	10	6	16	79	17	33	31	81	12	23	25	36	36
Louisville, Ky.	0	3	1	0	4	0	1	0	3	2	10	9	21	7	7	8	7	5
Memphis, Tenn.	0	0	0	0	0	0	0	0	1	0	1	1	3	3	4	9	4	4
Milwaukee, Wis.	5	4	4	9	17	2	2	8	15	14	13	54	80	3	4	3	18	8

(continued)

APPENDIX TABLE

PATENT GRANTS, BY PATENT CLASS, AND MANUFACTURING EMPLOYMENT, BY CENSUS MAJOR INDUSTRY GROUP, FOR ALL STANDARD METROPOLITAN AREAS FOR WHICH EMPLOYMENT DATA IS AVAILABLE, 1947–48

Standard Metropolitan Area	Number of patents issued (1947–48) in patent class number:[a]								Number (in thousands) of employees (1947) in Census major industry group number:[b]									
	123	M	29	82 90	M 29 82 90	23[c]	260[d]	18	37	33	34	35	33 34 35	28	28 29	28 30	All Mfg. Empl.	Total Population
Minneapolis-St. Paul, Minn.	6	1	3	2	6	2	1	3	3	2	9	20	31	4	5	5	12	10
Nashville, Tenn.	0	0	1	1	2	0	0	0	3	0	2	0	3	6	6	6	3	3
New Britain-Bristol, Conn.	4	2	0	0	2	0	0	0	0	2	16	17	34	0	0	0	5	1
New Haven, Conn.	0	2	0	0	2	0	1	5	1	5	4	3	12	0	1	3	4	3
New Orleans, La.	0	0	0	0	0	0	0	1	8	1	2	0	3	2	3	2	5	6
New York-N.E. New Jersey	33	78	43	19	140	93	58	89	81	38	83	90	212	102	118	116	160	123
Peoria, Ill.	2	0	0	1	1	0	0	0	0	3	1	25	28	1	1	1	4	2
Philadelphia, Pa.	5	16	12	8	36	28	30	26	33	28	48	47	123	28	45	37	53	34
Pittsburgh, Pa.	1	30	13	4	47	13	6	8	15	148	35	23	206	6	13	8	34	22
Portland, Ore.	0	1	1	1	3	0	1	0	3	4	4	3	11	1	1	1	5	6
Providence, R.I.	1	2	4	2	8	0	0	3	0	5	9	20	34	1	2	8	15	7
Racine, Wis.	1	0	3	2	5	0	0	0	0	2	3	10	15	1	1	1	2	1
Reading, Pa.	0	2	0	0	2	4	1	0	2	7	3	7	16	1	1	1	5	2
Rochester, N.Y.	1	1	1	6	8	0	1	4	3	1	3	9	13	2	2	1	11	5
Rockford, Ill.	0	1	4	6	11	0	0	0	2	3	10	11	25	0	0	0	4	1
Saginaw, Mich.	0	0	0	0	0	0	0	0	7	8	1	2	11	0	0	0	2	1
St. Louis, Mo.	10	2	3	2	7	4	7	5	19	24	19	21	64	17	24	18	24	16
San Diego, Calif.	3	2	1	0	3	0	0	1	12	0	0	0	0	0	0	0	2	4
San Francisco-Oakland, Calif.	3	6	1	6	13	13	20	4	20	11	15	14	41	11	20	11	16	19
Scranton, Pa.	0	0	0	0	0	0	0	0	2	0	2	1	3	0	0	0	2	3

(continued)

APPENDIX TABLE

PATENT GRANTS, BY PATENT CLASS, AND MANUFACTURING EMPLOYMENT, BY CENSUS MAJOR INDUSTRY GROUP, FOR ALL STANDARD METROPOLITAN AREAS FOR WHICH EMPLOYMENT DATA IS AVAILABLE, 1947–48

Standard Metropolitan Area	Number of patents issued (1947–48) in patent class number:[a]								Number (in thousands) of employees (1947) in Census major industry group number:[b]								All Mfg. Empl.	Total Population
	123	M	29	82 / 90	M 29 82 90	23[c]	260[d]	18	37	33	34	35	33 34 35	28	28 29	28 30		
Seattle, Wash.	0	0	1	1	2	2	0	3	20	2	4	3	9	1	1	1	5	6
South Bend, Ind.	20	0	0	0	0	0	0	2	22	0	1	7	8	0	0	0	4	2
Springfield-Holyoke, Mass.	6	0	4	1	5	0	2	7	2	2	4	20	26	4	4	9	8	4
Syracuse, N.Y.	0	1	2	0	3	2	0	0	5	6	4	16	26	2	4	4	5	3
Toledo, Ohio	3	1	2	0	3	0	1	6	15	5	8	12	25	2	4	2	7	4
Trenton, N.J.	1	0	0	0	0	0	0	0	4	2	7	5	14	1	1	6	4	2
Utica-Rome, N.Y.	1	1	0	0	1	0	0	1	1	6	5	7	18	1	1	1	5	3
Waterbury, Conn.	0	3	2	1	6	0	0	1	0	10	10	2	23	2	2	6	4	1
Wheeling, W. Va.-Steubenville, Ohio	0	1	0	1	2	0	0	1	0	23	9	1	32	1	0	1	5	4
Wilkes Barre-Hazelton, Pa.	0	0	0	0	0	0	0	0	0	2	1	2	4	0	0	0	4	4
Winston-Salem, N.C.	0	0	0	0	0	0	0	0	0	0	1	0	1	0	0	0	3	1
Worcester, Mass.	2	1	0	2	3	0	0	1	1	8	5	11	24	0	1	1	5	3
York, Pa.	2	0	1	0	1	0	0	0	1	2	4	9	16	0	0	0	4	2
Youngstown, Ohio	1	4	0	1	5	0	0	0	5	56	10	7	73	0	2	2	11	5

SOURCE: Derived from *Official Gazette of the Patent Office,* Dept. of Commerce, weekly issues 1947–48 and *Census of Manufactures,* 1947.

[a] Patent class number 123 is Internal-combustion engines; M is an aggregate of 75-Metallurgy, 266-Metallurgical apparatus, 78-Metal forging and welding, 148-Metal treatment, 80-Metal rolling, 205-Metal drawing, and 22-Metal founding; 29 is Metal working; 82 is Turning and 90 is Gear cutting, milling and planing; 23 is Chemistry; 260 is Chemistry, carbon compounds; 18 is Plastics.

[b] Census major industry group number 37 is Transportation equipment; 33 is Primary metal industries; 34 is Fabricated metal products; 35 is Machinery, except electrical; 28 is Chemicals and allied products; 29 is Petroleum and coal products; 30 is Rubber products.

[c] Data is for one year only, 1947.
[d] Figures are for a 12-week sample, the first week of each month of the year 1947.

The Future of Industrial Research and Development

YALE BROZEN

UNIVERSITY OF CHICAGO

RESEARCH in the laboratories of United States industry has grown for the past twenty-five years at a rate in excess of 15 per cent a year in dollar terms and 12 per cent a year in real terms. Growth in some industries has been even more rapid, of course, while in others it has fallen far short of these rates. Growth over the next fifteen years is projected at an annual rate of from 7 to 8 per cent. The portion of gross national product devoted to research and development is expected to rise from 1.9 to 3 per cent over this period with an ultimate ceiling at 5 per cent in the next century.

Profits and Research Performed

As research has increased, the profit performance of many segments of industry has changed in ways which appear to be related to their investments in this activity. Research spending in manufacturing industries is now much more closely related to *subsequent* sales and profits (see Table 1) than it was in the 1930's, when it amounted to less than 0.5 per cent of sales, and in the 1940's, when it was less than 1 per cent of sales.

The high correlation of research and subsequent profits points to the existence of a disequilibrium which may be indicative of a continued rapid growth of research spending in industrial laboratories. The correlation has, however, tended to deteriorate since 1957. This is one of the reasons for expecting a less rapid R and D growth in the future.

High research–high return industries are underinvesting in research and facilities. These industries will grow more rapidly than the low research–low return groups and, as a consequence, over-all spending on research will grow more rapidly than aggregate manufacturing sales even with a constant percentage of sales spent on research by each category.

Industries performing little research may be underinvesting in this activity. It seems apparent, however, that the low rate of spending in

NOTE: This paper is an abstract of an article entitled, "Trends in Industrial R and D," which appeared in the *Journal of Business*, July 1960.

TABLE 1

RESEARCH EXPENDITURES (1953 AND 1956) AND RATES OF RETURN (1957)
BY INDUSTRIES

Industry	Research Performed as a Percentage of Sales		Return on Net Worth
	1953	1956	1957
Aircraft and parts	8.9	17.6	17,8
Electrical equipment	4.3	5.3	12.6
Professional, scientific and controlling instruments	4.1	4.8	12.0
Chemical and allied products	2.1	2.3	13.2
Motor vehicles and other transp.	1.3	2.3	12.5
Machinery (except electrical)	1.3	2.1	10.7
ALL MANUFACTURING	1.3	1.7	10.9
Rubber[a]	.99	1.3	11.2
Petroleum products[a]	.57	0.80	12.4
Stone, clay, and glass	.55	0.70	12.3
Fabricated metal products	.40	0.57	9.3
Paper and allied products	.33	0.39	8.9
Primary metal[a]	.26	0.34	10.6
Food and kindred products	.11	0.15	8.6
Textile mill and apparel	.10	0.12	4.8

SOURCE: *Reviews of Data on Research and Development*, May 1958 and August 1959, and National Science Foundation, *Science and Engineering in American Industry, Final Report on a 1953–1954 Survey* (NSF 56–16, Washington, 1956), provided data on total research performed. Total sales in each industry were obtained from *The Economic Almanac 1958* (New York, Thomas Y. Crowell Company). Rates of return were taken from *Quarterly Financial Report for Manufacturing Corporations*, June 1958 (Federal Trade Commission—Securities and Exchange Commission).

[a] It should be noted that the rubber and petroleum industries may have an especially large understatement of book value (and overstatement of rate of return) relative to other industries because of the acquisition of government owned synthetic rubber facilities at favorable prices in 1955. The same is true of the primary metal industry because of its earlier acquisition of government owned aluminum and steel facilities.

the apparel, tobacco, food and beverage, textile, and iron and steel industries is primarily a consequence of the poorer scientific base available compared with that underlying the chemical, electrical, and instrument technologies.

Research Spending by Industry Categories

The great variation in research and development performance among industries is related to other factors besides the quality of the science base. New products, materials, or techniques appearing in an industry will lead to the spending of large amounts on research relative to sales. This relationship occurs partly because sales are low until a product is established and partly because much needs to be learned to perfect new products, to develop new applications and broaden markets, and to improve production processes. As these problems are solved and sales grow, the percentage of sales spent on research tends to drop unless more new products, materials, and processes appear (perhaps because of research in other industries) or improvements in the science base occur.

The scale of basic research performed in some industries (chemical, electrical, and petroleum) makes it likely that additions to the science base will occur at a rate which will prevent any decline in R and D performed relative to sales despite rapid growth of sales. Primary metal R and D seems likely to grow since a substantial proportion of the metal R and D budget is going to fundamental work. Also, products of basic research in universities and other nonprofit institutions and in government laboratories may appear in unexpected places and cause stagnating R and D programs to come to life.

Government Influences in Industrial R and D

Government support of work in industrial laboratories appears to be an important factor in causing the present high level of performance. Yet, some evidence to the contrary exists. So long as the government supported research in the synthetic rubber industry, research remained at low levels. Since the sale of government owned facilities and the ending of research subsidies, privately performed R and D has grown sufficiently to raise over-all performance by 50 per cent. George Stigler and David Blank present evidence which may indicate that government spending simply replaces private spending, often causing private outlays to fall by more than the amount of public funds spent.[1]

Other Factors Influencing R and D Outlays

Growth in per capita income spurs research partly because the income elasticity of demand for the products of high research rate industries is large. Also, a larger market provides more room for diversity in products. An item whose niche in a small market would provide insufficient sales to justify development expense becomes worthwhile in a large market.

[1] *The Demand and Supply of Scientific Personnel*, Princeton University Press for National Bureau of Economic Research, 1957, p. 59.

Low return industries are increasing their research and development spending, where possible, to improve their rate of return. Since the yield on additional capital is low in these industries, they turn their investment in the direction of moderate yield research projects which could not compete if high yielding equipment investment opportunities were available.

The restraining forces on R and D growth appear to be (1) the lack of growth in the *rate* of capital formation (which means little growth in an important market for the product of R and D), (2) the necessity of dipping deeper into the supply of talent as the amount absorbed increases, and (3) the absorption of a growing portion of gross saving by R and D which leaves less for further transfer from fixed asset investment in the future.

PART III
CASE STUDIES

Inventions in the Postwar
American Aluminum Industry

MERTON J. PECK

HARVARD UNIVERSITY

ALUMINUM is a striking example of an industry created by invention. Arthur Hall's discovery of the electrolytic process in 1889 provided a commercially feasible method of reducing aluminum, and the growth of aluminum consumption until it is now second only to steel owes much to subsequent inventions.[1] Inventions in the aluminum industry can be divided into two categories: first, new alloys, new processes in manufacturing products from aluminum, and new techniques for fabricating aluminum ingot that have permitted new commercial uses for aluminum; and, second, new techniques that have reduced the cost of aluminum ingot.

This distinction is based upon the roster of potential inventors. With the first group of inventions, the firms that could both profit from and have the technical knowledge for inventions include the independent fabricators, the manufacturers of end-products made from aluminum, and the makers of fabricating and manufacturing equipment as well as the producers of aluminum ingot. These different types of firms realize the profits from invention in varying ways, so that comparing the nature of the profits of invention for each class of firms with the actual record of invention tests the effects of various incentives and opportunities for invention. With the second group of inventions, the primary aluminum producers are the sole likely source of invention, for these firms alone have access to the technology and can profit directly from introducing inventions into their own operations.

Anti-trust action has transformed the structure of the industry from that of a single domestic seller·of aluminum ingot to a three-firm and later a five-firm oligopoly.[2] Consequently, the second question for

---

NOTE: This paper is drawn from a book-length study, *Competition in the American Aluminum Industry*, 1945–1955, Cambridge, Mass., 1961.

[1] For the early history of inventions in the aluminum industry, see Donald Wallace, *Market Control in the Aluminum Industry*, Cambridge, Mass., 1937, App. A.

[2] By volume, aluminum is second only to steel and by tonnage it ranks after steel, copper, lead, and zinc. Since aluminum has a low density, weight comparisons understate its relative importance. See *Aluminum, The Industry and the Four North American Producers*, New York, 1951, p. 8.

research is the effects of the change in market structure upon inventive activity for both classes of invention. Finally, even though the inventions here are grouped in terms of several distinct technical problems, these problems encompass most of the recent technical progress in the aluminum industry. What follows then comprises a history of inventions in the aluminum industry from 1946 to 1957.[3]

Sources of the Data

Invention is defined here as the introduction of a new product or production technique. The standard for novelty is low. It suffices if an invention is described as an advance in the state of the art in either the trade paper of the industry, *Modern Metals*, or another trade publication.[4] Such sources may be influenced by the public relations and advertising efforts of the inventor as well as by editorial judgments of readership interest. These sources, however, do impose the minimum level of significance as viewed by the trade press editors.

The inventions so recorded will vary widely in terms of their novelty and economic significance. An attempt has been made to distinguish between major and minor inventions upon the basis of the discussion in the trade press. Evaluating inventions, however, is a difficult problem even for those with more technical qualifications and with more reliable sources than the author's. What is reported here is the discussion in the trade press rather than an ex post analysis of the economic significance of various inventions.

Even though *Modern Metals* and other trade publications have an impressive record of accuracy and coverage, the preceding discussion indicates the limitations of these sources. The records and calculations of the individual firms were unavailable, a condition which further restricts the reliability of this study and makes the discussion unduly speculative. Therefore, the conclusions should be regarded as tentative, though perhaps no more so than is the case with other histories of invention.

Hypotheses as to the Origin of Inventions

The aluminum industry is usually considered to be synonomous with the primary aluminum producers: Kaiser, Reynolds, Alcoa, and since 1955, Harvey, Ormet and Anaconda. These firms mine bauxite, pro-

---

[3] For a discussion of this period, see Harold Stein, "The Disposal of Aluminum Plants," in *Public Administration and Policy Development*, Harold Stein, editor, New York, 1952.
[4] *Modern Metals*. Another standard source is the Bureau of Mines, *Minerals Yearbook*.

cess the bauxite into alumina, and reduce the alumina into aluminum pig and ingot. Approximately three-quarters of the pig and ingot is fabricated in the vertically integrated facilities of the primary producers.[5] Aluminum fabrications are sold to manufacturers for the production of a wide variety of end products, from aircraft and automobile components to building materials and pots and pans.

The increased consumption of aluminum over the last decades is in part dependent upon advances in the manufacturing techniques for aluminum as well as upon inventions in the aluminum industry narrowly defined. This is particularly so because aluminum is less workable by established production methods than steel or copper. Although these inventions might be considered outside the boundaries of the aluminum industry, the primary aluminum producers obviously profit from advances in the state of the manufacturing art that expand their $1\frac{1}{2}$ billion market for aluminum.

Indeed, this situation is highly conducive to invention by firms beyond the narrow limits of the industry. The three primary producers manufacture end-products so that they have direct experience with the technical problems involved.[6] Their sales engineers are in continuing contact with the end-product manufacturers so that the primary producers can facilitate the adoption of inventions in manufacturing processes. Kaiser, Reynolds, and Alcoa are among the 100 largest American manufacturing companies in the *Fortune* list.[7] All three have the extensive research organization of a large corporation.[8] Primary aluminum reduction is one of the most concentrated of American industries. Hence, if, as is sometimes argued, size and fewness are conducive to invention, the primary producers might well be the major contributors to the technical progress of their customers.

In contrast, the manufacturing processes for aluminum are only one of many technical problems confronting the end-product manufacturer. An end-product manufacturer would profit directly only from

[5] See data in *Small Business and the Aluminum Industry, A Report of Sub-committee No. 3 to the Select Committee on Small Business*, House of Representatives, 84th Cong., 2nd sess., H.R. 2954, 1956, p. 20. Hereafter this document will be cited as *Small Business and the Aluminum Industry*.

[6] For a description of the range of end-products manufactured by the primary producers see *Record*, United States vs Aluminum Company of America, S.D.N.Y., 1949, p. 1,791 (Hereafter cited as *Remedy Record*). Only about 10 to 15 per cent of aluminum ingot output is used by the primary producers in their own end-products.

[7] Alcoa was forty-third, Reynolds eighty-fifth and Kaiser one-hundredth in 1956. *Fortune*, July 1958, pp. 131–150.

[8] The research organizations as described in various articles in the trade press appear to have the character and size typical of a large manufacturer of producers' durables.

the incorporation of an invention in his own aluminum manufacturing process. Such profits would be relatively modest compared to the gains accruing to a primary producer from an invention resulting in even a small increase in the consumption of aluminum. Yet the end-product manufacturers, numbering over 24,000, have the law of large numbers in their favor.[9] Given the accidental character of invention, this factor might offset the differences in expected profits so that the end-product manufacturers would be a major source of inventions.

Aircraft manufacturers are a special category among the end-product manufacturers. The manufacturing techniques for aluminum represent an important technical problem for such firms. Furthermore, these firms have large engineering staffs and can charge a share of their research expenses to defense contracts.

Inventions in manufacturing techniques are often incorporated in new machinery so that the makers of equipment for aluminum manufacturing constitute a third source of inventions. An equipment maker profits from these inventions, both through a larger share of the equipment market and an expansion of the total sales of equipment that accompanies an acceleration in the rate of obsolescence of existing machinery and the increased use of aluminum. Compared to the end-product manufacturers who can utilize a new manufacturing technique directly only in their own operation, the equipment makers can capitalize upon the adoption of an invention by end-product manufacturers generally. This is offset by the smaller size of equipment makers relative to such end-product manufacturers as the aircraft companies, and their smaller number (several hundred firms compared to 24,000 end-product manufacturers).

The comparison of the probable expected profits from invention for the equipment makers and for the primary producers is even more difficult and nebulous. In general, the total profits from the sum of advances in manufacturing techniques are much greater for the primary producers than for the equipment makers simply because the sales of aluminum are so much greater than the sales of equipment. Yet the profits of invention for the equipment makers are more certain, immediate, and greater in proportion to the size of the firm. The equipment makers' profits are more certain since some inventions displace existing machinery rather than facilitate new applications for aluminum. The effects of invention cannot be foreseen with sufficient accuracy to enable the primary producers to discriminate accord-

[9] *Small Business and the Aluminum Industry*, p. 7.

ing to the results of invention, whereas the equipment maker benefits in either case. The equipment makers' profits are more immediate, because the sale of new machinery takes place over a relatively short time, whereas the increase in aluminum consumption from a new use made possible by the machinery occurs over a long time span. Finally, a single invention may change markedly an equipment maker's market share and so create a large percentage change in the firm's profits. Since aluminum has a wide variety of uses, any one invention is unlikely to increase markedly the profits of the primary producers.

In addition, the equipment makers are under more competitive pressures to invent. Relative technical merits are an important element in the sale of equipment so that a firm that does not invent may suffer a loss of market share. Since a loss of market share is said to be a greater stimulus to business effort than an equivalent gain, the existence of these competitive pressures would further favor the equipment makers as a source of inventions. In contrast, an increase in the demand for aluminum from an improvement in manufacturing techniques might be distributed among all the primary producers.

Up to this point only the profits directly realizable from the inventing firm's own operation have been considered. Clearly an end-product manufacturer could sell patent rights for a new machine to an equipment manufacturer and such transferability makes the economic position of the inventor less decisive. It is assumed here, however, that the market for inventions is sufficiently imperfect so that the sale of inventions does not alter substantially the relative profitability of invention for these three groups. This assumption is further strengthened by the nonpatentability of a minority of these inventions.

These views on the marketability of inventions imply that individual inventors and commercial research organizations will be a relatively minor source of inventions, since their profits from inventions are realized solely through the sale of patent rights. Universities, government laboratories, and foreign sources are considered as sources of invention outside the scope of market incentives and pressures.

Two other types of firms are a priori possible but unlikely sources of inventions in manufacturing techniques. Secondary aluminum producers make aluminum ingot from scrap and sell their ingot in competition with the primary producers. About 100 secondary smelters account for one-fifth of the total domestic aluminum output.[10] Inde-

---

[10] *Ibid.*, p. 19.

pendent fabricators buy ingot from the primary and secondary producers for fabrication and sale to end-product manufacturers. These firms account in total for only a quarter of the fabricating output.[11] Since both types of firms are individually small compared to the primary producers, they neither realize the profits accruing to primary producers from an increased demand for aluminum nor possess the research funds of a large corporation. Thus, they are likely to be a relatively minor source of inventions.

From this analysis of the nature of the expected profits from invention and the resources for research of the primary producers, the end-product manufacturers, and the equipment makers, it is possible to argue a priori that each will be the major source of inventions. Admittedly, this is a highly qualitative argument based upon the nature of expected profits rather than a quantitative examination of the net historical profits from past inventions for each group. Data is lacking for such a study.

Inventions in Four Technical Areas of the Industry

JOINING

To discover which of the three groups—the primary producers, the end-product manufacturers, or the equipment makers—is the major source of inventions in manufacturing techniques for aluminum requires the selection of a technical area that is important for an increase in the total demand for aluminum, of significance to a wide class of end-product manufacturers and with a substantial group of equipment makers. The joining of aluminum fulfills these specifications.

Not only is joining metal components common to the manufacturing of most end-products, but aluminum cannot be joined by conventional welding as easily as other metals.[12] Joining is a widespread technical problem among the end-product manufacturers, and so it is not surprising that the trade paper *Modern Metals* states, "It is pretty well known that the principal deterrent to the more extensive use of aluminum is the difficulty in joining."[13] Finally, there is a well established group of manufacturers of welding equipment for use with

[11] *Ibid.*, p. 20.

[12] Aluminum has a much lower melting temperature than steel. A tendency for oxidation and the diffusion of heat throughout the metal creates heat reactions. For a discussion see Reynolds Metals Company, *Reynolds Aluminum Alloys and Mill Products*, Louisville, 1948, p. 18.

[13] *Modern Metals*, April 1953, p. 46.

TABLE 1

SOURCES OF INVENTIONS IN FOUR TECHNICAL AREAS OF
THE ALUMINUM INDUSTRY, 1946–57

Source	Joining	Technical Area Finishing	Fabricating	Alloys
	(1)	(2)	(3)	(4)
Primary aluminum producers	6	1	10	30[a]
Independent fabricators	0	0	13	2
Secondary aluminum producers	1	0	0	1
End-product manufacturers				1
Aircraft	6	7	5	
Other	3	2	1	
Equipment manufacturers	26	13	37	0
Commercial research and development companies	3	3	1	0
Individual inventors	0	1	0	0
Universities	0	0	0	0
Government laboratories	1	0	2	1
Foreign sources	6	0	7	4
	52	27	76	39

SOURCE: A survey of inventions reported in the trade press and compiled by the author. A listing of these inventions, a brief description thereof, and the citations in the trade press can be obtained from the author.

[a] The breakdown here is Alcoa, 11; Kaiser, 10; Reynolds, 6; Harvey, 2; and Limited, 1.

other metals. Since 1940 some of these companies have supplied specialized welding equipment for use with aluminum.

The sources of inventions in joining from 1946 to 1957 are summarized in column 1 of Table 1. The blanks and near-blanks drawn for secondary aluminum producers and independent fabricators were to be expected while the applied character of these inventions rules out the universities. The absence of any contribution by an individual inventor appears surprising in view of Jewkes' recent study which emphasized the contributions of individuals relative to those of corporate laboratories.[14] Those who might be termed individual

[14] John Jewkes, David Sawyers, and Richard Stillerman, *The Sources of Invention*, London, 1958, p. 82.

inventors have sometimes joined one of the companies within the industry for the final stages in the development of their inventions. Furthermore, many of the equipment makers have small engineering organizations that provide the institutional environment of the individual inventor. Even so, independent inventors appear to be an unimportant source of invention.

The relatively low contribution of the primary producers and the relatively high contribution of the equipment makers is more striking. According to the preceding discussion, this would indicate that the competitive pressures and the more immediate, more certain, and larger relative increase in profits for the equipment makers offset larger potential long-run profits from inventions and the greater resources of the primary producers. The end-product manufacturers as a group are not an important source of invention despite their large numbers. Among the end-product manufacturers the aircraft companies predominate, which can be explained by the factors discussed previously.

Four joining inventions have been mentioned repeatedly in the trade press. Of these, the Koldweld process appears to be the most significant. The idea originated with a Royal Air Force officer, Sowter, who observed that when two sheets of copper were cut with dull shears a weld sometimes occurred on the sheared edge. This phenomenon was well known, but Sowter attempted to establish the conditions under which a weld would result. Upon demobilization, Sowter joined General Electric Ltd., a British welding equipment manufacturer. A research program conducted by the company developed the Koldweld process for aluminum. Even though the original idea was conceived by an individual inventor, it was within a large corporation that the invention was converted into a commercially feasible process.[15]

The Koldweld Corporation was organized to license the process in the United States.[16] Under agreements with this corporation, the Utica Drop Forge and Tool Corporation developed and marketed a line of tools for the Koldweld process.[17] This process, the first departure from conventional heat welding, is particularly important for those uses of aluminum in which the molecular structure of the metal must

[15] W. A. Barnes, "Connecting Aluminum Conductors by the Koldweld Process," *Modern Metals*, October 1955, p. 62. A Swiss aluminum fabricator is reported to have independently developed a similar process at about the same time.

[16] "Fast Process Welds Aluminum Without Heating," *ibid.*, December 1949, p. 28.

[17] Barnes, "Now Available: Tools for Koldwelding Wire and Sheet," *ibid.*, April 1954, p. 57. Alcoa was reported as developing methods which extend the range of alloys that can be Koldwelded.

be preserved. (Heat welding changes the physical characteristics of aluminum.) The use of Koldwelding is spreading, although it is by no means in general use.

At present, the most common method of welding aluminum is the heilarc process. Heilarc welding was developed by the Northrop Aviation Corporation in 1940 and is considered a "tremendous boon to the light metals industry."[18] In the postwar decade the Air Reduction Company, a welding equipment manufacturer, has made significant improvements in this process.[19]

The last two inventions accorded special mention are methods of brazing. Brazing joins metals through the flow of molten metal between joints without melting the metals to be joined and hence changing their physical properties. It is used primarily in air conditioning, automobile, and aircraft components where preserving the original heat transfer properties of aluminum is important.[20] The Trane Company, a maker of aluminum components for aircraft and air conditioning, has developed a brazing process described as "the most significant heat transfer development in a quarter of a century."[21] The dip brazing process developed jointly by United Aircraft Products and Alcoa is said, "to increase production rates, cut costs, and give a more efficient product design."[22]

The origin of these apparently more major inventions corresponds roughly with the results obtained from the counting of the inventions, with one each coming from a British equipment maker, a domestic equipment maker, an end-product manufacturer, and one jointly from an end-product manufacturer and a primary producer.

FINISHING

Although aluminum does not rust, it is subject to corrosion and water staining. This has restricted the use of aluminum generally, although it is particularly crucial for aircraft components where aluminum gears, impeller blades, and so forth are subject to heat erosion and abrasion.[23] Because the incidence of this technical problem is concentrated in the aircraft industry, it is a less valid test of the relative role

---

[18] "Welding Aluminum," *ibid.*, July 1959, p. 26.
[19] *Ibid.*
[20] *Aluminum and Its Alloys*, Pittsburgh, 1950, p. 92.
[21] "Brazed Aluminum Heat Exchangers," *Modern Metals*, October 1951, p. 25.
[22] "Dip Brazing Cuts Costs," *ibid.*, April 1953, p. 40.
[23] *Ibid.*, February 1952, p. 72.

of different classes of inventors. Rather, the aircraft companies could be expected to be major sources of invention.

The computations in column 2 of Table 1 indicate that this is the case. Otherwise the results are similar to those for inventions in joining aluminum; namely, equipment makers are the major source of inventions and the primary producers are a relatively unimportant source. None of these inventions have been discussed extensively in the trade press.

FABRICATING TECHNIQUES

Fabricating converts aluminum ingot into sheet, rods, and bar castings for use by end-product manufacturers. The reporting of fabricating inventions in the trade press is incomplete for products such as aluminum sheet in which the primary producers account for over 90 per cent of the production,[24] apparently because such inventions are of interest to only a few firms. (Independent fabricators do purchase reroll stock for finishing. Most of the rolling inventions listed below are for this type of rolling.) Consequently, the inventions in fabricating techniques reported here are largely limited to the fabricating carried on by both the independents and the primary producers. The primary producers account for about 40 per cent of the production fabricated by both independents and primary producers, with their share of individual products varying from 10 per cent in casting to 75 per cent in cable.[25]

The independent fabricators also vary greatly in size according to the product line. Extruding is largely a small business field containing firms with assets of as little as $200,000. Cable wire, tubes, and shapes are produced by larger firms, though only a few, such as Revere Copper and Brass, are among *Fortune*'s 500 largest industrial corporations. Some 3,000 foundries cast aluminum but most of these are specialty job shops. The mass production of die castings for the automobile industry is concentrated among a dozen or so comparatively large firms.

The primary producers realize gains from inventions in fabricating techniques through the increased demand for aluminum. For example, extrusion output expanded at about three times the rate of all fabricating output from 1950 to 1955,[26] in large part because the newer extrusion presses reduced the cost of this type of fabrication. Yet, as with

[24] See data in *Small Business and the Aluminum Industry*, p. 20.
[25] *Ibid.*
[26] *Ibid.*

the inventions in manufacturing techniques, the gains of the primary producers are deferred and uncertain compared to those of the equipment makers. This is partially offset by the primary producers' direct gains through the utilization of fabricating techniques in their own operations. These gains are the more immediate reduction in costs rather than the longer-run profits from an increase in demand for aluminum.

The equipment makers occupy the same position with respect to the realization of profits as in the case of manufacturing techniques. The independent fabricators here are comparable to the end-product manufacturers in that they use the inventions directly in their own operations. The end-product manufacturers as the consumers of fabrications would profit from improvements in their supply.

As column 3 of Table 1 indicates, the equipment makers are the major source of fabricating inventions. Again, the more immediate and certain profits from invention for such firms appear to be the more effective stimulus for invention. Fabricating machinery, however, is often custom made for a specific fabricator with engineers from both the fabricator and the equipment maker working together on its design. Consequently, many inventions are the joint work of these two parties.

The three major inventions in fabricating technique originated abroad. Shell moulding, the most frequently discussed of the three inventions, utilizes a plastic shell as a mold rather than a more expensive metal die. Johannes Croning, a German engineer, invented the process in connection with wartime aircraft production. After the war Croning joined the Polygram Casting Co., Ltd., an English foundry, to further improve the process.[27] Polygram holds the English patent and has applied for an American patent. As of 1953 the patent situation was described as "confused."[28]

Three companies outside the aluminum industry were instrumental in the introduction of the Croning process in the United States. The Bakelite Division of Union Carbide and Chemical and Monsanto Chemical Company have promoted the process which requires the

[27] F. L. Church, "The Shell Molding Process," *ibid.*, April 1952, pp. 28–33.

[28] Polygram claims, ". . . it would be a serious mistake to assume that in its commercially practicable form [the Croning process] is open to free exploitation and that no Polygram license is necessary" (*Modern Metals*, March 1953, p. 30). Another group, Crown Casting Associates, has applied for an American patent. *Modern Metals* reports, "It has since been contended that the American patent claims are invalid and that an unlicensed foundry can without fear adopt the process in its own operations." (Church, "The Shell Molding Process," p. 28).

plastics they manufacture.[29] Shallenberger of the Stanford Business School and some of his former students have developed new machinery for shell casting.[30] Over 100 foundries had adopted the process by 1953,[31] and its reception was such that one metallurgist cautioned, "The Croning process, though promising, is no panacea."[32]

The Properzi continuous casting process was invented by an Italian engineer, again for wartime aircraft production. Properzi made further improvements after the war and the Nichols Wire and Aluminum Company, an American independent fabricator, introduced the process into the United States. Continuous casting permits a single machine to convert aluminum ingot directly into redrawn rod, thus eliminating several intermediate steps of the conventional production process. According to Properzi, "When contrasted to the multi-million dollar plants and large labor forces needed for conventional production of rod, it becomes obvious that continuous casting processes are revolutionary in their economic impact."[33] To date, however, the economic impact has been limited, despite the considerable discussion of the Properzi process. Adoption has been discouraged by the initial cost of the machine ($175,000) and the radical changes required in existing operating techniques. There are now seven installations in the United States.[34]

The last major invention in fabricating technique is the large forging press. During the war, German aircraft firms built four extremely large presses that could form entire aircraft subassemblies, thus reducing the number of aircraft parts and so simplifying assembly and increasing structural strength.[35] In 1948 the Air Force shipped two of these presses to the United States for installation in fabricating plants owned by Alcoa and Bridgeport Brass. (The Russians took the other two presses.)[36] In 1950 the Air Force commissioned the building of even larger presses to be operated by Wyman Gorden, Alcoa, Kaiser, Harvey, and Curtiss Wright.[37] These presses are

[29] *Ibid.*, April 1952, p. 29.

[30] *Ibid.*, August 1953, p. 26.

[31] *Ibid.*, April 1953, p. 29.

[32] E. Eliot, "Aluminum and Its Alloys in 1953—Some Aspects of Research and Technical Progress Reported," *Metallurgia*, February 1954, p. 82.

[33] *Modern Metals*, December 1953, p. 92.

[34] *Ibid.*, July 1953, p. 30.

[35] "The aircraft designer has long been attracted to the idea of abandoning many of his substructures at present fabricated from sheer and extrusion and using forgings" (Elliot, *op. cit.*, p. 82).

[36] *Modern Metals*, September 1956, p. 94.

[37] *Ibid.*, p. 96.

considered a major engineering advance but their commercial value has yet to be established.

None of these inventions were introduced into the United States by the primary producers, which is consistent with the relatively limited role of these firms in the invention of fabricating techniques.

END-PRODUCT APPLICATIONS

The new product uses of aluminum since 1946 are too numerous for listing here.[38] Examples are such diverse products as (1) tubing for irrigation purposes, (2) shelving and refrigeration units for refrigerators, (3) lifeboats, davits, and ship superstructures, (4) mine props and beams, (5) low-tension electrical wire, (6) building products such as store fronts, lighting fixtures, window frames, and wall panels. Most of these inventions involved less of an advance in the state of the arts than those in the preceding sections, although some new applications called for the solution of difficult technical problems. The end-product manufacturers are the major source of these inventions. In view of their numbers and direct economic interest, any other result would be surprising. But the primary producers are also important contributors to this kind of technical change, both through assisting end-product manufacturers and through devising new end-products.

Elsewhere the primary producers have been given low marks as sources of inventions. New end-products, however, promise a much more immediate payoff to a primary producer than the preceding types of inventions. Consider a shipyard deciding on the relative merits of steel and aluminum lifeboats. A primary producer assisting in the development of a new aluminum lifeboat can expect an immediate increase in its sales of aluminum. In contrast, a new method of welding or new fabricating techniques will increase the demand for aluminum only as these new processes become sufficiently widely diffused to increase the demand for aluminum. The concentration of the primary producers on end-product applications is reflected in the limited public descriptions of the sales and research organizations of the primary producers.[39]

[38] For a discussion of new applications, see the testimony of Mr. Wilson, president of Alcoa, in *Remedy Record*, pp. 953–970.

[39] See W. B. Griffin, "Kaiser Aluminum: More Metal for More Products for More People," *Modern Metals*, January 1956; E. A. Farrell, "Selling Aluminum," *ibid.*, July and August 1956; and F. L. Church, "Man of the Year: David P. Reynolds," *ibid.*, January 1955.

ALUMINUM ALLOYS

The primary producers are likely to be the major source of new alloys (column 4 of Table 1), for the other types of firms do not have access to the technology and cannot realize direct and immediate gains from such inventions.

The primary producers have apparently concentrated their inventive efforts in alloys.[40] New alloys can be directly incorporated into the product line of the inventor so that the profits are relatively immediate compared to the profits from inventions in fabricating and manufacturing techniques. But perhaps more significantly, an alloy is more likely to increase the primary producer's share of the ingot market than other inventions. (Alloys are usually patentable whereas most new end-product applications are not.) Furthermore, a new alloy yields a profit for a primary producer even when it displaces an existing alloy so long as the inventor's market share increases. On the other hand, a new manufacturing or fabricating technique adds to a primary producer's profits only to the extent that it creates new uses for aluminum. Since the economic effect of an invention cannot be foreseen at the outset of the research, this two-fold possibility increases the certainty of a primary producer's profits from a new alloy.

But if immediacy and certainty characterize the profits from inventions in alloys, it does not follow that new alloys have been the most effective inventions in increasing the over-all demand for aluminum. New alloys account for only a small fraction of the total sales of aluminum ingot, indicating that these inventions have apparently played a minor role in the increase in aluminum demand.[41] In contrast, the sale of extrusions, a product with significant changes in extruding techniques, has increased from a few per cent of the prewar total fabricating output in pounds to nearly 25 per cent of the 1958 output.[42]

Primary Producers and Equipment Makers as Sources of Invention

Primary producers are an important source of inventions for new product applications and alloys, while they contributed relatively

[40] Data on the allocation of research expenditures were unavailable to the author. This statement is based upon qualitative descriptions of the research programs.

[41] In 1948 patented alloys accounted for 9 per cent of Alcoa's sales. This company at that time held the most alloy patents. *Remedy Record*, p. 1,729.

[42] See data in *Small Business and the Aluminum Industry*, p. 20.

little toward advances in welding, finishing, and fabricating. Yet inventions in these last three categories have accounted for substantial increases in the demand for aluminum.

This is still consistent with the proposition that the primary producers direct their inventive efforts towards those sectors in which their profits are likely to be the highest, if profits are discounted for time and uncertainty. The significant finding is that the discounts required to explain the primary producers' behavior are of substantial magnitude and more than offset the greater resources of the large firms.

An alternative explanation is that the primary producers can count upon the inventions by others to exploit the technical opportunities in fabricating and manufacturing techniques. Therefore, the primary producers might concentrate their resources in the invention of the alloys where their activities might have a higher marginal value in increasing the demand for aluminum. Yet this view is inconsistent with the fact that the primary producers are active in the development of new end-product applications in which the end-product manufacturers are an effective alternative source of inventions. The critical difference appears to be the immediacy and certainty of the profits in the end-product applications.

In fabricating techniques, welding, and finishing, however, the rate of technical progress has been at least comparable with that in those sectors in which the primary producers are the major inventors. If a balance of payments between the small and the large business sectors were established for the flow of the benefits of technical progress, the primary producers might well be the debtor nation.

Within the small business group, the equipment makers are the major source of inventions. This is a pattern common to such diverse industries as textiles, coal mining, and railroading. Because the equipment makers in these industries are larger relative to their market than their customers are, it is sometimes argued that the differences in inventive activity are a result of differences in market power. In aluminum, however, the equipment makers are relatively small in their market compared to some of their customers and to all the primary producers. For the reasons set forth above, the nature of competition between the equipment makers as well as the nature of demand for their products suggests that equipment makers have a vested interest in technical change that transcends differences in market power.

Oligopoly, Monopoly, and Demand Increasing Inventions

The second research question here is the relationship of oligopoly and monopoly to the rate of invention. Two new primary producers, Kaiser and Reynolds, were established in 1945 by the purchase of production plants constructed by the government during the war.[43] Their entry ended Alcoa's prewar position as the sole domestic producer of primary aluminum.

Oligopoly is often considered more conducive to invention than monopoly simply because of the greater number of independent decisions and approaches. It is possible, of course, to have parallel approaches within a single research organization, but such a research strategy is discouraged by the cost of duplicative efforts and the difficulty of making truly independent decisions within a single hierarchical unit. Further, an oligopolist may sponsor more research activity for fear a rival may exploit the technical possibilities in order to increase his share. The simple case for monopoly is its ability to realize more fully the economies of scale in research, as well as the presumed higher rate of profit that may provide more funds for research.

A historical comparison between the years of one and several primary producers indicates that inventions have occurred at a higher rate in the postwar oligopoly. Some of the new applications represent the culmination of Alcoa's prewar technical pioneering. An industry nearly eight times its prewar size should be expected to have a larger absolute research effort and hence more inventions. Still, at least some part of this increased activity is assignable to the introduction of oligopoly. Notably, within a relatively short time Kaiser and Reynolds have generated inventions at about the same rate as Alcoa even though Alcoa is the largest firm of the three. In alloys, Alcoa has only one more invention to its credit than Kaiser and in new product applications, Reynolds appears to be the leader. This hardly suggests that if Alcoa were the only seller and so twice its present size, the total rate of inventions would be greater.

The second type of evidence concerns the effect of oligopoly upon marketing effort and, through that, the level of research. The existence

---

[43] There was no dissolution so that the problems of dividing a going research organization were avoided. However, during the war these plants were largely operated by Alcoa under management contracts.

of several sellers apparently led to a greater pace in marketing effort, which in turn created pressures upon the research organization to develop new applications for aluminum and bring forth new alloys. It was through this marketing competition rather than direct research rivalry that oligopoly appears to have had an impact upon the rate of invention.

However, the primary producers' search for customers did not create a greater interest in new fabricating techniques. Rather, the effect of an oligopoly here was a more indirect one. The transition to oligopoly increased the significance of the independent fabricators[44] and, with the increase in the number of independent fabricators, there was a corresponding increase in the number of equipment makers serving them. Granted that the sheer increase in size may account for some of the greater activity, an expansion in the role of the independent fabricator may have been necessary for an expansion in the research activities of the equipment makers.

Oligopoly and Invention in Aluminum Ingot

In the production of primary aluminum ingot the primary producers are the sole likely source of invention because there is no established "equipment" industry. This also holds true for the processing of alumina and the mining of bauxite, which are all vertically integrated operations of the primary producers.

The transportation of bauxite, a related process, provides an illustration of the value of independent and competing units in promoting technical change.[45] After the war, there was discussion about the value of specialized ore vessels for the carriage of bauxite ore. At the remedy proceedings in 1949, Mr. Reynolds, president of Reynolds Metals, spoke highly of these specialized ore carriers.[46] A few days later Mr. Wilson, president of Alcoa, testified,

> We have made a continued and constant study as to the type of ships and type of service which will result in the lowest transportation costs and have figured ore carriers, which I heard Mr.

[44] Accurate figures are hard to obtain. The number of independent fabricators increased from 12 to 168, excluding castings (*Small Business and the Aluminum Industry*, pp. 10 and 20). The competition between the primary producers resulted in a seeking out of the independent fabricators. Furthermore, a court order prohibited a repetition of the prewar "price squeeze" by the primary producers.

[45] I am indebted to Alan Strout of the Harvard Economic Research Project for this example. The interpretation here is my own.

[46] *Remedy Record*, p. 188.

Reynolds testify to . . . we have examined the possibility of an ore carrier, one or more ore carriers—and to date we do not believe there will be any economy in utilizing an ore carrier. They are very expensive pieces of equipment and as such cannot be used for any other purpose than just hauling of ore.[47]

Shortly thereafter Reynolds commissioned an English firm to construct the S. S. Carl Schmedemen, the first self-loading bauxite carrier. The ship went into service and received :"good reviews" in *Iron Age*, *The Engineer*, and *The Shipbuilding and Shipping Record*.[48] All those sources claimed a reduction in cost with such a ship, and one estimated the cost savings to be as much as one-third of the shipping costs with conventional equipment. Alcoa has since ordered two specialized ore carriers which may be more conclusive proof of their economic value.[49]

The ore carrier is typical of the technical changes since the war—fairly prosaic and originating in the general advances in technology. Alan Strout, of the Harvard Economic Research Project, describes the technical changes in aluminum reduction "as a procession of non-revolutionary though significant factor saving innovations."[50] He lists changes in location of production facilities, use of new fuel sources, increases in the size of reduction pots, greater amperage, introduction of a continuous process for alumina digestion and electrode formation, improvement in electrical generation and transmission, mechanization of material handling, and improvement in the electronic control system.

The prewar pattern of technical change is quite similar, except that there were several more major inventions to enliven the record.[51] The best known is the Soderberg process which utilizes an anode self-

[47] *Ibid.*, p. 726.

[48] *Shipbuilding and Shipping Record*, December 4, 1952; *The Engineer*, January 16, 1953, p. 98; and *Iron Age*, December 4, 1952, p. 209.

[49] *Shipbuilding and Shipping Record*, May 12 1955, p. 606. Such specialized ore carriers are now used in hauling other ores and are ranked "As one of the most important changes which has marked shipbuilding in recent years" (*Merchants Ships, 1954*, New York, 1955, p. 64). Even without Reynold's leadership, Alcoa would probably have adopted this general shipping practice eventually.

[50] Alan M. Strout, "The Aluminum Industry," in Harvard Economic Research Project, *Report on Research for 1956–57*, Cambridge 1957, hectographed, p. 71. I am indebted to Strout for several sources cited in the following pages.

[51] Donald Wallace, writing in 1937, states, "With a few exceptions, which will be noted in due course, no fundamental alterations of process or apparatus have occurred since the birth of the industry." (*Market Control*, p. 7). Similarly, speaking about the Bayer process since 1928, Mr. Wilson, president of Alcoa, testified, "[the Bayer process] has had only such changes as result in material handling and general processing equipment." (*Remedy Record*, p. 975).

baked in the reduction pot and continuously restored by additions of a carbon mixture. This process is considerably cheaper than using a pre-baked anode.[52] The continuous digestion, the lime and soda, and the starch processes were significant modifications of the Bayer process for converting bauxite into alumina. The Soderberg process was invented by a Norwegian producer and the Bayer process modifications by Alcoa.

Aluminum is still produced by the Hall process discovered in 1887, and alumina by the Bayer process discovered in 1920. There have been rumors of revolutionary discoveries in the offing. For example, Reynolds has patented a process to extract aluminum directly from bauxite, thus by-passing the production of alumina.[53] The British Columbia Aluminum Company has announced the reduction of aluminum by long-wave electrical energy.[54] The Bureau of Mines, Alcoa, Harvey, and Anaconda have large research programs directed at the production of alumina from domestic clays.[55] Yet, except for brief press announcements of "promising" results, this research has been to no apparent avail, and the Hall and Bayer processes are likely to be used for years to come.

Continuous minor improvements have made these two processes highly efficient. For example, the Bayer process recovered on the average 95 per cent of the alumina in the bauxite ores even before the war and today the recovery percentage is 97 per cent.[56] Similarly, the electrical input per pound of aluminum was 12 kilowatt hours in 1926, 10 kilowatt hours in 1940, and 7.8 kilowatt hours in a plant constructed in 1954.[57] At the same time, the Hall and Bayer processes appear to have exploited fully the electrochemical knowledge that accumulated at the turn of the century. Processes that have had continuous minor improvements and were initially major advances in the state of the art are difficult to surpass.

[52] Department of Commerce, Business and Defense Service Administration, *Materials Survey: Aluminum*, November 1956, pp. VI 8–10.

[53] *Modern Metals*, September 1948, p. 48.

[54] *Ibid.*, March 1952, p. 18.

[55] For a history of the early efforts see John V. Krutilla, "The Structure of Costs and Regional Advantage in Primary Aluminum" (dissertation submitted to Harvard University, 1952) and for more recent discussion see *Modern Metals*, October 1953, p. 28; May 1953, p. 88; and December 1955, p. 92.

[56] T. G. Pearson, "The Chemical Background of the Aluminum Industry," Royal Institute of Chemistry, *Lectures, Monographs and Reports*, No. 5, London, 1956, p. 34.

[57] The last figure is for the Anaconda plant, built in 1954. Edwin O. Wooster, "A Description of the Anaconda Aluminum Plant at Columbia Falls, Montana," an address at the Colorado Mining Association, February 7, 1956.

What is required is another major increase in scientific knowledge comparable to that which made possible the Hall invention. Donald Wallace traces the Hall invention back to "scientific research and formulation of general principles governing the relations of electric currents to chemical changes . . ."[58] Such advances in scientific knowledge are the culmination of a series of scientific discoveries and are relatively rare events. For this kind of technical change, economics, at least the kind involved in the study of markets, is irrelevant.

Concluding Comment

The conclusions, as stated in each section, are not particularly novel. Most economists would agree that oligopoly is more conducive to invention than monopoly. The evidence here supports this proposition, although at the reduction stage the changes in market structure made no observable difference in the rate and nature of invention. The finding that even large firms focus their inventive activities in areas where the profits are relatively immediate and certain is not surprising, although there are few statements as to the limits of inventive activity of a firm, largely because few have posed the question.

The role of the equipment makers demonstrates that a substantial part of the technical change in one industry is likely to stem from progress of another industry. The importance of growth industries for particular historical periods, such as the automobile and rayon for the 1920's, is a common theme in economic history. There may well be industries that are less obviously major carriers of technical change, not only for a single historical period but more or less continuously, by virtue of their position in the economy. To generalize here, however, requires more knowledge than now exists of interindustry flows of technical change.

[58] Wallace, *Market Control*, p. 4.

Invention and Innovation in the Petroleum Refining Industry

JOHN L. ENOS

MASSACHUSETTS INSTITUTE OF TECHNOLOGY

AN INNOVATION is the combination of many different activities. Generally an invention is made and recognized, capital is obtained, plant is acquired, managers and workers are hired, markets are developed, and production and distribution take place. As the innovation proceeds the original conception may be altered to make it more amenable to commercial realities. Accomplishing these activities consumes resources. At any point in the sequence failure may occur, delaying or even frustrating the innovation.

In studying the petroleum refining industry I observed several processing innovations following one another in time and generating technological progress.[1] I then sought their origins in terms of the original ideas and the men who conceived them. In this paper I shall discuss the relations between the inventions and the subsequent innovations, focusing on the intervals between them, the returns to the inventors and innovators, and the changes in the proportions in which the factors of production in petroleum processing were combined.

Invention and Innovation in the Cracking of Petroleum

As it comes from the earth, crude petroleum is a varying mixture of hydrocarbons of different molecular weights. In addition to separating the hydrocarbons physically according to their properties—boiling range, combustion characteristics, etc.—refiners have found it profitable to process certain of the hydrocarbons chemically. Most of their efforts have been directed at altering the heavier and lower-priced components. Most significant have been those processes designed to derive motor gasoline from the heavy hydrocarbons. Those processes involve the chemical process of cracking, or the splitting of large hydrocarbon molecules into smaller ones. When produced under the

NOTE: The author wishes to thank Zvi Griliches for his comments on the original draft.

[1] These innovations are described in the author's Ph.D. thesis, "History of Cracking in the Petroleum Refining Industry: the Economics of a Changing Technology," Massachusetts Institute of Technology, June 1958. The major portion of the thesis is to be published as *Technological Progress in Petroleum Refining* (Cambridge, The Technology Press, 1961).

proper conditions, the cracked molecules are an excellent fuel in internal combustion engines.

The first commercially successful process to crack heavy hydrocarbons into motor gasoline components was introduced in 1913. Since then there have been eight more process innovations, comprising three waves, one in the early 1920's, another in 1936, and the final one in the 1940's. Each successive wave has yielded improved processes, which have generally displaced those from an earlier wave.

For each of these successful innovations, I attempted to select the one or possibly two inventions which first revealed the general ideas. It is always difficult, if not impossible, to follow an innovation back to a single source. Sometimes an innovation will include several new elements, each of which required an invention. Sometimes it is possible to find the germs of an invention in still an earlier work. The selection, therefore, is quite arbitrary, and the accuracy of the data questionable.

Cracking is almost as old as the oil industry. The phenomenon had been noticed in the 1850's and utilized from 1860 on in the manufacture of kerosene. In cracking to yield kerosene, the process was carried on at atmospheric pressure. In 1889, however, a patent was obtained by two English chemists, J. Dewar and B. Redwood, on cracking and condensing under pressure.[2] When pressure was used, the product was found to boil in the gasoline rather than the kerosene range. W. M. Burton, a refinery manager for the Standard Oil Company (Indiana), added to this and other earlier ideas the specification that a relatively narrow hydrocarbon fraction, commonly called gas-oil, be cracked, rather than the entire portion of crude oil boiling above kerosene. Gas-oil is that fraction of crude petroleum lying in the boiling range between kerosene and heavy fuel oil. Depending upon the type of crude petroleum, gas-oil will account for 30 to 50 per cent of its total volume. This specification, plus the design of the physical apparatus required to carry out the cracking process, was stated by Burton and his assistant, R. M. Humphreys, around 1910. In 1913 the Burton process was first applied by Indiana Standard and operated by them and later by others most profitably for about a decade.

Burton's process was limited in that it could not be operated continuously; the cracking retort had to be shut down every day or so to be cleaned out. Besides the technical limitations, the process was well

<hr />

[2] For a description of Dewar and Redwood's and other early cracking processes, see Carleton Ellis, *Gasoline and Other Motor Fuels*, New York, Van Nostrand, 1921. The early work is summarized in Kendall Beaton, *Enterprise in Oil*, New York, Appleton-Century-Crofts, 1957, pp. 345–46.

supported by patents and the right to utilize it was not widely granted. As a result, attention was given to developing a continuous thermal cracking process. Within a few years of 1920 four major and several minor continuous thermal cracking processes were introduced.

One of the major processes was the Holmes-Manley process, based upon the invention of Joseph H. Adams, an independent inventor, who in about 1909 conceived of a continuous cracking operation. His ideas underlay a commercial process, the development of which was carried out by R. C. Holmes and F. T. Manley, two refining executives of the Texas Company.[3] The Holmes-Manley process (it took its name from the innovators rather than the inventor) was installed commercially in 1920.

The second of the major processes was named after its inventors, Jesse A. and Carbon P. Dubbs. The former, like Adams, conceived of the idea of a continuous process, the latter of a recirculation of the hot uncracked material so as to increase the yield of gasoline. These inventions were made in 1909 and 1919, respectively; the first commercial application occurred in 1922.[4] The Dubbs process was promoted by a new process design firm, Universal Oil Products Company.

The third major process, the Tube and Tank, was the product of Esso Research and Engineering Company, then the Development Department of the Standard Oil Company (New Jersey). Again it was the concept of a continuous thermal cracking process that underlay the innovation; in this instance it was also an independent inventor, one who specialized in petroleum chemistry, Carleton Ellis, who conceived of the idea and made patent applications in 1909. The patents were subsequently purchased by Jersey in order to give protection to a process already well advanced in its development.

The final important continuous thermal cracking process was the Cross, invented and developed by Walter and Roy Cross, chemists who worked first with pharmaceuticals and later with petroleum. As in the case of the Dubbs process, a process licensing firm, Gasoline Products Company, was established to promote Cross's design. Unlike Universal Oil Products, this firm lasted no longer than the Cross process itself, becoming insignificant in the 1940's.

---

[3] The Holmes-Manley and the other continuous thermal processes are best described in E. H. Leslie, *Motor Fuels*, New York, Chemical Catalog Co., 1923. For a discussion of the cracking patents and the litigation that arose over them, see G. S. Gibb and E. H. Knowlton, *History of the Standard Oil Company (New Jersey), 1911–1927, The Resurgent Years*, New York: Harper, 1956, pp. 547–559.

[4] The Dubbs process is described in Beaton, *op. cit.*, pp. 241–246.

The four inventions, by Adams, Dubbs, Ellis, and Cross, are quite similar in nature. Each advanced the idea of continuous processing, although each called for different apparatus and operating conditions.[5]

The decade of the 1920's was spent less in developing new processes than in improving the equipment and expanding the scale of the conventional thermal cracking operations. However, in terms of almost any measure other than originality—reduction of costs, saving of resources, expansion of output—the improvements made in the processes subsequent to their initial application were as significant as the innovations themselves.

It was the next invention and innovation in the historical sequence which most savored of the heroic. By devoting himself and his fortune to the study of catalysis, a French inventor, Eugene Houdry, developed the first practical catalytic cracking process.[6] Commencing after World War I, Houdry carried out research into the nature of catalysis and its effect upon the cracking operation. It was not until 1927, however, that he first successfully produced motor gasoline from a heavy petroleum fraction. Like the inventors of the continuous thermal cracking processes, Eugene Houdry was not originally employed by an oil company. He differed from them in that he alone directed the subsequent development of the invention into a commercial process. In the early 1930's he sought financial support; with the firms that supported him—the Socony-Mobil and Sun Oil Companies—he established the Houdry Process Corporation. By 1936 the difficulties in the design of the equipment had been overcome to the point where a commercial installation could be made.

The Houdry process was semicontinuous in nature, each of the major vessels being operated in a cycle of reaction (cracking the gas oil) and regeneration (burning the carbon off the catalyst). Product flowed through the vessel only during the reaction stage. It was recog-

---

[5] During the decade 1910 to 1920 it was relatively easy to obtain patent grants covering advances in the cracking art. It is doubtful that today, with the standard of invention higher, all of the four individuals would have been given patents. It was left for the courts to adjudicate the relative merits of each in a series of patent infringement cases commencing with the installation of the first Dubbs unit and continuing through the useful life of the continuous thermal cracking processes, and for the innovating firms to form patent pools in order to avoid litigation.

[6] The major effect of the thermal cracking processes had been to increase appreciably the yield of motor gasoline from a given amount of crude petroleum. The major effect of the catalytic processes was to improve the quality rather than the quantity of gasoline. Catalytic cracking was, therefore, particularly opportune, for it was at this period that the advantages of high octane gasoline were being appreciated and incorporated in the design of automobile engines.

nized that it was not efficient to have a single vessel serve both functions because of the difficulty in obtaining the proper operating conditions and in synchronizing the flows. So the Houdry process was significantly altered to make it continuous; the result was Thermofor Catalytic Cracking or the T. C. C. process, first installed in 1944. The T. C. C. process and another derivative of the Houdry process, the Houdriflow, required many inventions, although none of them was as substantial a departure as Houdry's original one. The new idea underlying the T. C. C. process was the existence of two vessels, in one of which the reaction and in the other of which the regeneration were continuously carried out. In later versions of the T. C. C. and in the Houdriflow installed after 1950 the new idea was to elevate the catalyst from the regenerator to the reactor vessel not by means of an endless chain of moving buckets, as originally done, but by means of a gas lift. The two major inventions, the separate reaction and regeneration vessels and the gas lift, were achieved by members of Socony-Mobil Oil's research department aided by Houdry Process. The inventions were attributed to no single individual, and the patents were all assigned to the inventors' employers. Invention in the petroleum industry had become institutionalized.

When the Houdry process was recognized to be a very useful one, all the major oil companies other than Socony-Mobil and Sun Oil— Houdry stockholders—were faced with the choice of adopting it or developing their own catalytic processes. A group of them, led by the Standard Oil (New Jersey), chose the latter course and deliberately tried to invent around the Houdry patents. In the relatively short period of six years they and their associates developed a new process, Fluid Catalytic Cracking, so-called because it incorporated a fluidized catalyst bed. Like the T. C. C. process introduced two years later, it utilized separate vessels for reaction and regeneration. Also like the T. C. C. process, the Fluid process was the result of a cooperative research and development program. It is, therefore, very difficult to ascribe the invention to a group of individuals, let alone a single one. However, the original patent for the fluidized bed was taken out by an independent inventor and oil industry consultant, W. W. Odell. Odell's application for a patent on a process of producing reactions using a fluidized bed of powdered catalyst was made in 1929; in 1936 an application was made to renew the patent to apply the invention to catalytic cracking. The majority of the developmental work, however, was carried out in the five years, 1938–42, preceding the first commercial installation. Improvements have been made in the three continuous catalytic cracking processes—the Fluid, the T. C. C., and the Houdriflow. Today they account for nearly all of the gasoline made from heavy hydrocarbons.

I have described a series of inventions and innovations pertaining to the manufacture of motor gasoline from a heavy hydrocarbon material. These inventions and innovations occupied a period of approximately forty-five years from 1913 to the present and permitted the manufacture of products of higher qualities and greater yields at successively lower costs. The processes utilized first heat and pressure and then catalysts to promote the cracking reaction. They were initially noncontinuous and subsequently continuous in operation. In almost all cases the inventions were made by men close to the oil industry but not attached to the major firms.

The Interval between Invention and Innovation

An invention may be of immediate usefulness or it may be visionary, requiring great advances in technology and tastes before adoption. Similarly, innovation, consisting of many activities with varying ease of accomplishment, may be completed quickly or slowly. With such variety is it possible that the intervals between invention and innovation display any systematic pattern?

First, we might ask what the pattern might be in theory. Let us assume that each of the various activities or events which together comprise an innovation is independent of the others; that the events follow one another in sequence; and that the amount of time required to accomplish each varies randomly, following some common but unspecified probability distribution. The interval for innovation would be the sum of the times for all the events. In statistics the distribution of the sum of a series of observations approaches the normal distribution, no matter what the original distribution of the single events. Finally, if we assume that the number of events comprising the innovation are legion, then we can conclude that the distribution of intervals between invention and innovation will be normal.[7]

[7] If we were to consider not the interval between invention and innovation but the probability that, given the invention, the innovation would actually occur, we would derive a different theoretical distribution. As before, innovation is defined as the successful result of several activities: selecting an invention, securing financial backing, establishing an organization, finding a plant, hiring workers, opening markets, etc. If any one of these activities should not be accomplished, then the innovation will not transpire. Therefore the event, innovation, is the *product*, not the *sum*, of many independent activities, the product being the correct combination because the resultant (innovation)

TABLE 1

TIME INTERVAL BETWEEN INVENTION AND INNOVATION
FOR NINE CRACKING PROCESSES

Invention		Innovation			Interval Between Invention and Innovation (years)
Nature of Invention	Date Made	Description	Name of Process	Date of First Commercial Operation	
Distilling hydrocarbons with heat and pressure	1889	Batch thermal cracking	Burton	1913	24
Distilling gas oil with heat and pressure	1910				3
Continuous cracking	1909	Continuous thermal cracking	Holmes-Manley	1920	11
Continuous cracking "Clean circulation"	1909 1919	Continuous thermal cracking	Dubbs	1922	13
Continuous cracking	1909	Continuous thermal cracking	Tube and Tank	1922	13
Continuous cracking of gas oil	1915	Continuous thermal cracking	Cross	1920	5
Catalytic cracking of gas oil and catalyst regeneration	1927	Semi-continuous catalytic cracking	Houdry	1936	9
Fluidized bed of catalyst	1929	Continuous catalytic cracking	Fluid	1942	13
Moving bed of catalyst; regeneration	1936	Continuous catalytic cracking	T.C.C. (elevator)	1944	8
Gas lift for catalyst pellets	1937	Continuous catalytic cracking	T.C.C. and Houdriflow (gas lift)	1950	13

is zero (i.e., does not occur) whenever any one of the activities (e.g., financing) is not accomplished. If we assume that the activities occur in sequence, that each activity is independent of the preceding one, and that the probabilities of successful completion of the activities are drawn randomly from a single distribution, then the likelihood of the innovation occurring when a particular activity takes place is dependent upon the value of the likelihood reached previously, and the *change* in the likelihood of the innovation occurring is a *random* proportion of the previous value. This is called the law of proportionate effect, and a variable subject to this law follows the log-normal distribution. For a description of the genesis of the log-normal distribution, see J. Aitchison and J. A. C. Brown, *The Log Normal Distribution*, Cambridge University Press, 1957, pp. 20–23.

Having hypothesized a pattern to which the intervals between invention and innovation might conform, we shall now see how this compares with the actual pattern. In my study of inventions and innovations in cracking I observed nine commercial processes. The data are summarized in Table 1. This affords us nine time intervals between the two events. In two cases, the Burton and Dubbs processes, I associated two inventions with each innovation. If we credit these as additional observations, we have a total of eleven. Giving each invention equal weight, we obtain for the sample of eleven observations an arithmetic mean interval between invention and innovation of 11.0 years and a median of 11. For the sample of nine observations the mean is 12.8 years and the median, 13. The standard deviations are 4.6 and 3.0, respectively.

Could these observations conceivably have been drawn from a normally distributed population of equivalent mean and standard deviation? With such a small sample it is difficult to answer this question with any degree of assurance. A visual comparison of the actual and theoretical distributions for the sample of eleven observations is given by Figure 1.

In selecting parameters for the theoretical distribution of intervals between invention and innovation we took those derived from our experimental results; we could equally well have calculated them from

FIGURE 1

Frequency Distribution of Intervals Between Eleven Inventions and Innovations in the Petroleum Refining Industry

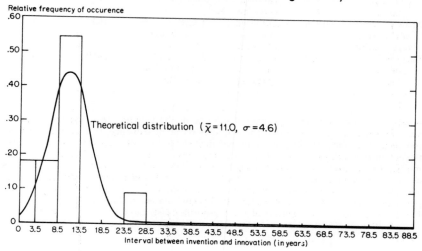

Relative frequency of occurence

Theoretical distribution ($\bar{x}=11.0$, $\sigma=4.6$)

Interval between invention and innovation (in years)

a larger sample drawn from the total universe of innovations. The sample presented in Table 2 was selected on the basis of ease of

TABLE 2

TIME INTERVAL BETWEEN INVENTION AND INNOVATION FOR THIRTY-FIVE
DIFFERENT PRODUCTS AND PROCESSES

Invention			Innovation		Interval Between Invention and Innovation (years)
Product	Inventor	Date	Firm	Date	
Safety razor	Gillette	1895	Gillette Safety Razor Company	1904	9
Fluorescent lamp	Bacquerel	1859	General Electric, Westinghouse	1938	79
Television	Zworykin	1919	Westinghouse	1941	22
Wireless telegraph	Hertz	1889	Marconi	1897	8
Wireless telephone	Fessenden	1900	National Electric Signaling Company	1908	8
Triode vacuum tube	de Forest	1907	The Radio Telephone and Telegraph Company	1914	7
Radio (oscillator)	de Forest	1912	Westinghouse	1920	8
Spinning jenny	Hargreaves	1765	Hargreaves'	1770	5
Spinning machine (water frame)	Highs	1767	Arkwright's	1773	6
Spinning mule	Crompton	1779	Textile machine manufacturers	1783	4
Steam engine	Newcommen	1705	English firm	1711	6
Steam engine	Watt	1764	Boulton and Watt	1775	11
Ball-point pen	I. J. Biro	1938	Argentine firm	1944	6
Cotton picker	A. Campbell	1889	International Harvester	1942	53
Crease-resistant fabrics	Company scientists	1918	Tootal Broadhurst Lee Company, Ltd.	1932	14
DDT	Company chemists	1939	J. R. Geigy Co.	1942	3
Electric precipitation	Sir O. Lodge	1884	Cottrell's	1909	25
Freon refrigerants	T. Midgley, Jr. and A. L. Henne	1930	Kinetic Chemicals, Inc. (General Motors and Du Pont)	1931	1
Gyro-compass	Foucault	1852	Anschütz-Kaempfe	1908	56
Hardening of fats	W. Normann	1901	Crosfield's of Warrington	1909	8
Jet engine	Sir F. Whittle	1929	Rolls Royce	1943	14
Turbo-jet engine	H. von Ohain	1934	Junkers	1944	10
Long playing record	P. Goldmark	1945	Columbia Records	1948	3
Magnetic recording	V. Poulsen	1898	American Tele-graphone Co.	1903	5
Plexiglas, lucite	W. Chalmers	1929	Imperial Chemical Industries	1932	3

(continued)

TABLE 2 (concluded)

	Invention			Innovation		Interval Between Invention and Innovation (years)
Product	Inventor	Date		Firm	Date	
Nylon	W. H. Carothers	1928		Du Pont	1939	11
Power steering	H. Vickers	1925		Vickers, Inc.	1931	6
Radar	Marconi; A. H. Taylor and L. Young	1922		Société Francaise Radio Électrique	1935	13
Self-winding watch	J. Harwood	1922		Harwood Self-Winding Watch Co.	1928	6
Shell moulding	J. Croning	1941		Hamburg foundry	1944	3
Streptomycin	S. A. Waksman	1939		Merck and Co.	1944	5
Terylene, dacron	J. R. Whinfield, J. T. Dickson	1941		Imperial Chemical Industries, Du Pont	1953	12
Titanium reduction	W. J. Kroll	1937		U.S. Government Bureau of Mines	1944	7
Xerography	C. Carlson	1937		Haloid Corp.	1950	13
Zipper	W. L. Judson	1891		Automatic Hook and Eye Company	1918	27

SOURCE: Safety razor: G. B. Baldwin, "The Invention of the Modern Safety Razor: A Case Study of Industrial Innovation," *Explorations in Entrepreneurial History*, December 1951, p. 74.

Fluorescent lamp: A. A. Bright and W. R. Maclaurin, "Economic Factors Influencing the Development and Introduction of the Fluorescent Lamp," *Journal of Political Economy*, October 1943, p. 436.

Television: W. R. Maclaurin, "Patents and Technical Progress—A Study of Television," *Journal of Political Economy*, April 1950, pp. 145–153.

Wireless telegraph, wireless telephone, triode vacuum tube, oscillator: W. R. Maclaurin, *Invention and Innovation in the Radio Industry*, New York, Macmillan, 1949, pp. 15–16, 33, 59, 67, 74, 85, 112.

Spinning jenny, water frame, spinning mule, steam engines: P. Mantoux, *The Industrial Revolution in the Eighteenth Century*, 2nd ed., New York, Macmillan, 1927, pp. 220–223, 228–235, 241–243, 323–324, 327–336.

Remainder: J. Jewkes, D. Sawers and R. Stillerman, *The Sources of Invention*, London, Macmillan, 1958, pp. 263–410.

access to the dates of invention (the earliest conception of the product in substantially its commercial form) and innovation (the first commercial application or sale). The individual observations may not be wholly accurate and the total is certainly not comprehensive. Moreover, placing in one class different numbers of observations from different industries at different points in chronological time may produce bias, for such factors as the industry, its stage of development,

FIGURE 2

Frequency Distribution of Intervals Between Thirty-Five Inventions and Innovations in All Industries

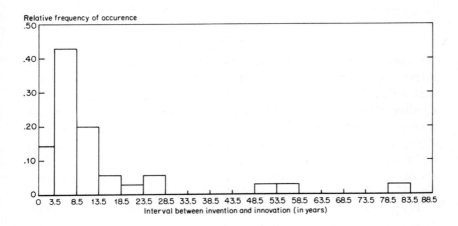

the size of the market, etc., may affect the interval between invention and innovation.[8]

The sample of thirty-five innovations yields an arithmetic mean of 13.6 years and a standard deviation of 16.3, an unlikely pair of statistics for a sample drawn from a normal distribution (see Figure 2). (If we were to eliminate the observation of the fluorescent lamp, the mean would be reduced to 11.6 years and the standard deviation to 12.3.) Looking casually at the data we can discern some variation among classes of innovations. Mechanical innovations appear to require the shortest time interval, with chemical and pharmaceutical innovations next. Electronic innovations took the most time. The interval appears shorter when the inventor himself attempts to innovate than when he is content merely to reveal the general concept. At any rate, whatever the reasons for the wide temporal variation, we cannot make any sophisticated comparison between the sample of all innovations and our own sample from petroleum refining using

[8] In mathematical terms we have assumed that the interval between invention and innovation is equal to a constant, a, plus an error term, u, where u is a random variable distributed normally about a zero mean. If u is not really random, i.e., if part of the variation in u can be explained by explicit factors, x, such as the industry, etc., then the x should be included in the relationship, too. The proper relationship would then be

$$y = f(a, x_1, x_2 \ldots x_n).$$

statistics applicable to normal distributions. The difference in the standard deviations of the two samples (13.6 vs. 16.3 years) does indicate, however, that the intervals between invention and innovation in the petroleum refining industry are less varied than those in industry as a whole.

Returns to the Inventor and the Innovator

We cannot draw any inferences as to what motivated the inventor merely by looking at the consequences of an invention, for the forces that influence behavior are complex and difficult to discover. Presuming, however, that the inventors hoped to make a profit from their inventions, we can see if these hopes were justified by the actual events. Again our sample of cracking innovations is not a perfect one, although this time it is not its small size that detracts from the generality of the results so much as the fact that all the innovations were very successful, this being the criterion for their selection.

Table 3 presents the relevant information; with the exception of the Holmes-Manley process for which the author made no estimates, the innovations cost in total roughly $60 million and returned roughly $2,200 million, with more still to come from the continuous catalytic cracking processes. The figures on returns from innovations are very crude, as one might expect. They are biased upward because all the returns from operating the processes are allocated to the innovations and none to the capital invested in the plant and equipment; they are biased downward for operating companies because the innovating firm's rate of profit was assumed to be equal to the royalty rate it charged others. These two biases somewhat offset each other, but the net effect cannot be estimated.

Individually and collectively the invention of cracking processes was a profitable activity. The amounts and variation in costs were not very great; only for Eugene Houdry was the sum substantial. The variation in returns, however, was wide, running all the way from the standard wages paid to engineers and scientists to many millions of dollars. The majority of the personal profits were made before 1930, for the subsequent institutionalization of research has deprived the corporate inventor of the prospect of a very large return.

Perhaps the most significant observation is the lack of correlation between what the inventor and the innovator received. In fact, the two sums are, if anything, inversely correlated. The explanation may lie in the size and the organization of the innovating firm, and in the

TABLE 3

PROFITABILITY OF SUCCESSFUL INVENTIONS AND INNOVATIONS IN PETROLEUM REFINING

	Invention				Innovation		
Description	Inventor	Estimated Personal Cost	Estimated Personal Returns	Process	Innovating Company	Estimated Cost	Estimated Returns
Distillation of heavy hydrocarbons under heat and pressure	J. Dewar and B. Redwood	Not available	Not available	Burton	Standard Oil Company (Indiana)	$200,000	$100,000,000 (less capital investment in plant and equipment)
Batch thermal cracking process and apparatus	W. M. Burton	None	Salary plus $433,333 bonus				
Continuous thermal cracking	J. H. Adams	Not available	Not available	Holmes-Manley	The Texas Company	Moderate	Large (less capital investment in plant and equipment)
Process and apparatus	R. C. Holmes and F. T. Manley	None	Salary				
Continuous thermal cracking	J. A. Dubbs	None	Salary $25,000	Dubbs	Universal Oil Products Company	$7,000,000	$140,000,000
"Clean circulation"	C. P. Dubbs	Small	Salary plus $17,500,000				
Continuous thermal cracking	C. Ellis	Not available	$225,000	Tube and Tank	Standard Oil Company (New Jersey)	$3,500,000	$300,000,000 (less capital investment in plant and equipment)
Process and apparatus	Employees of Standard Oil Development Company	None	Salaries				

(continued)

311

TABLE 3 (concluded)

| | Invention | | | | Innovation | | |
Description	Inventor	Estimated Personal Cost	Estimated Personal Returns	Process	Innovating Company	Estimated Cost	Estimated Returns
Continuous thermal cracking	W. and R. Cross	Not available	$1,500,000	Cross	Gasoline Products Company	$500,000	$4,500,000
Catalytic cracking	E. Houdry	$3,000,000 (Houdry and Associates)	$13,000,000	Houdry	Houdry Process Corporation	$11,000,000	$39,000,000
Fluidized bed Process and apparatus	W. W. Odell Employees of Standard Oil Development Company	Not available None	Not available Salaries	Fluid catalytic cracking	Standard Oil Company (New Jersey) and others	$30,000,000+	$300,000,000+ (less capital investment in plant and equipment)
Moving bed	Employees of Socony-Mobil Oil Company	None	Salaries	T.C.C.	Socony-Mobil Oil Company	$3,500,000+	$32,000,000+ (less capital investment in plant and equipment)
Gas lift for catalyst pellets	Employees of Socony-Mobil Oil Company and Houdry Process Corp.	None	Salaries	Houdri-flow	Houdry Process Corporation	$1,500,000+	$4,000,000+

SOURCE: J. L. Enos, "The History of Cracking in the Petroleum Refining Industry: the Economics of a Changing Technology," unpublished Ph.D. thesis, Massachusetts Institute of Technology, June 1958, Chaps. I–VI.

extent to which the inventor was associated with the innovation. The largest firms will receive the greatest absolute returns because they can apply innovations most widely. They are also the firms that are most likely to have permanent research and development organizations with salaried inventors. Their over-all returns, however, from research and development will not be as substantial as the history of the cracking processes would intimate, for they are paying the salaries of uninventive investigators as well.

We might expect that an inventor who helped to apply his invention would receive a greater return than one who was not associated with the innovation. Examining the cracking inventions, I found five inventors—Burton, Holmes and Manley, Carbon P. Dubbs, and Houdry—who also filled certain portions of the role of innovator; and eight—Dewar and Redwood, Adams, J. A. Dubbs, Ellis, W. and R. Cross, and Odell—who had little or no connection with the innovating firm. In the remaining four instances no single individual was responsible for the inventions; the ideas flowed from the research departments of the innovating firms. From the data in Table 3 it appears that those inventors who also took part in the subsequent innovations did receive greater returns than the others, but again the sample is so small that little confidence can be placed in the conclusion.

Changes in Factor Proportions

In an economy, scarce resources are allocated so as to satisfy conflicting and limitless needs. Through invention, a given output of product can be produced with a smaller total consumption of resources. Invention, by saving resources over-all, increases satisfaction and justifies itself.

One way of saving resources is to economize simultaneously on each of the factors of production in such a way that factor proportions remain unchanged. An invention of this nature would permit the same amount of product to be made with less of factor A, less of B, less of C, and so on, all in the same proportion. The greater the total saving, the more profitable the invention. If the invention has negligible effect on the total demand for any of the factors of production or if factor supply elasticities are all equal, then there will be no changes in the distribution of income.

The second way of saving resources through inventions is to substitute abundant resources for those which are scarce. In this case, factor proportions are changed. It is possible that less of each of the factors may be used; it is equally possible that more of the abundant resources may be used than before, together with less of the scarce ones. If the former, the invention will surely be adopted; if the latter, it will be adopted only if total costs of production are reduced. The money saved by economizing on the scarce factors must more than offset the increase in cost consequent upon using more of the abundant factors.

It might be well to define "abundant" and "scarce" precisely. A scarce factor is one whose cost is expected in the future to increase relative to that of the other factors. This could be a function of present supply elasticities. Assuming no change in the supply schedules through time, the scarce factor is the one with the more inelastic supply schedule. The relatively rising cost may also result from changing conditions on the supply side of the factor, i.e. increasingly inelastic supply schedules through time.

If relative factor prices are expected to change in the future, for whatever reason, new techniques would be developed which would substitute the abundant factor for the scarce one. For example, if in the future the price of labor is expected to rise relative to that of capital, we would argue that invention would proceed in the direction of substituting capital for labor.

Theoretically, this argument is indisputable. The important point, however, is whether or not it is consequential. If it is, the direction of invention in the future can be predicted with some accuracy. Quite easily, one can prognosticate future rates of growth for the various factors of production. In the United States, for example, it is believed that the stock of capital will grow faster than population will. The direction of invention, therefore, will be to substitute capital for labor.

Let us now see if abundant resources have been substituted for scarce ones, using data from four of the cracking process innovations.[9] First we shall have to establish the trends in the appropriate factor prices. The inputs to petroleum cracking are raw materials, labor, capital, and fuel. In Table 4 price series for these factors are given first on an index number basis and then relative to labor. The labor price series is derived from various wage statistics on the average

---

[9] Because several of the nine cracking innovations were very similar in terms of factor consumption and costs, we have only four entirely different sets of conditions. In their economic aspects the four continuous thermal cracking processes—Holmes-Manley, Dubbs, Tube and Tank, and Cross—were almost identical, particularly toward the end of their sway, as are the three continuous catalytic cracking processes today.

hourly rate paid to refinery workers. The fuel price is equal to the cost of heavy fuel oil; that of raw material, to the cost of gas-oil. Two different price series are tabulated for capital: one was derived from statistics on the average rate of return on investment for the petroleum industry as a whole, and the other from the cost of construction of refinery equipment. The assumption underlying all the price series is that additional resources may be acquired at a cost equal to the return on the outstanding stock.

Looking at Table 4, we observe that the price of labor has risen substantially since 1913, the rise being interrupted only once, during the depression of the 1930's. The other price series moved more erratically, although some trends can be discovered. The price of fuel fluctuated at a relatively high level until the mid-1920's, after which it declined substantially until 1931. From 1931 until 1948 it rose steadily at about the same rate as the price of labor. It declined until 1953 and then appeared to be rising again. For raw material price we have no observations for the period from 1923 to 1938, but during the other years the general direction of movement was similar to that of the price of fuel, although the fluctuations were milder. Our two series for the price of capital show different behavior. That based on construction costs follows the same general pattern as labor, although with milder fluctuations. The series based on rate of return shows the greatest fluctuations of all, the price varying from a negative figure in 1931—revealing losses for the industry as a whole—to a figure in 1948 over four times that achieved in 1939. It reveals a temporal pattern similar to that of the fuel price, fluctuating at high levels from 1919 to 1922, declining rapidly until 1931, rising steadily until a peak was reached in 1948, and remaining at a relatively high level thereafter.

Relative to labor, all prices fell from 1913 to the middle of the depression, those of raw material and fuel falling most rapidly, that of capital less so. Excepting the war years, from the middle of the 1930's until about 1948 construction cost rose less rapidly than labor whereas the price of fuel and the rate of return rose more rapidly, the latter rising the most rapidly of all. During the 1940's the price of raw material rose relative to wage rates at a rate midway between those of fuel and capital. Since 1948 the relative prices of all three factors have declined relative to labor, rate of return the most, construction cost the least.

We shall now turn from changes in relative factor prices to changes

TABLE 4

CHANGES IN FACTOR PRICES, PETROLEUM REFINING, 1913–55

YEAR	Labor	Fuel	PRICE INDEXES (1939 = 100) Raw Material	Capital Con-struction	Rate of Return	Fuel	RELATIVE PRICES (ratios, relative to labor) Raw Material	Capital Con-struction	Rate of Return
1913	n.a.	119	79.6	52.1	n.a.	n.a.	n.a.	n.a.	n.a.
1914	n.a.	108	78.6	47.3	n.a.	n.a.	n.a.	n.a.	n.a.
1915	30.2	111	83.9	49.2	n.a.	3.7	2.7	1.6	n.a.
1916	30.4	161	134	62.7	n.a.	5.3	4.4	2.1	n.a.
1917	47.8	155	180	84.9	n.a.	3.2	3.8	1.8	n.a.
1918	58.9	203	210	99.3	n.a.	3.4	3.6	1.7	n.a.
1919	73.0	88	220	105.6	268	1.2	3.0	1.4	3.7
1920	83.0	400	400	139.1	292	4.8	4.8	1.7	0.27
1921	85.0	167	181	104.0	22.6	2.0	2.1	1.2	0.27
1922	77.5	138	175	82.7	134	1.8	2.2	1.1	1.7
1923	78.5	n.a.	175	99.7	116	n.a.	2.2	1.3	1.5
1924	79.0	272	n.a.	103.9	137	3.4	n.a.	1.3	1.7
1925	78.0	250	n.a.	101.0	200	3.2	n.a.	1.3	2.6
1926	78.0	174	n.a.	99.4	197	2.2	n.a.	1.3	2.5
1927	79.1	127	n.a.	97.5	92.8	1.6	n.a.	1.2	1.2
1928	n.a.	91.1	n.a.	97.8	174	n.a.	n.a.	n.a.	n.a.
1929	n.a.	77.3	n.a.	95.9	179	n.a.	n.a.	n.a.	n.a.
1930	n.a.	75.6	n.a.	91.8	80.6	n.a.	n.a.	n.a.	n.a.
1931	n.a.	42.0	n.a.	84.7	19.8	n.a.	n.a.	n.a.	n.a.
1932	n.a.	50.5	n.a.	73.9	20.2	n.a.	n.a.	n.a.	n.a.
1933	67.1	60.1	n.a.	74.0	27.0	0.90	n.a.	1.1	0.40
1934	78.0	92.3	n.a.	81.8	53.7	1.2	n.a.	1.0	0.69
1935	82.1	94.4	n.a.	81.8	96.2	1.1	n.a.	1.0	1.2
1936	84.7	92.3	n.a.	87.9	139	1.1	n.a.	1.0	1.6
1937	96.7	115	n.a.	97.4	185	1.2	n.a.	1.0	1.9
1938	100	107	115	100	90.7	1.1	1.2	1.0	0.91
1939	100	100	100	100	100	1.0	1.0	1.0	1.0
1940	101	120	98.4	101	122	1.2	0.98	1.0	1.2
1941	107	130	105	104	165	1.2	0.98	0.97	1.5
1942	118	135	108	109	124	1.1	0.92	0.92	1.1
1943	125	138	103	113	154	1.1	0.82	0.91	1.2
1944	130	138	103	115	183	1.1	0.79	0.88	1.4
1945	134	138	103	117	165	1.0	0.77	0.87	1.2
1946	148	169	123	131	202	1.1	0.83	0.89	1.4
1947	162	268	191	153	300	1.7	1.2	0.94	1.9
1948	185	348	274	173	424	1.9	1.5	0.94	3.3
1949	194	200	219	182	256	1.0	1.1	0.94	1.3
1950	200	233	234	191	287	1.2	1.2	0.95	1.4
1951	216	256	240	205	311	1.2	1.1	0.95	1.4
1952	228	171	230	213	270	0.75	1.0	0.93	1.2
1953	240	164	224	227	268	0.68	0.45	0.95	1.1
1954	246	186	236	235	241	0.76	0.97	0.95	0.98
1955	255	246	245	240	252	0.96	0.96	0.94	0.99

SOURCE: Labor, Fuel, Raw Material and Construction Price Indexes: J. L. Enos, "The History of Cracking in the Petroleum Refining Industry," Tables 1, 2, 3, and 4, pp. 509–516.

Rate of Return, 1923–1955: Rate of return on net worth for the petroleum industry, *Petroleum Facts and Figures*, American Petroleum Institute, 9th ed., 1950, p. 442; 12th ed., 1956, p. 341, changed to index numbers on the basis 1939 = 100. 1919–1922: Income after taxes as a percent of capital plus surplus for fifty-two large petroleum refiners, R. C. Epstein, *Industrial Profits in the United States*, New York, NBER, 1934, App. Table 6, pp. 622, 625 and 632, placed on a similar index number basis.

n.a. = not available.

in factor proportions. In order to take advantage of all the data on cracking, we shall look at the entire sweep of technological progress.

Let us arbitrarily divide technological progress into two phases, the alpha and the beta. The alpha phase will consist of the invention, its succeeding development in both laboratory and pilot operations, and finally its installation or production in the first commercial plant. At the end of the alpha phase it is in competition with the product of existing processes. Therefore it is possible at this stage to measure its performance in economic terms. The beta phase consists of the improvement of the innovation. Improvements can be of three types: the construction of larger units to take advantage of inherent economies of scale; the adoption of ancillary advances by other industries, and the increase in operating skill or know-how. The alpha phase is quite similar to Schumpeter's "innovation," for it is the innovator who carries the development of the process or the product through its first commercial application. The innovator may also carry the development into the beta phase by making additional improvements; equally likely, it may be imitators who recognize that the original design or operation is not necessarily the best. Schumpeter, by using the terms innovators and imitators, implied that the latter firms make less of a technical contribution. This is not necessarily so, for the beta phase of technological progress may be as significant as the alpha, especially in highly technical industries where considerable advantage can be gained from the skillful application of the art.

In Table 5 factor inputs and factor proportions for four different cracking processes are listed both at the end of the alpha phase, when the first commercial application was made, and at the end of the beta, when improvements virtually ceased. Since each process innovation in the sequence tended to replace immediately the process already in existence, the end of the beta phase of the existing process was caused by and was coincidental with the end of the alpha phase of the new one.

TABLE 5

CHANGES IN FACTOR PROPORTIONS, FOUR CRACKING PROCESSES, 1913–55

Process		Consumption of Inputs (per 100,000 ton-miles of transportation output)				Index Numbers (Houdry alpha phase = 100)				Factor Proportions (ratios, relative to labor)		
Name	Phase in Process History[a]	Labor (man hours)	Fuel (10^8 BTUs)	Raw Material (000 gallons)	Capital (current dollars)	Labor	Fuel	Raw Material	Capital	Fuel	Raw Material	Capital
Burton	End of Alpha (1913)	56.0	28.9	13.6	65.5	1190	993	209	244	0.84	0.18	0.21
	End of Beta (1922)	9.1	15.6	8.4	50.6	194	538	129	189	2.8	0.66	0.97
Tube and Tank	End of Alpha (1922)	12.3	12.6	8.9	34.8	262	434	138	130	1.65	0.53	0.50
	End of Beta (1938)	4.4	9.0	5.2	18.7	94	310	80	70	3.3	0.85	0.74
Houdry	End of Alpha (1938)	4.7	2.9	6.5	26.8	100	100	100	100	1.0	1.0	1.0
	End of Beta (1942)	n.a.	n.a.	n.a.	n.a.	n.a.	n.a.	n.a.	n.a.	n.a.	n.a.	n.a.
Fluid catalytic cracking	End of Alpha (1942)	0.8	6.6	4.8	16.7	17	228	74	62	13	4.4	3.6
	Mid-Beta (1955)	0.4	2.2	3.5	25.0	8.5	76	54	93	8.9	6.4	10

SOURCE: J. L. Enos, "The History of Cracking in the Petroleum Refining Industry: the Economics of a Changing Technology," unpublished Ph.D. thesis, Massachusetts Institute of Technology, June 1958, Tables 1, 8, 12 and 13, pp. 613, 627, 634, and 636.

n.a. = not available.

[a] Alpha phase is from invention to first commercial application: beta phase is improvement of the innovation.

One conclusion that we can draw from the data in Table 5 is that the beta phase is as significant in its economic effects as is the alpha. There appear to be greater reductions in factor inputs, per unit of output, when a process is improved than when it is supplanted by a better one.[10] Another conclusion is that technological progress has achieved an absolute reduction in each of the factors of production, the reduction being relatively greatest in the consumption of labor, least in capital, and intermediate in raw material and fuel. Taking the whole period 1913 to 1955, the ratios of factor consumption at the beginning to those at the end are 140:1 for labor, 14:1 for fuel, 4:1 for raw material, and 2.5:1 for capital. The over-all trend in factor substitution has been capital for raw material for fuel for labor.

When we examined factor prices, we were able to make only one generalization concerning trends in relative price changes for the entire period 1913–55—that the price of labor has risen relative to all the others. Comparing the trend in the relative price of labor with the trend in the relative consumption of labor, we find that they move in opposite directions, the former rising while the latter falls. The factor that increased most in price was the factor that was reduced most in use.

Although this generalization appears to hold for the complete act of technological progress, it does not hold for the alpha and beta components, invention-innovation and improvement. Comparing the alpha and beta stages of a single process, we find that in every instance except one (the consumption of fuel in the Fluid Catalytic Cracking process) the direction of process improvement was to substitute the other factors of production for labor. Comparing the alpha stage of one process with the beta stage of the earlier one, however, we find the contrary result. In two of the three cases (Tube and Tank vs. Burton and Houdry vs. Tube and Tank) representing six of the nine instances, the direction of invention-innovation was to substitute, relatively, the scarcest factor, labor, for the other factors of production. Invention-innovation may well be neutral in its effect upon factor proportions, while improvement consists of factor substitution. Only in the beta phase of technological progress is it the scarcest factor that is economized the most.

---

[10] This argument is developed to a greater extent in the author's paper, "A Measure of the Rate of Technological Progress in the Petroleum Refining Industry," *Journal of Industrial Economics*, June 1958, pp. 187–194.

Let us neglect labor and look at the changes in proportions and in the relative prices of the other factors. An assumption of perfect foresight about changes in relative factor prices on the part of inventors is too unrealistic; a better one might be that inventors, equipped only with past data and with imperfect memories, assume that relative factor prices will move in the future as they have in, say, the preceding decade. We shall make this assumption in the following comparisons.

Taking first the inventions and innovations, we find that the result of the introduction of the Houdry process was to substitute capital for fuel. In the ten years preceding Houdry's invention (1917–27), there was observable little change in relative factor prices of the two, both series fluctuating widely. The result of the introduction of the Fluid process was to substitute fuel for raw material for capital. Odell's invention of the fluidized bed was made in 1929; again no trend is evident in relative factor prices for the preceding decade. The substitution of one factor for another took place in spite of little change in relative factor prices.

Perhaps we would have better results if we took process improvements. During the period 1922–38 when the Tube and Tank and the other continuous thermal cracking processes were pre-eminent, the reduction in the consumption of the factors was greatest for fuel and less (about equally) for raw material and capital. Looking at movements of relative factor prices in the earlier period 1915–27 we find it difficult to generalize, although it does seem probable from the data that the price of fuel did not increase relative to the other two factors. During the period 1942–55, in the Fluid and other continuous catalytic cracking processes capital was being substituted for raw material for fuel. The trend of relative factor prices in the period 1932–45 was such that the price of fuel was rising relative to raw material. Based on substituting abundant for scarce resources, the predicted substitution would be raw material for fuel. In this case the prediction is correct. Because the trend in the relative price of capital differs depending upon which index we use, rising relative to fuel if rate of return is used as the measure of the price of capital, falling if construction cost is used, we cannot make any prediction as to the direction of substitution.

In conclusion, it may be possible in the case of process improvement to predict from earlier trends in relative factor prices the direction in which factor substitution will occur. In petroleum refining the data do not refute the hypothesis that improvement of techniques is achieved partially through the substitution of abundant for scarce resources. We are not justified, however, in extending this idea to radically new techniques, as changes in factor proportions necessitated by innovation bear little relationship to previous trends in relative factor prices. In process innovations it is probably the technological factors that are governing.

The Origins of the Basic Inventions Underlying Du Pont's Major Product and Process Innovations, 1920 to 1950

WILLARD F. MUELLER

UNIVERSITY OF WISCONSIN

E. I. du Pont de Nemours & Company is often cited as the leading and most successful practitioner of basic and applied research. In truth, its success as an innovator has made it a symbol of the deterministic doctrine which makes firm bigness a prerequisite to inventive capacity and success.

Its officials characterize Du Pont both as a firm grown big because of inventive superiority, and as an example of inventive superiority made possible by firm bigness. Du Pont President Crawford H. Greenewalt pointed this out when he said, "For the Du Pont Company and I believe this is also true for the chemical industry, I can say categorically that our present size and success have come about through the new products and new processes that have been developed in our laboratories."[1] Greenewalt further contended that Du Pont's record of laboratory accomplishment is itself based on Du Pont's size. As he puts it, the tasks confronting the firm a hundred years ago "were not very big, and a relatively small pool of talents and abilities could accomplish them. Today the tasks are correspondingly larger, and they require a larger pool of talent to accomplish them."[2]

Du Pont, of course, has been an innovator in many fields. But what were the sources of the basic inventions underlying its *most important* product and process innovations? Were these innovations rooted, as President Greenewalt contends, on "the new products and processes that have been developed in [its] laboratories?" It is the purpose of this paper to attempt to answer this question. Perhaps doing so will provide some additional empirical content for our scantily filled economic boxes labeled, "sources of inventive activity."

To answer this question for Du Pont, I shall restrict my analysis to the company's experience during the period 1920–50. For nearly all of its more than 100 years of growth before 1920 Du Pont was a manufacturer soley of explosives and related products. But shortly

---

[1] *Study of Monopoly Power*, Hearings before the Subcommittee of the House Committee on the Judiciary, 81st Cong., 1st sess., p. 546.

[2] *Ibid.*, p. 59.

after the turn of the century it began diversifying into various fields not directly related to explosives; and by 1920 it had taken great strides toward becoming a diversified chemical firm.[3]

The definition of what constitutes important inventive activity at first sight seems beyond workable construction. It is impossible to state categorically where unimportant inventions end and important ones begin. All scientific inquiry and progress involve a continuing accretion of knowledge, with each piece of knowledge seemingly inseparably related to prior accumulations of knowledge.

But in reality we generally can identify inventions as being distinct from mere additional accumulations of scientific knowledge, because they result in something of unique economic importance. Thus, my definition of an important invention is based on its economic result. If a product or process resulting from a unique organization of scientific knowledge has been of significant economic importance to Du Pont's growth, I have considered it as being based on an important invention. I shall further avoid problems of defining what constitutes a really important Du Pont product or process by limiting the analysis to products and processes that have been of obvious economic significance.

It should be noted that this paper is concerned mainly with the inventions underlying *new* products and production processes, and *major* changes in existing products and processes. I recognize that the cumulative effects of many small changes in existing products and processes may have an important aggregate effect on product quality and production costs. The reason for placing special emphasis on the social and economic processes generating *new* products and processes is that they involve a basic breakthrough in scientific knowledge—often based on fundamental research—upon which subsequent product and process improvements are based. The justification for investigating the sources of technology underlying *new* products is that different economic and social forces may be responsible for generating the inventions underlying new products than for bringing about product improvements.

Table 1 lists twenty-five of Du Pont's most important product and process innovations from 1920 to 1950, and is based largely upon a similar list appearing in the October 1950 issue of *Fortune*.[4] All the

---

[3] For a discussion of its growth before 1920 and the sources of the technology underlying that growth see Willard F. Mueller, "Du Pont: A Study in Firm Growth" (unpublished Ph.D. dissertation, Vanderbilt University, 1955).

[4] *Fortune's* list included forty-eight products and processes illustrating Du Pont's

TABLE 1

DU PONT'S TWENTY-FIVE MOST IMPORTANT PRODUCT AND PROCESS INNOVATIONS
BETWEEN 1920 AND 1950, RATED FROM 1 TO 5 ON THE BASIS OF THEIR
RELATIVE COMMERCIAL AND TECHNOLOGICAL IMPORTANCE

Year Introduced	Product and Process Innovations	Relative Importance (5 Denotes Greatest Importance)
1920	Viscose rayon	4[a]
1923	Duco lacquers	3
1923	Tetraethyl lead (bromide process)	3[a]
1924	Tetraethyl lead (chloride process)	2[a]
1924	Cellophane	4[a]
1926	Synthetic ammonia	1
1927	Moistureproof cellophane	3
1927	Methanol and higher alcohols	1
1928	Dulux finishes	2
1929	Acetate rayon	3[a]
1931	Freon	2
1931	Neoprene	2
1931	Titanium pigments	2[a]
1934	Cordura high-tenacity rayon	2
1936	Lucite acrylic resin	1
1939	Nylon	5
1940	Polyvinyl acetate and alcohols	1
1941	Rutile titanium dioxide	1
1942	Fermate fungicides	1
1943	Teflon	1
1944	Alathon polyethylene plastic	1
1948	Orlon acrylic fiber	3
1948	Titanium metal	3[a]
1949	Polymeric color film	1
1949	Fiber V (Dacron)	3[a]

SOURCE: Based on "The Story of the Greatest Chemical Aggregation in the World: Du Pont," *Fortune*, October 1950, p. 114, except for viscose rayon, tetraethyl lead (chloride process), plain cellophane, acetate rayon, and titanium pigments which were added by the author.

[a] This is the author's estimate of the relative importance of these products and processes. In all other cases the relative importance is that given each product by *Fortune*.

"research and development record for three decades: 1920–49" ("The Story of the Greatest Chemical Aggregation in the World: Du Pont," *Fortune*, October 1950, p. 114). It rated each of these products and processes "with rough approximation" from one to six "on the basis of commercial importance and technical significance." Since little information is available on the items it ranked as least important (one), and since the significance of these items is debatable, the products and processes listed in Table 1 include only those ranked by *Fortune* as of two or above in importance. I have deleted one item, "improved X-ray film," included in *Fortune*'s "two" category, because no information about it is available and because according to Dr. James K. Hunt of Du Pont, "This product did not belong in quite the same category as the other items." (letter from technical advisor of Public Relations Department, Wilmington, Delaware, August 5, 1954). I have added five products not included in *Fortune*'s list: Viscose rayon, acetate rayon, and titanium pigments, because they are obviously more important than many of products and processes listed have contributed significantly to Du Pont's growth (in every case Du Pont was the first or one of the first American concerns manufacturing the product), and most are likely to continue to do so for some time. In 1948 these products and their closely related derivatives made up about 45 per cent of Du Pont's total sales. The circumstances surrounding the acquisition or development of these products and processes and their importance to Du Pont's growth are set forth below.

Product and Process Innovations

VISCOSE RAYON, 1920. Du Pont first became interested in rayon during its World War I diversification program. It conducted research to develop a nitrocellulose process for making artificial silk (later called rayon) but failed.[5] It also negotiated to purchase the highly profitable American Viscose Company, the country's sole viscose rayon producer, but it considered the price asked excessive.[6] Failing to develop its own rayon process and to buy the only rayon concern operating in America, Du Pont turned to Europe. In 1919 it executed an agreement with the Comptoir des Textiles Artificiels whereby the Comptoir gave exclusive rights to its viscose rayon technology to the newly created Du Pont Fibersilk Company. This company was owned jointly by Du Pont (60 per cent) and the Comptoir (40 per cent).[7] Only one other American concern (American Viscose) was in the field at the time Du Pont received access to patents protecting that valuable new product.

Viscose rayon has been one of Du Pont's major products ever since 1920. As late as 1948 rayon sales amounted to $102 million or about 10 per cent of total Du Pont sales.[8]

DUCO LACQUERS, 1923. According to Irénée du Pont, Du Pont accidentally discovered Duco Lacquer in 1920 while conducting research on photographic films. As he described it, on July 4, 1920, the power house was shut down shortly after a barrel of nitrocellulose

---

the products included in *Fortune*'s list; tetraethyl lead using the ethyl chloride process, because Du Pont probably would have been forced out of tetraethyl lead production had it not obtained access to this process; and plain cellophane as well as moistureproof cellophane, because without the first the second would have been impossible.

[5] *U.S.* v. *E. I. du Pont de Nemours & Company*, 118 Fed. Supp. 48 (1953), Testimony, p. 5343 ff. Hereafter this case is referred to as the Cellophane Case.

[6] *U.S.* v. *E. I. du Pont de Nemours & Company*, 126 Fed. Supp. 235 (1954), GX 1244. Hereafter this case is referred to as the Du Pont-G.M. Case.

[7] Cellophane Case, Tr. 5343.

[8] Cellophane Case, GX 577, p. 7323.

solution had been prepared in connection with research on photographic films. The shut-down prevented experimentation with the solution for forty-eight hours. When the experimenters resumed their work, "to their amazement the contents of the drum had become so limpid and so fluid that you couldn't cast it on a wheel."[9] This suggested to them that they might "put some pigments into [it] and make lacquers with very heavy pigment carrying power . . . and they found it would work, and that was 'Duco'."[10] The nitrocellulose lacquer was a great improvement over existing nitrocellulose finishes.[11] It was of special commercial significance because it reduced the time required to finish a car from days to hours.[12] Although accurate estimates of Du Pont's Duco sales are not available from published sources, such sales have doubtless run into millions of dollars annually since the mid-twenties.

TETRAETHYL LEAD (BROMIDE PROCESS), 1923. Thomas Midgeley, Jr. of General Motors discovered the ethyl bromide process for making tetraethyl lead.[13] Du Pont and General Motors made an agreement on October 6, 1922, whereby Du Pont was to build a tetraethyl lead plant with a daily capacity of 1,300 pounds. The agreement set the initial price of the chemical made by Du Pont at $2.00 a pound, which the parties felt was adequate to enable Du Pont to amortize the cost of its plant in one year. A Du Pont report on the "Origins and Early History of Tetraethyl Lead Business" stated that "the intent was plainly . . . to be that the contract should be 'a continuing one,' the Du Pont Company undertaking to produce exclusively for General Motors, and General Motors agreeing to take its full requirements from the Du Pont Company, except in the event of the latter's inability or unwillingness to produce the entire quantities required."[14] The first Du Pont tetraethyl lead was sold in February 1923, and by the middle of the year the product had gained public acceptance.[15]

TETRAETHYL LEAD (ETHYL CHLORIDE PROCESS), 1924. Du Pont had just succeeded in getting tetraethyl lead production under way when Standard Oil of New Jersey discovered a superior manufacturing process—the ethyl chloride process. President Irénée du Pont, recognizing

[9] Du Pont-G.M. Case, Tr. 2131.
[10] *Ibid.*
[11] Letter from James K. Hunt, dated July 30, 1954.
[12] "The Story of 'Duco' Nitrocellulose Lacquer," E. I. du Pont de Nemours & Company (mimeographed), p. 3.
[13] Du Pont-G.M. Case, Tr. 3525.
[14] Du Pont-G.M. Case, GX 773, p. 8.
[15] *Ibid.*

the superiority of Standard's process, wrote to Alfred Sloan of G.M. in June 1924 that "the ethyl chloride method will be found cheaper both as to construction cost and operating cost than the ethyl bromide method."[16] Had Standard manufactured and sold its own tetraethyl lead, Du Pont would have been in an inferior competitive position. Fortunately for Du Pont, however, it was able to make an agreement with Standard which gave it the right to the new process.[17] Between 1926 and 1948 Du Pont manufactured all of the country's tetraethyl lead. Its importance to Du Pont in recent years is indicated by its 1948 sales of tetraethyl lead which amounted to $30 million or about 3 per cent of total Du Pont sales.[18]

CELLOPHANE, 1924. Du Pont's association in rayon with the Comptoir des Textiles Artificiels was directly responsible for Du Pont's entrance into cellophane. During Du Pont's negotiations with the Comptoir on viscose rayon in 1919, a Comptoir official also introduced the company to a "transparent viscose film, known as cellophane." Cellophane was being manufactured by one of the Comptoir's associated companies, La Cellophane Société Anonyme.[19] La Cellophane had made cellophane since 1917, utilizing a process developed by Jacques E. Brandenberger, who in 1912 had begun producing a thin flexible cellulose film of the general type still manufactured today.[20] On January 6, 1923, Du Pont received an option from La Cellophane to acquire its rights to manufacture cellophane in North and Central America.[21] Cellophane has been one of Du Pont's most spectacular and profitable products.[22] By 1948 Du Pont's sales of it had grown to $74 million, or about 7.4 per cent of its total sales.

[16] *Ibid.*, GX 660.
[17] *Ibid.*, GX 675.
[18] *Ibid.*, GX 837.
[19] Cellophane Case, GX 1, p. 4.
[20] Although the origins of cellophane chemistry date back to 1846, it was not until 1892 that two English chemists, G. F. Cross and E. J. Bevan, developed the viscose method of reducing cellulose to a solution. By using an acid, they regenerated the cellulose solution into films of pure cellulose. Not until 1908, however, did Brandenberger make sufficient improvements in that process to make it commercially significant. He began producing his transparent viscose film, which he called cellophane, shortly after (*ibid.*, GX 28, p. 142).
[21] *Ibid.*, GX 392, p. 5429. The option provided that, in the event Du Pont became interested in entering cellophane manufacture, a jointly owned subsidiary should be formed with Du Pont owning 52 per cent and La Cellophane 48 per cent of its common stock.
[22] For a discussion of Du Pont's earnings in cellophane see, George W. Stocking and Willard F. Mueller, "The Cellophane Case and the New Competition," *American Economic Review*, March 1955, pp. 29–63.

SYNTHETIC AMMONIA, 1926. Du Pont got its first technical information in this field in 1916 when it acquired the American rights to the Birkeland-Eyde arc process of fixing nitrogen which had been discovered in Norway. Du Pont never used that process and took no further steps toward entering the industry until 1924. In that year it acquired the American rights to the Claude process from the Société Anonyme l'Aire Liquide of France, for $2.8 million. Using the process it built its first plant at Belle, West Virginia, in 1925. At about the same time it also acquired four American ammonia concerns—three distributors and one manufacturer. Although Du Pont expanded its position in the market through these acquisitions, its technology remained inferior to that of some of its rivals—notably Allied Chemical and Dye Corporation. After having tried and failed to get the German technology on synthetic ammonia, it obtained the American rights to the important Casale process by purchasing the Niagara Ammonia Company in 1927. That process was superior to the Claude process and Du Pont constructed an entirely new plant to exploit it. Beginning in 1929, Du Pont further buttressed its technical position in synthetic ammonia by a patents and processes agreement with Imperial Chemical Industries, Ltd., England's leading chemical firm. With technology from these various sources Du Pont developed a modified Claude-Casale process subsequently known as the Du Pont process.[23] No breakdown is available of the amount spent by Du Pont in developing its modified process and for plant investment.

MOISTUREPROOF CELLOPHANE, 1927. Shortly after beginning production in 1924, Du Pont recognized as cellophane's greatest defect its imperfect resistance to moisture.[24] In October 1924 Du Pont made its initial appropriation authorizing research aimed at developing a moistureproof process, providing for hiring one researcher and the expenditure of between $5,000 and $10,000.[25] By 1927 Du Pont had found a satisfactory moistureproofing process and began commercial production. In 1929 it received its basic patents covering that development. The importance of the process is indicated by the fact that in recent years the bulk of Du Ponts' cellophane sales (80 per cent in 1948) have been of the moistureproof variety.

---

[23] In 1948 sales of Du Pont's ammonia department amounted to $88 million (Du Pont-G.M. Case, DP 445). These sales included some products other than synthetic ammonia products, and no breakdown is possible. However, it seems quite likely that synthetic ammonia products constituted the greater part of these sales.

[24] Cellophane Case, DX 388.

[25] *Ibid.*, DX 393-94.

Uncertain that its initial moistureproof patents could be enforced against potential entrants into the cellophane field, Du Pont took steps to strengthen its moistureproof patent position. By 1930 it had patented "various modifications of moistureproof cellophane." A Du Pont employee explained that the patents were taken out "not only to strengthen the company's patent position, but also in an endeavour to prevent competition by a similar article."[26]

Between 1930 and 1934 Du Pont took additional steps to bolster its patent position when it authorized a research project for this specific purpose. In 1934 President Yerkes of Du Pont Cellophane reported on the success of this project.

> This work was undertaken as a defensive program in connection with protecting broadly by patents the field of moistureproofing agents other than waxes which were the only class of material disclosed in our original cellophane patents. The investigation on this subject did in fact lead to the discovery of a number of classes of materials which could serve equally well for moistureproofing agents, whether in lacquers or in other vehicles. Each of these classes has been made the subject of a patent . . . altogether 13 patent applications are being written as a result of the work done under this project, all in view of strengthening our Moistureproof Cellophane patent situation.[27]

The $19,503 spent on that research project was very likely more than was spent for the total research involved in developing the initial methods of moistureproofing cellophane used by Du Pont. As noted above, the first authorization for the earlier research was made in October 1924 with an appropriation between $5,000 and $10,000. That total expenditures for developing the initial process were not great is indicated by the fact that total "technical activities expenses," which included all types of technical work designed to improve production and process, came to only $32,048 during 1925 and 1926.[28]

Although Du Pont did not incur any of the expenses involved in the basic research leading to the invention of cellophane, and only modest expenses in developing its moistureproof process, it did spend large amounts in subsequent years for "research" aimed at cutting

---

[26] Letter from the general manager of the Cellophane Department to W. S. Carpenter, Jr., Chairman of the Board of Du Pont Cellophane, August 26, 1938 (*ibid.*, GX 2469, p. 3161).

[27] *Ibid.*, GX 488, p. 6478.

[28] *Ibid.*, DX 387.

manufacturing costs and improving quality. The company estimates that between 1924 and 1950 it spent $24,361,065 on cellophane research and technical development.[29] Of this sum, almost 99 per cent was spent after 1929 and 75 per cent after 1939. Although no breakdown is given of how all that money was spent, in 1935 about 26 per cent of the cellophane research budget of $588,372 was spent on chemical control, 66 per cent on product and process improvements, and 7 per cent on the development of additions to established lines of products. None of that cellophane budget went for fundamental research.[30]

METHANOL AND HIGHER ALCOHOLS, 1927. Methanol was first synthesized by the great French chemist Sabatier in 1905. After the Germans developed synthetic ammonia shortly before World War I, another French scientist concluded that the principles employed in ammonia synthesis might be applied to synthesize methanol as well. His speculations proved correct and he was granted his first patent in 1921.[31] The Germans simultaneously developed a method for synthesizing methanol. In February 1925 the first German synthetic methanol arrived in the United States, and by May total American imports exceeded a quarter of a million gallons.[32]

Shortly after Du Pont learned of the French and German success in synthesizing methanol, it began work on a production process of its own. The close relationship between synthetic methanol and synthetic ammonia no doubt made Du Pont's know-how in the latter field helpful in developing a synthetic methanol process. After two years' concentrated work, Du Pont's efforts paid off in 1926 when it (accompanied almost simultaneously by Commercial Solvents) began producing the first American synthetic methanol.[33] When Du Pont hired Roessler and Hasslacher in 1930 it added somewhat to its methanol technology by getting access to the starch patents covering copper catalysts for the conversion of carbon dioxide and water to methanol.[34] Du Pont soon discovered that in making synthetic methanol it was possible to regulate conditions so that not only methanol

[29] *Ibid.*, DX 387.
[30] *Ibid.*, GX 490, p. 6502. The breakdown of its 1934 cellophane research budget was about the same as in 1935 (*Ibid.*, GX 489, p. 6490).
[31] Williams Haynes, *American Chemical Industry, The Merger Era*, New York, Van Nostrand, 1948, Vol. IV, pp. 170–171.
[32] *Ibid.*, p. 172.
[33] *Ibid.*, p. 176.
[34] *Ibid.*

but also other higher alcohols could be obtained, e.g. propanol, izobutanol, active amyl alcohol, and di-isoprohyl carbinol.[35]

DULUX ENAMELS, 1928. Dulux enamels represented a substantial improvement in resin base finishes. William S. Dutton, in his biography of the Du Pont Company, reported that the basic resin essential for making Dulux was discovered by General Electric scientists.[36] Du Pont acquired the rights to General Electric's discovery and carried it into commercial production. These finishes have been used most extensively in refinishing automobiles and as original finishes for refrigerators. No estimates of the relative importance of dulux sales are available, but apparently they have contributed significantly to Du Pont's finish business for many years.

ACETATE RAYON, 1929. Acetate rayon is a fundamentally different and in many respects a superior product to viscose rayon.[37] Before 1929 the Celanese Corporation was the only American concern manufacturing it. Since Celanese was selling its acetate rayon at twice the price of viscose, profits probably were very high.[38] At any rate, Du Pont began looking about for a means of entering that industry during the mid-twenties. It again turned to France. In 1927 it acquired the manufacturing and sales rights to acetate flake from the Société Chimique Usines du Rhône, and in 1928 similar rights to the cellulose acetate yarn process were acquired from the Société Rhodiaceta. By 1948 Du Pont's total acetate rayon sales amounted to $32 million, about 3 per cent of its total sales.[39]

FREON, 1931. Thomas Midgely of General Motors, who had discovered tetraethyl lead about a decade earlier, discovered a revolutionary refrigerant in the late 1920's,[40] subsequently called Freon. Although General Motors had initially considered manufacturing the product itself,[41] Du Pont's close kinship with General Motors apparently paid off again. In August 1927, General Motors and Du Pont formed a jointly owned subsidiary, Kinetic Chemicals, Inc., in

[35] "A Story of Progress," *Du Pont Magazine*, June 1939, p. 7.
[36] William S. Dutton, *Du Pont, One Hundred and Forty Years*, New York, Scribner, 1942, p. 300 n. *Fortune*'s study of Du Pont in 1950 also reported Dulux as not being a Du Pont original ("The Story of the Greatest Chemical Aggregation in the World: Du Pont," p. 114).
[37] Jesse W. Markham, *Competition in the Rayon Industry*, Harvard University Press, 1952, pp. 88–89.
[38] Haynes, *op. cit.*, p. 383.
[39] Du Pont-G.M. Case, GX 577, p. 7323.
[40] *Ibid.*, Tr. 3605.
[41] *Ibid.*, GX 838.

which Du Pont received a 51 per cent interest.[42] The importance of freon refrigerant is demonstrated by the fact that it has become the "almost universal refrigerant."[43] By 1944 Kinetic's sales amounted to $12 million.[44]

NEOPRENE, 1931. Neoprene, the first general purpose synthetic rubber made in this country, is another Du Pont original. Although Father Julius A. Nieuwland of Notre Dame University conducted the fundamental researches underlying neoprene,[45] he was "not even casually interested in the search for a satisfactory synthetic rubber," but in acetylene gas. The credit for applying his basic discoveries to synthetic rubber goes to Du Pont's brilliant chemist, Wallace Carothers, who also discovered nylon. Although public information is not available on Du Pont's neoprene sales, they undoubtedly have been substantial.

TITANIUM PIGMENTS, 1931. Shortly before 1920 American, Norwegian, and French researchers made the basic discoveries underlying commercial titanium compounds. But it was not until the late 1920's that titanium pigments—used chiefly in paints—became commercially important. In 1930 Du Pont recognized that titanium pigments were likely to replace lithopone to a large extent. To take immediate advantage of that new and growing field, in 1931 Du Pont acquired control of Commercial Pigments Corporation, one of the country's two producers.[46] Du Pont's subsequent growth in the field was rapid. By 1940 sales reached about $16 million.[47] No more recent sales information is available.

CORDURA HIGH-TENACITY RAYON, 1934. William H. Bradshaw, research director of the Du Pont Rayon Company, developed a stretched and twisted viscose fiber of exceptional strength.[48] Du Pont introduced

[42] *Ibid.*, GX 850. Du Pont acquired G.M.'s interest in Kinetic in 1949 for $9.7 million (*Moody's Industrials*).

[43] Du Pont-G.M. Case, Tr. 3923.

[44] *Ibid.*, GX 886.

[45] Williams Haynes, *American Chemical Industry, Decades of New Products*, New York, Van Nostrand, 1954, vol. V, p. 390. Du Pont acquired rights to Father Nieuwland's basic patents in 1931 (Du Pont-G.M. Case, Tr. 4963).

[46] Commercial Pigments had acquired its basic titanium pigments patents and process from the Société de Produits Chimiques des Terres Rares on March 24, 1927. *U.S. v. E. I. du Pont de Nemours & Company*, 63 Fed. Supp. 513 (1945) (National Lead Case, GX 175, p. 974, hereafter referred to as the National Lead Case).

[47] In 1940 total American sales amounted to about $40 million. Du Pont supplied about 40 per cent of this, National Lead about 50 per cent, and American Zirconium Company and Virginia Chemical Company the remainder (National Lead Case, DP 92, pp. 4389–92).

[48] Haynes, *American Chemical Industry, Decades of New Products*, Vol. V, p. 371.

the fiber, which it called cordura yarn, for cord tire fabrics. Du Pont classifies the result of that development as an important product "improvement" rather than as a new product.[49] Du Pont rayon tire yarn sales in 1948 amounted to $40 million or about 4 per cent of its total sales.[50]

LUCITE, 1936. Du Pont received the vital technology for methyl methacrylate plastic, which it introduced as lucite,[51] from Imperial Chemical Industries, Ltd., of England. Beginning in the early 1930's, Du Pont received from I.C.I. seven methyl methacrylate patents, covering methacrylate monomers, lucite molding powder, lucite dentures, lucite molder sheets, lacquers, finishes, and adhesives and cements.[52] Du Pont paid I.C.I. only $121,680 for these vital product and process patents.[53] The importance of lucite to Du Pont is illustrated by its post-World War II sales, which amounted to between $20 million and $40 million a year.[54]

NYLON, 1939. Nylon was solely a Du Pont invention and doubtless ranks as one of the most outstanding accomplishments of modern industrial chemistry and private-industry sponsored research.

Du Pont research that ultimately led to nylon began about 1928. The year before, under the direction of C. M. A. Stine, Du Pont initiated a program of fundamental research. In accordance with the primary objective of this program, which was to discover scientific knowledge regardless of immediate commercial value, Du Pont began a number of chemical explorations. One of these projects was headed by Wallace H. Carothers, who continued work he had begun at Harvard on condensation polymers.[55]

His early work at Du Pont yielded considerable fundamental

---

[49] Letter from James K. Hunt, August 3, 1954.

[50] Cellophane Case, GX 837.

[51] Lucite, which is called Plexiglas by Rohm & Haas, was used extensively during World War II in making bomber noses.

[52] *U.S. v. E. I. du Pont de Nemours & Company*, 100 Fed. Supp. 504 (1951), Tr. 3655 ff, hereafter referred to as the I.C.I. Case. Rohm & Haas, which had been engaged in methyl methacrylate research since the 1920's, applied for an American patent covering its discoveries in this field about the same time as I.C.I., thereby causing the Patent Office to declare an interference between these two claims. By 1935 seven interferences had been declared between Rohm & Haas and I.C.I. (representing Du Pont) claims. Rohm & Haas and I.C.I. settled these interferences on March 5, 1936 by agreeing to grant each other nonexclusive royalty free licenses under all their existing and future United States patents relating to the use, manufacture, and sale of acrylics and methacrylics. *Senate Committee on Patents*, 77th Cong., 2nd Sess., pp. 615, 685, 819–822.

[53] I.C.I. Case, DX 1532, p. 9160.

[54] *Ibid.*, Tr. 3655 ff.

[55] Testimony of Crawford Greenewalt, I.C.I. Case, Tr. 1881.

knowledge of polymerization (how and why small molecules unite to form "giant" molecules), which initially was only of "academic value."[56] Then, "quite by accident," one of his assistants made a fortunate discovery. President Greenewalt explained what happened as follows: "Well, one day one of Carothers' associates was cleaning out a reaction vessel in which he had been making one of those polymers, and he discovered in pulling a stirring rod out of the reaction vessel that he pulled out a fiber; and he discovered its unusual flexibility, strength, and the remarkable ability of these polymers to cold draw.[57] The discovery had obvious commercial implications for Du Pont, which already was in the textile business as a rayon maker. Although this particular fiber was not very strong or elastic and was softened by hot water, its discovery suggested that some related compound might possess characteristics suitable for producing commercial fibers.[58] There followed "a concentrated effort in the laboratory to synthesize a polyamide which might form the basis for a commercial textile fiber."[59] Carothers and his associates tried time and again, and at one time prospects were so dark that Carothers discontinued his investigations.[60] Fortunately, however, he resumed his search and on February 28, 1935, synthesized the superpolymer used in manufacturing the first nylon.[61]

The original nylon, polymer 66, was made in the laboratory by extruding a synthetic fiber through a spinneret improvised from a hypodermic needle. Du Pont scientists and engineers next tackled, during the following two years, "the development on a laboratory scale of the manufacturing processes for the intermediates, the polymer and nylon yarn, and the development on a semi-works scale of the chemical engineering data for the erection and operation of a large-scale plant."[62] Upon completing its semi-works plant and after pronouncing nylon commercially feasible, Du Pont announced on October 27, 1938, its intention to build a new commercial plant at Seaford, Delaware, with an annual capacity of 3 million pounds. Before the first unit of this plant began operating, late in 1939, Du

[56] James K. Hunt, "Nylon: Development, Physical Properties, and Present Status," Wilmington, E. I. du Pont de Nemours & Company, undated, p. 1.

[57] I.C.I. Case, Tr. 1881.

[58] Hunt, "Nylon: Development, Physical Properties, and Present Status," p. 2.

[59] E. K. Bolton, "Development of Nylon," *Industrial and Engineering Chemistry,* January 1942, p. 5.

[60] Hunt, "Nylon, Development, Physical Properties, and Present Status," p. 2.

[61] Bolton, "Development of Nylon," p. 6.

[62] *Ibid.*

Pont decided to increase its capacity to 4 million pounds;[63] and before the plant was completed, its capacity was increased to 8 million pounds.[64] Early in 1940 the company announced plans to construct a second plant at Martinsville, Virginia; and in July 1948, it opened a third plant at Chattanooga, Tennessee.[65] By 1948 Du Pont's nylon sales had grown to $120 million; and Du Pont estimated its 1948 earnings before taxes at $37.9 million on an operating investment of $83.9 million.[66]

Public statements on the costs and risks of bringing nylon to the commercial stage are, at best, misleading and commonly inaccurate.[67] But a Du Pont document made public in a recent antitrust case sheds considerable light on this question. In 1938 a representative from Imperial Chemical Industries, Du Pont's leading international patents and processes partner, made two visits to Du Pont for the specific purpose of studying the discovery and development of nylon. He reported to I.C.I. that Du Pont's research expenditures in the early years of nylon research "were relatively modest, but as promising indications evolved the pace was quickened."[68] According to this source, by the time Du Pont had reached the point where it could build a pilot plant, expenditures amounted to $787,000. The pilot plant, which was completed in 1938, was designed and built at a cost of $391,000.[69] Another "development" cost cited by this source was approximately $782,000 (about the same as that spent on all pre-pilot-plant research) for sales development.[70] I.C.I.'s representative

[63] Hunt, "Nylon: Development, Physical Properties, and Present Status," p. 4.
[64] Bolton, "Development of Nylon," p. 9.
[65] Hunt, "Nylon: Development, Physical Properties, and Present Status," p. 4.
[66] Cellophane Case, GX 577.
[67] Typical of the misrepresentations made of nylon's research costs is the following statement from *Time* ("The Age of Research," July 9, 1956, p. 75). "When Dr. Carothers found a way to simulate the long chain molecules found in natural silk, Du Pont applied his findings to the development of nylon, which reached mass production in 1939, after five years and $27 million spent on applied research."
[68] Imperial Chemical Industries memorandum from the chairman to Mr. Cushion, I.C.I. Case, GX 626, p. 2317. I believe the statements made by this individual can be accepted as an accurate account of the facts because of the close relations existing between these two concerns for about a half-century. There seems to be no reason to believe that Du Pont would have intentionally understated its research and development costs to I.C.I. After all, Du Pont wanted to impress I.C.I. with its value as a patent and process partner, and the record indicates the I.C.I. visitor was impressed. For a discussion of the close and continuing technical relations between I.C.I. and Du Pont, see Mueller, "Du Pont: A Study in Firm Growth," pp. 234–256, 318–324.
[69] These figures were originally expressed in pounds sterling. I converted them to dollars at the then current exchange rate of $4.89 per pound.
[70] *Ibid.*

concluded that "the total cost of research and development can thus be taken at [$1,960,000]."

The previously mentioned first commercial nylon plant, for which $8,600,000 was authorized for construction,[71] apparently did not represent much of a gamble or require great additional development expenditures. E. K. Bolton, Du Pont chemical director, later said of it, "Except in size, the Seaford plant was practically a duplication of the semi-works plant in all details. Each step of the process and the equipment for it had been worked out thoroughly on a pilot scale, and it was unnecessary to gamble with untried methods and equipment on a full-plant scale."[72] Moreover, the market development expenditure apparently indicated a satisfactory demand for nylon before work began on the full-scale plant. According to Bolton, "Hoisery manufacturers had evaluated the yarn and pronounced the stockings to be of commercial utility."[73]

POLYVINYL ACETATE, 1940. Polyvinyl acetate is used in manufacturing what is popularly known as safety glass. The resin formed from polyvinyl acetate is used as an interlayer in glass to prevent shattering. Du Pont received its basic patents for polyvinyl acetate from I.C.I., and has been manufacturing it since 1941.[74] Although available sources do not cite production figures, a company official claims it was one of the most important products Du Pont received as a result of its patents and processes agreements with Imperial Chemical Industries of England.[75]

RUTILE TITANIUM DIOXIDE, 1941. Because of this pigment's superior "hiding power and more concentrated capacity," it represented an important improvement over previous titanium pigments. Although hiding power had been increased consistently since titanium pigments were introduced, Du Pont's rutile titanium dioxide represented the first appreciable increase."[76] That important product improvement was the result of Du Pont's own research efforts, but almost simultaneously with its introduction by Du Pont, National Lead (Du Pont's only significant rival at the time) introduced a similar product as a result of independent research.[77] No information is available on

[71] Haynes, *American Chemical Industry, Decades of New Products,* Vol. V, p. 36.

[72] Bolton, "Development of Nylon," p. 9.

[73] *Ibid.*

[74] I.C.I. Case, Tr. 3664.

[75] *Ibid.*

[76] "Titanium—The Common Rarity," Public Relations Department, E. I. du Pont de Nemours & Company (mimeographed), Wilmington, February 1952, p. 4.

[77] National Lead Case, DP 70, pp. 43, 52.

the research and development costs of this product or on its commercial importance.

FERMATE FUNGICIDES, 1942. Fermate, named after the first and last syllable of its chemical name, ferric dimethyl dithiocarbonate, is a fungicide and beetle repellant, for use in protecting many fruit, vegetable, and flower plants. Du Pont presumably developed the fungicide in its own laboratories,[78] but no information is available on its development costs or sales.

TEFLON, 1943. This remarkable plastic is "resistant to the attack of chemicals that would destroy gold or platinum," and "is a highly efficient electrical insulation, even at high temperatures, and particularly at the high frequencies of television and other electrical equipment."[79] *Fortune* described Teflon's discovery as a "research accident" growing out of Du Pont's systematic research efforts.[80] According to that account, Roy J. Plunkett was working with tetrafluoroethylene in the hope that it might have useful refrigerating properties. After synthesizing some tetrafluoroethylene he stored it in a cylinder for a few weeks. When he opened the cylinder he discovered that some of the compound had polymerized. Thus, "Accidently, Dr. Plunkett had turned up the most heat-resistant plastic and the most inert organic compound ever discovered."[81] No information is available about the subsequent development cost. *Fortune* expressed the view that after the discovery of its polymerization, Du Pont "had no difficulty devising a commercial process."

ALATHON POLYETHYLENE PLASTIC, 1944. Polyethylene is one of the lightest and most versatile of modern plastics. Its uses are numerous and *Fortune* referred to it as "the fastest growing plastic on the market."[82] Among its best-known uses today are ice-cube trays, food boxes, flexible refrigerator bowls, cosmetics containers, and plastic bags.[83] Imperial Chemical Industries invented and developed polyethylene shortly before World War II,[84] and disclosed the invention

---

[78] News Release, Public Relations Department, E. I. du Pont de Nemours & Company, June 4, 1942.

[79] "Memorandum on 'Teflon,' Tetrafluoroethylene Resin," E. I. du Pont de Nemours & Company (mimeographed), Wilmington, June 1953, p. 2.

[80] "The Story of the Greatest Chemical Aggregation in the World: Du Pont," pp. 130–32.

[81] *Ibid.*

[82] *Ibid.*, p. 129.

[83] "Alathon Polyethylene Resin—Many Purpose Plastic, A Memorandum," E. I. du Pont de Nemours & Company (mimeographed), Wilmington, October 31, 1953. Alathon is the trade-mark name of the plastic.

[84] I.C.I. Case, GX 668, p. 2494.

to Du Pont under their patents and processes agreement. Upon learning of the great military importance of the plastic (used as an insulator in radar units), Du Pont immediately sent a mission to England to obtain the necessary technical information.[85] Soon after that, Du Pont began manufacturing polyethylene "entirely at the request of the United States Government and solely for war purposes,[86] I.C.I. having waived all claims for royalties on the plastic manufactured for war purposes.[87] After the war Du Pont received a formal license to manufacture polyethylene for commercial purposes, and up to May 31, 1950, it had paid I.C.I. royalties of $272,200 under that agreement.[88] Although Du Pont had conducted some independent work along similar lines, President Greenewalt pointed out that it could not have manufactured polyethylene without obtaining a license from I.C.I.[89] In 1948 Du Pont's polyethylene sales amounted to $1.3 million.[90]

ORLON ACRYLIC FIBER, 1948. Orlon is the second important discovery resulting from Du Pont's basic research in synthetic fibers. This fiber has outstanding resistance to sunlight, is quick drying, holds its shape, and is more resistant to outdoor exposure than any other preceding fiber.[91] Du Pont initiated its orlon research in 1941 when its rayon pioneering research section decided that acrylonitrile might polymerize into a good yarn.[92] These expectations proved well founded, and before the war ended it had turned out in a pilot plant some of the new fiber for limited use in the war effort. By 1947, after orlon's development had reached a point where full-scale production seemed warranted, Du Pont drew up plans for its first plant, costing about $17 million, located at Camden, South Carolina and with an estimated annual capacity of about 7 million pounds.[93] Even before operations began in October 1950, Du Pont completed plans to build a second plant (across the street from the first), costing about $25 million and with an estimated capacity of about 30 million pounds.[94]

---

[85] *Ibid.*, DX 1193 and DX 1194.
[86] *Ibid.*, DX 673, p. 2545 and DX 1249, p. 8100.
[87] *Ibid.*, DX 1197, p. 675.
[88] *Ibid.*, DX 2219.
[89] *Ibid.*, Tr. 1871.
[90] I.C.I. Case, Tr. 1580, DX 1205, pp. 7887–92.
[91] "Facts About 'Orlon' Acrylic Fiber and the May Plant, Camden, S.C.," E. I. du Pont de Nemours & Company (mimeographed), Wilmington, undated, p. 1.
[92] "The Story of the Greatest Chemical Aggregation in the World: Du Pont," p. 112.
[93] *Ibid.*, p. 106.
[94] *Ibid.*

No detailed breakdown of the research and development costs of orlon are available. President Greenewalt mentioned $25 million as the total cost of research, development, and initial investment. That included $5 million for bringing orlon from the research stage through the pilot-plant and market-development stages, and $20 million for the initial plant investment.[95] Another Du Pont source stated that "Du Pont has invested more than eight years of intensive research and development work, and an estimated $22,000,000 in 'Orlon'."[96]

TITANIUM METAL, 1948. The discovery and introduction of titanium metal may well rank with that of aluminum. This remarkable metal is almost as strong as steel although weighing 40 per cent less.

In 1943 the United States Bureau of Mines obtained access to a German-owned titanium metal process seized by the Alien Property Custodian. A little later the originator of that process, Wilhelm Kroll, who had fled the Nazis in 1940, joined the Bureau of Mines where he continued his work. Under Kroll's direction the process was improved and by 1946 the Bureau of Mines had a titanium metal pilot plant in operation.[97] After the Bureau of Mines published its report, "Metallic Titanium and Its Alloys" in 1946, a number of American manufacturers manifested immediate interest. Du Pont and National Lead, now the country's two dominant titanium dioxide manufacturing concerns, began working on commercial processes immediately. By September 1948, Du Pont announced that it had a pilot plant in operation.[98] By 1950, its capacity had grown to 55 tons and it accounted for the bulk of the country's production of 75 tons in that year.[99] In 1951, Du Pont completed its first semicommercial plant, thereby pushing production to 700 tons during 1952.[100]

Mr. E. A. Gee of Du Pont's Pigment Department testified that the company had spent more than $4 million on titanium research up to November 1953, and that at the time it was continuing its research at a cost of about $1 million a year.[101] Du Pont's total investment for

[95] Crawford H. Greenewalt, "A New Industry Comes to Town," Speech at the Opening of the May Plant at Camden, South Carolina, October 6, 1950, E. I. du Pont de Nemours & Company, p. 7.
[96] "Facts About 'Orlon'," p. 1.
[97] "Titanium: The New Metal," *Fortune*, May 1949, 124.
[98] *Ibid.*, p. 124.
[99] *Ibid.* Also, "Memo on Titanium." Public Relations Department, E. I. du Pont de Nemours & Company (mimeographed), p. 1.
[100] *Ibid.*
[101] Testimony before the Special Subcommittee on Minerals, Materials, and Fuel Economies, of the Committee on Interior and Insular Affairs of the U.S. Senate, November 23, 1953. Excerpts of testimony furnished the author by Du Pont.

research and initial production reportedly approximated $9 million as of that time. [102]

POLYMERIC COLOR FILM, 1949. Du Pont's polymeric film developed to compete with others used in the important colored motion picture film field, substitutes a synthetic polymer for a gelatin emulsion used in all other color films except Technicolor. The process, instead of dyeing the film, builds the color directly into the polymer.[103] This product is another first for Du Pont growing out of its pioneer work in polymers begun in 1928 by Carothers. However, although polymeric color film was included in *Fortune*'s list of important product discoveries, Du Pont still had not begun commercial production of it as of August 3, 1954.[104]

DACRON POLYESTER FIBER, 1949. Dacron fiber (first called Fiber V by Du Pont) possesses many qualities superior to those of any other fiber; for example, it is wrinkle resistant, even when wet, and has high resistance to stretch.[105] Du Pont introduced this new synthetic fiber commercially in the American market in the spring of 1953. Much of the basic chemistry underlying dacron goes back to Carothers' work on high polymers. Whereas Carothers first experimented with polyesters in his efforts to build giant molecules, he soon concluded that polyamides offered greater promise.[106] As noted above, his work in polyamides led to the discovery of nylon.

But while Du Pont concentrated on polyamides, English scientists made further investigations of polyesters. About 1940 Calico Printers' Association, Ltd., began research on polyesters in an effort to develop a synthetic fiber.[107] By 1941 they had prepared laboratory-scale quantities of polyethylene terephthalate polymer, called terylene, which could be used in making fibers, but World War II delayed further work on it.[108] Imperial Chemical Industries acquired Calico in 1947 and began pilot-plant production during 1948.[109]

When Du Pont learned about the new fiber from I.C.I. it "negotiated for the purchase of patent rights then owned by Calico Printers'

---

[102] *Ibid.*

[103] "The Story of the Greatest Chemical Aggregation in the World: Du Pont," pp. 130–31.

[104] Letter from James K. Hunt, August 3, 1954.

[105] "The Du Pont Company and Its Products," E. I. du Pont de Nemours & Company (mimeographed), Wilmington, May 1953, p. 11.

[106] "Dacron Polyester Fiber," E. I. du Pont de Nemours & Company (mimeographed), Wilmington, August 27, 1953, p. 2.

[107] *Ibid.*

[108] *Ibid.*

[109] *Ibid.*

Association, Ltd."[110] Du Pont subsequently received eight different basic patents relating to dacron from I.C.I. under their patents and processes agreement,[111] and proceeded to develop the processes necessary for its production.[112]

Dacron has proven of even greater commercial importance than orlon. Du Pont reports its total research, development, and initial plant investment in dacron at about $65 million.[113] Of this amount, it reports that it spent between $6 and $7 million before it was able to begin building its first commercial plant.[114] This presumably includes expenditures for original research, development, and pilot plant.[115]

Summary and Conclusions

Of the twenty-five important product and process innovations discussed above (which together constituted about 45 per cent of Du Pont's total sales in 1948),[116] ten were based on the inventions of Du Pont scientists and engineers. If we break down these twenty-five innovations into new products and product and process improvements,[117] we find that of the eighteen new products, Du Pont discovered five and shared in the discovery of one other (see Table 2). Of the seven most important product and process improvements, Du Pont was responsible for five.

[110] Mr. L. L. Larson, Textile Fibers Department, Du Pont Company. Talk before the American Association of Textile Technologists, New York City, May 2, 1951. Reprinted by Public Relations Department, E. I. du Pont de Nemours & Company (mimeographed).

[111] I.C.I. Case, DX 1549, p. 2999, DX 1543. Another Du Pont source states that Du Pont acquired the rights to dacron in 1946 ("The Du Pont Company and Its Products," p. 12).

[112] Emmette F. Izard, research associate of Du Pont's Film Department Research Laboratory, received the Jacob F. Schoellkopf medal for, among other things, his "contributions to the development of a process for the production of polyester fiber and film" ("News Release," Public Relations Department, E. I. du Pont de Nemours & Company, April 14, 1953).

[113] Andrew E. Buchanan, "The Outlook in Fiber Competition," Speech before the Denver Agricultural Club, May 25, 1953. Reprint by E. I. du Pont de Nemours & Company, p. 7.

[114] *Ibid.*

[115] If Du Pont followed the same means of estimating these costs as it did in the case of nylon (see above), they may also include initial sales promotion.

[116] Since Du Pont had not begun commercial production of "Dacron," "Orlon," and titanium metal in 1948, this may understate the present importance of the products and processes appearing in Table 1.

[117] This breakdown does not imply that the discovery of new products is necessarily more important than the discovery of major improvements in existing products or processes. Moreover, in some cases it is difficult to decide arbitrarily whether a particular discovery is a new product or an improvement in an existing one. Few products are ever completely new. The classification appearing in Table 2 is the author's.

TABLE 2

SUMMARY OF NEW PRODUCTS, AND PRODUCT AND PROCESS IMPROVEMENTS,
INTRODUCED BY DU PONT, BY SOURCE OF BASIC INVENTION, 1920 TO 1949

New Products	Original Source of Basic Invention	Product and Process Improvements	Original Source of Basic Invention
Viscose rayon	Other	Duco lacquers	Du Pont
Tetraethyl lead (bromide process)	Other	Tetraethyl lead (chloride process)	Other
Cellophane	Other	Moistureproof cellophane	Du Pont
Synthetic ammonia	Other	Dulux finishes	Other
Synthetic methanel	Other and Du Pont[a]	Cordura high tenacity rayon	Du Pont
Acetate rayon	Other	Rutile titanium dioxide	Du Pont
Freon refrigerants	Other	Fermate fungicides	Du Pont
Neoprene	Du Pont		
Titanium pigments	Other		
Lucite	Other		
Nylon	Du Pont		
Polyvinyl acetate	Other		
Teflon	Du Pont		
Alathon polyethylene	Other		
Orlon	Du Pont		
Titanium metal	Other		
Polymeric color film	Du Pont		
Fiber V (Dacron)	Other		

SOURCE: These products and processes are classified on basis of discussion appearing in the text.

[a] Du Pont shared this discovery with others.

Of Du Pont's five new product discoveries, only neoprene, nylon, and orlon have achieved substantial commercial significance to date. On the other hand, most of the new products developed by others but introduced into the American market by Du Pont have been very important in Du Pont's growth. Especially important have been viscose rayon, tetraethyl lead, cellophane, synthetic ammonia, acetate rayon, freon, titanium pigments, lucite, polyethylene, and titanium metal. Many of these were big money makers before and during World War II, and practically all seem likely to continue to be important for some time. Du Pont enjoyed large innovator's profits in rayon during the 1920's[118] and grew rapidly in this field up to 1948. Its earning record in cellophane has been phenomenal over a twenty-five year period.[119] Since Du Pont had no competitors in tetraethyl lead between 1923 and 1948, this too must have been a profitable field. Freon, which had

[118] See Stocking and Mueller, "Cellophane Case," p. 62.
[119] *Ibid.*

become the almost "universal refrigerant" by 1948, must also have been a profitable venture. By 1948 lucite sales already exceeded $20 million a year, and in polyethylene Du Pont had a stake in the "fastest growing plastic on the market." Titanium metal and dacron will doubtless be important factors in Du Pont's growth for years to come.

Of Du Pont's seven most important *product and process improvements*, five were Du Pont originals. Especially important were Duco, moistureproof cellophane, and cordura fiber. Duco has been an important seller ever since the mid-twenties. Most of the cellophane sold today is of the moistureproof variety. Du Pont sales of rayon tire yarn in 1948 came to $40 million; much of this presumably was cordura.

The above sample strongly suggests that Du Pont has been more successful in making product and process improvements than in discovering new products. Except for nylon, orlon, and neoprene, Du Pont's major product innovations have been based upon technology acquired from others. Next to be considered is the significance of these findings in relation to the frequent statement that Du Pont's bigness has created a perfect environment for inventive activity resulting in important *new* products and processes and *major* improvements in existing products and processes.

The record during the period of this study does not support such a generalization. Although Du Pont has expanded its research expenditures as it has grown—from slightly under $1 million annually shortly before 1920 to $38 million in 1950—there has not been a proportional acceleration in the number of *important* inventions (as defined herein) coming from its laboratories. Nylon still remains its greatest success story. Neoprene, discovered in 1931, probably has been exceeded only by nylon and orlon; and the latter was an outgrowth of its basic discoveries underlying nylon.

It is well to recall here that the basic research leading to the invention of nylon and neoprene was done during the late 1920's and early 1930's, when Du Pont's total research and technical budgets averaged $5 million a year, about one-sixteenth of its 1958 budget. Yes, the Du Pont that initiated the research leading to nylon and neoprene was truly a small firm by today's standards. Its sales in 1928 were only one-seventeenth as large as they were in 1959. Furthermore, by 1950 its nylon sales alone were larger than its 1928 sales of all products.

Du Pont's success in making major product and process improvements did not increase proportionately to its increasing research expenditures during 1920–50. Its greatest achievements of this kind were duco lacquers and moistureproof cellophane. Both of these were developed in the 1920's.

The above conclusions must be qualified in several important respects.

First, because I have concentrated my analysis on the inventions underlying Du Pont's most important innovations, I have left unmentioned many of Du Pont's successes. While I cannot quantify my judgment on this score, I believe that, if I had been able to identify the technical sources of Du Pont's many less spectacular innovations, the quantity of such accomplishments would be found to be more closely correlated with the size of Du Pont's research expenditures during 1920–50.

Second, it is possible that this analysis has treated too short a period in Du Pont's growth to permit generalizations.[120] Perhaps since 1950 Du Pont's inventive achievements have accelerated. But unfortunately it has not been possible to gain access to reliable information concerning the company's inventive activities since 1950.[121]

No opprobrium is intended by the preceding analysis of the sources of the inventions underlying Du Pont's most significant innovations. Du Pont's management must be commended for its aggressive and farsighted search for new products and processes, and for continually looking outside as well as within Du Pont's laboratories for them. It recognized new opportunities when they arose and backed them with a tremendous push of money, of product and process improvements, of mass production, and of salesmanship.

But a fundamental question is raised by these findings. To what extent can we as a nation rely on, and become dependent upon, the fundamental research efforts of a relatively few large industrial firms. Although such firms may be perfect vehicles of applied research and innovation, they may not have adequate economic incentives for

[120] I have found, however, that during its growth as the country's largest explosive maker Du Pont relied even more heavily on the inventions of others than it has since becoming a diversified chemical concern (based on an unpublished paper by the author on the sources of Du Pont's innovations during its first 100 years of growth as an explosives manufacturer).

[121] I obtained much of the information concerning the sources of Du Pont's inventions during 1920–50 from Du Pont Company documents appearing in various antitrust cases. These documents often gave accounts of the sources of Du Pont's inventions which were substantially different from those in generally available secondary sources.

sponsoring the ideal environment for conducting the basic research leading to the inventions underlying important innovations, or they may not be able to create that environment.

Apropos the question of adequate incentives, Richard R. Nelson of the Rand Corporation concludes his excellent theoretical analysis of the economics of basic research by saying, "though private profit motives may stimulate the firms of private industry to spend an amount on applied research reasonably close to the figure that is socially desirable, it is clear . . . that the social benefits of basic research are not adequately reflected in opportunities for private profit, given our present economic structure."[122]

Apropos the environment which big businesses create for conducting basic research, Clarence Cook Little, Director of the Jackson Memorial Laboratory and former President of the University of Michigan put it this way: "Scientific research is an intensely personal effort . . . like the artist, the creative scientist must be permitted to pursue his own ideas unhampered by restrictions of organized groups. The large groups have made extremely important contributions only when an original discovery, made by a single individual, is already available for further technical development."[123]

Obviously, case studies alone cannot prove or disprove theories. But I hope this one will contribute to the slowly growing empirical evidence useful in testing what are still largely unverified theories of the sources of inventive activity.

COMMENT

ZVI GRILICHES

An economy can grow, in a per capita sense, either by an increase in the amount of available resources per head, or by an improvement in their quality and utilization, by getting "more" out of them. The latter has come to be known as "increases in productivity," and it is clear, by almost any conventional method of measurement, that it has been the most important component of economic growth in the United States in recent decades. The growth in productivity can in turn be

---

[122] Richard R. Nelson, "The Simple Economics of Basic Scientific Research—A Theoretical Analysis," *Journal of Political Economy*, June 1959.

[123] Quoted with permission of T. K. Quinn, former vice-president of General Electric, in *Giant Business, Threat to Democracy: the Autobiography of an Insider* (New York, Exposition Press, 1953), p. 112.

divided into two parts: (1) the improvements in efficiency due to the elimination of various disequilibria, i.e., movements toward and along the known production boundaries; and (2) the expansion of the boundaries themselves due to the accretion of new knowledge. The first encompasses the diffusion of already known new techniques and the elimination of various inefficiencies, including taking advantage of existing economies of scale. The second includes advances in science in general, inventions and discoveries (patentable and unpatentable), and the development of practical versions and applications of more general inventions and new scientific principles.

Economists have long been identified with the study of the efficient allocation of a given set of resources within the context of a particular, fixed state of the arts. Recently some attention has begun to be paid to factors affecting the rate of diffusion of new techniques. This conference, however, is concentrating on the even more difficult and challenging problem of the production frontier itself. Its focus is on the knowledge producing industry, its output, the resources available to it, and the efficiency with which they are being used. Thus we are faced with the problems of measuring the rate of accretion of new knowledge (the output of this activity), measuring the resources devoted to the production of new knowledge (the inputs), determining the existence and nature of the relationship between inputs and output (the production function), investigating the factors determining the rate of production and the composition of output in this industry (product and factor prices), and discovering and describing the social private arrangements that would be most conducive to productivity and increases in this industry.

For these purposes, however, inventions may be the wrong unit of measurement. What we are really interested in is the stock of useful knowledge or information and the factors that determine its rate of growth. Inventions may represent only one aspect of this process and be a misleading quantum at that. They are arbitrarily defined discrete large jumps in the stock of certain kinds of (largely patentable) knowledge. They may represent only a small fraction of the growth of knowledge in general, and their fluctuations may not be very well correlated with changes in the over-all rate of growth.

On the other hand, if we restrict our attention solely to the consideration of shifts in the production function, we may miss some very important contributions of invention to the process of economic growth. Inventions may affect the rate of economic growth not only by increasing the productivity of certain inputs but also by preventing a fall in their productivity. The latter influence may be very difficult to detect, even in the best of all statistical worlds. But the fact that the private rate of return has remained high enough for net investment to continue through so many decades is in itself a very important factor in economic growth and could be largely due to "inventions."

Turning, however, explicitly to shifts in the production frontier, I find the theoretical concepts in this area very unsatisfactory for our purposes. In what sense is this a fixed and inelastic frontier? What do we know about different previously unrealized points on it and about what is outside of it? Is the frontier equally impermeable throughout its length? I find the concept of a production function, frontier, or possibilities curve to be a very unsatisfactory tool of analysis when one tries to turn it around and use it to answer questions about itself.

FIGURE 1

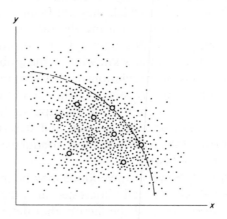

Some of these problems are illustrated in Figure 1. Let x and y stand for quantities of different products or different kinds of performance levels that could be associated with a given, fixed set of resources. Let the circles stand for currently and previously achieved levels of productivity. Let the dots represent points that could be achieved, at some as yet undefined cost, given the current state of knowledge. The probability of achieving a given performance combination within a given time period and cost level would then vary from point to point and is represented in the figure by the frequency of the points. The denser the shading the higher is the probability of achieving it within a given cost-time constraint, and the lower is the expected cost achieving it (neglecting the time constraint). Presumably, points lying between, behind, or around already achieved levels could be "developed" with little uncertainty and cost. This is one interpretation of what is meant by development expenditures. Points further out may require substantial research expenditures to be realized, and the undotted area may be so unexplored and uncertain that even a subjective probability calculus would be of little help here. This, then, is the area of "basic" research.

Since all these distinctions are distinctions of degree rather than kind, the definition of what is "within the state of the arts" and the drawing of a production frontier becomes very difficult and arbitrary. One could define a production frontier, represented by the broken line in the figure, by putting to the left of it all the points that could be achieved (at some specified probability level) within a given time and cost constraint. But both this and the two-dimensional nature of the figure abstract from what may be the most important aspect of the problem—differences in the cost of achieving different productivity or performance levels.

Leaving the definition and measurement problems aside, the first substantive question to be asked is whether an increase in inputs in the knowledge producing industry would lead to more output. Is there any relationship between inputs and output here? Unless this question is answered in the affirmative, there is really no point in proceeding toward the usual prescription of economics, the manipulation of incentives and inputs to achieve particular goals. That there is such a relationship may appear self-evident to many of us, but actually there is very little evidence in support of it. Thus we are indebted to Minasian (and similar earlier work by Terleckyj) for showing that research and development expenditures seem to accomplish something, that more R and D implies more output, measured in this case by the growth in productivity. Since many firms are spending money on R and D, one would expect that they are getting something in return (at least on the average), but it is good to have one's preconceptions confirmed by a careful and detailed study of actual expenditures.

Similarly, Nelson's work shows the inventors of the transistor looking for, among other things, knowledge that would lead to better amplifying devices and finding it. In the same vein, Peck's study of the aluminum industry implies that different kinds of inventions are produced by those groups that are most likely to benefit from them. While none of these studies comes anywhere near supplying us with a production function for inventions, the Enos and the Marshall-Meckling papers emphasizing the large component of randomness and sheer uncertainty in it, nevertheless they do establish the existence of some relationships between input and output in this activity. These relationships are not very strong or clear, but they do tell us that there is something in the data, that there are regularities worth studying, and keep our hopes alive.

The next major area of discussion is the existence and identity of factors and incentives affecting the level and direction of inputs in inventive activity. It is quite clear that *successful* invention is a reasonably well paying activity; this can be inferred from the Enos and Minasian papers (it would be interesting to compute the private rate of return on R and D expenditures from Minasian's data). We know nothing, however, about the rate of return to inventive activity as a whole, including the unsuccessful efforts. Is it positive or negative? Even if it were negative, would that mean that we have too few inputs in this area? Not necessarily. Inventors may be tinged by megalomania and willing to risk investing in an activity whose average return is zero or negative, as long as the variance is high enough. This assumption may not be too far-fetched since it is probably true of such diverse groups as speculators on commodity and stock exchanges, investors in Broadway shows, and actors and artists in general. The question that has to be asked is not whether the private rate of return is low or high but whether it is too low and its variance too high to induce the "right" amount of inputs.

It is also quite clear that the direction of inventive activity is affected by the relative profitability of different lines of endeavour as perceived by the inventors. Peck's data, Nelson's study of the transistor, and Schmookler's study of the variations in the rate of inventive activity in different industries all point in that direction. If one conceives of a production-possibilities surface indicating the various combinations of commodities that could be produced from a given set of resources and within a given state of the arts; and if the term commodity is interpreted broadly to include different dimensions or performance characteristics of commodities—e.g., speed, volume of pay load, range, and achieved height for airplanes—there is little doubt that the relative prices of these different commodities and characteristics strongly affect the direction of inventive activity. It is probably no accident that little work is being done on increasing the speed of automobiles. Both the private and social returns from such work are likely to be low. On the other hand, work is continuing in an attempt to improve the fuel utilization of cars.

It is less certain that the direction of inventive activity is affected by relative factor prices except as these enter directly into the profitability calculations. Are inventions "neutral" on the average? Will different factor price ratios induce different kinds of invention? The theoretical answer given by Fellner implies no tendency away from neutrality in a competitive economy. Given the assumption that it costs the same to advance 10 per cent along any factor-ratio ray (this is effectively on equal ignorance assumption), the highest returns are to be had from an advance along the currently optimum ray. Even if inventors anticipate changes in factor prices and move out along another ray, the effect of this on factor shares is moot. It will depend on the form of the production function, on how it changes as it is pushed outward and upward, and on whether the anticipated factor price changes actually materialize.

Some support for Fellner's proposition is provided by Enos. On the basis of his data one cannot reject the hypothesis of the neutrality of invention in petroleum refining, at least in the "alpha" stage. The "beta" stage, the development and improvement stage, shows a somewhat larger drop in the labor coefficient than in the capital coefficient. Given the paucity of cases and the quality of data, one cannot make much out of it. Moreover, it is not at all clear what the theory would predict for petroleum refining. The relative shares of capital and labor in petroleum refining in 1929 were approximately 0.7 and 0.3. Thus a 10 per cent reduction in the capital coefficient would have been more profitable than a 20 per cent reduction in the labor coefficient, and one would have expected inventions to be "capital saving" there. Actually, we can say very little about it, since all our data concern average productivities, whereas our theory is about marginal productivities. In general, it is my hunch that relative factor prices play a much smaller role in determining the direction of inventive activity than differences in the relative returns from different kinds of inventions (relative product prices).

This conclusion gains force from considerations raised in the third area of concern: the most efficient way of using a given set of inputs. Noting the tremendous uncertainties involved, Klein proceeds to argue that the whole strategy of employing ones resources has to be different in this area. The basic idea is to stay flexible and search for significant new knowledge, rather than to try to produce a particular gimmick to perform a particular task. It may prove easier and more efficient to break through into a different area from the one originally desired. The cost of inventing may be lower there and once the production frontier has been pushed out, it will be relatively easy to colonize some intervening or neighboring areas and develop the desired gimmick. We may get farther if we do not care too much about where we are going. In other words, the cost of moving the production frontier may be different at different points along it, and lower for parallel and oblique than for ortagonal shifts in it. Thus if one wanted to achieve point *B* in Figure 2, it might be cheaper to break through along the ray *O C* to *D*, assuming that the frontier is more "permeable" at this point, and only then move from *C* to *B*. Moreover, it is possible

FIGURE 2

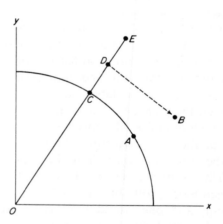

that in trying to break out one actually achieves point *E*, making *B* suboptimal. *B* would now never be reached even though it was the original destination. In short, the differences in the cost of producing inventions utilizing particular factor combinations, the apparent inefficiency of having too definite a goal in the invention process, and the inherently large component of randomness in the final outcome, all lead to inventions that are not well correlated with base-period factor prices or price trends.

Granting the importance of Klein's point, I doubt, however, that the contrast between the efficiency minded manager and the inventor is as sharp as he makes it out to be. The true entrepreneur, one with some leeway in his decision making, also operates in a very uncertain environment. It may be optimal for him, too, to be flexible and searching (on this see the earlier work of Stigler and Simon).

Given the paucity of our knowledge about so many aspects of this problem, probably too much attention has been paid by economists to the relation between market structure and inventive activity. I do not deny that the relation between the form of industrial organization and inventiveness may be of interest to the industrial organization man, I only doubt its importance to the invention and economic growth oriented researcher. Whatever evidence we have (see the Mueller and Peck papers, Worley's paper, and the recent book by Jewkes *et al.*) points to no particular relationship between monopoly, oligopoly, or competition and inventive activity. Neither the empirical evidence nor the theoretical discussion has established the presumption of a correlation between the degree of market control and the rate of inventive activity. Even if there were some relationship between the two (positive or negative), it could at best have only a second order effect. It would be quite inefficient, I believe, to try to affect the rate of inventive activity in the United States by manipulating the antitrust laws.

COMMENT

KENNETH J. ARROW, THE RAND CORPORATION

I would like to consider some theoretical implications of the case studies presented at this conference. My comments will be grouped under four heads: (1) the spread of information in the economic system; (2) the problems of appropriability and competition connected with the innovation process; (3) the optimal dynamics of invention; and (4) the implications for the estimation and meaning of macro-economic production functions over time.

Information

Invention is a process in which information is both the output and an input. The effectiveness of the invention process in a firm will depend then on the informational resources available to it, just as its productive effectiveness will depend in part on natural resources owned by it. Also, of course, the productive efficiency of the firm will depend on its acquisition of information, partly from its own inventive activity and partly from outside sources.

From the case studies, particularly those of Mueller and Peck, it can be inferred that the diffusion of information is by no means a cost-free process, even apart from artificial barriers in the form of patents and secrecy. As Mueller's example of dacron shows, even when information about new productive processes is supplied by another firm, a considerable investment must be made to make use of the knowledge. Further, it is not easy for Du Pont's rivals to develop competing products which deviate sufficiently from the original to avoid patent infringement, even when the fundamental knowledge can be inferred from Du Pont patents (e.g. nylon). Peck, in his discussion of the leadership of the primary producers in developing alloys, as opposed to their relative backwardness in other innovations, points to the fact that information about alloys is a by-product of the primary producing process. Other firms, for example, end-product manufacturers or independent fabricators, who would have an interest in new alloys, could acquire the background information only at a much greater cost.

To sum up, the transmission of information is costly, and certain types of information arise as a by-product of the basic production process of the firm. It follows that the information pool available to society is considerably greater than that available to any member or economic agent.[1]

The obstacles to the flow of information across company barriers are far from absolute, however. According to Mueller, many of Du Pont's innovations are derived from information supplied by others; Enos also cites several cases of patent transfers. Further, Peck has shown that in many cases end-product innovations and manufacturing techniques are developed by primary producers and given to the natural consumer of the information. Even when the information is not supplied officially, imitations can be devised, e.g., the rise of rival cracking processes. Imitation, which is a form of spreading of information, is, of course, costly, but it can be accomplished when sufficiently profitable.

---

[1] A study of the social and individual informational pools for several cultures in the southwest United States has been carried out by John M. Roberts as part of the Harvard Values Study Project.

One interesting feature of all three of these studies is the relatively low price paid for information. Patent royalties are generally so low that the profits from exploiting one's own invention are not appreciably greater than those derived from the use of others' knowledge. It really calls for some explanation, why the firm that has developed the knowledge cannot demand a greater share of the resulting profits —ideally all except a competitive return on the capital invested. One possible explanation is that the costs of development are large and comparable to the costs of imitation, so that there is little to squeeze. Further, the high costs of development, being fixed costs, favor large firms and so create a monopsony or oligopsony situation.

Appropriability and Competition

The above observations suggest, though they do not prove, that the rewards for invention in the form of royalties are trivial. The basic reward must then come in the form of monopoly profits including, in many cases, those from market sharing to which patent exchanges may be auxiliary. Now the possibilities of monopolization vary among industries and, in particular, among different stages in a production process. This has been exemplified in the work of both Peck and Enos. The inventive activity may take place, not in the industry which benefits directly, but in supplying industries. Equipment makers appear to be in a peculiarly strategic position for invention to the extent that it is accompanied by differentiation of the equipment product. Primary producers operating under oligopoly can expect only a share of the market resulting from any innovation with respect to end-products, and so have a reduced incentive to innovate. In practice, this is offset in part by the expectation that the beneficiary of an innovation will give its trade to the innovating company for some period of time; this is an indirect form of royalty payment, though one that would be hard to capture statistically.

The appropriability of the results of invention may come about in one of two ways: either there may be, for other reasons, barriers to entry so that the rewards for invention can be appropriated by a firm which is, at least to some extent, in a monopolistic position; or the costs of imitation may be so high, for either technical or legal reasons, that competition cannot erode the profits from invention. In the second case, the invention may be appropriated either through monopoly or through patent royalties. The former possibility is certainly the more likely if the costs of transmission, including that of associated development, are high.

The typology sketched here and suggested by the papers of Enos, Mueller, and Peck may be useful in locating the industrial sectors in which the appropriability of invention is apt to be greatest. Of course, appropriability is not the sole determinant of the locus of inventive activity; the cost of production of the information also matters, and this will depend on the technological possibilities of the moment and the information available to a firm as a by-product of its usual activities.

Optimal Dynamics of Invention

The papers of Klein, Marschak, Marshall and Meckling, and Nelson are at a more micro-economic level than those of Enos, Mueller, and Peck. As in the usual rational theory of the firm, they are trying simultaneously to study how decisions are made and how they ought to be made. The primary stress is on the uncertainty of research and its implications for policy. Two factors dominate: the possibility of flexibility, through multiple lines of development and the cessation of unpromising lines, and the acquisition of information over time. These aspects are not completely unique to invention; they also appear in ordinary production processes under uncertainty in many cases, and the analysis of such situations was begun by Hart[2] many years ago.

One cautionary note on the implications of the view of Klein and his colleagues is in order. There is great stress on decentralization of decision making in research with a view to securing the parallel development of alternative approaches, since none is certain. But decentralization secured in this way is not identical with decentralization through the price system and, indeed, is in many respects incompatible with it. Parallel development of research projects, in order to be efficient, requires continuous interchange of the information accumulated during the process in order to permit elimination of inferior projects at the earliest possible time. In the absence of such interchange of information, for example, if it is prevented by competitive or interservice rivalry, there is liable to be either an excessive cost for retention of projects which are, in fact, inferior to others, or to avoid these costs an unwillingness to enter upon a sufficient number of projects.

[2] A. G. Hart, *Anticipations, Uncertainty and Dynamic Planning*, New York, Kelley and Millman reprint, 1951, Chap. IV; "Risk, Uncertainty, and the Unprofitability of Compounding Probabilities," *Studies in Mathematical Economics and Econometrics*, O. Lange, T. O. Yntema, and F. McIntyre, editors, University of Chicago Press, 1942, pp. 110-118.

Implications for Estimation of Production Functions

The presence of innovations introduces a number of problems into the estimation of production functions, particularly, though not exclusively, estimation from time series. The technique, stemming from the pioneer work of Douglas, has been developed more recently, with greater reference to technological change, by Valavanis-Vail and Solow.[3] The production function itself is a relation between output and factors, usually capital and labor, but under competitive conditions marginal productivity relations imply that the parameters of the production function can, in part, be inferred from data on wages and profits, and this combination of methods has become standard. The papers of Enos, Peck, and Mueller suggest, however, some problems in the interpretation of these functions, a few of which I list here.

1. At any given moment of time the aggregate production function is supposed to reflect the technological knowledge then available. However, it appears from the case studies that the *distribution* of technical knowledge can also be a significant factor in the performance of the economy as a whole. If some criterion for measuring the accessibility of productive knowledge to individual entrepreneurs could be devised, it might be introduced as a relevant variable in explaining, for example, the differences in performance among countries at a given moment of time.

2. Invention and capital-labor substitution are hard to distinguish. If the capital-labor ratio changes, capital goods will tend to be embodied in different forms (bulldozers rather than shovels), which may be regarded as inventions only in the sense that no one had found it profitable to construct them previously. In this connection, one might offer an interpretation of Enos' observation that capital-labor substitution is not found in invention and development per se but only in the subsequent phase of improvement of the invention in practice. Possibly the latter phase might be regarded as adjustment to the optimum with respect to a given production function, while the former phase alone constitutes a shift in the production function. This suggests a model of neutral technological change with lagged adjustment to an optimum.

[3] P. H. Douglas, "Are There Laws of Production?" *American Economic Review*, 1948, pp. 1–41; S. Valavanis-Vail, "An Econometric Model of Growth, U.S.A. 1869–1953," *American Economic Review*, Papers and Proceedings, 1955, pp. 215–218; R. M. Solow, "Technological Change and the Aggregate Production Function," *Review of Economics and Statistics*, 1957, pp. 312–320.

3. The rates of return on inventive activity as given by Enos seem very high and would be hard to reconcile with the marginal productivity assumptions used in the estimation of production functions. To the extent that they are valid, they support again the idea of a "dynamic" estimation of the production function in which there is a lag in the achievement of a maximum-profit position and also in the diffusion of technological knowledge throughout the economy. These effects have been demonstrated in the work of Griliches and Mansfield.[4] But there is reason to argue that the rates of return are too high; they disregard not only the capital invested but also the costs of unsuccessful innovations which should, properly speaking, be charged against the successful ones.

[4] Z. Griliches, "Hybrid Corn: An Exploration in the Economics of Technological Change," *Econometrica*, 1957, pp. 501–522; E. Mansfield, "Technological Change and the Role of Imitation," presented at a meeting of the Econometric Society, December 1959.

PART IV
NONMARKET FACTORS

Intellect and Motive in Scientific Inventors: Implications for Supply

DONALD W. MACKINNON

INSTITUTE OF PERSONALITY ASSESSMENT AND RESEARCH
UNIVERSITY OF CALIFORNIA, BERKELEY

Two major types of inventors have been noted: inventors working as researchers in an industrial organization, sometimes referred to as captive inventors, and inventors working on their own as individuals, sometimes called independent inventors. Inventors of the second type may be self-employed, devoting all their working hours to invention, or they may be engaged in full-time employment having nothing to do with inventing. The latter, despite the fact that they devote only their spare time, mainly weekends and evenings, to inventive activity, are nevertheless often so absorbed in it that being an inventor becomes for them their major professional identity. Still other independent inventors engage in inventive activity only as a hobby.

Report is here made on a group of inventors employed in industrial research and a group of individual inventors whose inventive activity varies from being a hobby to being serious part-time self-employment.[1] The data on these two groups of inventors take on added significance since it is possible to relate them to data gathered in the study of other creative groups: research scientists, mathematicians, architects, and writers.[2]

The design of the over-all research provides for the study of creative persons in these several fields so that eventually something can be said about what characterizes creativity generally, regardless of the special field in which it may manifest itself, and a delineation made of the characteristics of the creative worker and his mode of work in each of the areas studied.

[1] In preparing this report and in testing the independent inventors I have been ably assisted by Wallace B. Hall, who in addition has been responsible for the preparation of the statistical data here reported.

[2] These studies are part of a larger investigation of creative work and creative workers in the arts, sciences, and professions being carried out in the Institute of Personality Assessment and Research at the University of California, Berkeley, supported in part by funds granted by the Carnegie Corporation of New York. The statements made and views expressed here are, however, solely the responsibility of the author.

With the exception of the independent inventors, who participated only in a six-hour program of psychological testing, the creative groups were intensively studied by the assessment method which was developed in the Office of Strategic Services during World War II for the purpose of studying highly effective persons. The method as employed in the researches here reported involves bringing the individuals to be studied together during a weekend in an assessment center where they meet with each other and with a staff of psychologists, participate in a series of experiments, take tests of personality traits, attitudes, interests, and values, and are interviewed concerning their life histories and their professional careers.

In a study of the creativity of 45 research scientists employed in three industrial firms and engaged in research and development in guided missiles and electronics, it was discovered that 27 were inventors, 18 noninventors.[3] The criteria for inventor were that the research scientist be a patentee, had applied for a patent, or made a disclosure; criterion for noninventor was that he failed to meet any of the criteria for inventor. Hereafter the two groups will be referred to as research scientist inventors and research scientist noninventors.

The independent inventors for whom data will be reported are 14 adult males engaged in full-time employment unrelated to inventive activity but who devote varying amounts of their free time to such activity and all of whom conceive themselves as inventors as witnessed by their membership in the International Inventors Association.[4] The other creative groups with whom the inventors will be compared are nationwide, though small samples, of 20 writers (poets, novelists, and essayists), 12 women mathematicians, and 40 architects.[5]

In assessing our several creative groups we have found a characteristic and distinguishing pattern of interests as indicated by scores on

[3] This study of professional research scientists was conducted by Harrison G. Gough and Donald G. Woodworth. I am indebted to them for making their data available and permitting me to examine the characteristics of the two subgroups of inventors and noninventors.

The industrial laboratories in which these 45 research scientists work are those of the Dalmo-Victor Company, San Carlos, California; the Lockheed Corporation Laboratories, Sunnyvale, California; and Varian Associates, Stanford, California.

[4] I wish to express my appreciation to those members of the Association who consented to be studied, and especially to Laurence J. Udell, Secretary-Treasurer of the Association, for his invaluable aid in eliciting their participation.

[5] I am indebted to project directors Frank Barron for data on the writers and Ravenna Helson for data on the women mathematicians. I have directed the study of architects with the assistance of the project's co-director, Wallace B. Hall.

certain scales of the *Strong Vocational Interest Blank*.[6] From sample to sample there has been some slight variation, but the general pattern has been for original and creative subjects, as well as for highly effective persons as first reported by Gough,[7] to show relatively high scores on such scales as artist, psychologist, architect, author-journalist, and specialization level, and relatively low scores on scales such as purchasing agent, office man, banker, farmer, carpenter—and most interestingly—policeman and mortician.

This pattern of interests as revealed on the *Strong Vocational Interest Blank* can best be interpreted as indicating that more original and creative subjects are generally less interested in matters of small detail or concerned with them primarily for their wider meanings and implications, less concerned with regulation and control, possessed of greater cognitive flexibility, and interested in ideas and in communicating them accurately to others.

Table 1 lists the interest scales of the S.V.I.B. on which the research scientist noninventors, research scientist inventors, and independent inventors earned high (A, indicated by an asterisk, or B+) scores. It is immediately apparent that both the inventors and noninventors of the research scientist group have many more as well as broader

TABLE 1

MEAN SCORES OF A OR B+ ON STRONG VOCATIONAL INTEREST BLANK
SCALES FOR THE THREE GROUPS

Research Scientists Noninventors	Research Scientists Inventors	Independent Inventors
*Psychologist	*Psychologist	*Engineer
*Architect	*Architect	*Production Mgr.
Physician	Mathematician	Farmer
Mathematician	*Engineer	Carpenter
Engineer	*Chemist	
*Chemist	Production Mgr.	
Math and Sci. Teach.	Math and Sci. Teach.	
Personnel Director	Public Administrator	
*Public Administrator	Musician	
Social Worker	Senior CPA	
Musician		
Senior CPA		

* Specialization level.

[6] E. K. Strong, Jr., *Manual for Strong Vocational Interest Blanks for Men and Women, Revised Blanks*, Palo Alto, Consulting Psychologists Press, 1959.

[7] H. G. Gough, "Some Theoretical Problems in the Construction of Practical Assessment Devices for the Early Identification of High Level Talent," Berkeley, University of California (mimeographed), 1953.

interests than do the independent inventors, and they are more certain of these interests and almost certainly pursue them with greater energy (as their higher scores on the specialization scale indicate). Actually there is an interesting progression in number of fields of high interest from independent inventors (4), to research scientist inventors (10), to research scientist noninventors (12).

Qualitative differences in the interests of the three groups are also evident. The independent inventors are in their interests clearly oriented toward things rather than people, and though this interest in things also characterizes the research scientists there is in their case an added interest in and orientation toward persons, and this is even more characteristic of the noninventors than of the inventors among them. There is a progression in range of interests from things to people as one moves from independent inventors to research scientist inventors to research scientist noninventors.

Another difference to be noted in the pattern of high interests of the three groups is a predominant interest in details and in concrete physical objects on the part of the independent inventors in contrast to a greater interest in wholes, complex configurations, and the ideational and the abstract on the part of the research scientists and especially those who are noninventors.

These differences in interest patterns of the independent inventors and the research scientists, including both inventors and noninventors, suggest that the two groups should differ also in socioeconomic status, level of education and training, and in occupational level, and indeed they do.

Of the 45 research scientists, 80 per cent come from families of middle or upper middle class status with fathers in skilled, semi-professional or professional occupations. All but five of the group have had some formal graduate training, and 28 of them have Ph.D.'s in their specialties. Employed as industrial research scientists, they are 100 per cent in professional positions. In age they range from 24 to 54 with a mean age of 35 years. In regard to these several variables, the inventors among the research scientists are not significantly different from the noninventors.

Of the 14 independent inventors, only 64 per cent come from families of middle class or better. Forty-two per cent of their fathers were in skilled trades, only 21 per cent were in professional or semiprofessional occupations. Only three in the group hold a baccalaureate degree, while two completed one year of college. One completed one year of high school while another finished two years. Exactly one-half of the group completed four years of high school. As for their type of employment, eleven are in skilled trades, one in semiskilled, one in semiprofessional, and one in professional work. In age they range from 29 to 71 with a mean age of 47 years.

These marked differences between the industrial research scientists and the independent inventors suggest that they must differ also with respect to intelligence. On the *Concept Mastery Test* (Terman, 1956)[8] the research scientists' mean score was 118.2 with a standard deviation of 29.4, the mean score of the independent inventors being 50.8 and the standard deviation, 34.7. Despite this great difference in measured intelligence between the independent inventors and the research scientists as a group, there was no significant difference in the test scores of inventors and noninventors among the research scientists: research scientist noninventors 117.3, standard deviation 30.9; research scientist inventors 118.9, standard deviation 28.2. It is of some interest to compare the performance of our three groups with that of other groups tested by the Terman test. Table 2 presents these data.

It is to be expected that, on a test of verbal intelligence with such a high ceiling, creative writers will surpass all others. But, in view of our concern with the relation of intelligence to inventive activity, it is surprising to discover our sample of independent inventors scoring as a group lower than any other group to whom we have administered

TABLE 2

MEAN SCORES AND STANDARD DEVIATIONS FOR VARIOUS GROUPS
ON THE CONCEPT MASTERY TEST, FORM T

Group	Number	Mean	Standard Deviation
Writers	20	156.4	21.9
Subjects of Stanford Gifted Study	1004	136.7	28.5
Women mathematicians	41	131.7	33.8
Graduate students	125	119.2	33.0
Research scientists: inventors	27	118.9	28.2
Research scientists: noninventors	18	117.3	30.9
Creative architects	40	113.15	37.7
Undergraduate students	201	101.7	33.0
Spouses of gifted subjects	690	95.3	42.7
Air Force captains	344	60.1	31.7
Independent inventors	14	50.8	34.7

[8] L. M. Terman, *Concept Mastery Test, Manual, Form T*, New York, Psychological Corporation, 1956.

the *Concept Mastery Test*. The inventors among the research scientists as well as the noninventors in that sample, on the other hand, earned very respectable scores, scoring at about the level of graduate students.

In view of the marked difference in mean intelligence scores between our two groups of inventors one might well guess that they differ also in the amount of inventive activity engaged in or the success with which they carry on their inventive efforts. Actually, however, the mean number of patents held by the independent inventors is 1.25 while the mean number held by the research scientist inventors is only 0.88. This difference is, of course, not significant, but at least in terms of this criterion the group of inventors scoring higher on intelligence shows no superiority to the group scoring appreciably lower. It must be noted, however, that proportionately more of the research scientist inventors are patentees (48 per cent), as against 36 per cent of the independent inventors.[9]

There is evidence, too, that the research scientist inventors engage in more inventive activity or at least more often move in the direction of patenting their inventions in so far as they, more often than the independent inventors, make disclosures and apply for patents. An inventive index—a weighted score for inventive activity in which a disclosure is given a weight of 1, an application a weight of 2, and a patent granted a weight of 3—has been computed for each inventor studied, and the mean inventive index calculated for the two samples of inventors. The mean inventive index for research scientist inventors is 10.5, with a standard deviation of 13.0; for independent inventors it is 4.3 with a standard deviation of 8.5.

If one considers, however, that the research scientist inventors are employed full-time in inventive activity while the independent inventors engage in such activity only in such leisure time as they can make for themselves, and if one remembers further the striking difference

[9] The general level of inventive activity is low for both groups studied. The mean number of patents held by the research scientist inventors, 0.88, is almost certainly an underestimation of the inventive activity in this group, and probably is to be explained by the fact that for the most part members of this group have been working on classified research supported by government contracts, in connection with which patent applications are not likely to be made. The mean number of patents held by the independent inventors, 1.25, may well underestimate their inventive activity also, since for the most part members of this group have been handicapped by lack of financial resources. No outstandingly successful inventor was included in the sample of independent inventors, and despite the almost certain underestimation of inventive activity in both samples of inventors there is reason to believe that, indeed, in both groups the level of inventive activity was relatively low.

in measured intelligence between the two groups, it is most surprising that the differences in their inventive activity and inventive accomplishments are not greater.

It is interesting to note in this connection that the inventor who, of all those studied by us, holds the largest number of patents, 11 in all, is not one of the research scientists but an independent inventor with a score of 6.0 on the *Concept Mastery Test*. This is the second lowest score earned by any of the subjects we have tested. The lowest score earned by any of the research scientist inventors was 72. If, instead of looking only at the final total score of this most inventive inventor in the two samples, one examines the way in which he earned it, a most interesting finding emerges.

The test is "a measure of ability to deal with abstract ideas at a high level" and consists of two parts: Part I, Synonyms-Antonyms, is essentially a vocabulary test of knowledge; Part II, Analogies, is a test of word knowledge, general information, and reasoning ability. Instructions for the test specify that one should not guess but should instead answer only those items for which the correct response is known. Score for Part I of the test is number right minus number wrong, for Part II number right minus one-half number wrong. Total score is score for Part I plus score for Part II. With this method of scoring it is clear that a subject who guesses when he does not know is apt to be penalized, and will be if he is wrong. The total score consequently does not indicate the total number of correct responses a subject gives, which in the case of our inventive inventor is 87 rather than 6. It would appear then that this individual has a fair amount of correct knowledge which he can record, but also a good deal of wrong information which he does not hesitate to give.

One wonders, then, if this might not be a salient trait of the inventor who succeeds, namely, that he is willing to take a chance, to try anything that might work, even in taking a test of intelligence. But one also wonders whether this might not be more characteristic of inventors who possess less general information, who are relatively less intelligent, and who are in general less well educated—in other words, the independent inventors of the present study.

Table 3 shows the mean total correct score (which ignores and does not penalize for wrong answers) on the *Concept Mastery Test* for independent inventors and the two groups of research scientists. The relative standing of the three groups re intelligence is in no way changed by this new method of scoring the test. The noninventors and

TABLE 3

MEAN TOTAL CORRECT SCORES AND STANDARD DEVIATIONS FOR THREE
GROUPS ON THE CONCEPT MASTERY TEST, FORM T

Group	Number	Mean	Standard Deviation
Research scientists–Noninventors	18	137.9	22.7
Research scientists–Inventors	27	139.0	24.6
Independent inventors	14	85.2	32.2

inventors among the research scientists are not distinguishable in respect of the amount of correct knowledge which they have, but both groups are clearly set apart from and markedly superior to the independent inventors.

The difference in intelligence test performance between both groups of the research scientists and the independent inventors is further indicated in Table 4, which gives for the three groups the ratio of the total number of wrong answers to the total number of answers given on the same test. A ratio of 0 would mean that no errors or wrong guesses

TABLE 4

RATIO OF TOTAL ERRORS TO TOTAL QUESTIONS ANSWERED ON THE
CONCEPT MASTERY TEST, FORM T, FOR THREE GROUPS

Group	Number	Mean	Standard Deviation
Research scientists–Noninventors	18	0.17	0.10
Research scientists–Inventors	27	0.15	0.06
Independent inventors	14	0.35	0.12

had been made. The research scientists are either quite accurate or quite cautious in taking the test; at least both groups give relatively few false answers. In contrast the independent inventors make proportionately more erroneous responses. It may be noted that the difference in mean ratio between independent inventors and research scientist inventors is significant at the 0.001 level with a t of 5.68.

With these data we are now in a position to answer the query raised above as to whether the tendency to take a chance, to try anything that might work (as revealed in the analysis of performance on the *Concept Mastery Test*), is more characteristic of less well endowed and less well educated inventors (the independent inventors) than of inventors more intelligent and better educated (the research scientist inventors). The answer can be found in the correlation of the *Concept Mastery Test* ratio (total errors to total number answered) with the inventive index already described. For the research scientist inventors the correlation is −0.16, for the independent inventors, +0.49. The difference is significant beyond the 0.06 level and strongly suggests that the more inventive a research scientist inventor is, the less inclined he is to take chances, i.e., to offer erroneous answers in taking an intelligence test; while the more inventive an independent inventor is, the more disposed he will be—and this indeed to a marked degree— to try anything that might work.

These analyses of the intelligence test performance of independent inventors, in contrast to research scientist inventors, reveal an attitude and set which appear to characterize them very generally. It is, in part, a lack of critical attitude toward themselves, their ideas, and their abilities, which frees and liberates them for actions and responses that more self-critical, inhibited, and conforming individuals could never bring themselves to make. One would expect a person with such an attitude to have a rather good opinion of himself. Such a person would consequently not be embarrassed by failure, the very thought of which would inhibit others. The willingness "to cut and try," so long observed to be characteristic of the inventor in his inventive activity, appears to apply to one type of inventor—the less intellectually gifted and less well educated. It appears to characterize him no less when he is taking an intelligence test than when he is engaged in other activities. Such an attitude toward work can, on a purely statistical basis, increase the probability of a correct response being made or an inventive solution being achieved. In his inventive striving our independent inventor does not penalize himself for trials that do not work, but in the arbitrary scoring of an intelligence test, as we have seen, he is penalized, with the result that his measured intelligence correlates only imperfectly with his effective intelligence in any situation calling for an inventive response.

If the attitude or mental set with which one takes a test of intelligence can have such consequences as have just been reviewed, and if, as would seem to be the case, such sets operate not only in the intelligence testing situation but in work and life situations as well, it is reasonable to suppose that other sets and orientations toward work may also distinguish the inventor from the noninventor as well as one kind of inventor from another.

Gough and Woodworth undertook to discover in their study of

the 45 research scientists, for whom data are being presented through-out this paper, whatever stylistic differences might exist in their subjects' attitudes and habits and views of themselves as researchers.[10] To this end, in collaboration with a group of engineers and research scientists, they assembled a list of 56 statements and phrases descriptive of the various ways in which industrial researchers go about their work and perceive themselves. The following selected statements will give some idea of what the complete list is like: (1) pursues details and ramifications of research problems with great thoroughness; (2) likes to play his hunches in research and is guided by his subjective impressions; (3) prefers to work alone—is not a "team" research man; (4) likes to talk out his research ideas and get other people's reactions; (5) somewhat given to bluffing and claims to know more than he does.

The second task was to ask each subject to sort these 56 statements over a 5-step scale of relevance to himself in frequencies of 5, 12, 22, 12, and 5, ranging from the 5 statements most descriptive of him to the 5 items least applicable to him. The next task was to intercorrelate the sortings made by each of the 45 subjects and then to factor analyze the matrix of intercorrelations. From this matrix eight "person-factors" or types of researchers were extracted.

Subjects having the highest loadings on each of these stylistic factors were identified. The eight stylistic types were then studied in relation to assessment data drawn from other sources to reveal what psychologically characterized each of the types. In the light of this analysis, Gough and Woodworth have described and labeled the eight types of industrial researchers found in their study as follows:[11]

TYPE I: THE ZEALOT. This man is dedicated to research activity; he sees himself as a driving, indefatigable researcher, with exceptional mathematical skills and a lively sense of curiosity. *He is seen by others* as tolerant, serious-minded, and conscientious, but as not getting along easily with others and as not being able to "fit in" readily with others.

---

[10] H. G. Gough and D. G. Woodworth, "Stylistic Variations among Professional Research Scientists," *Journal of Psychology*, Vol. 49, pp. 87–98.

[11] It should be noted that the original classification into the type categories is based on self-perceptions and self-definitions, as embodied in the Q-sort phrases. However, the later explication of the type-psychology includes the evaluations and descriptions contributed by assessment observers. The summary statement for each type thus includes (1) a formulation of the key elements from the self-descriptive classificatory Q-sort phrases, and (2) an inductive sketch of the personological components of each type as seen by psychologist observers.

TYPE II: THE INITIATOR. This man reacts quickly to research problems, and begins at once to generate ideas; he is stimulating to others and gives freely of his own time; he sees himself as being relatively free of doctrinaire bias—methodological or substantive—and as being a good "team" man. *Observers describe him* as ambitious, well-organized, industrious, a good leader, and efficient. They also characterize him as being relatively free of manifest anxiety, worry, and nervousness.

TYPE III: THE DIAGNOSTICIAN. This man sees himself as a good evaluator, able to diagnose strong and weak points in a program quickly and accurately, and as having a knack for improvising quick solutions in research trouble spots. He does not have strong methodological preferences and biases, and tends not to be harsh or disparaging towards others' mistakes and errors. *Observers see him* as forceful and self-assured in manner, and as unselfish and free from self-seeking and narcissistic striving.

TYPE IV: THE SCHOLAR. This man is blessed with an exceptional memory, and with an eye for detail and order. However, he is not a research perfectionist nor an endless seeker for ultimates. He does not hesitate to ask help when blocked in his work, and feels that he can adapt his own thinking to that of others. He is well-informed in his field, and is not given to bluffing. *Observers describe him* as conscientious and thorough, and as very dependable, but as lacking confidence and decisiveness of judgment.

TYPE V: THE ARTIFICER. This man gives freely of his own time, and enjoys talking shop with other researchers. He is aware of his own limitations and does not attempt what he cannot do. He sees himself as having a special facility for taking inchoate or poorly formed ideas of others and fashioning them into workable and significant programs. *Observers see him* as honest and direct, getting along well with others, and as usually observant and perceptive and responsive to nuances and subtleties in others' behavior.

TYPE VI: THE ESTHETICIAN. This man favors analytical over other modes of thinking, and prefers research problems which lend themselves to elegant and formal solutions. His interests are far-ranging, and he tends to become impatient if progress is slow or if emphasis must be put upon orderliness and systematic detail. His own view of experience is primarily an esthetic one. *Observers see him* as clever and spontaneous, but as undependable and immature, somewhat lacking in patience and industry and indifferent about duties and obligations.

TYPE VII: THE METHODOLOGIST. This man is vitally interested in methodological issues, and in problems of mathematical analysis and conceptualization. He is open about his own research plans and enjoys talking about them with others. He has little competitive spirit and tends to take a tolerant view of research differences between himself and others. *Observers characterize him* as a considerate, charitable person, free from undue ambition; at the same time they report a certain moodiness and an occasional tendency toward complicated and difficult behavior.

TYPE VIII: THE INDEPENDENT. This man eschews "team" efforts, and dislikes and avoids administrative details connected with research work. He is not a driving, energetic research man, although he does have a lively sense of intellectual curiosity. He prefers to think in reference to physical and structural models rather than in analytical and mathematical ways. *Observers describe him* as active and robust in manner and hard-headed and forthright in judgment. He appears relatively free from worry and self-doubt, but inclined to behave impolitely or abruptly.[12]

It is of some interest to inquire concerning the frequency with which each of the eight types occurred among the independent inventors as well as among the inventors and noninventors of the research scientist group. The answer to this question can be given (cf. Table 5),

TABLE 5

PERCENTAGE OF THE EIGHT STYLISTIC TYPES OF RESEARCH SCIENTISTS AMONG RESEARCH SCIENTIST–NONINVENTORS, RESEARCH SCIENTIST– INVENTORS, AND INDEPENDENT INVENTORS

	Research Scientist– Noninventors	Inventors	Independent Inventors
I. The zealot	39	15	14
II. The initiator	6	33	36
III. The diagnostician	0	19	36
IV. The scholar	11	7	0
V. The artificer	6	7	0
VI. The esthetician	11	7	0
VII. The methodologist	22	4	0
VIII. The independent	6	7	14
Indeterminate type	0	0	14

[12] Gough and Woodward, *op. cit.*, pp. 93–94.

since each of the independent inventors of the present study also sorted the fifty-six statements to describe himself.

In determining the stylistic type for each subject, his own sorting of the fifty-six items was correlated with the sorting for each of the eight types. If an individual's sorting failed to correlate 0.50 with any of the sortings for the eight types he was judged to represent none of them; his own stylistic type was indeterminate with respect to the eight types established in the Gough and Woodworth study. If an individual's sorting correlated 0.50 or better with the sorting for more than one type he was judged to represent that type with which he showed the highest correlation. In cases where an individual's highest correlation was the same (0.50 or better) for more than one type he was judged to represent them equally. Thus the percentage of types for the three samples does not always sum to 100.[13]

Among research scientist noninventors the zealot occurs most often, followed by the methodologist, then, with tied frequencies, the scholar and the esthetician. The initiator, artificer, and independent appear infrequently, each accounting for 6 per cent of the group, while the diagnostician never once appears in this subsample.

The picture which one thus gets of the research scientist who is not interested in inventing is that he tends to be dedicated to scientific goals, mathematically skilled, and interested in methodological problems (zealot and methodologist). The same traits, though perhaps less highly developed, doubtless characterize the next most frequently occurring types—the scholar and the esthetician.

The low frequencies with which the initiator, the artificer, and the diagnostician occur suggest that noninventors will not often appear in the guise of the active, outward-going trouble shooter, the man interested in things and in action, and the team man generous of his time with others.

The academician, the intellectual interested in ideas, in elegant mathematical solutions, in methodological niceties—in short, the research scientist who would probably be happier in an academic post rather than in industry—this is the picture which one gets of the industrial research scientist who is not engaged in invention.

---

[13] If, instead of applying this criterion for type, each independent inventor is assigned to that type with which he correlates most highly (even though less than 0.50) the indeterminates turn out to be either initiator or diagnostician. The distributions become for the independent inventors: the zealot, 14 per cent; the initiator, 43 per cent; the diagnostician, 43 per cent; and the independent, 14 per cent, with the remaining five types having a frequency of 0 per cent.

The picture obtained earlier from the profile of the *Strong Vocational Interest Blank* of the independent inventors as persons more oriented to things than to ideas and to people is reconfirmed by the frequency with which the stylistic types are found among them. They are the initiators, the men of action "free from doctrinaire bias," whether methodological or theoretical. They are the diagnosticians, the trouble shooters. Some of them will work with considerable zeal just as some of them will work with considerable independence, but one does not find among them scholars, estheticians, or methodologists. One might have expected to find artificers among them but one does not, quite possibly because the type isolated by Gough and Woodworth represents a very high level research designer and apparatus man and because the artificer type as defined is too much given to working and researching with others while independence appears to be much more emphasized among the lone and individual inventors.

As one might expect, the frequencies with which the several stylistic types occur among the research scientist inventors, in general, fall between the frequencies with which they occur among the other two subgroups. As with the independent inventors, the most frequently occurring types are initiator and diagnostician. Zealots occur with about the same frequency as they do among the independent inventors, though the frequency of the independent type approximates more nearly that with which it occurs among the noninventors.

Especially to be noted is the virtual absence of the methodologist among inventors of both types. Again the inventor appears as one intolerant of methodological issues which, if accepted, would force him to proceed along certain prescribed channels. If there is any method to which he is committed, it is the one that provides him with the maximum freedom for action; for the research scientist inventor this may be in large measure "trial and error" guided by some theoretical considerations, and for the independent inventor it may be predominantly "cut and try" guided by more practical considerations.

The differences between independent inventors, research scientist inventors, and research scientist noninventors with respect to the stylistic variations which they reveal in their approaches and attitudes toward their work suggest that they may also differ in the values they hold. Their differing patterns of interests as revealed on the *Strong Vocational Interest Blank* show that indeed they do.

In an earlier report it was shown that creative individuals have a pattern of values different from less creative persons.[14] On the Allport-Vernon-Lindzey *Study of Values* designed to measure in the individual the relative strength of the six values of men as described by Eduard Spranger—the theoretical, the economic, the aesthetic, the social, the political, and the religious—creative architects, research scientists, and mathematicians show a high elevation on two values: the theoretical and the aesthetic.[15] As Figure 1 shows, the highest mean value for research scientists is the theoretical followed by the aesthetic; for architects, the aesthetic value is highest with the theoretical value in second place; while for creative mathematicians, the two values are well above average and approximately equally high.

It is not surprising that the theoretical value is highest for the research scientists, or that the aesthetic value is highest for architects. It had not been anticipated, however, that the two highest values for

FIGURE 1

Profiles of Values for Architects, Research Scientists, and Women Mathematicians on the Allport-Vernon-Lindzey Study of Values

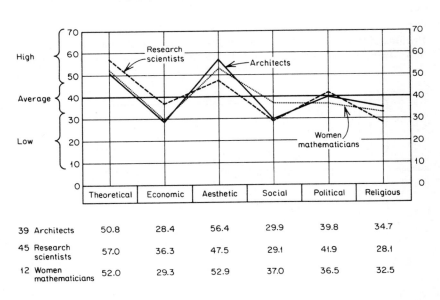

	Theoretical	Economic	Aesthetic	Social	Political	Religious
39 Architects	50.8	28.4	56.4	29.9	39.8	34.7
45 Research scientists	57.0	36.3	47.5	29.1	41.9	28.1
12 Women mathematicians	52.0	29.3	52.9	37.0	36.5	32.5

[14] D. W. MacKinnon, "Identifying and Developing Creativity," in *Selection and Educational Differentiation*, T. R. McConnell, Editor, Berkeley, Center for the Study of Higher Education, 1960.

[15] G. W. Allport, P. E. Vernon, and G. Lindzey, *Study of Values: Manual of Directions*, (rev. ed.), Boston, Houghton Mifflin, 1951.

architects, research scientists, and mathematicians would be the theoretical and the aesthetic or that they would be of so nearly the same strength in each group, for the developers of this test had described the aesthetic attitude as diametrically opposed to the theoretical. The theoretical man is usually thought of as having a cognitive orientation seeking primarily to observe and to reason, whereas the aesthetic man is described as one who judges all experience from the standpoint of fitness, grace, and symmetry. It may be that for most persons there is some conflict between theoretical and aesthetic values. If so, it would appear that the creative individual has the capacity to tolerate the tension created in him by opposing strong values, and in his life and work effects some reconciliation of them.

The profile of values for the research scientists as shown in Figure 1 is, in Figure 2, redrawn for the two subgroups of research scientists discussed throughout this paper—inventors and noninventors. Figure 2 also shows the profile of values for the independent inventors. For each of the subgroups the theoretical is the highest mean value, but it should be noted that while this value falls in the high range for the

FIGURE 2

Profiles of Values for Independent Inventors, Research Scientist-Inventors, and Research Scientists-Noninventors on the Allport-Vernon-Lindzey Study of Values

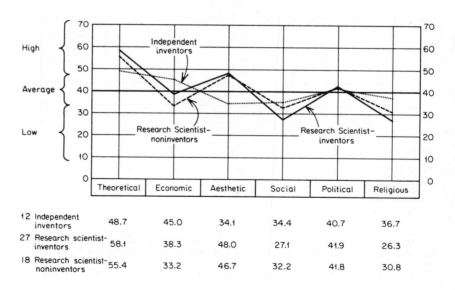

	Theoretical	Economic	Aesthetic	Social	Political	Religious
12 Independent inventors	48.7	45.0	34.1	34.4	40.7	36.7
27 Research scientist-inventors	58.1	38.3	48.0	27.1	41.9	26.3
18 Research scientist-noninventors	55.4	33.2	46.7	32.2	41.8	30.8

two subgroups of research scientists, it is of only average magnitude for our sample of independent inventors.

The differences are even more striking with regard to the aesthetic value. While this is the second highest value for the research scientists, inventors as well as noninventors, it is the lowest of all values for the independent inventors, whose second highest value is economic rather than aesthetic. It is of interest to note, also, that the independent inventors score higher than the other two groups on social and religious values, while there is no difference among the three groups with regard to political values.

The failure of the independent inventors' profile of mean values to show high peaks on both theoretical and aesthetic values, which all our highly creative groups have shown, suggests that in general the creativity of our independent inventors may be less and will certainly be of a different type and form or both, from that of the other groups. Specifically, one might hazard the opinion that the independent inventors are less impressed by elegant solutions of intricate and abstract theoretical problems and relatively unmotivated to deal with them. Rather it is the functional and utilitarian aspects of problems which intrigue them. It is the "desire to improve"[16] already existing physical inventions, to make them more efficient and more useful that looms large in the motivational structure of the independent inventors. The economic drive, argued by Bennett to be the primary motive for inventive activity,[17] plays a more salient role in the case of these inventors who, in general, come from families of relatively low socioeconomic status and have been unable to improve their own position. But even in this group it is not the economic value which is highest; it is the theoretical value, though less highly developed than in the other creative samples we have studied.

The implications of the researches here reported for questions concerning the supply of inventors can be discussed in only the most restricted and tentative fashion. It must be emphasized that the samples for which data have been presented are small, and individual differences within each sample are rather large as the reported standard deviations for the various group means indicate. Thus the differences between the several groups discussed are far from definitive. They are

---

[16] The second most frequently mentioned motive for inventing of the respondents in Rossman's study of inventors (J. Rossman, *The Psychology of the Inventor: A Study of the Patentee*, Washington, D.C., The Inventors Publishing Co., 1931).

[17] W. B. Bennett, *The American Patent System: An Economic Interpretation*, Baton Rouge, Louisiana State University Press, 1943.

at best suggestive, and require further study in larger samples. They do, however, possess considerable psychological verisimilitude and for this reason have been judged worthy of discussion.

It must be emphasized that of the three classes of inventions and inventors often described we have so far sampled only two. None of the subjects studied by us have produced basic, extensive, labor-producing and factor-producing inventions. We have caught in our assessment net none of the truly great or outstanding inventors, either captive or independent. Our subjects, instead, have been drawn from the other two classes of inventors: on the one hand, those who have produced developmental, intensive, improving, labor-saving and factor-displacing inventions and, on the other hand, producers of minor inventions which result in the production of gadgets and the improvement of already existing devices.

To what extent the traits and attributes found to characterize the inventors in the present study would be found in basic inventors we cannot say. What is rather striking in our data are the clear-cut differences between our research scientist inventors and our sample of independent inventors. Whether these differences would be so sharp had our sample of independent inventors been a larger and more representative sample of the population we cannot say with certainty. My guess is that our sample underrepresents the more intelligent, better educated, more successful, and more affluent independent inventors. The small measure of success which our independent inventors had achieved both in their personal lives and in their inventive activity may well have motivated them to volunteer for study in the hope and expectation that participation in the research would in some way increase their own effectiveness. A wider and more adequate sampling of independent inventors would almost certainly have yielded still other types. And the most plausible assumption to be made about those who produce basic inventions is that, if studied, they would reveal still other types of inventors.

Rather than supporting the notion that all inventors are of a single type, our data and the implications to be drawn from them point to the existence of a multiplicity of inventive types. If this is so, one can be somewhat more optimistic about the future supply of inventors than are those observers who have concluded, erroneously in my judgment, that there is only one type of inventor, and he is to be found today almost entirely in large industrial laboratories.

COMMENT

Thomas S. Kuhn, University of California, Berkeley

Before discussing MacKinnon's paper, I am compelled to a confession. Examining the names and professional qualifications of the other participants in this conference, I doubt my suitability for the role I have been asked to play. Almost certainly I am the only member of the group who has never taken a course in either economics or psychology; very probably I am among the few who have never computed a correlation coefficient or who are forced, while reading over the conference proceedings, to pause in temporary puzzlement every time they encounter a phrase like "marginal utility." In this company, in short, I am a rank outsider. That isolation indicates no lack 'of interest in the problems under discussion. On the contrary, at least three of my recurrent roles—as ex-physicist, as practicing historian of science, and as interested citizen—repeatedly confront me with several of the central problems of this conference and often in a most acute form. But the nature of my professional background and concerns does mean that I approach the problems of this conference from a viewpoint very different from that of most other participants. That difference will certainly be reflected in my comments, and under the circumstances, it seems appropriate to make the sources of my viewpoint clear at the very start.

Let me turn now to the illuminating paper contributed to this conference by my Berkeley colleague, Donald MacKinnon. (It is one of the ironies of academic life that I should first meet him at a conference 2,000 miles from home.) That paper attempts to discover, from a variety of psychological tests, the distinctive research styles and personalities of three selected groups: research scientists who are not inventors, research scientists who are inventors, and independent inventors. The result is an investigation that I find particularly interesting, for experience as a historian has long since convinced me that the scientist and the inventor are often profoundly different types and that they characteristically flourish under rather different cultural and social circumstances. Evidence on this point is therefore what I particularly sought in MacKinnon's investigation, and I am delighted to report that it can be found there in a particularly striking form. But to isolate that evidence and to see its force, we must first examine those aspects of the investigation that would make it particularly easy for a hostile critic to dismiss the whole. Because design weakness is inevitable in any exploratory study, I shall not elaborate negative criticism. But it cannot be avoided entirely, because the most dubious aspects of the sampling procedures employed provide essential background for what seems to me the single most striking point that emerges from the research.

Look first at the two groups that MacKinnon has investigated most thoroughly. They are research scientist noninventors and research scientist inventors. To isolate them for investigation MacKinnon has split into two parts a single group of industrial scientists who were initially selected as a homogeneous sample for another study.[1] Those members of the initially homogeneous group who possessed at least one patent, patent application, or disclosure have been labeled "inventors"; the remainder of the group are "noninventors." It then turns out that only 48 per cent of the inventors are patentees and that the average number of patents per inventor is 0.88.

But can we be sure, except in the obvious numerical sense, that we are really dealing with two distinct groups? In industrial research all sorts of accidents may help to determine who gets his name on a patent application or disclosure, particularly if the invention derives from a group project. In addition, as many of the contributors to this conference have emphasized, policy about what to patent and what to keep secret varies immensely in different industrial situations. One may well suspect, therefore, that if there is an inventor type, many of its exemplars will be found among MacKinnon's "noninventors," while many of his "inventors" may not be of the inventor type at all. It is even conceivable that, as industrial scientists, his whole group should be labeled "inventors." Comparison with a sample drawn from university scientists would at least have lent his study more authority. These considerations do not suggest that MacKinnon's segregation of inventors from noninventors *must* be without significance, but they do raise questions. It can, for example, surprise no one that on almost all the tests the research scientist inventors and the research scientist noninventors show almost identical scores. Only a man trained in the subtlest forms of statistical analysis will feel any assurance that he can tell the two groups apart. But can we conclude anything from this as to the similarity of research scientist inventors and noninventors?

[1] H. G. Gough and D. G. Woodworth, "Stylistic Variations among Professional Research Scientists," *Journal of Psychology*, XLIX, 1960, pp. 87–98.

MacKinnon's third sample, the fourteen independent inventors, presents even more profound problems. Who are these people? They have in common their membership in the International Inventors Association, and they share a willingness to volunteer for psychological study. In addition, they are united by the fact that for them invention is only an avocation. Certainly they see themselves as inventors, but it is not clear that we should accept their image. Only 36 per cent of the group possesses a patent and the average number of patents per individual, while higher than that for the research scientist inventors, is only 1.25 per cent. Furthermore, these men are described as relatively little educated and as relatively unsuccessful, both personally and inventively. It is, therefore, not surprising to find that their test results are almost always very different from those of the other two groups. But there seems little reason to suppose that these quite striking differences have much of anything to do with their being "independent inventors." That could be the source of the differences but it surely need not be. Perhaps, for example, they are simply less privileged people.

Under these circumstances there is only one sort of result that participants in this conference should feel forced to accept as fully relevant to the problems that concern them. The similarity between MacKinnon's first two groups and the marked differences between these two and his third need not illuminate those problems. But what would necessarily be both illuminating and convincing would be a test result that displayed marked differences between MacKinnon's first group, the research scientist noninventors, and his second, the research scientist inventors. This discrimination would be even more striking if the same test showed a marked similarity between the two superficially different groups of inventors.

Now MacKinnon does get just such a result, though it is somewhat hidden by his method of presentation. It is contained in his Table 5 which I shall here somewhat simplify and rearrange. In doing so, let me dismiss for the moment—as possible statistical artifacts or as what, in my earlier career as a physicist, I called "dirt"—those entries which contain only one or two individuals. Simultaneously let me regroup the four remaining stylistic types, the ones that contain an obviously significant proportion of the members of at least one of the samples. Immediately a surprising result begins to emerge. Fully 61 per cent of MacKinnon's noninventors are to be found in the combined group representing research styles I and VII, though less than

20 per cent of either of the inventor groups falls there. On the other hand, if research styles II and III are grouped together, they are found to contain only 6 per cent of the noninventors but 52 per cent of the research scientist inventors.and 72 per cent of the independent inventors. These are the results summarized below in tabular form.

| *Research Styles* | *Research Scientist–* | | *Independent* |
| | *Noninventors* | *Inventors* | *Inventors* |
	(per cent)		*(per cent)*
I and VII	61	19	14
II and III	6	52	72

The summary displays just the sort of result I have suggested that we cannot afford to ignore. The two groups of research scientists, which elsewhere for obvious reasons, have looked very nearly identical, are here sharply distinguished. Simultaneously, the two groups of inventors, which have elsewhere and again for obvious reasons, looked very different, here show marked similarity. This finding may well point to a profoundly significant mode of discrimination. I, therefore, hope that MacKinnon and his colleagues will pursue it further, both with the data already at hand (there is vastly more of it than his paper shows) and with more refined tools of investigation. For example, a restudy of the Q-sort deck used in the investigation to determine which items are particularly responsible for the differentiations above should permit the design of a still more decisive testing tool.[2]

Discussion of what will emerge from this additional investigation should await the results of the research itself. The thumbnail epitomes of the eight stylistic types provided by MacKinnon are too brief to be more than suggestive. Yet they are suggestive, and I cannot quite resist concluding with a few speculative words about them. Presumably the commentator has a license that the author of a formal paper does not. Let me exploit it in order tentatively to note three likely differences between stylistic types I and VII, which include the bulk of

[2] A cursory inspection of the Q-sort deck used by Gough and Woodworth as well as of the results they got with it (*ibid.*, pp. 89–91) suggests, for example, that more attention be given to "unpopular" stylistic characteristics, ones that nobody in a research organization will quite wish to own to. "Has strong research biases" and "enjoys philosophical speculation" were characteristics of this sort in the Gough and Woodworth research. If I read the paper correctly, few scientists gave either of these characteristics high personal relevance, but the inventors rejected the first more strongly than the scientists, and the scientists rejected the second more strongly than the inventors.

MacKinnon's noninventors, and types II and III, which include the majority of his inventors.

Notice first that both types I and VII, unlike types II and III, give evidence of real difficulty in interpersonal relations. That difficulty could be part of a pattern of partial withdrawal from society, resulting concern with greater abstraction, and a concommitant low evaluation of practical and social service problems. Or again, notice, what is probably not at all surprising, that types II and III, the inventors, are both characterized by an unusual quickness of response and by a marked gift for improvisation. (This part of MacKinnon's finding, being drawn from the Q-sort, may refer only to the self-image, not to the actuality. But that would not deprive it of significance.) By contrast, the scientist noninventor is probably slower and perhaps also more self-critical and inhibited. As a historian, I have the impression that there is significant biographical support for this discrimination.

Finally, notice that groups II and III, the inventors, are just the ones whose members declare themselves markedly free from methodological and substantive bias. This finding seems congruent with the inventors' consciousness of uncommon rapidity and skill in improvisation as well as with the fact, noted by Gough and Woodworth, that the members of groups II and III are more prone to philosophical speculations than are the members of groups I and VII, the scientists.[3] Taken together these clues point clearly to a larger pattern that is at least implicit in Merrill's excellent contribution to this conference, and that I have developed elsewhere from historical sources.[4] That pattern suggests that the basic scientist, unlike the inventor, requires for his work a deep immersion in a pre-existing tradition. Such a tradition, acquired through professional training, informs him of the unsolved problems confronting his profession and tells him what will be acceptable as solutions to them. Without an immersion in that tradition he could scarcely operate as a scientist at all. The inventor, in contrast, requires little similar immersion. His problems tend to be externally, not professionally, defined and, in addition, his criterion of success is, of necessity, social adoption. Something of this same distinction seems to me dimly visible in MacKinnon's data.

[3] *Ibid.*
[4] T. S. Kuhn, "The Essential Tension: Tradition and Innovation in Scientific Research," in *The Third (1959) University of Utah Research Conference on the Identification of Creative Scientific Talent*, Calvin W. Taylor, editor, University of Utah Press, 1959, pp. 162–177.

Perhaps these tentative conclusions will not withstand the results of further investigation. Nevertheless, it is just because it may well permit conclusions of this sort that MacKinnon's paper seems to me so very challenging and so clearly worth pursuing.

Organization and Research and Development Decision Making Within the Decentralized Firm

ALBERT H. RUBENSTEIN

NORTHWESTERN UNIVERSITY

THIS investigation is focused on the specific relationships between certain corporate organizational characteristics—especially in decentralized firms—and their consequences for (1) operation of the research and development activity and (2) the results achieved through R and D.

In the first section, the general conceptual framework is described briefly. The succeeding section deals with several aspects of this framework and describes how they are being investigated.

Specifically, this paper deals with the way in which decisions significant for R and D are influenced by constraints related to the organizational form and economic characteristics of the large decentralized firm. Of particular interest are significant constraints deriving from the manner in which divisional performance is controlled and evaluated and the way in which the R and D resources of the company are deployed. Other phases of the investigation are described elsewhere.[1]

NOTE: The work reported in this paper was initiated at Massachusetts Institute of Technology and is being continued at Northwestern. It has been supported by grants-in-aid from: The Sloan Research Fund of the School of Industrial Management, M.I.T.; The McKinsey Foundation for Management Research, and several industrial companies.

[1] The study is now in its third year. It involves over 100 large decentralized manufacturing companies in six major industries. *Phase One* traces the historical relationship between corporate decentralization and the deployment of research and development resources and activities in the firm. The organizing principle for operating divisions is examined, as well as the initiation and termination of operating divisions. *Phase Two* examines the dynamics of the relationship between corporate headquarters and the operating divisions with respect to R and D policies and programs, in approximately 25 companies. *Phase Three* concentrates on the measurement of idea flow within and between laboratories of three companies.

Some reports of various phases of the study are: Robert W. Avery, "Enculturation in Industrial Research," *IRE Transactions on Engineering Management*, March 1960; Robert W. Avery, "Technical Objectives and the Production of Ideas in Industrial Laboratories," January 1959, unpublished; Donald B. Cotton, "Some Data on the Relation between Divisionalization and Deployment of Research and Development Laboratories in Decentralized Companies," January 1959, unpublished; Albert H. Rubenstein and Robert W. Avery, "Idea Flow in Research and Development," *Proceedings of the National Electronics Conference*, October 1958; Albert H. Rubenstein, "Organization of Divisionalized Research and Development," paper presented at the Operations Research Society Annual Meeting, November 1957; Albert H. Rubenstein, "Organizational Change, Corporate Decentralization, and the Constraints on Research and Development," presented at the Institute of Management Sciences, June 1959.

A Model of R and D Decision Making in the Firm

Figure 1, "A Schematic Diagram of the R and D Process in the Firm," is an abstract representation of the major variables and relationships which constitute the framework for this study. Briefly, the major variables are these:

1. The *objectives and mission* of the R and D activity in a company reflect the purposes for which management has established and continues to support it. Occasionally these purposes are spelled out in specific, operational terms for all involved to see and use as guides in decision making. Most frequently they are not. The statement of objectives or mission, if an explicit one is provided, is often vague and general. Part of the ambiguity or vagueness stems from a lack of clear understanding by top management of the capabilities and limitations of R and D in the firm. Consequently, few industrial research programs are "designed" with the aid of clear and quantitative specifications.

FIGURE 1

A Schematic Diagram of the R and D Process in the Firm

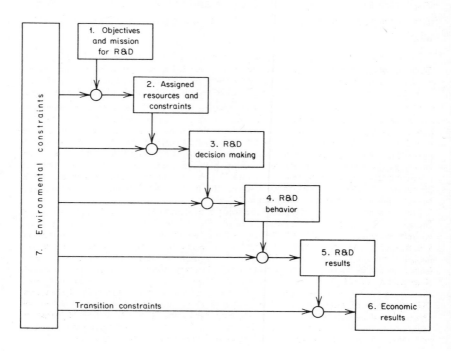

2. Assigned *resources and constraints* are provided by the company to enable the R and D activity to operate and to provide some measure of control over that activity. In general, the resources provide the means for carrying out the mission and the constraints are the rules of the game under which R and D is performed. The distinction between resources and constraints is not a clear one. In general, constraints tend to limit the alternatives of choice and action for the people in R and D. On the other hand, the assignment of resources can also limit alternatives. For example, one might consider the number and kind of people assigned to R and D as resources but, at the same time, that number constitutes a constraint on the laboratory's field of activity and the intensity of that activity. "One" chemist might be considered a resource, but "only one" chemist might be considered a constraint. The terminology of this investigation does not clearly distinguish between resources and constraints but views them as having a collective influence on decision making.

3. *R and D decision making* is an important variable. Since this is not a purely mechanical or deterministic system, constraints do not lead automatically to a specific, predictable pattern of R and D behavior. As in any process involving the interactions of people, there is a great deal of uncertainty about the response of individuals and groups of people to environmental circumstances.

Therefore, the relationships between constraints and behavior are ones of influence rather than determination. There is no guarantee that an intended constraint upon the behavior of laboratory personnel will be effective, e.g., that a restriction of the channels of communication will result, in fact, in the elimination or blockage of a given channel of communication.

It is highly likely, however, that if the researchers know about this intention to restrict communication, it will influence their behavior in conforming or not conforming to the restriction. In order for the constraints to affect behavior, then, a continuous process of decision making—conscious and unconscious—must occur within the R and D activity. Choices must be made continually on matters such as which problems to work on, how to work on them, how far and in what direction to pursue them, when to terminate them, and so on. A detailed catalogue of relevant decisions will be presented below.

4. *R and D behavior;* a major concern of this investigation is the process whereby constraints are perceived and transformed by decision making into actual behavior within the R and D activity.

Many aspects of R and D behavior are of interest and a number have been studied by students of research organization. In this investigation two aspects are of particular interest: (1) The actual distribution of effort among various classes of R and D activity, i.e. the R and D portfolio. This is a quantitative description of the allocation of time and other resources among tasks such as customer service, new product development, exploratory studies in a new field, etc. (2) The actual communication among the company's various R and D laboratories and between them and other segments of the company and the outside world. In particular, emphasis is placed on the flow of ideas between a given laboratory and its environment rather than merely on a gross measure of communication.

R and D behavior, in terms of what is worked on (project portfolio) and how the work is carried on (idea flow) is expected to strongly and directly influence R and D results.

5. *R and D results* are the direct product of R and D activity. They may be primarily scientific, technical, or informational. In general, they are an intermediate step in the realization of the mission, since they must be further transformed before economic results are achieved.

The achievement of a technical result, such as a solution to a problem of manufacturing process or product configuration, does not automatically insure that this result will be applied and that economic benefits will be forthcoming. In most cases, other activities in the firm—engineering, production, sales, finance—must act on the results in such a way as to ensure economic benefits.

At this stage another set of constraints appears which can further influence the success of the entire R and D process as measured by economic results. These may be called *transition constraints*. They are additional factors in the environment of the R and D activity which tend to limit the available alternatives of choice and action.

Examples of these constraints are: relations between R and D and departments which will ordinarily use their results; willingness or ability to innovate; financial condition of the company which may restrict the amount of capital available for exploiting research results; actions of competitors; shifts of interest within the company and within individual divisions.

6. *Economic results* are the final product of the R and D process. They reflect but do not directly measure the contribution made by R and D results to the welfare of the company in terms of increased profits, decreased costs, growth of assets or sales, increased good will,

etc. The "credit" for the total contribution to welfare must, of course, be shared by all of those activities involved in the process from statement of mission to economic results.

A number of practical attempts have been made to measure and allocate this credit directly to R and D but these efforts, even where useful empirically, are lacking in economic validity. The idea of "credit" for research achievements is not prominent in this investigation. Instead, an attempt is made to assess the contribution of particular projects and programs to the welfare of the company, without trying to divide the credit among functional activities such as research and development, production, marketing, etc.

An additional consideration adds complexity to analysis of the R and D process. Figure 1 suggests that the main direction of influence between the factors described is from constraints to behavior to results. Certainly influence is also exerted in the other direction. For example, the degree of success achieved by R and D in either research results or economic results has an effect on the future constraints which are imposed on it, or to which it responds.

Because of the complexity of the R and D process and the current lack of systematic knowledge about it,[2] all the relationships described are in the form of partial explanations. Hence, R and D decisions do not *determine* R and D behavior, but they do strongly *influence* it. Sometimes this influence is negative, e.g., if a decision is made not to undertake work in a given field, the chances are that nothing of importance will be achieved by the company in that area. Discoveries, however, can be made by accident; and projects can be "smuggled" into the R and D portfolio despite decisions to the contrary.

This paper deals primarily with the upper half of Figure 1, and traces the chain of perceived constraints on R and D decision making from top corporate management to the bench researcher. Other papers resulting from the investigation deal with such aspects of the R and D process as economic results, transition constraints, and more detailed analyses of objectives, mission, and R and D behavior.

---

[2] For example, we have not even been able to say with confidence what the significant research achievements have been in various industries over a given period, and which firms have been responsible for the achievements. A start has been made on this in some of the other studies reported in this volume and in three Masters' theses done in connection with this project and submitted at Massachusetts Institute of Technology. The latter include: Charles F. Langenhagen, Jr., "An Evaluation of Research and Development in the Chemical Industry," June 1958; William Miles, "An Evaluation of Research and Development in the Textile Industry," June 1959; and Alexander S. Ninian, "The Role of Research and Development in the American Steel Industry," June 1959.

It is necessary to point out that we are a long way from a complete explanatory or predictive theory of research management. We lack basic information on the nature of "other" influences and their consequences. This investigation has selectively focused on what appears to be the main stream of influence in R and D decision making within the decentralized firm, with additional classes of relationships (colleagues and outsiders) acknowledged and described where possible, but not investigated in detail. The design of the investigation is intended to yield descriptions of a significant portion of the total influence under which the R and D process operates, with the balance to be investigated in other ways and at other times.

The test of significance is a qualitative one, arising from the data itself. If a particular constraint or class of constraints is found to have had important consequences for the behavior and accomplishments of the R and D activity in more than a single instance, it is incorporated into the general explanatory scheme which is developing as the investigation proceeds. If a given constraint is encountered in only one situation, an attempt is made to relate it to other classes of constraint, of which it may be a special case.

In summary, the output of this investigation is not conceived of as a series of detailed case studies of how R and D is influenced in a number of specific companies, with an analysis in depth of the specific circumstances, events, and personalities that influenced it in each company. Rather, it is thought of as a general, if approximate, description of how R and D is influenced in a large, decentralized company. The particular circumstances, events, and personalities should provide more or less predictable variations from the expected behavior suggested by the general description or "theory."

R and D Decision Making in the Decentralized Firm

An important task in this phase of the investigation is the cataloguing of the various classes of decisions made *by* R and D and *about* R and D which can have a significant effect on its contribution of economic results to the firm. Certainly each move by each researcher or member of the management hierarchy which relates to R and D can have some important effect on the outcome of specific projects, programs (related groups of projects), and the R and D activity as a whole. A chemist's decision to study material A first, rather than materials B,

C, or D, may have far-reaching consequences, as the history of science amply demonstrates.[3]

In this investigation, we are concerned with decisions about these subjects: organizational form (internal organization of R and D, e.g. organization by project or by function, relations between functions); specific projects and major project phases; programs (groups of related projects); fields (general technical areas not yet formalized as programs); ideas (suggestions or recommendations for work which have not yet been formally designated as projects or programs); transition (progression from the laboratory to market); personnel (recruiting, hiring, promotion, recognition, and reward).

The classes of decision that apply to these subjects yield a large number of specific types of decisions of particular interest. Our sample consists of the largest companies in each of several industry groups. Each of these companies has an R and D activity of some sort in operation. We, therefore, start our examination of decision making in R and D with the assumption that there is an existing R and D activity—organized, funded, otherwise constrained, and behaving in a given way. Our attention is focused on the decisions made about and by R and D which tend to change its current behavior or to overtly reconfirm its current behavior.

CONSTRAINTS ON R AND D DECISION-MAKING

As suggested by Figure 1, decision making by members of the R and D activity is influenced by their perceptions of the constraints intended by people above them in the company hierarchy and by their perceptions of the additional constraints imposed by the environment, e.g. the actions of colleagues, competitors, and other people working in their field; economic conditions; the state of the art; the body of scientific knowledge; the body of scientific opinion; and many other factors of possible influence.

Although the results of the investigation thus far argue against the existence of a unique organizational form or set of specific constraints on the R and D activity in companies that have been technologically successful, there is reason to expect that there is a set of sufficient although not necessary patterns of constraints which are associated with successful R and D. That is, there may be a number of patterns

[3] See, for example, I. Bernard Cohen, "The 'Happy Accident' and its Consequences," Chap. 3 in *Science, Servant of Man*, Boston, Little, Brown, 1948.

of constraints which can, alternatively, provide the milieu or environmental conditions conducive to "chance" discovery.[4]

In this investigation, attention has been focused on several specific constraints which appear to have particular relevance for the behavior and results of R and D in the decentralized company, although they may also be relevant to R and D activity in any setting. Some of them derive directly from the very nature of the decentralized company, others appear to be accentuated by the specific circumstances of the decentralized company.

The prominent features of the typical large decentralized firm may be recognized as including a top management group, several corporate staff activities (e.g., research management), and a series of relatively autonomous operating divisions, which carry on the direct productive functions of the business such as production, engineering, and distribution. The exact organizational structure and distribution of functions varies among firms and among industries. The salient features for our purposes are the organization of the corporation's business into relatively "autonomous" operating units—generally along technological or market lines—and the establishment of measures of performance for the purposes of control, incentive, and reward.

The following specific constraints are being investigated in this study:

METHODS OF EVALUATING AND REWARDING DIVISIONAL PERFORMANCE. What measures of performance are used; how frequently are they applied; how is divisional performance related to the compensation of divisional officers, etc.

ORGANIZATIONAL DEPLOYMENT, LOCATION, AND STATUS OF R AND D. How many laboratories; what is the chain of command; how large are the various laboratories; is R and D represented on the Board of Directors or the executive committee, etc.

ASSIGNED MISSION OF R AND D IN THE COMPANY. Does R and D have complete responsibility for technological innovation; what fields, programs, or projects are explicitly assigned to R and D; how closely are divisional laboratories expected to support current divisional activities, etc.

COMPANY POLICY ON DIVERSIFICATION, ACQUISITION, AND MERGER. Will the company welcome, resist, or be indifferent to engaging in new lines of business; has the company historically

[4] Karl Deutsch speaks of "designing for the improbable" (private communication).

researched its way or bought its way into new businesses and new technologies, etc.

METHODS OF FUNDING R AND D. Do the divisions fund their own R and D; does the corporation "tax" the divisions for support of a central or corporate research facility; does the central lab (if one exists) charge divisions for its services; do any of the laboratories have outside sources of funds (e.g. government contracts), etc.

SIZE AND RATE OF CHANGE OF THE R AND D BUDGET. Is the company's over-all expenditure on R and D increasing, remaining relatively stable (except for increases due to costs), decreasing, changing gradually or radically; how does the size of the R and D budget relate to company sales, profits, dividends, advertising budget; etc.

RESEARCHER ATTITUDES AND BELIEFS. How do the goals of the organization relate to those of the researcher; how well is he aware of the company's interests and capabilities; what are his relative interests in science and business, etc.

PROJECT SELECTION AND APPROVAL PROCEDURES. At which point in the hierarchy may projects be approved; are formal methods such as mathematical formulae used in project selection; is there a research advisory committee and if so, what are its powers and what is its membership, etc.

This phase of the study, in which the constraints on decision making regarding R and D are being investigated, has been carried out in varying degrees in about two dozen companies. The principal methods being used are several forms of interview, ranging from relatively free discussions about the effects of decentralization on R and D, or recent changes in corporate structure or policy that may have affected R and D to relatively structured interviews aimed at replies to specific questions about particular constraints or events or historical situations; questionnaires directed at tracing the constraints on flow of ideas and the R and D portfolios of particular laboratories; and examination of records for information about R and D expenditures, company policy and policy changes, organization structures, promotional histories, etc.

Organization and Research and Development Decision Making Within a Government Department

PAUL W. CHERINGTON, MERTON J. PECK, AND FREDERIC M. SCHERER

HARVARD UNIVERSITY

THIS paper examines some organizational aspects of military R and D decision making. For the purposes of our discussion we visualize R and D as a continuous spectrum of activities that can for expository purposes be divided into discrete steps, as follows:

Step I. The formation and empirical verification of theories about parameters of the physical world.

Step II. The creation and testing of radically new physical components, devices, and techniques.

Step III. The identification, modification, and combination of existing components and devices to provide a distinctly new application practical in terms of performance, reliability, and cost.

Step IV. Relatively minor modification of existing components, devices, and systems to improve performance, increase reliability, reduce cost, and simplify application.[1]

For those who like a more conventional terminology step I can be equated with basic science, step II with applied research, step III with advanced engineering and development, and step IV with engineering. Since several of the papers presented in this volume are concerned with the nature of these steps and their interaction, we shall not discuss them in any detail here.

It is commonly said that the technical problems of weaponry are increasing. Certainly, two changes distinguish the post-Korean projects from those of 1946 to 1949. First, step I and II activities play a larger role in the missile and supersonic aircraft developments of the 1950's, although the bulk of the effort remains in stage III. Second, the effort at stage III has become more complex.

In this kind of technical environment, the crucial decision to initiate a weapons program, to provide for its funding, and to administer its execution can be formulated in terms of two kinds of considerations.

---

[1] This tabulation is adopted from David Novick, "What Do We Mean By Research and Development," *Illinois Business Review*, November 1959.

First, what is the relationship between cost in terms of both dollars and time and the performance of the weapon, that is, what might be called the development possibility function. Second, what is military utility or value of various combinations of cost, time, and performance. Conceptually, it is apparent that the decisions in weapons projects are identical to those in the theory of the firm. But in view of the great uncertainties involved a purely formalistic and static analysis would tell us very little about how weapons projects are administered.

The approach we have been assigned is to examine some of the aspects of the organizational framework for weapons projects. Each of the various groups involved can be viewed as one element or force in the decision process that we ordinarily visualize as taking place inside the skull of an idealized decision maker. In this way, we can distinguish some of the factors that underlie a complex development decision.

Patterns of Organization

Having set forth the several levels of research and development, it is appropriate to examine the pattern of organization within which decisions concerning them are made. Figure 1 sets forth a highly simplified, over-all organizational chart, using the Air Force by way of illustration. This chart shows all of the major groups that are apt to become involved in a decision to go ahead with a step III development project for a major (and probably controversial) system. A decision involving a step I research project would probably involve many fewer groups and perhaps only some subunit of the Air Research and Development Command, which would enter into a contract for a few thousand dollars with a university, specifying that one or two individuals would work in a fairly broad area.

For present purposes, we shall confine our attention to a decision to begin serious development of a major weapon system (step III).

There are a number of ways in which such a development may be initiated. A contractor may propose it. It may result from a special study by a group such as the RAND Corporation. It may be proposed by a subunit of either the ARDC or an operating command. But the first formal document proposing development of such a system probably originates in the headquarters development staff.

Various development possibilities and their military value are appraised and integrated into a program recommendation by the

FIGURE 1
Groups Involved in a Major Air Force Program Decision

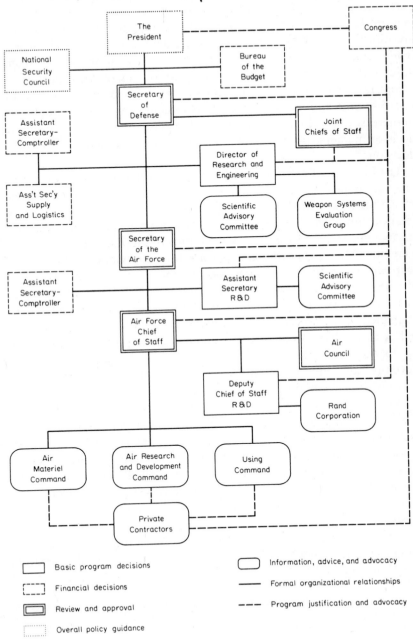

headquarters research and development staff of the particular military service. Participating in these determinations are civilian counterparts in the offices of the service secretary and perhaps the Secretary of Defense. Information and often complete recommendations are obtained from the service's procurement and research agencies, from commands which will use the proposed weapon system, from industrial contractors, and from a variety of independent groups.

Several hundred persons are apt to have a hand in the process of coordinating and clearing the development proposal through the numerous offices in Washington and the field. These are not ultimate decision makers, but some of them may help to shape the ultimate decision.

The location of the crucial decision to proceed with a development program depends upon the quantity of resources required, the degree of certainty attached to cost and military value expectations, the relationship of the particular program to programs of other agencies, the extent to which overall national policy is affected, and many other elements. Most program decisions are formally made by the service secretary upon the recommendation of the military chief. However, if neither of the two revises the recommendations of his staff, who has made the decision? And decisions of the services can be altered or overruled by the Secretary of Defense and his staff. When top national policy is involved, weapons development decisions have been passed up to the President, e.g. it was President Roosevelt's decision to develop the atomic bomb and President Truman's decision to move forward into the hydrogen bomb.

What can be stated is that the program decision is a function of the United States executive branch. The Congress has on occasion attempted unsuccessfully to cancel programs (such as the Air Force's Mace guided missile) and to have programs initiated (such as its efforts to accelerate development of a nuclear propelled bomber). But its power over program decisions must be exercised mainly through persuasion (a not insignificant factor) and through broad budgetary controls.[2]

This suggests another aspect of the program decision—the determination of resource levels, usually in dollar terms, once the program has been approved. Again, the locus of program decisions is not

[2] For an excellent discussion of the U.S. organization for weapons program decision making, see *Hearings* on Organization and Management of Missile Programs, H.R. Committee on Government Operations, 11th Report, 1959, especially pp. 151–152.

easily described. Initial program budgets are usually prepared by military procurement agencies on the basis of information submitted by contractors. The budgets are then revised successively by the service headquarters staff, by the service secretary's comptroller and research and development staffs, by the Secretary of Defense's staff, by the Bureau of the Budget, and finally by Congress.[3] Even when Congress makes its annual appropriation, the level of spending on any one program is not absolutely determined, for the executive agencies can withhold money (as was done in the Polaris and Nike Zeus programs, to cite only two instances) and can divert money from other categories to conduct programs for which funds were not appropriated (as in the Mace case[4]).

In sum, very many hands and heads participate in any weapon system program decision, with the result being a lengthy and complex decision making chain. Almost inevitably the chain will include both advocates and skeptics, and an important dissent can seriously delay a program considered urgent by others. These characteristics of the U.S. program decision making process have been studied and criticized repeatedly in recent years. As retired Lt. General James M. Gavin, former chief of the Army Office of Research and Development, wrote,

> It has been the decisions that have been, at times, shockingly in error, not only the decisions themselves, but their tardiness. And the principal object of any reorganization now should be to accelerate and improve the quality of the decision-making processes.[5]

Nevertheless, as noted earlier, our immediate object is simply to point out the economic features and problems of the program decision making process, not to recommend specific corrections. To that end it is particularly useful to look for a moment at the terminal links in the decision chain: the information inputs at one end and the final decision making locus at the other end.

Let us begin by considering the final decision locus. Critics of the

---

[3] Cf. *Hearings* on Research and Development, H.R. Committee on Government Operations, 32nd report, 1958, especially pp. 100–102 and pp. 116–146.

[4] Cf. *Hearings* on Organization and Management of Missile Programs, *op. cit.*, p. 65.

[5] *War and Peace in the Space Age*, New York, Harper, 1958, p. 163 ff. Other examples include the Rockefeller Report, *International Security: The Military Aspect*, Garden City, Doubleday, 1958, pp. 27–35; and the Robertson Report.

weapons decision making process have often questioned the need for secretarial reviews and concurrences. However, analysis of commercially sponsored developments suggests that their wonderment may be misdirected—it is perhaps more amazing that so much authority is delegated to generals and assistant secretaries. Even in the largest U.S. corporations, projects involving more than roughly $100,000 are critically evaluated by at least a vice-president, and often by the company's president and board of directors. Yet, in contrast, Air Force weapon system project officers (usually lieutenant colonels) have authority to approve program changes involving up to $350,000, and the Air Research and Development Command can begin new programs costing up to $1 million and authorize program changes worth up to $5 million on its own initiative. Major weapons programs, however, involve tens to hundreds of millions of dollars. The interest of top Pentagon decision makers when these sums are at stake is not surprising.[6] The significant question is not whether these top officials should be interested; it is whether they are in a position to comprehend the full range of issues involved in a technically complex program decision. But this matter must be deferred until the issues themselves are better defined.

Turning to the inputs of information for such decisions, most of the various groups shown in Figure 1 add information about strategic worth and technical feasibility. Two outside groups, the weapons contractors and the scientific advisory committees, deserve some special attention at this point.

Role of Contractors

In recent years, private contractors have taken an active part both as sources of information and as advocates of the weapons development in which they participate. With respect to the former role, contractors are perhaps the most important source of new weapons ideas.[7] Besides ideas, they provide information on the technological feasibility of new concepts and data on estimated development costs

---

[6] In other nations weapons acquisition decisions are also matters of top-level interest, often at the expense of rapid decision making. For one account of delayed top-level decisions, see "Swiss Fighter Choice Referred to Council," *Aviation Week*, October 26, 1959, p. 103.

[7] Cf. the testimony of Air Force Association president Peter J. Schenk in *Hearings* on Employment of Retired Military and Civilian Personnel by Defense Industries, Subcommittee for Special Investigations of the H.R. Committee on Armed Services, 1959, p. 396; and the Robertson Report.

and schedules—the basic elements of what we have called the development possibility map. In addition, practically every major weapon system prime contractor has an operations analysis group which studies the military value of new weapons possibilities—the other half of our theoretical program decision model.

Such contractor furnished information could be a valuable input into the program decision making process. On occasion, however, advocacy becomes mixed with education in unwholesome proportions. Particularly troublesome are unrealistic cost and time estimates submitted to "sell" a company's proposals. Moreover, contractors are so prolific in generating new weapons proposals that frequently the ideas are not fully evaluated by military planners who lack the time or perseverance required to plow through the chaff for a few kernels of wheat. As a result, even though contractors are potentially the best source of information on weapons possibilities, the admixture of advocacy with information prevents realization of the source's full value.

Of considerably less significance to the program decision making process, but of apparently greater public concern, are the efforts of contractors to promote their programs through public communications media and personal selling. The full-page advertisements purchased by producers of the competing Bomarc and Nike Hercules antiaircraft guided missiles provoked President Eisenhower to utter his much-quoted comment in 1959 about the "munitions lobby."[8] A House of Representatives committee termed such advertising "dangerous and unhealthy."[9] The same committee conducted extensive investigations into the employment of retired military officers by defense contractors for the purpose of their sales contacts and into the entertainment of military decision makers by contractors.[10] A more subtle means for generating widespread interest in specific weapons programs are company press releases (approved, of course, by the military agencies) describing in detail technical features and accomplishments of their development efforts.[11] Such releases are published

---

[8] *New York Times*, June 4, 1959, p. 14. The advertisements appeared in leading Washington, D.C., and New York newspapers on April 8 and 21, and May 27, 1959.

[9] *Hearings* on Employment of Retired Commissioned Officers, p. 15.

[10] *Ibid.*; and also by the same Subcommittee, *Supplemental Hearings* Released from Executive Session Relating to Entertainment, Furnished by the Martin Company of Baltimore, Md., of U.S. Government Officers, 1959.

[11] See, for example, the rash of optimistic articles on the Titan ICBM development in the January 11 and 18, 1960, issues of *Aviation Week* and the January 25 issue of *Missiles and Rockets*, just when the Titan program entered a period of crisis, with cancellation

readily by trade magazines anxious to report the newest developments in their fields, and the result is a substantial literature on otherwise secret weapons programs.

It must be said in fairness that much of the advocacy surrounding
U. S. weapons programs is not of a malicious or mercenary sort. Both
contractors and sponsoring services usually have a genuine belief that
their weapons programs are essential to the national defense. If this
sincerity does not come from pride in invention, it soon develops just
as a result of constantly living with the idea. However, selling a new
program to all the skeptics in a decision making chain is not easy.
Indeed, history shows that were it not for zealous advocacy, many new
military developments would never have received approval until it
was too late. Under these circumstances, personal contact with "the
right people" is an effective means of getting ideas accepted. Similarly,
creating public demand for a program through advertising and feature
articles is a way of winning over or bypassing balky decision makers.
Nevertheless, there is a deep-seated presumption in the United States
that the government (perhaps unlike private consumers) should not
be "sold" on new weapons; that it is intelligent enough to recognize its
needs and make rational decisions without coaxing.

Use of Scientific Consultants

Given the tendency for advocacy to creep into the presentations of
both contractors and sponsoring military agencies, and recognizing
their own inability to deal with the vast array of technical questions
in weapons program decisions, top military and civilian officials have
felt the need for some objective source of creative ideas and technical
evaluation. One solution has been the widespread employment of
professional scientists as special consultants to the government.
Beginning with the National Defense Research Committee formed in
1940 (the group that sponsored the Manhattan Project and the Radia-
tion Laboratory), the scientific advisory committee has come to play
a truly significant role in U. S. weapons decisions. After World War
II, the counsel of leading scientists and engineers was instrumental
in the decision not to promote the development of ballistic missiles
and later (when a committee of scientists predicted the breakthrough
in hydrogen warhead technology) in the decision to develop ballistic

---

under serious consideration, after several highly unsuccessful tests. On the program's
uncertain position at the time, cf. "Martin Girds for Titan Crisis," *Business Week*,
January 9, 1960, p. 69.

missiles with maximum urgency. Scientific advisory committees similarly influenced decisions to undertake the Polaris submarine launched ballistic missile development, not to cancel (in 1959) the Bomarc antiaircraft guided missile program, to proceed cautiously on the Nike Zeus anti-missile project, and to proceed with or abandon a variety of other weapons developments. By 1960, practically no high-level weapons decision maker was without a full complement of standing and *ad hoc* scientific advisory committees.[12]

The role of scientific consultants and advisory committees in program decisions can be stated in terms of a theoretical program decision model. First, they determine whether or not a weapon system of certain technical characteristics is feasible or not (whether or not a development possibility curve exists); second, they assess the development cost and time required to obtain weapons of those characteristics (estimating the position and shape of our development possibility curves); and third, they make independent technical evaluations of the strategic worth of proposed weapon systems (building up what we have called the military value function).

Naturally, not all scientific advisory committees perform all of these functions, and when they do, they do not perform them equally well. Such committees appear to be most useful in appraising the technical feasibility of proposed weapon systems, that is, in judging whether given systems can be developed or not. In this role the scientist's familiarity with the fringes of the state of the art is a valuable asset. But in projecting development costs and schedules, either *ab initio* or through the evaluation of contractor submissions, the scientist often has less to offer. The reason why is summarized from testimony of guided missile and satellite expert Werner von Braun:

> It is helpful to have a scientific advisory committee at a time when you kick the question around whether a certain proposal is sound or desirable and in the country's interest and whether the performance promises made are sound, and so forth. . . . But the missile business, particularly once a missile project really gets going, involves many questions which are, I would say, non-

[12] For a chronological "who's who" of committees in the guided missile field from 1950 through 1959, see *Hearings* on Organization and Management of Missile Programs, *op. cit.*, 1959, pp. 712–777. A more compact 1957 list appears in *Hearings* on Inquiry into Satellite and Missile Programs, Senate Committee on Armed Services, Preparedness Investigating Subcommittee, 1958, pp. 352–355. The contributions of scientific advisory committees are described at length in *Hearings* on Organization and Management of Missile Programs, 1959, *op. cit.*, especially pp. 12–15 and 69–74.

scientific in nature; they have something to do with project management or time schedules. For example, a physics professor may know a lot about the upper atmosphere, but when it comes to making a sound appraisal of what missile schedule is sound and how you can phase a research and development program into industrial production, he is pretty much at a loss. . . . I believe an established missile program, like the Jupiter, has much more similarity with an industrial planning job than with a scientific project. . . . I would say [Jupiter] was 90 per cent engineering and 10 per cent scientific, and in these scientific areas we love scientific advice.[13]

Recognizing the value of scientific advice both in broad feasibility evaluations and detailed problem areas, von Braun nonetheless suggested a more fundamental reason for the proliferation of scientific advisory committees:

Sir, there are many areas where we even go to them and ask for their advice, but I think to expect a scientist to have all the answers to everything—my personal feeling, to be frank about this, is as follows: I believe that the prestige factor plays a very important part in these things. When confronted with a difficult decision involving several hundred million dollars, and of vital importance to the national defense, many Pentagon executives like to protect themselves. It helps if a man can say, "I have on my advisory committee some Nobel prizewinners, or some very famous people that everybody knows." And if these famous people then sign a final recommendation, the executive feels, "Now, if something goes wrong, nobody can blame me for not having asked the smartest men in the country what they think about this."[14]

Even in the assessment of technological feasibility, the task of a scientific advisor is not as narrow as one might imagine. There is a tendency to think of the state of the art as something very objective—either an accomplishment is technologically possible or it is not, and that is all there is to it. But, more frequently, this is not so. There are

[13] *Hearings* on Inquiry into Satellite and Missile Programs, *op. cit.*, pp. 591, 592, 589, and 590. The order of the comments has been rearranged.
[14] *Ibid.*, p. 591.

two major factors: whether a given accomplishment is possible for the best group of scientists and engineers available; and whether a given group can accomplish the task. What is quite possible for one development group to accomplish may be extremely difficult for another development group, merely because the former group is more competent or has specialized experience. There are wide variations in competence between development groups both within individual companies and between firms. Consequently, a good technical feasibility evaluation must consider not only the state of the art in a very objective sense, but also the competence, insight, motivation, and other characteristics of those who propose to develop the weapon. By failing to include these latter subjective elements, some scientific advisory committees have missed the mark badly in their evaluations.

Organizational Influences

The foregoing discussion is perhaps sufficient to illustrate the enormous complexity of the structure through which R and D decisions must pass when major step III projects are involved. But there are a number of additional influences that are brought to bear on the final decision that have their antecedents in the organizational structure. They may not be immediately apparent from an examination of the formal organizational chart. These may be briefly summarized as (1) objectivity versus confidence, (2) the influence of the operators, (3) the level of priority, (4) the fit with roles and missions and, (5) the influence of external forces.

OBJECTIVITY VERSUS CONFIDENCE

When the state of the art is uncertain, weapons decisions must often be based on interpersonal confidence rather than objective analysis.[15] The history of technology is replete with situations where innovations were supported not because the underlying logic was overwhelming but because someone with funds believed in someone with an idea.[16]

One illustration of the influence of "confidence" will suffice. A situation involving hundreds of millions of dollars is to be found in

[15] Along the same line but in a more traditional vein, see F. H. Knight, who observes that the basic problem of organizational responsibility and control is judging men's powers of judgment, not the facts of the situation (*Risk, Uncertainty, and Profit*, Boston, Houghton Mifflin, 1921, p. 292).

[16] There are also sufficient examples of failure under these conditions to provide one explanation of the tendency of program decision makers to gain assurance from several sources.

the conflict over whether the Nike Zeus antimissile missile system should be produced. Critics of the program in top decision making positions feared that, because of technological uncertainties, the system would not meet its performance promises or that the development would not be completed on schedule. Nevertheless, the Army had "tremendous confidence" in the system, largely because of the Army's successful experience with the same development team in the Nike Ajax and Nike Hercules programs.[17] To resolve this conflict, an independent committee of top scientists was appointed. Published information indicates that the committee accepted as given the development group's performance and schedule promises, confining its inquiry mainly to the question whether a weapon system of the proposed performance would provide military value commensurate with its cost.[18]

INFLUENCE OF THE OPERATORS

It is no secret that most military organizations are heavily oriented toward immediate operational capability—how can we fight right now. This is reflected in the fact that a chief of staff is typically an operating or combat man and that the headquarters operations staff is typically the most influential of the several functional staff groups. In the process of developing a proposal for a major advanced weapons system and pushing it through the decision making machinery, the influence of the operators bulks large. This has the tendency—but it is no more than that—to place emphasis on nearer-in projects and to mean that more speculative and farther-out projects are rejected, or are carried out as Step II component developments.

LEVEL OF PRIORITY

A major factor affecting both the level at which key decisions are made and the speed with which they are made is the level of priority of the project. The priority may be determined by an enemy threat, by a technological breakthrough or possibly by a competing project of a rival service. In the case of decisions affecting high priority pro-

[17] Cf. the testimony of Maj. Gen. Robert J. Wood, U.S. Army Deputy Chief of Research and Development, *Hearings* on Department of Defense Appropriations for 1960, H.R. Committee on Appropriations, Part 6, page 422. The fiscal year 1959, 1960, and 1961 Congressional appropriations documents abound with comments on the Nike Zeus controversy.

[18] Cf. "Defense Group Evaluates Zeus Potential," *Aviation Week*, November 2, 1959, p. 30; and "Zeus Delayed by Technical Doubt, Budget," *Aviation Week*, February 8, 1960, p. 32.

jects, the organizational machinery can be, and often is, made to work with considerable rapidity. Some of the steps normally undertaken are eliminated, some of the organizational units are short-circuited, and the ones retained are made to take coordinating action more rapidly. It is perhaps significant that in both the Navy and the Air Force, special organizations have been established to handle and make key R and D decisions on high priority missile projects.

FIT WITH ROLES AND MISSIONS

Some special decisions have to be made (usually at the top level of the service) when a project decision brings into issue the role or mission of the service. For example, in the air defense field, antiaircraft batteries had been assigned to the Army, air defense aircraft to the Air Force. With the advent of air defense missiles, the respective roles and missions of the services in the air defense field became a matter of controversy. Each service had a weapon presumably capable of destroying enemy bombers, and the only distinguishing feature was that the Army weapon (Nike) was a so-called point-defense weapon while the Air Force, in the Bomarc, had an "area-defense" weapon. This distinction was not sufficient to keep the weapons from being sharply competitive. This competition, and its potential threat to the services' role in the air defense mission, had a considerable influence not only on the initial R and D program decision but on a variety of subsidiary decisions as the respective programs proceeded.

What is usually referred to as interservice rivalry often has its origin in this type of roles and missions ambiguity. It thereupon may become an influential factor in various R and D decisions.

INFLUENCE OF EXTERNAL FORCES

There are, of course, a host of external forces which tend to influence R and D program decisions and which are the product both of the internal organizational complex of the Department of Defense and the services and of the relationship of the DOD to other parts of the government. The most familiar are the budgetary influences on program decisions as exercised by the Treasury, the Budget Bureau, the President and, ultimately, by the Congress. But there are many others.

The decision makers may be urged to delay the announcement of the cancellation of a major R and D program until after an election on the grounds of political expediency. They may be urged to give a contract for a new program to contractor A rather than contractor B on the grounds of a high level of unemployment in contractor A's territory and in view of the fact that contractor A's capability is almost on a par with B's.

The fact that such courses are urged, perhaps by powerful external organizations, does not mean that they are automatically followed. On the other hand, depending on the power of the external organization, they undoubtedly receive consideration unless deemed wholly unreasonable. The DOD and each service must, after all, live in an environment of accommodation with other branches and agencies of government.

It is sometimes claimed that political factors play a large role in R and D decisions, especially in the matter of source selection. It is our impression that political influence on R and D decisions is greatly overrated. But it would be absurd to deny that it is not attempted and that it tends to complicate R and D decisions.

Some Society-Wide
Research and Development Institutions

ROBERT S. MERRILL

UNIVERSITY OF MINNESOTA

THIS paper is concerned with institutional or organizational determinants of directions of research and development activity. In Western industrial societies, R and D of many kinds is carried out in a variety of different society-wide institutional settings. For example, the National Science Foundation distinguishes four major R and D sectors: industry; colleges and universities; other nonprofit institutions; and federal government agencies. In addition, each of these sectors includes several subsystems. If we want to understand the determinants of directions of R and D, we need to understand how these different institutional systems operate and how they are interrelated to form an overall system.

With the recent increase of interest in R and D has come a considerable increase in quantitative data about R and D and in descriptions of relevant institutions. But, except for work on industrial R and D making use of economic theory,[1] there seems to be relatively little effort to formulate systematic notions about how the institutional subsystems operate. It seems to me that even crude "models" of the other R and D subsystems would serve two useful functions at this stage of our study. They would serve as guides in selecting important questions for empirical research. And they would serve as a basis for developing more rigorous and sophisticated theories.

The particular aim of this paper is to present some preliminary ideas about the workings of four R and D subsystems: "pure" academic natural science research, academic medical research, academic engineering research, and government agricultural research. These were chosen because they differ from one another and from the market-patent system. Therefore, they may suggest something of the

NOTE: I want to thank Jacob Schmookler, Scott Maynes and, especially, Joseph Spengler for helpful comments on earlier drafts of this paper. The defects remaining are mine alone. Much of the work was done while at the Research Center in Economic Development and Cultural Change, the University of Chicago.

[1] Richard R. Nelson, "The Economics of Invention: A Survey of the Literature," *Journal of Business*, Vol. 32, 1959, pp. 101–127 and, by the same author, "The Simple Economics of Basic Scientific Research," *Journal of Political Economy*, Vol. 67, 1959, pp. 297–306.

variety of the institutional arrangements which affect R and D. The sketches are presented as hypotheses, not proven facts, and preliminary hypotheses at that.

Certain limitations of the discussion need to be mentioned at the outset. First, my concern is with determinants of directions of R and D activity within each subsystem. No effort is made to discuss the factors which influence the total amount of funds made available to each subsystem. Second, I have made the assumption that the outside groups and organizations that finance much of the research in the academic subsystems discussed do not have major net effects on the directions of research within these systems. This begs a question which is the subject of considerable contemporary debate, especially with reference to government financing. However, I believe the assumption is a useful first approximation. Moreover, I think improving our understanding of the internal workings of the academic subsystems is a necessary step in developing ways of empirically determining the role of outside subsidizers.

Academic Science Research

The first example of a society-wide R and D subsystem I would like to discuss is that of "pure" or theoretical natural science research as carried out in universities. The distinguishing feature of "pure" scientific research is the aim of advancing knowledge and gaining deeper understanding for its own sake. More work has probably been done on developing a picture of how academic science functions as a system than on any other nonindustrial R and D subsystem. This provides exceedingly helpful guides. In particular, I am much indebted to Polanyi for many of the ideas used here.[2]

My procedure is first to outline some of the crucial features of the institutional setting of academic science. I then try to show, in a simplified way, how these features lead to an over-all pattern of allocation of personnel and resources among different lines of research within academic science. Next I discuss the particular content of the scientific values used in judging the scientific significance of substantive research work. Finally, I discuss factors that influence the production within academic science of knowledge useful as inputs to further research rather than as "final outputs."

[2] Michael Polanyi, *Science, Faith and Society*, Oxford, 1946; ——, *The Logic of Liberty*, Chicago, 1951; ——, *Personal Knowledge*, Chicago, 1958.

INSTITUTIONAL SETTING AND OPERATION

Certain features of the university setting of academic science seem especially important in influencing directions of research. The first important feature is the acceptance by influential segments of modern Western societies of the idea that a major function of universities is the advancement of knowledge. In "national" universities, in which the great bulk of scientific research takes place, the faculty, the administrators, and the trustees are concerned with advancing the reputation of their institutions as centers of scientific and scholarly investigation. Departments in major universities are similarly concerned with their reputations, which depend primarily on the excellence of the research carried out by department members. For this reason, a major determinant of appointment and advancement in a science department is the publication of research of scientific significance.

A second major feature of the university setting is the fact that the accepted judges of the merit of published scientific research—of the extent to which it advances knowledge—are professional colleagues throughout the country (and abroad) and especially those "universally recognized as the most eminent."[3] Professional opinion and advice are relied on in making decisions about university appointments.[4] Moreover, foundation and government research funds are usually allocated on the basis of advisory judgments by professional scientists concerning the probable scientific worth of research proposals submitted.

A final feature of importance is the freedom or autonomy granted the individual university faculty member to use the time he has available and the personnel and facilities he is able to obtain to conduct the research he wants to carry out.

These institutional features obviously influence the directions of academic science research. Their effect is to allocate personnel and resources among lines of research in a way that tends to "maximize" the expected scientific significance of the results obtained, subject to the constraints imposed by the availability of funds, personnel, and other resources. This effect is brought about in the following way.

Each academic scientist working in his specialty and motivated by a concern for his academic career if by nothing else, will pursue those

---

[3] Polanyi, *The Logic of Liberty*, p. 54.
[4] See Eric Ashby, *Technology and the Academics*, London, 1958, for a good discussion of how university academic government works in the British Commonwealth.

lines of research which he expects will yield the most significant results. Results are published and discussed, and their scientific merit evaluated by professional colleagues in the specialty. As reputations are established, academic departments, striving to enhance their standing in their disciplines, will try to appoint or promote those scientists pursuing especially successful lines of work. Scientists advising on the granting of fellowships and grants-in-aid will behave similarly. These actions perform a twofold function. They reinforce the goal of advancing knowledge by tangibly rewarding productive scientists with income, tenure, academic rank, prestige, and professional influence. In addition, departments trying to attract promising scientists will offer such advantages as increased time for research, access to more and better graduate students and technical assistants, better library and other research facilities, interested and competent colleagues, etc. Such competition within and between departments means that the more productive scientists in a specialty obtain better research conditions than do others. This tends to increase the output of scientifically significant results obtainable from given resources.

Similar forces within academic science shift resources between specialties within each discipline. Departments will tend to seek scientists in specialties that are yielding especially exciting results. In addition, graduate students will be attracted to such specialties. Established scientists in "active" specialties usually will be able to obtain more than average funds for supporting the training and research of graduate students. Moreover, they will be able to point to the wider career opportunities in such specialties as compared to those judged less promising. In these ways, trained personnel (and facilities) in a discipline are shifted toward those specialties which appear to be the most scientifically productive at a given time. Obviously, this also tends to increase the scientific significance of the research results obtained with the funds available to the discipline.

Finally, there are also forces in academic science that tend to increase the proportion of research resources available to active disciplines as compared to that available to disciplines where work of less scientific promise is going on. Scientists of one discipline will tend to exaggerate its scientific importance relative to others, and there are obvious incentives for each discipline to try to obtain as large an amount of funds as possible. The resolution of these conflicting claims for research support, insofar as they are resolved within the system of academic science, falls on persons in positions where they need to consider the over-all scientific significance of different possible uses of resources—persons responsible for decisions affecting a whole division, school, college, or university. They have incentives to move resources to disciplines where work of high scientific significance appears possible. In addition, newcomers to academic science are more likely to select careers in rapidly advancing disciplines than in those that are comparatively stagnant.

All these institutional arrangements result in a system which tends to maximize the expected scientific value of the research done with available resources. The scientific value of research results is judged by scientists themselves and these judgments, operating through the institutions discussed, are the means by which the community of academic scientists governs itself. Insofar as this is true, it is clear that we need to understand the standards, criteria, preferences, or principles which are used by scientists in judging the scientific value of research proposals and results.[5] On what basis are some results deemed important and exciting while others are judged to be insignificant and not worth following up? Working out ways of studying this question empirically appears to be a crucial step in advancing our knowledge of the determinants of the directions of academic science research. In the following section I want to discuss this aspect of the subsystem of academic science further.

JUDGING SCIENTIFIC VALUE IN ACADEMIC SCIENCE

Judgments of the scientific significance of research in academic science have certain general features that need to be kept in mind. First, there is great uncertainty in scientific research—it is really a search into the unknown. This means that judgments are tentative estimates or guesses which are needed in making decisions, even though they may turn out to be wrong after the fact. Second, the criteria or standards used in judging scientific research are largely implicit. Such explicit formulations as exist are maxims or pointers, not precise criteria that can be routinely applied by any appropriately trained person. It is generally recognized among scientists that some persons are far better judges than others.[6] Third, even though there is a common core of values in the traditions of science to which scientists appeal in supporting their judgments, it is recognized that consensus is by no means

---

[5] To avoid misunderstanding, let me say that the term "value" is used here in the general sense of "utility" or "use value," and not, as is usual in economics, in the sense of exchange value or price.

[6] See Polanyi's remarks about Rutherford (*Science, Faith and Society*, pp. 76–77).

always possible in particular cases. What one scientist thinks will be promising may be regarded as useless by others. When disagreements arise, scientists are formally free to follow their own judgment and attempt to demonstrate through further research the validity of their ideas.

All this puts the student who wants to understand the selection of directions of academic scientific research in a difficult position. Essentially his problem is to develop testable propositions about how directions of research vary with circumstances from qualitative information about the way scientists make judgments. In this section I want to discuss some of the criteria that seem to be operative in scientific decisions in an effort to suggest some of the kinds of systematic empirical research which would be useful in increasing our understanding of the directions taken by research in academic science.

We may begin by dividing judgments of the value of proposed or published scientific contributions into two kinds. On the one hand, there are judgments concerning the value of substantive contributions to science—direct contributions to knowledge of the subject matter under investigation. They are the scientific discoveries of empirical facts, regularities, concepts, and theories which take their place in the textbooks which summarize what is known. In addition to these "final outputs" of scientific research, there are other contributions whose significance lies primarily in their role as aids to further research. They serve primarily as knowledge "inputs" rather than as final outputs. Let us discuss these two kinds of evaluation, in order.

Evaluation of Substantive Contributions

I believe the most useful statement of the criteria used in judging substantive contributions in academic science is that of Michael Polanyi.[7] Let us consider the criteria used to judge contributions on a given subject, and then discuss how findings in different fields may be compared.

Within a given subject-matter field, Polanyi thinks two criteria are of primary importance: (1) the precision, accuracy or certainty of a contribution; and (2) its systematic relevance or profundity—the breadth of its coverage and the variety of its implications.[8] These

---

[7] Polanyi, *The Logic of Liberty* and *Personal Knowledge*. Schwab, dealing with a somewhat different problem, has developed an interesting set of distinctions which could also be used for this purpose (Joseph J. Schwab, "What Do Scientists Do?" *Behavioral Science*, Vol. 5, 1960, pp. 1–27).

[8] Polanyi, *Personal Knowledge*, pp. 135–136.

criteria "apply jointly, so that deficiency in one is largely compensated for by excellence in the others."[9] A contribution which is very accurate and reliable but very narrow in its scope may be valued as highly as a contribution which is less precise but more general. Such judgments are made on the basis of the knowledge available at the time. They may be drastically altered as a result of changes in the state of knowledge. Consider the precision measurement of atomic weights.[10] At one time, the atomic weights of the elements were thought to be important clues to the basic nature of matter. Later, the discovery of isotopes showed that this was not so, that the important weights were isotopic masses. Precision work that was awarded a Nobel prize in 1914 was thought to be of little interest by 1932.

The relative importance accorded these two values thus becomes an important factor affecting the directions of scientific research. Responses to new knowledge may provide a way of estimating the weight given these values. One would expect that in a discipline or scientific tradition which evaluated precision highly, research would change markedly in response to the discovery of new ways of achieving greater precision, but not shift very much with discoveries affecting the systematic relevance of findings. Conversely, in disciplines or traditions where systematic relevance is given the greater weight, an opposite pattern of response to changes in knowledge would be expected. Comparative studies of responses to the same or similar changes in knowledge should enable us to empirically document the role of these values in various fields of science. Moreover, such studies would provide tests of the extent to which these values account for the selection of lines of research in particular fields.

Let us now ask how contributions of equivalent precision and systematic relevance in different subject-matter fields are compared. Here, Polanyi thinks a third criterion operates, the criterion of "intrinsic interest." Some subjects are just more interesting than others, apart from any relation they may have to practical concerns. To quote Polanyi:

> In science, as in ordinary perception, our attention is attracted by things that are useful or dangerous to us, even though they present themselves less distinctly and coherently. This sets up a competition between practical and theoretical interests. . . . But

[9] *Ibid.*, p. 136.
[10] *Ibid.*, p. 136.

things are also interesting in themselves, and their intrinsic interest varies greatly. Living animals are more interesting than their dead bodies; a dog more interesting than a fly; a man more interesting than a dog.[11]

Thus, insofar as academic science is "pure" science, concerned with knowledge for its own sake, intrinsic interest is the guiding criterion in evaluating the scientific value of similar contributions to our knowledge of different subjects. We here encounter the long debated issue of the influence of practical or utilitarian values on directions of academic science research. Polanyi's distinction between practical and intrinsic interest in a subject suggests ways this problem might be studied empirically.

Polanyi appears to assume that everyone judges the intrinsic interest of various subjects in the same way. However, it seems likely that there are cultural and subcultural differences in the amount of intrinsic interest accorded particular subjects. But, if such cultural differences exist, it also seems probable that they would manifest themselves in relatively stable differences in the proportion of effort devoted to the same scientific subjects in different societies. Practical interests, on the contrary, can be expected to change rapidly even in a single society and to differ from society to society in ways that are correlated with extrascientific conditions which can be studied. Practical interest in particular military, agricultural, industrial, or medical problems certainly exhibit such variations. Therefore, it ought to be possible to study the role practical interests play in the selection of lines of research by studying empirically the extent to which directions of research vary and shift with differences and changes in conditions affecting practical interests. Such study is complicated by the fact that the state of knowledge, or what Cohen calls the scientific situation,[12] also changes rapidly and, as we have seen, also affects directions of research. However, it should be possible to distinguish the effects of these different kinds of changes.

We thus have the picture of the "pure" scientific significance of substantive contributions to academic science being judged according to some weighted total of their precision, systematic relevance, and intrinsic interest. In addition, practical interests may also play a role in judging the value of research results. The possible role of practical

[11] *Ibid.*, p. 138.
[12] I. Bernard Cohen, *Science, Servant of Man*, Boston, 1948, pp. 31–32.

interests raises another problem that requires explicit discussion. We have assumed so far that the only role practical interests play in academic science is possibly giving greater weight or importance to the scientific study of certain topics than they otherwise would have. We have assumed that practical interest in a subject does not alter the scientific character of the research done. However, it is relatively easy to show that practical interest in a subject can also alter the direction taken by the research. This possibility is clearly seen in industrial "basic research" in examples such as the following. Shell Development undertook a study of the mechanisms of hydrocarbon oxidation.[13] This is a theoretical or scientific subject, but was picked because the phenomena were important in Shell operations. In the course of this work discoveries were made concerning the role of hydrogen peroxide. Since hydrogen peroxide was a commercially interesting substance, the focus of the research shifted to the study of reactions that would produce it in larger yields. That work, in turn, led to still other commercial production methods. Thus, even though the research apparently started out as a scientific study, it was really not that. Rather, it was a strategy for making inventions; a way of uncovering clues from which useful processes or products could be developed. Gershinowitz comments as follows:

> In the large sense there can be no such thing as undirected research in industry. It may start out thus, but essentially it is directed into types of activity that the managers of that research laboratory have confidence will some time have application. Therefore, I think it is very important that there shall be somewhere a place in the research setup of the nation where really undirected investigation can take place. Here a man who is working on the kinetics of oxidation of hydrocarbons will not be distracted into studying the kinetics of reactions to make hydrogen peroxide. Here he will continue to work on what he began and let only the results of his own activities determine the direction he wants to go.[14]

In cases like this, practical interest in a scientific subject turns the investigation into a search for practically useful clues. This is not

[13] Harold Gershinowitz, "Industrial Research Methods and Industrial Research Programs as Affecting Academic Research," *Changing Patterns of Academic Research*, Sigma Xi, Rensselaer Chapter, Rensselaer Polytechnic Institute, 1957.

[14] *Ibid.*, p. 21.

what Polanyi calls technically justified science, in which the aim is deeper understanding of a subject of practical interest.[15] Instead it is a way of making inventions by doing enough scientific investigation to uncover useful new ideas which then become the center of attention. Such research ought to be called something like exploratory science-invention to distinguish it from technically justified science. Exploratory science-invention leads to some advances in general knowledge but these are likely to be limited, since work is continually diverted to the exploration of practical possibilities.

Thus, in examining the role of practical interests in academic science, we need to know how such interests affect the relative amount of work done in various subject-matter fields and the extent to which research becomes exploratory science-invention instead of technically justified science. How much exploratory science-invention is carried out in academic science will depend on a number of institutional factors. It will depend, for example, on the extent to which investigators are rewarded for advancing scientific knowledge, apart from any useful clues they may uncover, as compared with the attention given findings of direct practical relevance. It will also depend on how committed researchers are to a scientific career. If an academic chemist, for example, is not strongly committed to science, he may select lines of research that promise practically significant findings which would make him an attractive employee in industrial research.

It seems clear that unless the community of academic scientists is strongly committed to the importance of advancing knowledge and is supported in this commitment by significant segments of the larger society, this goal will not be fully affective in guiding the direction of research. It is possible, for example, that the apparently greater value placed on the humanistic search for truth and the academic life in Europe as compared to the United States has something to do with the apparently greater output of high quality science there. There certainly is evidence that it is very difficult to transplant academic science effectively to countries where its values and traditions are not understood.[16] Careful comparative study of the attention devoted to selected lines of research in different countries might enable us to document and test empirically these impressions.

[15] Polanyi, *Personal Knowledge*, p. 179.
[16] *Ibid.*, p. 182; also Polanyi, *The Logic of Liberty*, p. 56.

Knowledge Capital in Academic Science

So far we have discussed only standards used to evaluate substantive contributions as final outputs of academic science research. But research also produces kinds of knowledge whose significance does not lie in their contribution to knowledge of the subject being investigated but rather in the usefulness of such knowledge in undertaking further research. This is true of the development of new scientific instruments such as the cyclotron; of new methods of chemical analysis, physical measurement, or observation; of new methods of experimental design, manipulation, and control, and so on. Moreover, certain kinds of background research produce knowledge which is chiefly useful as an aid to research.[17] Cohen mentions the usefulness in organic analysis and synthesis of the vast collection of data on melting and boiling points and similar properties of countless organic compounds.[18]

Knowledge that is useful as an input to further research can be thought of as knowledge capital. An addition to the stock of knowledge capital aids further research by opening up new possibilities or by reducing the cost or time required to explore already existing possibilities. From this point of view, it is clear that substantive contributions can serve as knowledge capital as well as final outputs. Fruitful substantive contributions are precisely those which seem to open up new significant research possibilities.

All of this means that to understand the selection of directions of academic science research we must understand how the capital value as well as the substantive value of research results are judged. The basic logic used goes something like this. First, an effort is made to estimate the net additions to substantive knowledge which are likely to be produced in the forseeable future as a result of the knowledge capital contribution being evaluated. Then the scientific significance of these expected additions is estimated and imputed to the knowledge capital and to the research that produced it. In other words, an effort is made to judge the significance of an addition to knowledge capital by estimating its expected net effect on the output of substantive scientific results in the near future. It is obvious that such estimates are difficult to make, that scientists will often disagree, and that the estimates will often turn out to be wrong. But at least rough judgments

---

[17] Cohen, *op. cit.*, p. 53.
[18] *Ibid.*, p. 252.

have to be made if work on scientifically useful aids to research is to be promoted, and a reasonable guess is better than nothing at all. Furthermore, as time goes on and the impact of a given piece of research can be assessed on the basis of more evidence, evaluations of additions to knowledge capital can be corrected and the rewards to scientists producing them changed accordingly.

It follows from this argument that the producer of knowledge capital as well as the producer of results of substantive significance will tend to benefit privately according to the social benefits to science which stem from his work. Within the subsystem of academic science there appears to be no external economy problem comparable to that which Nelson has pointed out in the case of "basic" research carried out by firms in a market-patent system.[19] Probably the best way to test these notions empirically and to increase our knowledge of the determinants of research devoted to the production of knowledge capital would be to compare work on similar research aids in academic science and other subsystems such as private industrial research.

CONCLUSIONS

If the preceeding picture of the way the subsystem of academic science operates is a useful first approximation, it suggests that a key problem in understanding the selection of directions of scientific research is obtaining better knowledge of the scientific values or criteria used in making professional evaluations of the significance of different lines of research. This seems to require the study of the way decisions vary with differences in relevant circumstances such as the state of knowledge, practical interests, institutional organization, etc. The discussion attempted to suggest ideas which would be useful in the design of such research.

Academic Medical Research

I now turn to some of the R and D subsystems devoted to the improvement of practical arts. Practical arts are concerned with the achievement of useful results. It is usefulness in actual practice under a particular set of prevailing conditions relative to available alternatives that is the basic test of advances in a practical art. Meeting such specifications gives to technology and its improvement a character and complexity significantly different from that of pure science. However, in the absence of a really adequate analysis of the kinds of

[19] Nelson, "The Simple Economics of Basic Scientific Research."

knowledge involved in the improvement of a practical art, the following discussion will be limited to features that emerge in making broad institutional comparisons.

The first example of a R and D subsystem devoted to improving the practical arts to be considered is academic medical research. By academic medical research I mean the research activities of full-time or part-time staff members of medical schools and teaching or other hospitals who, in addition to teaching and often providing medical services, also engage in medical research. Included is a broad spectrum of R and D activities. They range from clinical research concerned with the introduction, testing, and improvement of specific advances in medical practice on through experimental and clinical studies devoted to uncovering useful new leads, to the research carried out in the so-called preclinical medical sciences such as anatomy, physiology, bacteriology, biochemistry, etc.

Let us first examine some of the important features of the institutional organization of academic medical research to see what clues we can get concerning determinants of the direction of research activity in this subsystem. To a considerable degree, the institutional arrangements are like those of academic science. First, academic medical research is largely subsidized from outside the system in the same ways that academic science is. Second, the prestige of medical schools and associated institutions depends to a considerable extent on the reputation they build up as contributors to the advancement of the medical arts and sciences. Third, donors of funds and administrators generally defer to professional judgments of the value of medical research results and follow medical advice in the allocation of funds. Fourth, established academic medical investigators are given autonomy to decide what lines of research they want to pursue with the means they are able to obtain. Therefore, persons following a research career in medicine are in a situation where they have incentives to do research that will be considered significant by professional opinion.

However, some workers in academic medical research are in an institutional position that differs significantly from that of the typical academic pure scientist. It appears that many of the positions in clinical departments in medical schools and teaching hospitals are part-time positions or positions in which the incumbent is allowed to practice for fees and to retain at least a portion of the fees earned.[20]

[20] *Medical Research: A Midcentury Survey*, Boston, Little, Brown for the American Foundation, 1955, Vol. 1, pp. 214 ff.

Anyone thus employed has a stake in a private practice and is not necessarily committed solely to a research career. So long as he performs his official functions well enough to retain his position, it is possible for him to orient his research along lines significant for his practice. He could focus his work on attempts to make improvements in medical practice that would enhance his reputation as a practitioner and thus his income derived from practice. Such economic incentives could operate even if, as is the case in medicine, professional standards dictate prompt and full publication of research findings and open access to the knowledge and use of new techniques. A reputation as an originator and longer experience with a new procedure may attract fee paying patients even when an innovation has become widely diffused. Similar incentives to direct research toward improvements which attract fee paying patients could also operate on an institutional level. Clinics, out-patient departments, and hospitals affiliated with medical schools may seek to attract patients who will improve their budgetary position, and research workers associated with such institutions could be given incentives to direct their activities in such directions also.

Within the constraints that regulate access to medical research funds and positions and that control medical practice, there is probably a certain amount of academic medical research oriented toward the financial benefit of the investigator or the institution with which he is affiliated. The extent and significance of such influences on the selection of lines of research can only be ascertained when methods have been developed for distinguishing such research from that selected on other bases. Crucial to such study would be a determination of the kinds of medical advances that attract financially rewarding patients and the kinds of improvements that have no significant effect of this sort. That distinction would provide a framework for detailed empirical study to see what effect, if any, this difference has on the allocation of effort to lines of research.

My impression is that most academic medical research is focused on obtaining results that will be judged highly by the profession and not on direct financial gain. In this context the key question is what criteria are used to judge the medical significance and value of advances in the medical arts and sciences. Two general possibilities suggest themselves. On the one hand, the traditions of medicine are those of a service profession devoted to meeting the medical needs of the people it serves. Insofar as these traditions govern the evaluation of research, medical advances would be judged according to their significance in meeting the medical needs of society. On the other hand, given the position of academic medical research as a major research arm of a profession whose practitioners obtain income by providing services to the public, there is the possibility that medical advances could be judged according to their significance in economically benefiting the profession as a whole. I doubt whether the economic criterion is very significant. It is difficult to see how most medical advances significantly increase the average income of the medical profession. Professional policies in other areas, such as those affecting the number of medical practitioners, seem much more important. Furthermore, pressures from the lay public and from subsidizers of medical research tend to reinforce the traditions within medicine stressing the preeminence of meeting the medical needs of the public. It therefore appears likely that professional standards for judging the significance of advances in medical knowledge stress the extent to which advances enhance the ability of the profession to meet its social obligations.

The question then becomes, what professional criteria are used to judge the extent to which an improvement helps in meeting public medical needs? A number of criteria are often mentioned in this connection, such as amount of reduction in mortality rates, in morbidity rates, in average duration of illness, in severity of aftereffects, in amount of suffering, and so forth. These and other more specific criteria appear to derive from general social values in Western societies. However, so far as I know, little study has been made of how these criteria or others are used in professional medical judgments of improvements in the art. In particular, we do not know the relative weights given various criteria in reaching over-all judgments. There is evidence of the use of the kinds of criteria mentioned. For example, the Steelman report which is based, at least in part, on professional medical advice includes the following statement: ". . . if the Federal Government is financing a broad program of medical research, the problems under investigation should bear a reasonably close relation to those causes of illness and death which are most common in the population and in which the public, therefore, has the greatest stake."[21]

How far and in what ways such criteria guide professional judgments and decisions concerning directions of academic medical

[21] John R. Steelman, *The Nation's Medical Research,* Vol. 5 of *Science and Public Policy,* Washington, 1947, p. 86.

research are questions clearly needing study. In modern times, due to demographic changes and to changes in the medical arts themselves, the importance of various diseases as causes of illness, death, suffering, etc. has often changed radically. Systematic empirical study of the effects of such changes on the directions of academic medical research ought to shed considerable light on what criteria are used and the relative importance accorded different indices of medical need. In such a study, the effect of changes in medical knowledge on expected costs of making comparable advances in different medical fields would have to be taken into account. One would not expect that resources would be allocated to research on diseases in direct proportion to the severity of the medical problems they present. Such an allocation would not take into account differences in the expected difficulty and cost of making comparable improvements in the prevention or treatment of different diseases. Expected costs obviously vary greatly from disease to disease and change as the state of medical knowledge changes. These facts complicate the study of the criteria used to evaluate the importance of different lines of academic medical research, but I doubt if the difficulties are insurmountable.

The professional standards and values used to judge the probable medical importance of specific advances in medical practice can be used directly in making decisions about the importance of research on particular medical problems. They can also be used to evaluate alternative lines of exploratory science-invention. The question of the allocation of resources to technically justified medical *sciences* and to fields within them seems to me to raise additional issues. I suspect empirical study would show that much of the academic medical research within the preclinical disciplines (e.g. anatomy, physiology, biochemistry, and even bacteriology, pathology, and pharmacology) is carried out as technically justified science. That is to say, much of the research in these fields is concentrated on gaining a deeper general understanding of the subjects studied and not on obtaining clues of direct practical significance. These fields are professionally organized, have their own journals, and their own foci of interest. We should be able to test this guess by studying how directions of research in the preclinical medical sciences vary in response to changes in knowledge opening up new lines of scientific study as compared with their response to changes in the importance of practical medical problems related to their subject matter fields.

If the preclinical medical disciplines do function to a considerable extent as technically justified sciences, how do we account for their elaborate development and for their ability to maintain a strongly scientific as against a practical orientation? Theoretically, one might argue that research in these fields is supported on the basis of some estimate of the average long-run rate of production of knowledge of practical medical significance; and that their scientific orientation is supported as a necessary condition for obtaining the particular kind of practically significant knowledge they produce. Nowadays many of the arguments for supporting basic research, including academic science, are of this sort.

However, the difficulty so often encountered in practical fields in generating support for activities that produce long-run, uncertain, broad, and difficult-to-trace benefits suggests that additional factors are involved. One possibility is that part of the support is based on the intrinsic interest of the phenomena studied in the medical sciences. This possibility could be explored by detailed study of the attention paid to specific topics relative to the prospects of practically significant findings and the prospects of precise and systematically coherent results. A major sign of intrinsic interest in a subject is support of research on it in the absence of practical implications and in the face of inability to produce as precise or profound findings as are possible in other fields. In addition, it seems probable that there has developed within medicine and among groups concerned with the support of medical research the conviction that scientific understanding of the art is a good thing in the long run for the profession, apart from any effort to assess practical benefits relative to costs. Wide variations appear to exist among the practical arts in the importance attached to understanding of the scientific principles involved. Though such variations may reflect the different practical benefits derived from advances in related scientific knowledge, I doubt if this fully accounts for the facts. Systematic comparison of the development of technically justified science research auxiliary to medicine with that related to agriculture, mining, metal working and other industrial fields would shed light on this question.

To sum up, the subsystem of academic medical research as a system for improving a practical art appears to have a number of distinctive characteristics. For example, it differs from industrial research in its orientation toward meeting medical needs rather than market demand; in its open publication of findings; in the absence of intra-industry external economy problems; and in the development of special traditions supporting technically justified medical sciences. The reality of these characteristics and their effects on directions of research could be studied most directly in cases where similar kinds of medical research are carried out both within the academic subsystem and by pharmaceutical houses and surgical or other medical supply firms.

Academic Engineering Research

In this section I want to discuss only one question concerning academic engineering research suggested by comparisons with academic medical research. By academic engineering research I mean the research carried out in engineering schools, institutes of technology and related applied science departments. Unlike the situation in medicine, by far the largest amount of research on specific practical problems in engineering is done by firms operating in the market-patent system.[22] Despite this fact, it appears that technically justified engineering sciences receive less academic support than comparable medical sciences. An exploration of this problem may provide leads concerning additional institutional factors affecting research in R and D subsystems concerned with the improvement of practical arts.

Finch provides an interesting summary of the difference between academic medical and engineering research in the United States:

> In engineering, as in the case of medicine, the work of natural scientists has never provided all the scientific knowledge and understandings which are essential to continued professional growth. In engineering the practical mechanics of heat (engineering thermodynamics), of electrical machines and circuits, of liquids and gases (hydraulics and fluid mechanics), of solids (elasticity and strength of materials), more recently of soils, foundations, and earth structures (soil mechanics)—all these and other basic engineering studies were, over a century ago, designated by the Germans as engineering science. They were based to be sure on the facts of natural science, but they have been developed by engineers in directions, scope, and understandings which would not claim the interest, time, and efforts of workers in pure science. Exactly the same situation has existed in the medical field, but here the scope, function, and importance of medical

[22] For a review of work on industrial research see Nelson, "The Economics of Invention: A Survey of the Literature."

science is well understood and fully recognized. American engineering, on the other hand, faces today the task of making equally clear the place and importance in technological progress of research in engineering science.[23]

A corollary of this underemphasis on engineering science in U.S. academic engineering research is a greater emphasis than one might expect on specific practical problems like those dealt with in industry and on the study of such problems in an empirical, practically oriented way. Let me again quote Finch:

> . . . many problems of engineering research involve the study and analysis of various forms, devices, structural or machine units, as well as a scientific explanation for physical, chemical, or other phenomena encountered in engineering practice. These are not necessarily development or industrial research problems, though they may arise in the activities of industry. . . . Unfortunately, however, such activities can very easily deteriorate into mere routine testing or empirical formula or coefficient hunting which may have little or no value in extending the frontiers of engineering knowledge and should seldom be referred to as research.[24]

There is still other evidence that U.S. academic engineering research has tended to be empirically rather than theoretically oriented. There is historical evidence that we borrowed from Europe when engineering practice itself required increased use of theoretically based methods. Finch notes:

> Just before World War I some German books on stress analysis and similar subjects began to attract special attention. But the fact that the state of American engineering science was not all it should be and that American engineers were ill prepared to cope with the new problems which were becoming of importance is reflected very clearly in the rapid rise to prominence of numerous newcomers to our shores whose education had been acquired in Europe.[25]

My impression is that Europeans continue to play a significant

[23] James Kip Finch, *Engineering and Western Civilization*, New York, 1951, p. 315.
[24] Finch, *Trends in Engineering Education*, New York, 1948, pp. 89–90.
[25] Finch, *Trends in Engineering Education*, p. 19.

role in the more theoretical aspects of academic engineering teaching and research. Finally, it may be noted that the increased importance of theoretical knowledge in engineering since World War II has resulted in a marked increase in the employment of mathematicians and physicists by industry for both R and D and engineering practice. This suggests that academic engineering training and research continues to lag behind the needs of practice.

The question then arises: what factors in the organization of U.S. academic engineering account for this apparent underemphasis on research in the engineering sciences? Two contributing factors may be suggested. One is the stress academic engineering institutions place on their function of providing services to local industry. Another possibility is that professional standards in U.S. academic engineering, outside a few research oriented institutions, stress the importance of immediately useful research results rather than more theoretical advances. It has been said that the practical orientation of U.S. engineering stemmed from a situation where the high cost of labor relative to other costs resulted in a lack of emphasis on economical use of materials and on precision of design.[26] Though the problems of engineering practice have been changing and are now changing even faster,[27] traditions based on the early situation have apparently altered more slowly.

Another factor involved lies in the area of relations between academic engineering and academic science. Wickenden describes the efforts of German technical schools to obtain academic status comparable to that of other scientific institutions and to obtain the right to grant a fully recognized research doctorate.[28] This effort to establish fundamental research on technical subjects as a way of gaining stature in the academic world apparently had much to do with the development of the engineering sciences in Germany. Similar theoretical research interests on the part of academically trained engineers are reported for England[29] and Europe generally.[30] Though that interest

[26] *Ibid.*, p. 13.

[27] See, for example, Arthur R. von Hippel, *Molecular Science and Molecular Engineering*, New York, 1959.

[28] W. E. Wickenden, *A Comparative Study of Engineering Education in the United States and Europe*, Society for the Promotion of Engineering Education, Bulletin No. 16, 1929.

[29] R. L. Meier, "Research as a Social Process," *British Journal of Sociology*, Vol. 2, 1951, pp. 91–104.

[30] *The Organization of Applied Research in Europe, The United States and Canada*, Vol. I, *A Comparative Study*, Organization for European Economic Co-operation, Paris, 1954.

may have adverse effects on the practicality of the work done on industrial problems (see above references), it undoubtedly contributes to the development of technically justified engineering sciences. In the cases cited, the concern of academic engineering groups with their general academic status apparently stems from the stronger humanistic interests and the higher status of scholarship prevalent in Europe as compared with the United States.

We need to work out ways of testing empirically such impressions concerning the possible effects of differences in academic engineering traditions on the directions taken by academic engineering R and D. Empirical comparisons of the attention devoted to engineering sciences in different countries could be made. Differences between fields within engineering, such as the older and newer fields,[31] need to be explored. Such studies would give us a basis for judging empirically the magnitude and nature of the differences in emphasis in various spheres of academic engineering research. We would then be in a position to study systematically the organizational, cultural, and other factors influencing R and D decisions in academic engineering.

Government Agricultural Research

I now turn to a different kind of R and D subsystem organized and operating in a governmental rather than an academic setting. The example chosen is governmental agricultural research as carried out by the U.S. Department of Agriculture and State agricultural experiment stations.[32] Like academic engineering, governmental agricultural research services an industry operating in the price-market system. However, in contrast to industrial firms, agricultural operators carry out comparatively little research of their own so that government research constitutes the major source of agricultural R and D except in agricultural machinery and equipment, fertilizers, and insecticides and so on, where industrial firms also play a role.

The directions taken by government agricultural research are influenced by the organizational setting in which the research agencies operate. The research units in the USDA are divisions within a

[31] W. Rupert Maclaurin, "Technological Progress in Some American Industries," *American Economic Review*, 1954, pp. 182–184.

[32] For general background see: Carleton R. Ball, *Federal, State and Local Administrative Relationships in Agriculture*, Berkeley, 1938; A. Hunter Dupree, *Science in the Federal Government*, Cambridge, 1957; Alfred Charles True, *A History of Agricultural Experimentation and Research in the United States 1607–1925*, U.S. Dept. of Agriculture, Misc. publ. 251, 1937.

hierarchically organized federal government department while the state experiment stations are state government agencies administered by directors. It seems reasonable to assume that the heads of these units, like the heads of most governmental agencies, are in a situation where their own careers and their opportunities for performing public services which they feel are important depend on their ability to maintain and preferably to expand both the financial support and the tasks assigned to their organizations. Government agencies are usually concerned with developing that kind of support and influence which is helpful both in the bargaining within and between government departments during the budget making period and in the political processes of getting legislative support for their programs and the appropriation of funds to finance them. Fundamental to this objective is the political support of sizeable, politically influential segments of the relevant electorate and their elected representatives.

A major way government agencies that provide services to a clientele can develop public support is to supply especially desired services, as agricultural research strongly oriented towards the needs of farmers. Presumably, the main type of benefits desired by farmers from research agencies are services that help them economically through increasing their incomes. Therefore, government agricultural research organizations will probably seek to maximize the economic benefits to the industry of the work they are able to do within the budgetary, administrative, and legislative constraints under which they operate. T. W. Schultz, for example, argues that:

> Undoubtedly other tastes and preferences, other than a "maximization" of economic value of the output enter into the decision relations determining the director's choices. However, even a casual look at the behavior patterns of directors in approving research projects suggests that economic considerations, broadly conceived and when taken over a span of years, are of primary importance.[33]

In addition, Schultz characterizes the results in the following way:

> The political mechanism does not cut with a razor's edge; it is a blunt contraption at best; and yet, it appears that in making

[33] Theodore W. Schultz, *The Economic Organization of Agriculture*, New York, 1953, p. 113.

funds available for agricultural research, with all its imperfections, it compares favorably, for example, with the public and private efforts that went into the settlement of the American frontier.[34]

If the organization of government agricultural research can be approximated by some such model, then certain consequences for the way this R and D subsystem functions may be noted. Since research is supported by public funds, research findings are made freely available to the public not only as information (as in the case of patents) but also for use in practice by all farmers and farm firms. Furthermore, such agencies have strong incentives to communicate their results fully and promptly and also to be sure that the results are accurate and reliable. Competition among agencies, concern of researchers for their careers, and the checks provided by farmers who use recommended practices all tend to discipline the communication of results more effectively than is the case when results are made available in the form of patent claims.[35] Further, the position of the agencies enables them to benefit (in the form of political support) from broadly useful improvements they develop, whether patentable or not. Thus, in their decisions about prospective benefits of lines of research, they are able to take into account the social benefits of intraagricultural (or at least intrastate intraagricultural) external economies in a way that firms in a market-patent system are not able to do.[36] In these ways, the system of government agricultural research works like that of academic medical research and differs from that of private industrial research.

Government agricultural research, however, also differs from academic medical research in ways that influence the directions of R and D activity. In the first place, practical benefits to agriculture are defined in essentially economic market oriented terms (subject to the modifications resulting from strong governmental regulation and subsidy) rather than in professional terms reflecting general social values operating outside the market expression of consumer demand. In short, government agricultural research services an industry operating in a regulated price-market system, not a service profession like medicine which tends to provide services on a need

[34] *Ibid.*, p. 118.
[35] On patents see the remarks of James B. Conant in *Science and Common Sense*, New Haven, 1951, p. 331.
[36] Cf. Nelson, "The Simple Economics of Basic Scientific Research."

basis. In the second place, the socially or politically expressed demands of the clientele on investigators appear to differ significantly in the two research fields. In the case of medical needs, lay members of society may express their interest in the solution of various medical problems, but beyond that they generally defer to professional opinion in decisions about what specific kinds of research ought to be done. The situation appears to be different in agriculture. Many farmers are skilled and often professionally trained practitioners of the arts of agriculture; they are analogous to practicing physicians rather than to patients. Therefore, they are likely to believe that they can evaluate the significance of particular agricultural problems and decide the kinds of research needed. They are likely to express their demands for research services in highly specific terms. The result is that government agricultural agencies may be forced to carry out the research farmers think will benefit them most, rather than follow professional judgments based on a wider acquaintance with scientific, technological, economic, and other developments affecting agriculture.

Other features of the standards or criteria farmers use to evaluate the research results provided them are also significant. It makes a difference, for example, whether farmers judge the economic benefits of research on the basis of results derived from recently received and used improvements or on the basis of results obtained over a longer period of time. If research directors feel that support for their work depends on their responding immediately to each new crisis or problem that arises, their choice of lines of research will be largely limited to specific projects capable of yielding benefits quickly. They will be in a position analogous to that of business firms fighting for survival who direct their R and D toward immediately useful improvements. If, on the other hand, farmers realize the benefits of longer-term lines of investigation on major unsolved problems, then research directors are in a position where the politically feasible alternatives among which they can choose are significantly broadened.

The support of long-term research would appear to depend on the extent to which agricultural interests defer to the expert judgment of investigators or defer to people in their own ranks who have made it their business to become informed about the issues involved in decisions about directions of agricultural research. This will also affect expenditures of funds on activities producing knowledge capital, such as work on improving research techniques and instruments; on making fundamental scientific advances in practically important fields not otherwise supported; and on building up bodies of broadly useful background data.

Thus, the operation of the subsystem of government agricultural research depends significantly not only on the internal organization of the system and on the arrangements affecting the way its clientele can influence research decisions, but also on the set of standards and beliefs that guide farmers in the exercise of their powers.

So far as I know, little systematic empirical research has been done on the facets of government agricultural research discussed here, though there appear to be a number of possibilities. The role of economic conditions in affecting the selection of directions of research could be studied by making interregional, intertemporal and even international comparisons of responses to various economic and other conditions. In addition, there are possibilities for comparisons between different R and D subsystems. For example, what are the differences between industrial and government research on similar problems in agricultural engineering or in the utilization of agricultural products? How does research in veterinary medicine compare with that in human medicine? Using a model like that sketched here may help in the design of such research.

Conclusions

Our exploration of some society-wide R and D institutions suggests certain general conclusions. First, I think it is evident that R and D includes a variety of nationwide institutional systems which are not only descriptively different but also functionally different in the patterns of R and D they generate. Second, it appears possible to develop models of the operation of these systems analogous to the models that economic theory provides for the competitive price system and its variants. Third, such models would be useful in guiding empirical research, in explaining the directions taken by R and D, and in evaluating the efficiency of alternative institutional arrangements for the performance of different R and D tasks.

Viewed more broadly, this paper has tried to apply the general approach of economics to the analysis of the organization and operation of institutional systems which differ considerably from those usually studied by economists. In this respect, it is similar to the work of Downs and Dahl and Lindblom on politico-economic institutions[37]

[37] Anthony Downs, *An Economic Theory of Democracy*, New York, 1957 and Robert A. Dahl and Charles E. Lindblom, *Politics, Economics and Welfare*, New York, 1953.

and to the work of Simon on hierarchic formal organizations.[38] The work of these writers suggests that it may be possible to develop theories that will enable us to explore the relations between (1) organizational structure, (2) type of task, (3) environmental conditions, and (4) task performance for a wider variety of institutional arrangements than are usually considered in economic analysis. It seems to me that the study of R and D provides both an incentive and an opportunity for broadening still further our knowledge of alternative institutional systems for the performance of social tasks.

COMMENT

JOSEPH J. SPENGLER, Duke University

Robert Merrill focuses attention upon the manner in which R and D is organized and directed within those subsystems of our societal system in which nonmarket forces play a major role and actual and prospective monetary profits supposedly play a relatively small part. Two types of subsystems are examined: theoretical science, in which practical application is not emphasized, and applied science, in which the major emphasis is put upon practical application (as, for example, in the fields of medicine, agriculture, and engineering).

It is assumed that, within each of these subsystems, the direction given to inventive activity depends very largely upon three conditions: (1) the alternatives considered; (2) the consequences associated with each alternative; and (3) "the 'preferences' or 'values' used to judge the desirability of the various alternative-consequence combinations." Attention is focused upon the last of these three presumably because, in the absence of a monetary common denominator to measure gross costs and gross benefits, some sort of indicator, albeit ill-defined, is required if one is to choose among alternatives. By contrast, the management of a business firm, when confronted by alternatives with which consequences are associated, usually would attempt to translate both alternatives and consequences into continua of estimated monetary costs and estimated monetary returns. Having allowed for the uncertainties involved, it would then choose an alternative and pursue it roughly up to the point where its pursuit paid no better than that of any other available choice. By such action the business firm would maximize its return above costs, given the inputs at its

[38] James C. March and Herbert A. Simon, *Organizations*, New York, 1958.

disposal and the time horizon in terms of which decisions affecting profits are made. Of course if, as organization theory postulates, the "welfare function" of the firm includes other elements besides those immediately affecting net return over cost, the management would take these elements into account also; nonetheless its assessment and balancing of alternatives and consequences would run predominantly in terms of monetary costs and benefits.

It seems to be assumed that the set of alternatives available for consideration is essentially given. There is not much allowance, therefore, for the fact that decision makers, by their current actions, can or will substantially alter the set of alternatives confronting them in the future. Consequently the analysis of decision making within the subsystems studied seems to run largely in terms of the short run and to be based upon the assumption that the decision maker cannot significantly modify the environment of alternatives to which he is responding.

I find myself hard pressed to put behavior within any of these subsystems on a par with behavior in a profit dominated economy. I cannot find in any of the subsystems a clear-cut analogue of the price system which serves to organize and equilibrate the profit dominated behavior of all the private business firms composing the economy. Nor do I find enough analogues to the business firm which continually acts to maximize profits or some more composite success indicator, given actual and prospective buying, selling, and accounting prices, together with the particular industrial setting in which it finds itself. Even though one postulates the alternatives present in a subsystem, one needs to identify the specific decision makers together with the constraints faced by each and the organizational arrangement that binds these decision makers into a subsystem and somehow distributes scarce resources among them in a manner making for the stability and perpetuity of the subsystem.

Before turning to Merrill's analysis of particular subsystems, several implications of his study should be noted. By definition, that part of the realm of theoretical science which is not dominated by profit seeking firms is largely removed from the control of market forces, subject to the constraint that virtually all of the inputs utilized in theoretical science are scarce and hence must be rationed. By definition, also, any practical-art realm is much more dominated by market forces than is any theoretical realm, for the tastes and demands which a practical art subserves are largely shaped by market factors and by a considerable awareness of the opportunity costs involved in any particular course of action. Of course, one subsystem of the practical art sort may be more shaped by market forces than is some other.

I turn now to Merrill's analysis of the direction of R and D within the realm of theoretical science. Control is exercised largely by scientists participating in the particular cultural traditions of science and bent upon promoting "the aims and values embodied in this tradition." Science is organized, not by prices, but by the "professional judgments of achieved and expected performance" which are based upon "culturally transmitted standards of scientific significance and value." The overriding standard is described as that of deepening our understanding of nature, or of maximizing our advance in knowledge. Accordingly, interest and resources tend to be shifted, at the margin, to fields of science in which something is happening, that is, to fields in which new findings or methods have given rise to "new and wider opportunities for achieving greater precision or profundity" and for extending an affected field's systematic relevance and increasing its intrinsic interest. "Practical interest" is a subsidiary source of attraction.

Unfortunately, Merrill does not present supporting empirical evidence but instead counts heavily upon M. Polanyi's arguments. He does, of course, note that European scientists set greater value upon purely academic science than do American scientists, presumably because of differences in cultural tradition. One might argue, however, that a comparative scarcity of resources for relatively expensive practically oriented research may also be influential; after all, such scarcity helps account for the relative importance, in poor countries, of more cheaply produced training in the humanities and legal science.

Three allocative levels seem to be involved, though Merrill does not specifically identify the inputs relevant at each level: (1) recruitment of scientists into a given field of science; (2) recruitment of practitioners in a given field of science into a particular area of that field; and (3) allocation of auxiliary inputs among the scientists engaged at any given time in the various fields and sub-fields of science. One must become a physicist (instead of an economist) before one can become a solid-state physicist and, having become a solid-state physicist, one must get the auxiliary inputs if one is to carry on effectively. The standards emphasized by Merrill seem to be most applicable at level (3); they are not very applicable at level (1), and only modestly so at level (2). In any event, the comparative availability of funds (or resources) for remuneration and research will have much to do with whether a college graduate commits himself to some given field of science; it will also affect his choice of a specialty. One might discover the allocative forces operative by sampling and classifying scientists by major scientific category, specialty, age, type of institution with which connected, interspecialty shifts (if any), and principal reasons for choice of major category of science and of specialty within it. I incline to the view that awareness of differences in economic prospects, together with the ready availability of opportunities for advanced study (which also are economically determined), has much to do with the choice made.

The standards emphasized by Merrill seem most applicable at level (3) and within given fields. Even so, their influence is subject to restriction. When funds are not earmarked for particular fields, a certain amount of conventional egalitarianism affects their allocation; it is considered "unfair" to give "too much" to certain fields even though a strong case may be made for so doing. When funds are earmarked, activities tend to expand most rapidly in those areas in which earmarked funds expand most rapidly. In either situation it is likely, of course, that the amount of support given particular kinds of projects will be greater than otherwise if the instruments these projects produce are likely to be of use on other projects; then investment in the former set of projects results in external economies.

In the second part of his paper, Merrill examines research and development in terms both of its application to the solution of specific problems and of its use in the general improvement of a practical art. Three practical arts, medicine, agriculture, and engineering, are examined. Criteria of practical usefulness are held to operate in the field of medical research as well as in that of government-sponsored agricultural research, particularly in the selection of specific problems for solution. This is true also in engineering but in that field one also finds a considerable institutionalization and utilization of resources to improve engineering in general, seemingly more than in the field of medicine which draws upon a larger number of specialized sciences.

Within the field of medicine the direction given research is dominated by professional standards incorporated in the tradition of medical science; it is in light of these standards that the comparative importance of medical needs and the degree of their satisfaction is assessed. Because findings are promptly publicized they are expeditiously evaluated, as are the research techniques, and the like, associated with them. Even so, nonscientific determinants may also be operative; for example, the attitudes of patients sometimes affect applied medical research and the same is true of foundation financing, be it rational or otherwise. It is questionable, of course, whether standards used to define what is good medical practice have much to do with how investigators are recruited or with how resources are allocated among them. The prospect of economic advantage probably plays a major part in determining what research is undertaken. Careful inquiry might disclose what particular tastes and interests animate those whose funds help give direction, be it economically warranted or not, to medical research.

Applied research and development in the field of government sponsored agricultural research is largely controlled by governmental agencies. The criterion of prospective economic usefulness appears to determine what is to be done. It is not disclosed how this criterion is applied. Nor is it disclosed whether the criterion of usefulness is better defined and more closely conformed to in this field than in that of medical research in which, at least until recently, the role of government has been small.

Engineering is described as less influenced by scientific specialists than is medicine and, also, as far more completely under the influence of profit seeking firms, inasmuch as they employ most of the engineers engaged in R and D. Some support is given to basic research, principally by larger firms and a few research-oriented engineering schools. It is noted, however, that the increasing capacity of theoretical engineering research to give rise to widely applicable results as well as to contribute to the *general* improvement of engineering is making for greater support of basic research.

Merrill does not report which of the three practical arts considered is most closely oriented to the market and hence most under its influence. Engineering appears to be the most market-dominated of the three, with government-sponsored agricultural research second, and medical research third. In the field of engineering, the market seems largely to determine how much money is available for research and the uses to which it is put. In the field of agricultural research, the market influences what is done in far greater measure than it influences how much is done. The same is true of medicine but to a lesser extent.

In each of these three fields one might endeavor to determine the extent to which the market governs what research is undertaken, and then seek to explain the residuum in noneconomic terms. This approach, if it could be carried out, would provide us with a better estimate of the relative importance of nonmarket factors than we presently have. It might also disclose the role of market forces to be quite important even when nonmarket forces are supposed to be playing the major role. After all, as Pareto and Marshall and others have suggested, market forces sometimes resemble icebergs in that much of their influence is exercised from submerged situations and, hence, hidden from superficial examination.

The basic problem with which Merrill deals requires further analytical clarification. (1) Each subsystem, together with its allocative machinery, must be defined and bounded. (2) Values must be separated into those present *within* a subsystem (where they may constrain the operation of the allocative machinery) and those present *outside* the subsystem. The values *outside* the subsystem must be classified in turn into those which are largely shaped within the market (e.g. ordinary consumer tastes) or outside the market (e.g. those that generate dispositions to supply funds for defense and offense, space travel, specialized medical research, etc.). (3) The sources of the personnel and other resources available to any particular subsystem must be carefully identified, as must the circumstances which govern this availability through time. (4) The levels at which the allocation of personnel and inputs takes place need to be differentiated.

Given analytical distinctions of the sort indicated, it will be found that most of the personnel and resources available to any of the subsystems treated by Merrill flow in from the outside. They do so largely in consequence of values generated outside the subsystem, either within the market or outside the market. Furthermore, even when these values have been originated and organized outside the market (e.g. by the action of special interest groups expressed through government agencies or private foundations), their realization is accomplished through the market. Funds are made available and individuals and auxiliary equipment are "hired" to accomplish the objective ends to which the values point. These individuals and equipment could not otherwise be engaged to objectify the values in question; for only very rarely will individuals engage in a line of activity irrespective of the remuneration offered and the other alternatives available. Moreover, even within a subsystem, material advantage will be largely counted upon to attract men and materials to one sector and from others. In sum, advocates of given courses of research action must rely largely upon the use of material rewards; for, as Rochefoucauld implied, material self-interest usually swallows up virtue. What is most in need of explanation is why certain courses of action come to be preferred by given individuals and how those individuals go about the business of raising the material means with which to induce competent persons to implement such courses of action.

Scientific Discovery and the Rate of Invention

IRVING H. SIEGEL

THE PATENT, TRADEMARK, AND COPYRIGHT FOUNDATION OF
GEORGE WASHINGTON UNIVERSITY AND THE U.S. COUNCIL OF
ECONOMIC ADVISERS

THIS paper discusses relations between scientific discovery and invention considered as *concepts* and as *phenomena*. The two entities are connected, as symbols and as realities, with the generation, treatment, and use of information, which is increasingly being recognized as a fundamental economic and technological "stuff" comparable to matter and energy. They enter into the logical sequences of ideas and events that culminate in the economic exploitation of new material and nonmaterial inputs, production methods, and products. In the contemporary setting, they represent typical goals of formal research and development projects, on which billions of dollars of public and private funds are being spent annually in the United States. They provide opportunities and avenues for cultural change, including economic growth and progress (which may be measured in terms of per capita real income and real output per man-hour, respectively); and they influence, although they cannot alone determine, the pace and directions of such change.

Concepts of Scientific Discovery and Invention

The terms scientific discovery and invention signify both acts and results of acts, both processes and outcomes. When used in plural form, they clearly refer to outcomes rather than processes; and when the singular form is preceded by the indefinite article, an outcome is connoted. Although in legal and other literature the terms discovery and invention are often coupled and treated as equivalent, they are assigned different meanings here. A distinction is intended even when, for the sake of simplicity, the adjective scientific is omitted. Discovery is the act of wresting a secret from nature; and a secret that is won is

---

NOTE: A full revised version of this report appears in the *Patent, Trademark, and Copyright Journal*, Fall 1960, under the title "Scientific Discovery, Invention, and the Cultural Environment."

a discovery. More specifically, a discovery may be a "new" fact, principle, hypothesis, theory, or law concerning natural (including human) phenomena that are observable directly or through their effects. Novelty is to be determined from the standpoint of a nation or a civilization rather than from the viewpoint of an individual; what is new to a person other than the recognized pioneer may represent a rediscovery or just the diffusion of existing knowledge. Nevertheless, the "first" discoverer is not always accorded as much honor, if his name is remembered at all, as a later discoverer whose work has borne more fruit. Every discoverer actually builds upon a foundation of "old" knowledge that has become part of the cultural heritage, and the acknowledgement of his contribution depends on the manner in which he presents his findings and on the ripeness of his time.[1] Too much primacy may be dismissed, in retrospect, as prematurity.

Invention may be regarded as purposeful and practical contriving based on existing knowledge (theoretical and applied) and uncommon insight or skill; that is, as the act of bringing to workable condition a potentially economic or usable process or product (an invention) that has a significantly novel feature. Again, tradition is relevant, and novelty is supposed to be judged from the standpoint of a nation (e.g., according to the standards of a patent system) or a civilization (e.g., against the background of all "prior art"); and, again, honor for primacy may be bestowed without a fine regard for historical literalness or the sensibilities of disgruntled inventors. Patriotism, insularity, indifference to exact definitions and specific patent claims, or ignorance may encourage attribution of an invention to a citizen of one country instead of another. But a preference in favor of native inventors may also reflect the fact that an invention has a cultural context, that it tends to be credited on the basis of its local development and significance rather than its abstract availability.

---

[1] To avoid repetition of the "classic" cases of men of science against the world, I mention three great young chemists who even defied their own professors: van't Hoff and Arrhenius, who had the good fortune to enlist the aid of an Ostwald, and Couper, whose humbling by Wurtz left Kekulé to bask alone in glory. See Bernard Jaffe, *Crucibles: The Story of Chemistry*, Premier reprint, 1957, pp. 140–154; P. Cook, "The End of Chemistry Is Its Theory," *Science News*, October 1959, pp. 33–48; and Eduard Farber, *The Evolution of Chemistry*, New York, Ronald, 1952, pp. 164–166, 174–175, 222–225, 265–268.

Two other infrequently cited instances of professionally resisted advance come to mind—the insightful, though unrigorous, applications of mathematics to electrical engineering by Oliver Heaviside (inventor of the "operational calculus") and Gabriel Kron (pioneer in the analysis of stationary electrical networks and rotating electrical systems by means of matrices and tensors). Once accepted, the contributions of these two men proved valuable in mechanical engineering and more remote fields.

On "Rates" of Discovery and Invention

Since events are more discrete than the acts that lead to them, the volume of scientific or inventive activity during any period of time is not perfectly correlated with the number of discoveries or inventions completed in the same interval. This divergence, however, is only one of many factors that should discourage a quantitative interpretation of the phrase "rate of invention" included in the title assigned to the present paper.

A much more relevant factor is the wide variation in the quality and significance of discoveries and inventions (considered as events), for a simple count of such events provides no clue to the number of "units" of significant novelty involved. As already noted, every scientist or inventor actually enters *in medias res*, from the standpoint of his culture, even though he may think he starts *ab ovo*. A scientist may either add a small increment to the fund of knowledge or propose or effect a grand reorganization or synthesis; he may show either unusual persistence or genuine creativity, deftness of hand or incisiveness of mind, a tolerance of perspiration or a touch of inspiration.[2] Happy accidents may befall some prepared minds and shorten the path to success or provide new goals,[3] while mischance may frustrate others no less deserving. Once a pioneer is acknowledged, his work tends to resist depreciation as successors offer more elegant solutions of the same problems on the basis of newer knowledge.[4] A hero may also be overcredited by common opinion with the achievements of his

[2] What weights would be appropriate for combining in one measure these three major qualitatively different achievements involving the speed of light: Michelson's painstaking measurement of this constant, Lorentz's use of this speed as a limit in his "transformation equations" relating to the mass and length of moving objects, Einstein's use of it in his expression for converting mass into energy? Once Mendelejeff's periodic table of the chemical elements becomes established, should a new significance be attached to such ridiculed anticipations as Newlands' "law of octaves"? Is Fermi's calculation of the neutrino into existence a comparable feat to Maxwell's insistence on a mathematical symmetry that led beyond Ampère to the electromagnetic theory?

[3] On the role of accident, see I. B. Cohen, *Science, Servant of Man*, Boston, Little, Brown, 1948, pp. 36–50, 107–108; and W. I. B. Beveridge, *Art of Scientific Investigation*, Modern Library paperback, 1957, pp. 37–55. Also of interest is Ernst Mach's 1895 essay on "The Part Played by Accident in Invention and Discovery," published in his *Popular Scientific Lectures*, La Salle, Ill., Open Court, 1943, 5th ed., pp. 259–281. Of course, recognition of the role of chance may be traced back to much earlier observers (e.g., Francis Bacon).

[4] Michelson's mechanical determinations of the velocity of light, refined over a half-century, were inherently much less accurate than the measurements subsequently made by many little-known workers in Federal laboratories using radar, radio waves, molecular vibrations, and "atomic clocks."

predecessors, colleagues, and assistants;[5] and his true accomplishment may be ungenerously appraised by his peers or by members of a different profession.[6] In an age of sophisticated formal research activity, it is easy to ridicule the empiricism of a Goodyear—and fail to recognize persisting elements in the testing of catalysts or medicines, in the minor modification of drug molecules, and in the screening of molds for antibiotics. Finally, the march of history may confer new significance on a discovery or invention thought to be minor or trivial in an earlier context.[7]

Other papers presented at this Conference deal with problems of measuring the rate of invention, so it is not necessary to discuss here the inadequacies of patent statistics, the uneven economic import of patented inventions, and similar matters. Three pertinent facts that have struck the author in the course of his work with the Patent, Trademark, and Copyright Foundation are: the wide neglect of patent "claims" as units of registered inventions; the manifold uncertainties still surrounding the legal concept of invention; and the necessity for somehow taking account of reinventions, trade secrets, know-how, and employee suggestions in the consideration of the universe of inventive activity.

Discovery and Invention Seen in a Broader Context

Modern circumstances require that increasing attention be given to the roles of discovery and invention in economic and other cultural change, and that more explicit consideration be given to these two

[5] This is true not only of broad syntheses such as Newton's or Einstein's but also of limited projects involving team research—e.g. the production of transuranium elements. The reader may find it instructive to check the names he recognizes in the list of credits shown for elements 98–101 by Albert Ghiorso and G. T. Seaborg, "Synthetic Elements: II," in *New Chemistry*, New York, Simon and Schuster, 1957, p. 137.

[6] Recall the attitude of physicists like Maxwell and Rowland toward inventors of practical things as simple as the telephone (Cohen, *op. cit.*, pp. 61–63). Much more recently, sociologists and anthropologists have espoused cultural theories of invention and discovery that minimize the role of the individual. A prominent anthropologist, L. A. White (*Science of Culture*, New York, Grove reprint, pp. 213–214), has stated that Urey's isolation of heavy hydrogen (a feat winning the Nobel prize) did not require "intelligence of a high order" although it did demand more technological knowledge than the more familiar feat of "opening a recalcitrant jar of pickles."

[7] The Seebeck, Peltier, piezoelectric, magnetostrictive, and Edison effects are among the many discoveries that have acquired importance through time. Swan's artificial-fiber filament was not good for an incandescent light, but it pointed the way to rayon. Goddard's early work in rocketry and Jansky's discovery of radio-wave emanations from distant stars acquire increasing significance as our government gives urgent support to space science and technology. Patents on stereophonic recording expired before popular interest in an alternative to monaural disks was awakened.

categories (or the activities they embrace) in the economic treatment of information. Among the relevant circumstances are: the multiplication and enlargement of corporate research programs; the annual outlay of billions of public dollars for private contract research; the clarification of accounting rules (e.g. in the Internal Revenue Code of 1954) regarding the treatment of private research costs; the increasing importance of the scientific and technological dimensions of national defense; the private acquisition of commercially valuable patents and experience through military contracts and subcontracts; the extensive exchange of technical information through inter-company arrangements and trade literature; the constant efforts to restrain domestic production costs (through process improvements) and to expand the horizons of domestic consumption (through introduction of new, acceptably-priced products); the intensifying competition with foreign industry for markets at home and abroad; the depletion of high-grade domestic mineral deposits; and the impressive advance in information-handling technology (e.g., electronic communications and data processing).

The new circumstances require, for example, a breakdown of the Schumpeterian triple sequence (invention, innovation, and imitation) into more stages and the interpolation of others. They also demand the establishment of subdivisions in the categories basic research, applied research, and development—to distinguish educational activities (which typically involve rediscovery and reinvention) from those that lead to discovery, invention, and innovation. Furthermore, they suggest the need for separate treatment of discovery and invention in sociological and anthropological theories, rather than their grouping as "new combinations and syntheses of cultural elements" that have a "platonic" existence and seem merely to await realization through the performance of minor acts of human catalysis; the recognition of sources, as well as effects, of scientific and technological advance; the recognition that discovery and invention interact; and re-examination of the functionality of the concept of cultural lag.

Finally, it is important in the contemporary setting to recognize not only the relation of discovery to basic research, or of invention to applied research and development, but also the relation of all these activities to operations involving information. As information takes its place beside matter and energy in the economic cosmogony, a spectrum of operations such as the following deserves attention:

1. Creation of absolute information[8] (discovery)
2. Processing
    a. Screening and correlation
    b. Reorganization and preliminary adaptation
    c. Coding and decoding
    d. Computing and logical analysis
    e. Abstracting and digesting
    f. Translation
    g. Recording and indexing
    h. Copying (as in printing, typing, or photography)
3. Storage, maintenance, and retrieval
4. Distribution and acquisition (as in radio and television broadcasting, interoffice communication, consultation, patent sale or licensing, and education)
5. Application
    a. Embodiment in hypotheses and theories (discovery), invention, reinvention, and know-how
    b. Utilization of invention, etc.
    c. Decision making

All of these unitary activities create time, place, form, or ownership utility; they are services that command a price. They may be expanded and regrouped to take account of the schemes used by Schumpeter, Usher, Maclaurin, and others. Analogues exist at various levels of aggregation—for example, the occupation, the department, the firm, the industry, the economy.

Analogues also appear at the various levels of biological existence, from the individual down to the cell, chromosome, and gene; and this fact will assume increasing importance in the study of creative and other behavior, life processes, and heredity. From an economic appreciation of material substance, including fuels, man has naturally progressed to an appreciation of energy in more abstract terms. Today, we are witnessing the emergence of information as an economic stuff with the recognition of the special value of energy signals in communication. The stage is also being set, through advances in the life

[8] A term used by L. Brillouin, "Thermodynamics and Information Theory," *American Scientist*, October 1950, pp. 594–599.

Alternatives to, or extensions of, the catalogue presented here will be suggested by a rapidly growing literature. See, for example, J. D. Trimmer, "The Basis for a Science of Instrumentology", *Science*, October 23, 1953, pp. 461-465; and papers by J. P. Guilford and J. S. Bruner in *Fundamentals of Psychology: The Psychology of Thinking* (Annals of the New York Academy of Sciences, Vol. 91, Art. 1, December 23, 1960, pp. 6-21 and 23-37.

sciences, for the identification of "vitality" as a fourth entity. The distinction will seem valid and desirable even though material, energy, and information processes underlie all manifestations of life. Examples of pertinent advances include, in addition to those already familiar in agriculture and medicine, the successful "imprinting" of animal behavior in early life, the treatment of viruses as living molecules, the increasing understanding of the role of specialized organs and molecules (such as adenosine triphosphate) in the biological "transduction" of energy, the recognition of the importance of intercellular communication for "homeostasis," and the awareness that intracellular communication via "replicating" nucleic acid molecules plays an outstanding part in specifying the inheritable features of a future adult organism.

Sequences and Interactions

It should be mentioned in passing that the private costs of acquiring new knowledge and giving up old knowledge would limit the practical force of the proposition that the marginal social cost of using an invention is zero. Even if no royalties had to be paid for patent licenses and the flow of new inventions could still be assured, potential users would still have to learn of the existence, technical nature, and economic applicability of the free inventions. They would also have to be willing to abandon knowledge and skills they already possess. In other words, costs of change (beyond the costs of reforming society so that the theorems of welfare economics would become more acceptable!) have to be taken into account.

Single-factor theories of development are attractive, but the assumption of interaction among the leading entities often provides a sounder first approximation than does linear causation in one direction. In considering the roles of discovery and invention in the real world, it is desirable not to preclude the possibility of their interdependence and their influence on, as well as their reaction to, economic, social (including political, legal, and familial), psychological, and international factors. The firm adoption of a theory of determinism—geographic, biological, or cultural—would hobble inquiry or, if we are more fortunate, lead to hypotheses that could quickly be contradicted.[9]

Although discovery logically precedes invention, experience indicates that the reverse order also occurs to the extent that an invention has considerable practical importance. Thus, the invention of all sorts of instruments and apparatus has proved essential to the progress of science. Behind these instruments, of course, lie other discoveries, but the tools of industry and the skills of workers and the vast store of accumulated technological information should not be overlooked. As we think further about such interrelations, the integrity of a modern society becomes obvious.

Sometimes, the heart of a scientific discovery is actually a physical invention or a mental invention, in which instances we may well say that discovery and invention proceed together. Thus, in the very broad territory covered by military research nowadays, a genuine scientific advance may be immediately reducible to practice and lead to a patent for a process or composition of matter. On the other hand, a scientific discovery that involves explanation rather than, or in addition to, observation may require the invention of convenient mental fictions—concepts or models—or entail the invention or reinvention of a type of (unpatentable) mathematics.

Although we are culturally conditioned to believe that technology is autonomous, that it follows a relentless if unpredictable course, that it molds almost everything else, we may easily verify that the arrows of influence also point in the opposite direction, as in many chemical equations. Thus, economic considerations affect the technological future, as is so well illustrated by the lag of nuclear power generation, despite flamboyant forecasts, and the widening use of by-product radioisotopes. The profitability of atomic power stations is still in doubt, despite the willingness of society to forego the recovery of billions of dollars of past investment in nuclear science and technology; conventional steam stations based on coal retain their competitive vigor, benefiting still from applications of "old-fashioned" knowledge.

Another factor that helps shape technology is military necessity,

---

[9] Cohen (*op. cit.*) properly stresses the importance of the "total scientific situation" in influencing the course of discovery and invention; and E. G. Boring, the psychologist, properly observes that the *Zeitgeist* may in some cases advance and in others hold back scientific and technological change, and that our knowledge of pertinent facts is always inadequate for correct prognostication ("Science and the Meaning of Its History," *The Key Reporter*, July 1959, pp. 2–3).

On interaction and forecasting, see also Bernard Barber, *Science and the Social Order*, Glencoe, Free Press, 1952, and four papers by I. H. Siegel: "Technological Change and Long-Run Forecasting," *Journal of Business*, July 1953, pp. 141–156; "Conditions of American Technological Progress," *American Economic Review*, May 1954, pp. 161–177; "The Role of Scientific Research in Stimulating Economic Progress," *ibid.*, May 1954, pp. 340–345; and "Changing Technology and Resources," presented at the Conference on Natural Resources and Economic Growth, Ann Arbor, April 7–9, 1960.

which now dictates, for example, the abandonment of manned aircraft for missiles in response to a foreign initiative. Firms are counting on the development of commercial supersonic liners at huge public expense; the prototype bomber (B-70) is regarded as essential for defense and national prestige. In the past, military necessity, plus a timely declassification, permitted the apparently profitable development and introduction of commercial jet airplanes despite the inadequacy of existing airports and the absence of helicopter shuttle service.

Finally, we should note the vigor of the foreign bid for a share in United States markets as an emerging influence on our technology. This challenge has brought back the domestic compact car, has probably speeded the domestic development of transistorized radio and television receivers, and will hasten the diffusion of steelmaking methods employing large amounts of oxygen. The adjustment of complementary research efforts of our firms will surely lead to new discoveries and inventions in the same and other general fields.

Interplay of New and Old Science and Technology

As future directions of change and growth are contemplated, it is important to recognize that considerable room still exists for discovery, invention, innovation, and investment in fields already familiar as well as in frontier areas. The advance into such new areas stimulates certain established technologies and provides new contexts for the revaluation and upgrading of old knowledge. The advent of atomic energy has already raised the national base of conventionally generated electric power and increased the demand for lead, steel, concrete, water, automobile transportation, and so forth; it has not simply created an interest in beryllium, zirconium, hafnium, the rare earths, uranium, thorium, and other comparatively exotic materials.

Even without speculating on the nature of future developments that will enrich existing science and invention, we may observe the reassuring pattern in recent years of the cross-fertilization of the old and the new. It is as though we could find space for new people by filling gaps between our cities rather than, say, by having to settle at once on Antarctica, a moon, or other planets. Consider the rising interest, in the present context, not only in atomic and solar energy and magneto-hydrodynamics but also in power technologies originating in the nineteenth century—the fuel cell (derived from Faraday), the thermocouple, and thermionics. Consider the startling discovery of a new color theory by Land that follows up neglected hints in patents granted to two men in 1914, overthrows the classical theory of Newton, Young, and Helmholtz, and is bound to simplify color photography.[10] Finally, the limited but significant revolt of the public against industry control of its taste in automobiles is sure to encourage broader competitive experimentation by makers with materials and power plants already known but used rarely or not at all.[11] Continuing suburbanization, expansion of tourism, further population growth, rising demands for education and health services, and the automatization of industry are more likely to occasion difficult adjustments of a familiar variety (such as location of responsibility for adequate capital formation, taxation, and welfare legislation) than to require sudden diversification of the nation's existing base of science and invention. In the military realm, however, where the pattern of competition and the timetable are not controlled by one nation, crash programs of one kind or another may continue to be required for national safety.[12]

COMMENT

THOMAS S. KUHN, University of California

One aspect of Irving Siegel's paper seems to me particularly striking, at least in the full version distributed to conference participants. Unlike more standard discussions of similar problems, Siegel rejects from the start all the usual simplifying schematic assumptions. From start to finish the author displays no fear of the full complexities of the job at hand, and, since a willingness to face difficulties seems an admirable characteristic, I can only admire and applaud his courage. My admiration is particularly warm because of my firm

[10] Francis Bello, "An Astonishing New Theory of Color," *Fortune*, May 1959, pp. 144 ff.

[11] See, for example, the article by Damon Stetson in the *New York Times*, March 14, 1960. Incidentally, the *General Motors Annual Report for 1959* notes (p. 12) that the Stirling thermal engine is under study: "New developments in material and design have revived interest in this 19th Century engine, noted for quietness and ability to burn wide variety of fuels."

[12] In a comment made in *Capital Formation and Economic Growth*, Princeton, 1955, pp. 572–578, I. H. Siegel noted that technological change occurs almost continually and almost everywhere in our economy, even though only the dramatic instances are usually singled out for attention; that the technical growing points of our economy should accordingly be sought in the activities and demands of (1) the household, (2) private industry, (3) government, and (4) other nations seeking trade or aid; and that Colin Clark's triple classification scheme should accordingly be altered to include these four additional categories from which new industries or subindustries arise.

conviction that all the difficulties to which Siegel points are entirely real. He is obviously, for example, quite right when he insists that neither patent counting nor national reputation is an adequate measure of a country's eminence in invention. Again, he must be right in his insistence that Schumpeter's triple sequence—invention, innovation, and imitation—is no longer adequate for the analysis of technological change, and that the analyst must now investigate a full spectrum of sequential activities. By the same token, I can only agree when Siegel does battle with all "single-factor" accounts of inventive and innovating activities. Furthermore, his sketch of the multiple factors—social, economic, psychological, and so on—whose interactions must be taken into account, seems to me eminently just. And these are only illustrations of the analytic difficulties to which Siegel points. In almost every other case as well I find myself in complete agreement.

Those remarks might, by themselves, serve as a full commentary on Siegel's paper, but I sense something else that must be said. The topic to which his title directs our attention is the relation of scientific discovery to inventive activity. That topic has urgent action corollaries for both national and industrial policy. Given such a problem, the multiplication of complexities—even, as in this case, real ones—need not necessarily supply the most fruitful approach to a solution. From my own experience, it seldom supplies the most fruitful approach to even the "purest" of scientific problems. These reflections lead me to voice a small but persistent fear that Siegel, in his admirable concern to face squarely the real complexities of the contemporary scene, may have succeeded principally in disguising the most important problem that, to me at least, his subject presents. In what follows I shall limit myself to the elucidation of that fear.

Unfortunately I am forced to begin with a terminological problem. Siegel uses the words "discovery" and "invention" in ways with which I have little quarrel but which are so far from my habitual professional usage that an attempt on my part to follow him is likely to create only confusion and obscurity. In his paper, invention is "purposeful and practical contriving based on existing knowledge"; for the corresponding spectrum of activities I shall use the terms technology, applied science, and, perhaps, engineering. Again, and more significantly, Siegel uses discovery to mean "a new fact, principle, . . . theory, or law"; for the activities that produce these results I shall employ the term science or, more appropriately, basic science. This change of terms will enable me to describe my worry in clearer and more familiar ways.[1]

Midway through his paper Siegel suggests that perhaps sociologists and anthropologists should adopt different treatments when analyzing discovery, on the one hand, and invention, on the other. (This differentiation corresponds to mine between science and technology.) But, except at this point and in his introductory definitions, Siegel scarcely employs separate treatments himself. On the contrary, his evidence is drawn indiscriminately from technology and science (most of it is, in fact, drawn from technology), and he concludes by deriving a single set of generalizations, explicitly applicable to both activities from this undifferentiated body of evidence. History of science provides grounds for grave doubts about both this procedure and the conclusions drawn from it. Furthermore, these doubts are unaffected by history's total failure to produce any definition that will invariably distinguish a scientific from a technological development. I am even dubious that such a definition could be given. There are too many historical episodes that lie squarely on the border and that would have to be described as neither science nor technology or as both. Nevertheless, it seems to me of first importance, in approaching Siegel's problem, to recognize that the two activities, science and technology, have very often been almost entirely distinct.

A few brief and vastly too simplified historical illustrations will clarify what I have in mind. In presenting them my object is at least to make plausible such generalizations as the following: until about a century ago science and technology most often flourished at different historical times; when, occasionally, they did flourish in the same period, they most often did so at different geographical locations. If these generalizations are even approximately correct (and in the nature of the case they cannot be more than that), they should at least suggest that historically science and technology have been relatively independent enterprises.[2] And they may suggest somewhat more. The

---

[1] This terminological shift probably has little importance to the problem at hand, but it can be of critical significance in the analysis, historical or logical, of science and of technology. In my own field, for example, it is often important to remember that, while scientists may *discover* new objects or phenomena, they must *invent* new theories. By the same token, one would distrust an analysis of technology which prohibited the inventor from discovering anything at all. At a higher philosophical level, of course, the distinction once again becomes problematic, but it still seems a necessary starting point.

[2] To use the word "independence" I have to neglect the very important stimulus which developments in technology and the crafts have repeatedly provided to the sciences since the beginning of recorded history. That stimulus is extremely important to the historian of

cultural matrix that has supported a flourishing scientific enterprise has not usually supported a progressive technology and vice versa. At least part of the historical pattern I shall sketch thus hints at an actual conflict between the two enterprises. I remind you, for example, that, excluding the last few decades about which no secure judgment is yet possible, the only nation that has achieved simultaneous eminence in both science and technology is Germany in the years from about 1860 to 1930.

Let me then throw the historian's usual caution to the winds (it proves remarkably difficult to do) and omit *all* qualifications. I suggest to you, first, that the greatest achievements of ancient technology are largely restricted to the period before 700 B.C., and that the major development of science comes almost entirely after that date. Again, it seems noteworthy that ancient science, when it did develop, was largely Greek but that Greece was technologically a debtor nation. The great technological power of classical antiquity was Rome, and the Romans made little use of Greek science and developed none of their own. That pattern of the separate locus of science and technology continues into modern times. The technological changes that helped to bring the Middle Ages to a close and that ushered in the Renaissance were almost completed by 1500. But the scientific discoveries that collectively constitute the Scientific Revolution were produced almost entirely after that date. Or, we may move into still more recent times and examine the situation at the very start of the nineteenth century. At that time, Britain was at the height of the Industrial Revolution, the acknowledged leader of Europe in the production and exploitation of technological innovations. But, simultaneously, England was widely felt to be a relatively backward country scientifically. At the beginning of the nineteenth century it was technologically backward France that led Europe in the sciences and that was universally acknowledged to do so.[3]

These are the sort of contrasts that lead me to urge the desirability, at least in a first approximation, of considering science and technology as separate enterprises and very likely in some conflict one with the other. I hasten to add, however, that the historian can delin-

---

science, but it has little bearing on the question here at issue. We are looking for an influence of scientific discovery and invention upon technology, and that seems to have been very nearly negligible before the nineteenth century.

[3] For an excellent and somewhat more extended account of much of the material in this paragraph, see R. P. Multhauf, "The Scientist and the 'Improver' of Technology," *Technology and Culture*, 1959, pp. 38–47.

eate this independence only by restricting attention to the period before 1860. Before that date, the facts and theories discovered and invented by scientists contributed little to progress in technological innovation.[4] Despite persistent rumors to the contrary, neither the Greeks, nor Galileo and Newton, nor even Black and Lavoisier taught the great technological innovators very much of what they needed to know about nature. Astronomy, dynamics, and inorganic chemistry—the principal fields in which these famous men made their most notable contributions—did not prove very relevant to major technological advances. Only with the development of the electric battery and of organic chemistry did science begin to achieve large-scale success in fields that promised direct and relatively rapid application. But these are nineteenth-century fields, and their exploitation had scarcely begun before the middle of the century. Once it did begin the whole pattern of relationships between science and technology changed rapidly and drastically.

Today that change is familiar to all. Since 1860 a number of industries have been revolutionized and many others have been brought into being by a massive influx of information and techniques from the basic scientific laboratory. In these industries one finds that characteristic twentieth-century institution, the industrial research laboratory, and in these laboratories one finds that characteristic twentieth-century figure, the new innovator-engineer whose satisfactory performance demands much basic scientific training. In any society where industries like these bulk large even the old approximate independence of science and technology is very hard to find. In our

---

[4] Note that I speak of the effect upon technology of scientific discovery and invention. If we were concerned instead with the effect of scientific method or of the scientific attitude upon technology, we would find that it became significant at least a century earlier. The need for this distinction between the effects of scientific method and those of scientific results is too seldom noted, and the consequence is a considerable confusion in the literature. See, for example, the two excellent papers by C. C. Gillispie and R. E. Schofield (*Isis*, 1957, pp. 398–415). Because one of these authors sees science as method, the other as accumulated fact and theory, their papers reach opposite conclusions about the relation of science and technology in the late eighteenth century from facts that both are quite willing to grant. The same confusion shows again and again elsewhere and can be at least partially dispelled by the same technique. For example, Smeaton's improvements of the Newcomen engine did not depend significantly upon prior scientific knowledge and Watt's may not have done so. But both these men, unlike the innovators in, say, the eighteenth-century textile industry, arrived at their improvements by the same sorts of laboratory techniques that their contemporaries were employing in the sciences. In the same period the same sort of methodological borrowing is also apparent in the inorganic chemical industry (see Henry Guerlac, "Some French Antecedents of the Chemical Revolution," *Chymia*, 1958, pp. 73–112).

day the two enterprises are intimately entangled as they have never been before.

Nevertheless, I see no reason to suppose that the entanglements, which have evolved during the last .hundred years, have at all done away with the differences between the scientific and technological enterprises or with their potential conflicts. A casual scrutiny of either the congressional debates and hearings on the National Science Foundation or of the editorials in the journal, *Science*, strongly suggests that these differences and conflicts are an integral part of contemporary life. The evidence I have tried to draw from MacKinnon's paper points in the same direction, and there is biographical evidence to the same effect, besides. I think, for example, of Edison's famous statement to his chief engineer: "We can't be like the old German professor who as long as he can get his black bread and beer is content to spend his whole life studying the fuzz on a bee!" That was the closing line in a devastating critique of one of the Ph.D.'s employed at Menlo Park, a man who, according to Edison, constantly got sidetracked and lost time because he insisted upon following up phenomena that were new to him.[5] Or, note what has happened to the triumvirate whose successful development of the transistor Richard Nelson has so well described for this conference. Only one of the three is still at Bell Laboratories; a second has now started his own industrial concern; and the third has joined the staff of a major university. Instances like these, reflecting the rather different goals and drives of the scientist and the technologist, can be multiplied *ad nauseam*. That being the case, it seems a great shortcoming in any paper on the relations of science and invention that it should do so very little to reflect their existence.

Let me close therefore by pointing to just two effects upon Siegel's paper of this failure to discriminate. I begin by considering the "spectrum of operations" which he outlines. To the extent that I understand the terms employed, I think that spectrum—from discovery, through processing, to application—fits applied science well enough. But, though scientists do many of the same things, I have great difficulty fitting the same spectrum to their enterprise. In part the implied order of operations seems wrong. More important, I can discover far too little place for the sorts of problem solving that scientists most characteristically undertake. Furthermore, I doubt

---

[5] H. C. Passer, *The Electrical Manufacturers, 1875–1900*, Cambridge, Mass., 1953, pp. 180–181.

that a few changes of phrase and the addition of new items to Siegel's list would much relieve my difficulties. On the contrary, a schema of a fundamentally different form seems to be needed. Instead of a single spectrum, consider two parallel ones, descending from a common pool labeled "Existing Knowledge." One of these parallel lines is to represent science, the other, technology, and their possession of a common origin indicates that both the scientist and the inventor-engineer depend for the source and structure of their enterprises upon what is already known.

This schema is obviously only a beginning, and in some respects it may be a misleading one. (Today, as I have already indicated, science and technology are by no means so clearly separate as the schema up to this point implies.) But the double spectrum has obvious advantages over the single one, among them, that it provides a basis for discussion of Siegel's topic, the interaction between science and technology or between science and inventive activity. The most obvious channel for interactions is through the pool of existing knowledge, from which both enterprises begin and to which both feed back. In the sorts of industries studied by Jacob Schmookler—agriculture, the paper industry, and railroads—it has probably provided the only significant channel. Like technology at large before 1860, these industries have profited only from past scientific achievements and not very often even from those. But the pool of existing knowledge does not provide the only channel for interaction or the only one illustrated in modern industry. Nelson's case history of the transistor shows that at least occasionally and temporarily the problems of the basic scientist and of the technologist can be the same. Identical overlaps could, I feel sure, be shown to occur even more frequently in the organic chemical industries, though even there they would probably not bulk very large. But they do occur, and my schematic revision of Siegel's spectrum therefore needs to be supplemented by a series of double headed arrows connecting the "science" line with the "technology" line at various distances from their common origin.

These remarks prepare the way for my second and concluding illustrative remark about the effect of failure to discriminate upon Siegel's paper. If one sees in the contemporary scientific-technological scene not a single enterprise, but two in constant interaction, then one may be prepared to discover that the social, economic, and psychological factors that Siegel so properly emphasizes have quite different effects upon the two. And if one has gone that far, then one may hesitate to conclude, as Siegel does, that "the base of science already appears sufficiently large and diversified . . . to accommodate as much growth as other factors in the environment will demand and allow." That statement may well be correct. But, since Siegel means by "science" the entire spectrum of activities from basic science through applied science to ingenious invention, there is no evidence for it in his paper. Perhaps he has proved his point for technology. One might also grant what he says about "the base of science." But one could do all this and still argue that the diversity of the contemporary scientific enterprise, as against that of contemporary technology, is neither so great as it has been nor as it should be. I shall not here argue that position, but I do regret that Siegel's paper does so much to prevent the questions that underlie it from even being asked.

PART V
EFFICIENCY
IN RESEARCH AND DEVELOPMENT

Predictability of the Costs, Time, and Success of Development

A. W. MARSHALL AND W. H. MECKLING

THE RAND CORPORATION

NOWADAYS, tales of how important discoveries or inventions have been made by accident or in contradiction to the best scientific evaluation are familiar to almost everyone. And the proposition that development of new products or processes is an uncertain business is generally accepted without serious dispute. But when it comes to translating this generality into uncertainties associated with particular current development proposals, or when it comes to discussing the implications of uncertainty for the way development projects should be managed, the apparent agreement in point of view is often quickly dissipated. To a large extent the differences that arise do so over the question of the extent of the uncertainty in development—over questions like, Are estimates of cost of production likely to be off by 25 per cent or by 300 per cent?

In its role as advisor to the Air Force on research and development policies RAND is continually forced to make use of predictions about particular development projects. Inevitably, we have become concerned over the confidence that can be attached to such predictions. In this paper we present the results of some recent research into the extent and nature of the uncertainty in new developments. Our general conclusions are:

1. Early estimates of important parameters are usually quite inaccurate, in two respects. First, such estimates are strongly biased toward overoptimism. Second, aside from the bias, the errors in estimates show a substantial variation. That is, even if estimates are multiplied by an appropriate standard factor to eliminate the bias, a nonnegligible source of error remains.

2. The accuracy of estimates is a function of the stage of development, i.e., estimates improve as development of the item progresses. This also means that estimates for development projects representing

NOTE: The authors are greatly indebted to Eugene Brussell for his pioneering research on the accuracy of cost estimates, and to Robert Summers for expanding Brussell's work and providing penetrating comments.

only "modest advances" tend to be better than those for more ambitious projects.

We hope in the balance of this paper to make these propositions more meaningful through analysis and discussion as well as presentation of some data.

One word of warning is perhaps in order. Most of our experience has been limited to military development (the Air Force in particular) and what we have to say is largely centered about the problems of development in that area. Although we feel our experience does have relevance to the problems of development generally, we are by no means confident that it applies with equal exactness in all areas. There are some good reasons for believing that privately financed projects may show different tendencies. In our data, estimates of cost of production of the type of equipment most closely resembling regular commercial equipment, i.e., cargo and tanker aircraft, appear to be quite accurate. This is probably partly because of the modest advances usually sought in these programs, and partly it is because for some of these there are commercially available substitutes.[1] There are, of course, many reasons why military development programs are likely to differ from ordinary commercial ventures. Military developments tend to explore very near the margin of technical feasibility; commercial development goes only so far as market profitability. The policy of cost-plus contracting followed in most military projects is not common practice in private developments. Under cost-plus contracting there is very little penalty attached to understating costs, hence contractors have a decided incentive to do so in order to get contracts. The tendency to underestimate costs is, therefore, not very surprising in military development.

The term research and development covers a wide spectrum of human activity ranging from the discovery of new principles to the construction and testing of operational equipment like a commercial aircraft that itself embodies very little that is really new and untried. In this paper we shall not attempt to cover this entire spectrum. Instead we shall focus on what might be called operational development as distinguished from basic research and exploratory development. By the former we mean, roughly, the effort to take ideas or components that have been tested experimentally and embody them

---

[1] This latter condition leads to a selective process and since we only observe the development of military cargo aircraft that are roughly competitive with commercial carriers no large factor increases in cost estimates from early to late estimates are found.

in useful equipment, as distinguished from the generation of new ideas and their experimental testing. The development of the first jet engine and of the transistor are examples of the latter, while the development of a jet aircraft or a transistorized bombing-navigation system are examples of operational development. Although this division is crude, it defines the area of discussion sufficiently for our purposes.[2]

Ultimately, the measure of success of any development project is the difference between costs and the value of output. But predictions regarding particular projects are seldom framed in terms of that criterion. Instead they take the form of estimates of separate ingredients of success such as costs, performance, etc.

To discuss predictability rationally then, we need an exhaustive classification of factors that affect success. One such classification that we have found useful consists of four subclasses: (1) costs (development and production); (2) performance;[3] (3) time of availability;[4] (4) utility.

Utility

Because the first three factors are largely quantitive[5] while the last, utility, is largely qualitative, most of our study of the problem of predictability has centered about the first three, and we shall concentrate on them here. But, in a paper purporting to discuss how well we can foresee the outcome of research and development, it would be a serious error of omission to neglect entirely uncertainties about utility.

This is particularly true of the development of military equipment. The utility of a potential weapon system usually depends on a host of circumstances about which there is great uncertainty. What weapon systems will the enemy have? What kinds of war or wars will it be necessary to be prepared to fight, and where? What will happen to political alliances in the future? What competing or complementary weapons will be developed? And more could be asked. The outcome

[2] This restriction on the subject matter is not imposed because basic research and exploratory development are less uncertain than operational development. In fact, an imposing list of examples where the best experts failed to foresee the potential of new ideas could be constructed. It is simply a matter of keeping the size of the problem within reasonable bounds.

[3] Performance is used here very broadly to include all the qualities of any equipment or system that contribute to its utility. For military equipment the kinds of qualities included are speed, range, accuracy, pay load, maintainability, operability, etc.

[4] Realistically, availability consists of a schedule of quantities available through time, though we shall consider here only the first operational availability.

[5] This statement is qualified because certain aspects of performance, like ease of handling, are not quantitative.

of a particular development can, and frequently does, hinge critically on answers to questions of this sort. Thus, ten years ago we did not foresee the rapid development of nuclear warheads by the Soviet and its concomitant strides in ballistic missiles. In fact we did not foresee our own development of hydrogen warheads and the implications of this for the utility of ballistic missiles. But these developments had a tremendous impact on the utility of other weapons such as air-breathing intercontinental missiles that we were then intent on developing. In other instances we have tended to overestimate the quantity or quality, or both, of enemy weapons. During the Taiwan air battle we were pleasantly surprised by the overwhelming superiority of the weapon systems we had supplied to the Nationalists. In short, although it is difficult to quantify uncertainties about the utility of proposed developments, there is no doubt that they exist and are highly significant.

The Equivocal Nature of Predictions

One of the main difficulties encountered in assessing the accuracy of development predictions is the fact that the predictions themselves are seldom formulated in a way that permits verification. Perhaps the most obvious (and most pernicious) example of this is the oft-repeated statement that something is "technically feasible" or "within the state of the art." The "something" referred to is usually a set of performance characteristics for equipment whose development is under consideration. Depending on the interpretation one supplies, assertions like these are generally either useless or irrefutable. If they are intended to mean only that such performance is physically possible, they are quite useless in deciding whether a particular development project deserves support. Since proposed developments seldom violate physical laws, at *some* time and at *some* cost the advertised performance can almost always be achieved. On the other hand, if they are intended to mean more than that—that such performance is attainable at an "interesting" cost and in an "interesting" time period—they are irrefutable until costs and availability are explicitly quantified. It is of course the latter meaning that is ordinarily conveyed, whether it is intended or not, and that meaning provides a kind of ideal prototype illustrating the source of much of the difficulty encountered in measuring the accuracy of development predictions.

In our classification of factors affecting the success of a development program, we listed (aside from utility) three parameters or classes of parameters—costs, performance, and time. In practice, trade-offs among these three are always possible. There is a production surface relating them. A given performance can be attained earlier if greater costs are incurred; or, for given costs, earlier availability is possible if lower performance is accepted, and so on. The relevance of these trade-offs to development prediction is fairly obvious. Predictions of any one parameter, e.g., performance, that do not specify what is assumed about the other two, are very elusive propositions indeed. For the predicted parameter may always be achieved at the sacrifice of either or both of the other two.

Cost Estimates

One variant of this kind of ambiguity that is particularly troublesome is the standard procedure for estimating costs. When early estimates are made of what it will cost to produce or develop something new, the estimator typically bases his estimate on the current design and the currently planned program for development. If he is estimating cost of production, he gets a total cost by costing the various components as presently conceived and aggregating those. If he is estimating the cost of development, he estimates the cost of test articles, engineering man-hours, etc., as presently planned and aggregates those. He does not specify what performance he is associating with the particular design nor does he indicate the date at which that performance is to be operationally available. He is simply costing a physical configuration or the physical resources contemplated in the current development plan, or both.

As development proceeds, however, these initial designs and plans are almost invariably changed, either because of unforeseen technical difficulties that forestall meeting performance requirements, or because the customer decides it is essential that the equipment be modified so as to keep pace with changing predictions of enemy capabilities, new operational concepts, and new technological possibilities. A guidance system that was supposed to weigh a few hundred pounds turns out to weigh a ton; a development program that was supposed to require fifteen test articles requires forty-five; revised estimates of enemy defense capabilities dictate additional pay load in the form of countermeasure gear; and more. This kind of thing is not the exception, but the rule. Such changes will have an important effect on costs, and the costs finally incurred will not be those of the initial design or the initial development program, but the cost of whatever actually is produced and whatever program actually is conducted. The difficulties this poses for verifying original estimates are obvious. If costs turn out to differ materially from original predictions, the estimator absolves himself on the grounds that he costed a different program or different product; and, since the initial program or product never emerges, it is usually not possible to know exactly what it would have cost.

In fact, however, absolution is not as simple as all that. The purpose of such cost estimates is to foster a better allocation of resources to research and development projects. Our interest in estimating costs emanates from our desire to economize by making better research and development decisions. In that context we are not concerned with what it would cost to construct particular physical configurations or to carry out particular plans. Instead, we are interested in what it will cost to get some level (or levels) of performance by some date (or dates). Suppose, for example, we are trying to decide whether to initiate the development of a new missile. An analysis of the potential of the missile must run in terms of the performance characteristics of the missile—range, pay load, vulnerability, reliability, etc.—attainable in a certain time period. Accordingly, it is the cost corresponding to the assumed level of performance that is relevant to making the decision, not the cost of a particular development program and a particular physical configuration.

In practice, estimates of the cost of particular development programs and physical configurations are universally married to particular performance characteristics in analyses directed toward making development decisions. In other words, such estimates are used as if they were in fact estimates of the cost of achieving the expected level of performance.[6] As a practical matter, therefore, it is appropriate to treat cost estimates, however they are generated, as if they were estimates of the cost of achieving the expected levels of performance by a given date. By so doing and by observing the changes in these estimates we have a measure of the uncertainty actually confronted in making research and development decisions.

In principle it would be possible to factor the total error in cost estimates as they are prepared into two parts: (1) the part due to errors in the costing of the configuration supplied to the cost estimator (i.e. the intrinsic error in cost estimating); and (2) the part due to

---

[6] Moreover, this is generally done with the active support of those who generate the cost estimates!

changes in the configuration as development progresses. In practice it has not been possible to carry out this separation. However, it is our belief that the intrinsic errors in costing a fixed configuration tend to be small relative to errors due to changes in the configuration in the costing of most major items of military equipment. This means that the main improvements in the accuracy of cost estimating, especially for items of equipment or weapon systems embodying moderate or large changes in technology, must be sought in improved forecasts of the final configurations or other statistical means of adjusting early estimates. However, large uncertainties will remain for these estimates in any case, and those uncertainties should be taken into account in their use. Perhaps estimates should be presented in such a way as to make this possible. As estimates are now produced, the results show this would involve at least adding to each estimate an estimate of its bias and mean square error. Ideally it would involve supplying the user with a complete set of sufficient statistics.

Turning now to the data, Table 1 summarizes some data on the history of estimates of cost of production[7] for twenty-two major items of military equipment.[8] For each item of equipment we have calculated

TABLE 1

TOTAL FACTOR INCREASES IN AVERAGE CUMULATIVE COST OF
PRODUCTION, UNADJUSTED

Fighters	Factor	Bombers	Factor	Cargoes and Tankers	Factor	Missiles	Factor
1	5.6	1	8.7	1	1.7	1	57.6
2	3.6	2	3.5	2	1.6	2	20.7
3	3.1	3	1.5	3	1.0	3	11.1
4	2.1			4	1.0	4	10.3
5	1.9					5	1.5
6	1.5					6	1.3
7	1.4						
8	1.2						
9	1.2						
Mean	2.4		4.5		1.3		17.1 (9.0)[a]
Mean, all classes 6.5 (4.1)[a]							

Note: Factor is the ratio of the latest available estimate to the earliest available estimate.

[a] Excluding missile case No. 1.

[7] Not including the cost of development.
[8] These studies of the accuracy of estimates of cost of production of military equipment are mainly the work of Eugene R. Brussell. We are particularly indebted to him since, so far as we know, his work is the only systematic attempt to study this problem.

the ratio of the latest available estimate of the cumulative average cost of production to the earliest such estimate available.[9] That ratio is labeled factor in Table 1. Thus if the latest cost estimate were three times the earliest available estimate, the factor would be three. Table 1 shows these factors for four classes of equipment—fighters, bombers, cargoes and tankers, and missiles. (This breakdown simply follows conventional military lines, but it is useful because, as we shall see later, the technical advance incorporated in new equipment correlates fairly well with this classification system.)

The ratio between the most recent estimate and the earliest estimate of the cost of production for these items ranges from a minimum of 1 to a maximum of 57. If we include the extreme missile case, number 1, the over-all mean factor increase is about 6.5; if we exclude it, the mean increase is roughly 4. It is worth noting that there exist substantial differences in the means among the four classes of equipment. For cargoes and tankers the mean factor was only 1.3, while for missiles it was 17.[10]

The factors presented in Table 1 are unadjusted. In particular, no adjustment has been made for changes in price levels, and no adjustment has been made for disparities between actual output and the output contemplated at the time the early estimates were made. Both of these adjustments tend to reduce the factors, i.e., reduce the size of the estimating error. Since changes in price levels have generally been upward, the factors are reduced when the latest estimates are deflated. At the same time experience indicates (at least for the kinds of military equipment considered here) that cumulative average cost of production is a decreasing function of total output. In practice, total output

[9] The data Brussell was able to get are particularly messy. Therefore, a good deal of judgment has had to go into the construction of these estimates of factor increases. But even after the most prudent treatment, the data from which the factors were generated leave much to be desired and a good deal of caution is needed in interpreting the results. The earliest estimate available for some systems was made later in development than for other systems. In some cases the latest available data were actual data on cost of production. In other cases, the latest available data were still estimates either because a program was cancelled or because development was incomplete. Sometimes it was not possible to determine just what the original estimator had included in his estimate in the way of subsystems, spares, etc. If the error in the cost estimates was generally small, e.g. 25 per cent, these deficiencies might be important. In fact, however, the error tends to be so large that the defects in the data are not too troublesome. In addition, on balance, the data were dealt with in such a way that these estimates are, if off in one direction or another, likely to understate the factor increases.

[10] The vehicles included in the six missile cases represent a much more heterogeneous assortment than for the other three classes of equipment. At least one of each of the following is included among the six: air-to-air missiles, surface-to-air missiles, air-to-surface missiles, and surface-to-surface missiles.

usually turns out to be much smaller than is originally anticipated to a large extent because costs turn out to be greater than anticipated. Therefore, when the original estimate is adjusted to take account of the reduced output, the effect is almost always to reduce the factor.

Strictly speaking, the unadjusted factors in Table 1 overstate the magnitude of the error in cost estimates. Why do we then bother to include Table 1? First, because a comparison of Table 1 and Table 2 provides an indication of the impact of the output and quantity adjustments. But second, and more importantly, because decisions are sometimes made with little or no appreciation of the functional relationship between costs and outputs. For example, system A, that is now under development, is estimated to cost $X million per copy based on some output, Q_1. Thereafter when system A comes up for consideration its cost is taken to be $X million without regard to output. Thus, even though the cost estimator is thinking in terms of a schedule of average costs associated with appropriate outputs, a single point on that schedule is sometimes the cornerstone for a decision.

Table 2 presents adjusted factors for the same twenty-two items of

TABLE 2

TOTAL FACTOR INCREASES IN AVERAGE CUMULATIVE COST OF PRODUCTION, ADJUSTED

Fighters	Factors A	Factors B	Bombers	Factors A	Factors B	Cargoes and Tankers	Factors A	Factors B	Missiles	Factors A	Factors B
1	3.9	4.0	1	6.2	4.0	1	1.4	1.6	1	14.7	6.4
2	2.6	2.5	2	2.8	2.8	2	1.5	1.5	2	9.4	6.0
3	2.0	2.0	3	1.1	1.2	3	1.0	0.9	3	4.4	2.7
4	1.5	1.5				4	1.0	0.8	4	7.2	7.1
5	1.7	2.1							5	1.5	1.3
6	1.2	1.2							6	1.1	0.8
7	1.0	0.8									
8	1.0	1.0									
9	1.1	0.6									
Mean	1.8	1.7		3.4	2.7		1.2	1.2		6.4	4.1

	A	B
Mean, all classes	3.2	2.4

equipment. The adjustment is twofold to take account of the two problems discussed above. First, an aircraft composite price index was used to deflate the latest cost estimates. Second, in each case the factor was adjusted to take account of any difference between the output on which the early estimate was based and the output on which the most recent estimate is based.

You will note that Table 2 contains not one but two sets of adjusted factors. We have elected to show two sets because of the tricky nature of the adjustment process. Discretion and judgment are called for in deciding what adjustments are most sensible. The two sets of factors in Table 2 were prepared by two different individuals,[11] and represent somewhat independent judgments as to what is appropriate. Both proceed essentially from the same unadjusted data, however.

As is evident from Table 2, the effect of the adjustments is to reduce the size of the factors. The mean factor for all twenty-two items is about cut in half, to 3.2 for the A set of factors and to 2.4 for the B set of factors. For the missile class as a whole, the mean factor is cut by about 2/3 or 3/4, depending on which set of factors is used. Most of the reduction incidentally is a result of the output adjustment rather than of the price level adjustment. For the twenty-two systems the price level increase from the date of the earliest estimate to the date of the most recent estimate ranged from 3 per cent to 52 per cent and averaged only 28 per cent.

The data in Table 1 and in Table 2 are consistent with the two main propositions made at the beginning of this paper. The cost estimates for these twenty-two items of equipment were decidedly biased toward overoptimism. Even after the adjustments, the most recent estimates on the average exceeded the earliest available estimates by some 240 to 300 per cent. Moreover, among the various items of equipment there were substantial differences in the size of the increase, ranging from slight decreases in some instances to factors of 6 or 7, using even the most modest set of factors.

The difference in the mean size of the factor among the different classes of equipment is also revealing. The smallest increase on the average occurred in the cargo and tanker class, while the largest increase occurred in the missile class. The explanation for this lies in our second main proposition to the effect that the size of the error in estimates is a function of the stage of development or the magnitude of the advance being sought. The performance demanded of new cargo and tanker aircraft, such as range, speed, and even sometimes pay load, is usually less than what has already been achieved in other air-

---

[11] One set of factors was computed by Eugene R. Brussell, the other set by Robert Summers.

PREDICTABILITY OF COSTS, TIME, AND SUCCESS

craft, particularly bombers. Moreover, the subsystems that together make up the air vehicle as a rule are "off-the-shelf" items. The engines, for example, are likely to have already been in operation for some time in other aircraft. Even the airframe is often only a slight modification of some design already in use. In brief, in terms of both performance and physical characteristics of the equipment, only very modest innovations are embodied in cargo and tanker developments. Very likely, the costing errors in these cases are almost totally due to the first of the two sources of error mentioned earlier. The factors for cargo and tanker aircraft probably represent an upper bound on the currently attainable level of accuracy in cost estimating.

At the other extreme, during the period covered by most of these estimates, missile development encompassed what was in many respects a new and radically different technology. Computers and other electronic equipment were required capable of solving complex guidance and control problems without the aid of man in the vehicle, and many of the missiles incorporated propulsion systems with which there had been little previous experience. Meanwhile performance was demanded that meant an order of magnitude improvement over anything we had achieved before.

In other words, the technology and the performance which characterize the missile programs of Table 1 and Table 2 called not for the kind of modest advances sought in cargo and tanker programs but for quite ambitious advances. This, we think, is the reason for the much larger bias and the larger variance exhibited by the missile estimates. Factor increases for cost estimates associated with a second generation of missile systems are likely to be nearer those shown for fighter and bomber aircraft.[12]

Further evidence on the same point is presented in Table 3. Technical experts were asked to classify our twenty-two development programs according to the technical advance sought in each—small, medium, or large. The consensus of that poll was then used to classify the factors as shown in Table 3. The results evidence a correlation between factor size and the size of the advance being sought—the mean factor being an increasing function of the size of advance.[13]

---

[12] Though the subject is not covered here, we have also compared predicted and actual development costs and found much the same story as for production costs. Actual costs generally prove to be much higher than originally anticipated, with a large variance in the error from one project to another.

[13] The relationship is even stronger if the effect of a third variable, namely the date of the estimates, is removed. Among the systems that represented large advances, the first

TABLE 3
FACTORS CLASSIFIED ACCORDING TO TECHNOLOGICAL ADVANCE

	Small		Medium		Large	
	Factor A	Factor B	Factor A	Factor B	Factor A	Factor B
	1.5	1.5	2.8	2.8	1.1	1.2
	1.7	2.0	2.6	2.5	1.0	1.0
	1.0	0.8	2.0	2.0	1.0	0.8
	1.4	1.6	1.2	1.2	6.2	4.0
	1.0	0.9	1.1	0.6	1.1	0.8
	1.5	1.5	1.5	1.1	14.7	6.4
					3.9	4.0
					4.4	2.7
					7.2	7.0
					9.4	6.0
Mean	1.3	1.4	1.8	1.7	5.0	3.4

Availability Predictions

As we have indicated above, time, or how long a development will take, is another important parameter in predicting the outcome of development programs. This is particularly true of military developments where each side struggles frantically to achieve technological superiority in its weapons.

Availability predictions, like cost predictions, exhibit both a decided bias toward overoptimism and substantial variation in the extent of the optimism. Table 4 gives the "slippage" in years for ten of the twenty-two systems covered in Tables 1 and 2, along with slippage factors.[14] Slippage is here defined as the difference between early estimates of first operational dates and actual first operational dates. The slippage factors are the counterpart of our cost factors. They are the ratio of actual time taken to get systems into operation to early predictions of the time it would take to make them operational. Data on availability is also often treacherous, requiring careful auditing and interpretation. Determining when a system actually became operational is a case in point. New equipment in the hands of the operating commands does not mean that an operational capability has been achieved. Which of several early estimates should be used is also frequently a problem. In general, for the systems in Table 4 we have

three were cases in which the earliest cost estimates available were, nevertheless, made fairly late in the program. They are thus based on much better information than was generally the case. For that reason the resulting factors were relatively small.
[14] Data on all twenty-two systems are not available.

TABLE 4

SLIPPAGE IN AVAILABILITY

System	Slippage (years)	Slippage Factors
1	5.0	2.5
2	3.0	1.6
3	3.0	1.5
4	3.0	1.5
5	2.0	2.0
6	2.0	1.5
7	1.3	1.3
8	0.7	1.2
9	0.5	1.2
10	0.3	1.1
Mean	2.0	1.5

used conservative dates—dates that make the error in estimated availability as small as is reasonably possible.

In spite of this, the errors in estimates of availability dates for those ten systems average 2 years and range as high as 5 years, while the factors range as high as 2.5 and average 1.5. Other studies of slippages, covering a much larger number of systems, tend to confirm the results of Table 4. Estimates of availability are almost invariably optimistic, with the error in estimates varying widely from one weapon system to another.[15]

Finally, it is worth noting that, like cost estimates, availability estimates tend to be more accurate the less ambitious the particular project and, of course, tend to be more accurate in the later stages of development than they are in the early stages.

Performance Predictions

The last important measure of success to be considered is performance. Availability and costs each could be expressed in terms of a single vector, time and dollars respectively. Performance, however, cannot be reduced to a single vector. Performance consists of a multitude of

[15] In connection with slippages a word is in order on so-called program stretch-outs. Sometimes program plans are revised and operational dates postponed because of insufficient development funds. But there are two variants of this. There is the case where development expenditures are held to levels below what was anticipated when initial plans were laid, and there is the case where development expenditures, although constrained, are nonetheless as large or larger than was initially planned. To call the latter a stretch-out is, at the very least, misleading. And as a matter of fact the former occurs only infrequently. None of the ten systems here were stretched-out in that sense.

attributes—range, speed, altitude, reliability, maintainability, vulnerability, operability, accuracy, etc. Most of these can be quantified, but others are largely qualitative, e.g., ease of handling. It will be necessary, therefore, to treat estimates of performance much more broadly than estimates of cost and availability.

Estimates of performance also differ from estimates of cost and availability in another important respect. Typically, in weapons development great emphasis is placed on performance. Most new weapons are developed around specific detailed performance requirements laid down by the military—requirements that are taken very seriously. The penalties incurred by contractors for not meeting performance requirements are more severe than those for failure to meet availability schedules or failure to live within original cost estimates. As a result, whenever circumstances dictate a retreat from early plans, it is usually the costs or availability, or both, that give ground. If, for example, technological difficulties with electronic equipment prohibit the attainment of the required performance on the original schedule at original costs, usually either the availability date is postponed, or costs are increased, or both. Degradations in performance are seldom tolerated.

This means that estimates of performance tend to be realized to a greater degree than estimates of either costs or availability. However, among the twenty-two systems in Table 1, most fell short of performance expectations in one or more respects. Range or accuracy was sometimes less than expected. More often than not, reliability was poorer than expected. But the amount by which performance fell short was usually small in comparison to the extension of time or the increase in costs that occurred. Moreover, in some instances performance actually turned out to be somewhat better than expected. In short, though estimates of performance tend to be slightly higher than what is finally achieved, they are much more nearly fulfilled than are predictions of cost and availability.

Summary

The data presented above are neither as comprehensive nor as unambiguous as one would like. Nevertheless, they do give a reasonably accurate picture of recent experience with predicting the outcome of development projects. The truth is that estimates have been quite inaccurate. Cost increases on the order of 200 to 300 per cent and extensions of development time by 1/3 to 1/2 are not the exception, but the rule. In addition, the size of the error in estimates has varied widely from one weapon to another.

The optimistic bias is not hard to understand. Contractors are anxious to have their proposals accepted by the military, and the military itself is anxious to have development proposals supported by the Department of Defense and Congress. The incentive to make optimistic estimates is thus very strong. On the other hand, the contractual penalties for having been overoptimistic are generally small. But apart from any bias, the military have been living for the last decade or so, and will continue to live for the foreseeable future, in a period of unprecedented technological revolution. Therefore there have been great uncertainties involved in all of their planning and perhaps especially in the R and D area. Errors were bound to be large on the average. The real problem is to explain why so large a portion of the error shows up statistically as bias rather than variance.

The variability in size of the errors observed in individual cases stems from two sources. One is just the basic uncertainty that characterizes all development work. The other is the difference in technological advance sought in different systems. For systems incorporating many new ideas and major improvements in performance the error tends to be larger than for less ambitious projects.

Steps can and should be taken to improve development cost estimates, especially to remove the bias. But even if this is done, significant uncertainties remain to harass the analyst and the decision maker. A more detailed analysis of the nature of these uncertainties and their implications for research and development decision making is the subject of the succeeding paper by Burton H. Klein.

The Decision Making Problem in Development

BURTON H. KLEIN

THE RAND CORPORATION

CONTINUING the theme introduced by my colleagues, Marshall and Meckling, I shall attempt in the first part of this paper to describe the nature of the uncertainties involved in development decisions. In the second part I shall turn more explicitly to a discussion of the decision making problem. My purpose is to point out in what key respects the decision making problem in development—especially in areas involving the rather ambitious advances that military development projects typically do involve—is different from that in production. Economists have said a good deal about decision making under uncertainty, but very little about decision making when the responsible person is in a position to do something about the uncertainties facing him. Finally, I shall briefly point out the similarity between the conclusions of this paper and an idea long ago advanced by Schumpeter.

The evidence on which this paper is based is in part the same described in the Marshall-Meckling paper, but it mainly comes from about fifty case studies we have made on military research and development projects, and a few we and others have made on nonmilitary projects (see, for example, Thomas Marschak's paper in this volume, "Strategy and Organization in a System Development Project"). As a basis for any generalizations we would like to have a much larger body of evidence, but two things prevented us from conducting this project as a statistical investigation. For one thing, gathering data on development programs is an extremely expensive kind of research. To find out the cost of development alone can sometimes take months of digging. For another, although we have started some work along these lines, it was not until we were well into the case studies that we began to see that there were some hypotheses that could be statistically tested.

But granting that it would be desirable to have a good deal more evidence, I think some fairly definite conclusions can be drawn from the work we have done to date. Moreover, I believe that the general conclusions of this paper are quite as relevant to civilian R and D as they are to military R and D, providing that in either case we are speaking of kinds of development aimed at ambitious advances.

Nature of Uncertainties Facing the Decision Maker

Before building a bridge, engineers carefully examine the physical environment in which it might be placed, take into account the kind and amount of traffic that will pass over it, the stresses to which it will be subject, and so forth. If the bridge is well designed to begin with, the probability is very high that it will not have to be extensively redesigned during its construction and that it will hold up about as expected. To be sure, unexpected things sometimes happen to bridges after they are built—the initial calculations sometimes prove to be wrong—but I have the impression that such events are rare.

In contrast, development involving the advances that military projects typically seek seldom goes according to plan. No matter how much attention is given to the initial design work, as development goes forward there are almost always a number of surprises. So far as space development projects are concerned, this much can be deduced from reading the newspaper accounts. But I do not think it is generally appreciated how uncertain a business development can be even without getting into space. In almost all the cases we looked into, the system that came out of development was quite different from the one initially conceived (e.g., as different as a Nash and a Buick), and often the system's actual role turned out to be quite different from its intended role. To illustrate this point let me refer to a study we did of six relatively recent fighter-plane development projects. All of these planes were designed for some particular mission, e.g., all-weather interception, ground support. All the aircraft manufacturers based their airframe designs on some particular engine design furnished by one of the engine manufacturers. In almost all these cases, there were also programs for developing specialized electronic and other kinds of equipment. To what extent did these plans materialize? Four out of the six planes ended up with different engines, three with different electronic systems.[1] In order to make them satisfactory flying

---

[1] Other weapon systems, as well as fighters, tend to come out of development with technological inputs different from those originally planned for them. For example, in looking into the development of 24 weapon-system projects initiated since World War II, we found only three programs in which the final engine coincided with the initial choice. Nine of these programs had three or more engines associated with them at one time or another, several, as many as five. Nor have the British been especially successful in making engine projects come out as planned. Although several British companies develop and produce both airframes and aircraft engines, and although the integrated companies have usually planned their aircraft around their own engines, these companies are seldom able to mate their own engines to their own airframes.

478

machines, five of the airframes had to be extensively modified; three of the fighters came out of development essentially different airplanes. Of the six planes, three ended up by having quite different operational roles from what was originally planned for them. Only one of the planes possessed the same technological ingredients and had the same kind of operational role that had been initially planned for it. This plane, however, will have a much less important role than was intended for it, in part because another fighter, whose development was started for a different kind of role, has already provided quite as good a capability.

The essential distinction between bridge building and development of fighter airplanes is that whereas the former is mainly a problem of how to take best advantage of existing information, the latter involves also a good deal of learning. In the one case the problem is how to make the best use of known alternatives; in the other, it is to find "good" alternatives. Later in this paper I will discuss the significance this difference has for the decision making problem in research and development. But before turning to this central matter, I want to say something more about the kinds of uncertainties involved in predicting the outcome of development projects.

These uncertainties fall into two broad classes: uncertainties about the cost and availability of various alternatives; and uncertainties about their future usefulness. As Marshall and Meckling have indicated, the utility of military hardware is not highly predictable. Between the time the development of any piece of military apparatus is started and the time it is ready to go into operational use—usually a period of some five to ten years—a host of things can happen to drastically change the demand for it. But it is not only the difficulty of predicting future market situations that makes the development problem unique. Future market situations can be very difficult to predict whether the market be civilian or military, whether the item in question involves a large or a nominal technical advance. Even in the case of bridge building, it may be assumed that predicting future demand is no trifling problem.

On the other hand, what does sharply differentiate activities like bridge building from activities like fighter plane development is that the latter is also characterized by considerable uncertainties on the supply side. In the one case the decision maker can proceed with a considerable degree of confidence that the information on technical characteristics, costs, and time to complete the project available to him at the beginning of the project will not significantly change; in the other he has to proceed under the assumption that it probably will change.

Why is it so difficult to foretell how alternative designs will turn out? In some instances discoveries have been made in development like the discoveries that come out of basic research. But even with no scientific discoveries made during the course of development, predictions often have turned out to be bad. As an illustration, consider the postwar experience of this country in airborne radar development. Almost all of the radars that have been developed since World War II are based on principles that were quite well known at the end of the war; in fact, the basic designs of many of the radars developed in the last fifteen years were conceived during the war. Yet it is very difficult to find any radar that, when a seemingly completed system was first tested, met its original expectation. Out of the dozen programs we examined, there were only two in which the development costs after a full-scale test of the radar did not exceed by several times the costs up to the time of such a test. And there were none in which the cost of meeting the unanticipated problems was negligible. Thus, even though the problems were not of a scientific nature, it can hardly be argued that a good deal was not learned during these programs.

What was learned? The learning that took place in these radar programs, or for that matter the learning that takes place in almost any kind of development program, can be roughly divided into three stages. In the earlier stages of a program the dominant problems are usually those associated with overcoming the major technological problems. The seriousness of these problems depends in good part on how ambitious the advances are that are being sought. In military research and development, even when the advance sought is relatively modest, a variety of technical problems almost invariably turns up. In the second stage of development the main problems have to do with getting the various pieces of a system to perform with a tolerable degree of reliability. In radar development, probably much more has been spent on overcoming reliability problems than on all other problems combined. As might be deduced from reading the newspaper accounts, it also has been a problem in ballistic missile development. Finally, there are the problems involved in mating the various subsystems, and in tailoring the equipment to work satisfactorily in the environment it will be used in, and in finding efficient means for getting it produced.

As one might suspect, in actual practice the learning process does not always follow this precise chronology. For example, in the initial design stage the developer will be concerned with problems of reliability and of how to combine various technical inputs. He knows from experience that some types of designs pose an inherently more difficult reliability problem than others; he also knows that some kinds of constraints are required to insure that the various parts of the system will be ultimately compatible. Conversely, he may find himself confronted with serious technical problems very late in the program. This may be because the development program was not conducted in a manner to uncover them early; or it may be because some of the "later" problems, e.g., reliability, turned out to be so serious that it was necessary to redesign the equipment, which, in turn, gave rise to a new series of technical problems.

Without implying that the three stages of learning, as I have outlined them, are in practice easily distinguished from each other, let me now try to suggest the nature of the problems that do come up.

Designing a compressor for a jet engine provides a fairly typical example of the kind of technological problem the developer has to solve. In a number of important respects the performance of an engine is dependent on the design of the compressor; hence the continuing emphasis on getting improved compressor designs. The root of the problem in compressor development is that, although on the basis of the fundamental equations of aerodynamics it is "theoretically" possible to predict the performance of any particular design, in actual fact it is possible to predict only in very approximate terms the characteristics required to provide a given performance. And in fact while some of the particular designs that satisfy the criteria of a "good" design may turn out to be good; others may turn out to be bad. This being the case, the chance of any design turning out to be a good one will depend partly on the experience and ingenuity of the engineers and partly on luck. But in any case, when a good design is finally hit upon, the outcome usually has been preceded by a tremendous amount of experimental work.

It can be argued, of course, that the basic reason for this kind of situation lies with science—that if the scientific basis were more complete, better and more precise predictions could be made. This I do not dispute. My point is simply that science cannot usually predict how a particular design will turn out. It is true that there are significant differences among technologies as to the kinds of predictions that can be made. In some branches of nuclear technology it has been possible to make quite accurate predictions. On the other hand, in other technologies—notably materials—the scientific basis for making any kind of prediction is very meager, with the result that progress is almost entirely made by trial and error.

Experience indicates that one of the most unpredictable things about a new piece of equipment is the problems that will be encountered in making it perform reliably, and the time that it will take to overcome these problems. One of the main reasons why development costs tend to be seriously underestimated is a tendency to minimize the reliability problems that will be encountered and the amount of testing and modification that will be required to overcome them. Quite apart from all the other problems, the simple problem of diagnosis has often proved to be a formidable one. Experts evaluating a test program have often not been able to agree among themselves as to the cause of a major malfunction. The process by which reliability problems are overcome can hardly be described as anything but a highly empirical one: a piece of equipment is run until it breaks down (which in the early stages of the program is not very long); a series of modifications is undertaken to correct the major causes of malfunction; and when the equipment can perform reliably under relatively easy conditions, it is then subject to more and more stringent conditions. In some cases the result of this process is a host of minor modifications; in others, it is some fairly major changes in the design of the equipment.

Before reliability work on the various parts of a major system has progressed very far, another major problem will have come to the forefront: how the various elements of the system can best be combined to perform some useful function. As indicated earlier, this problem certainly will have been considered in the initial design work, but in order that it can be considered very fruitfully, and in detail, development must have progressed to a point where a good deal is known about the kinds of trade-offs that are actually possible. These may differ considerably from the kinds of trade-offs initially believed possible. For example, whereas the weight of a guidance system of some specified characteristics may have been initially estimated at, say, 300 pounds, its actual weight may turn out to be four times that amount. And this in turn may force some major changes in other parts of the system. It may be found that in order to get a fire-control system working with an acceptable degree of reliability, some of its versatility has to be given up and the loss in capability partly made up in some other way. Or, as often happens, it may simply be found that a major component will not be available until much later than the rest of the system, and that some alternative device of quite different characteristics has to be substituted.

As development progresses a good deal is learned not only about the technological alternatives themselves, but also about the environment in which the system will operate. Almost invariably, the actual conditions under which a new piece of equipment will have to operate are found to be quite different from the assumed conditions. For example, after only a little experience in testing a missile it may be found that the kind of ground equipment needed to support it is of a quite different kind than was earlier assumed. It may be found that the design of the equipment requires far more skilled personnel to operate and maintain it than are available. Time after time, equipment has to be modified so that a large corps of engineers and scientists will not be required to maintain it.

Finally, it often turns out that new methods have to be developed in getting the equipment into production. Sometimes the problems are so basic as to require a good deal of research and development work on the production processes themselves. For example, in connection with developing the B-58 supersonic bomber a process for producing honeycombed aluminum structures was developed. Work on the development of the B-70 supersonic bomber will involve the pioneering of techniques for producing stainless-steel structures. The increasing emphasis that has been placed on the development of miniature devices of one kind or another has resulted in a number of new production problems.

Though sometimes there are serious problems involved in getting new kinds of equipment or devices produced, the evidence we have examined suggests those problems are usually much easier to overcome than the problems involved in their development. Ordinarily, comparatively little effort is required to overcome the production problems.

Though I might have gone further in characterizing the kinds of problems that come up in development, I trust enough has been said to indicate that in the course of development a number of different kinds of problems have to be solved—that development is essentially a learning process. Its main purpose is to find out how much new kinds of capabilities will cost, and how useful they can be made. As Meckling and Marshall point out in their paper, the very large uncertainties associated with cost estimates of not-yet-developed systems are mainly uncertainties about what it is that is being costed. These are the uncertainties I have been discussing.

But granted that a good deal of learning is involved in development, to what extent is the problem of making choices here essentially different from what it is in the familiar cases in which perfect knowledge is assumed from the outset? Granted that there is often a good deal more risk in making development decisions than other kinds, is the decision making problem here any different, essentially, from what it is in other less risky areas? To this question I now turn.

Central Differences between the Decision Making Problem in Development and in Production

DECISION MAKING STRATEGY

The fact that it is very difficult to make good estimates either of cost or demand does not in itself prove that the decision making problem in development is basically different from other kinds of decision making problems that involve choices among various kinds of alternatives. One might simply take the attitude that it makes no difference what kind of probability distribution is associated with the initial estimates; that the decision maker has no alternative but to make the best estimates he can, and to act as if he were dealing with certainties.[2] This situation is roughly illustrated by case A on Chart 1. The decision maker, we assume, is trying to decide whether to develop device A or device B, and that his decision will be entirely based on what he believes these devices will ultimately cost. It can be seen that in case A the initial subjective probability distributions are very wide, and that they remain very wide to the end of the project. Providing he has to make a choice, it is apparent that in this situation the decision maker will choose the device whose expected cost (the mean of the subjective distribution) is lower—in this example, device B. On the other hand, assume that the distributions can be significantly narrowed long before the end of the project—that the situation is more like that shown

[2] To be sure, under such circumstances the decision maker (if he could afford it) might decide to insure himself against future uncertainties by developing two airplanes instead of one. But the idea of taking contingencies into account in planning, while certainly an important aspect of the problem of making decisions under conditions of uncertainty, is a notion long familiar to economists.

CHART 1
Variance of Estimates as a Function of the Stage of Development

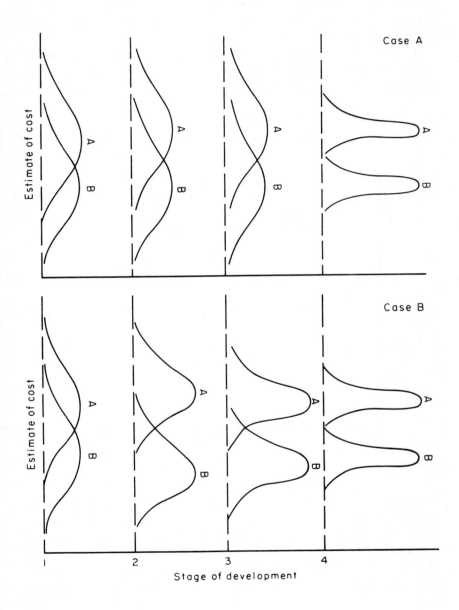

in case B. Then it is by no means apparent that, even though he must ultimately choose either device A or B, his best strategy will be to choose that device with the lower initial expected cost. The crucial question is the extent to which he is in a position to reduce these uncertainties, and at what cost.

To push this argument further, let us assume that the developer starts out with estimates of performance, cost, etc., whose accuracy is represented by point A on Chart 2. When development is completed,

CHART 2
Rate of Learning Hypotheses

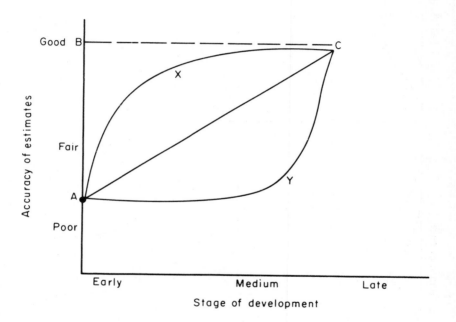

the accuracy of the estimates will have improved to B. If the actual world corresponds more or less to Y—if there are large indivisibilities in this learning process—then, although the decision maker may feel very uncomfortable about his initial estimates, he has only one thing to worry about: should he become involved in such a risky undertaking or should he not? If he does decide to go ahead with the project, he may as well act on the assumption that his initial estimates were good, for there is no way to find out except by committing himself to the entire project. If it costs $100 million to complete the development of the system in question, there is no way he can significantly improve his initial estimates except by spending the entire $100 million. It does not matter whether in choosing this particular alternative he happens to regard the initial probability distributions of cost, availability, and demand as highly compact or highly dispersed; he has to make choices on the basis of expected values. In other words, he has to proceed as he would in dealing with a conventional kind of optimization problem.

On the other hand, if the actual possibilities for improving the estimates lie in the neighborhood of the line AC, the decision maker may want to pursue a very different kind of strategy. Under these circumstances he can significantly narrow the uncertainties facing him long before the end of the program. His decision whether or not to adopt such a course of action will depend essentially on what it is likely to cost. If it is relatively inexpensive (as compared with total development costs) to carry projects into the initial phases of development— if the initial uncertainties can be significantly narrowed for a cost of not $100 million but, say, $15 or $20 million—then it is fairly apparent that the decision maker will want to play the game very differently. Under these circumstances, the basic nature of the decision problem will be much more like that involved in solving a crime than that involved in solving the typical kind of optimization problem. The essential problem for the developer is how to eliminate potential suspects quickly and efficiently.

Since it is a matter of such key importance, we have been interested in finding out all we can about the opportunities, as they actually exist, for improving information as development progresses. The general impression we have obtained from our case studies is as follows. In the first place, as might be expected, we have found that there are considerable differences among development programs. For example, it is quite obvious that if the advances sought are relatively modest (e.g., as in developing a transport plane), the uncertainties are ordinarily much more easily resolved than if the advances sought are relatively ambitious (e.g., as in developing a new kind of missile). The possibilities for early learning will also depend on the kind of technology involved. Pursuing multiple approaches to difficult technological problems is a good deal cheaper in some fields than in others: in relation to total development costs, the cost of getting preliminary test results is much cheaper in developing missile guidance systems than it is in developing large solid-propellant missile engines. Finally, the rate of learning will depend also on the spirit in which the development program is conducted—when the developer is very keen to learn, he usually finds ways to make the learning process more divisible.

But, though there are considerable differences among development programs, we feel that cases involving very large indivisibilities in learning—cases approaching Y—are in fact rare. And while it is often true that some important problems are not resolved until late in the development process (and sometimes never), it is also often true that very modest expenditures can buy a considerable amount of information. Consider, for example, the experience in ballistic missile development. As might be expected, it has been found that there is no way of predicting exactly how an entire system will work short of assembling it and testing it a number of times. On the other hand, it also has been found that a surprisingly large amount of information can be obtained by relatively inexpensive kinds of development work and testing that can be done on the ground, for example, static test firings of engines or sled tests of guidance systems. Even after the test firings have begun, it usually is not efficient to test an entire system until a whole sequence of preliminary tests has been conducted. Or take the problem of developing a jet engine. Here again serious unanticipated problems may crop up late in development—after more than, say, $150 million has been spent. But experience has also indicated that the test of a preliminary model aimed at a demonstration of its novel components, costing perhaps $5 to $15 million, can make possible much better predictions of an engine's ultimate performance than predictions based simply on a design study. And by the time roughly one-third to one-half of the entire development has been paid for, it usually has become fairly apparent which engines are going to turn out to be good and which are not.

Fairly recently we began some work aimed at more rigorously testing the "early learning" hypothesis. The general idea behind this study is to find out how rapidly estimates of availability, cost, and performance improve as a function of development time and development cost. If the accuracy of the estimates is found to improve at a linear or increasing rate, we would regard this as confirmation of the hypothesis. To date, our efforts along these lines have consisted of a fairly crude analysis of a small number of availability estimates, and a much more sophisticated analysis of a somewhat larger body of cost estimates. Though the second study has not been completed, I was able to persuade Robert Summers to throw caution to the winds, and provide me with some of his preliminary results.

Our analysis of availability estimates—which was undertaken more or less as a pilot investigation—was restricted to 8 missile programs, for which there were 35 estimates of availability made at various stages of the programs. In order to get an absolute measure of the error in the estimates, the estimated time to go (ETG) was subtracted from the actual time to go (ATG). To obtain a relative measure, the error rate was computed as $\dfrac{\text{ATG} - \text{ETG}}{\text{ATG}}$. On the basis of this concept, an error of five years in an estimate made ten years from the actual time of completion would be equivalent to an error of one year in an estimate made two years from the time of completion (0.5 in either case).

As might be expected, there was a fairly substantial difference among the programs with regard to the rate of improvement in the estimates. In one of the programs, the predictions made after development was started actually turned out to be a good deal worse than the initial prediction, and there was no significant improvement in the estimates until rather late in the program. However, in all the other cases, improvement in the estimates was fairly continuous; in five of them the error rate declined very rapidly. The adjusted errors[3] as a function of development time are plotted on Chart 3. As the chart indicates, the errors fell quite steadily as development progressed. Plotting the error rate against development time would indicate an approximately constant rate of improvement in the estimates.

Roughly the same conclusion—improvement in the accuracy of the estimates at about a constant rate—is indicated by the preliminary results of our analysis of cost estimates. These results are based on 22 weapon systems, both aircraft and missile, for which we had 71 usable observations. As in the availability study, the weapons chosen were those on which we were able to get information (though at no small cost) and, though we obviously cannot be sure, we have no reason to believe that the errors made in costing these systems were any larger than the errors that have been made in costing other aircraft and missile systems.

---

[3] Since the number of observations was relatively few and since we are here primarily interested in comparing the manner the errors decline rather than comparing the differences in the absolute errors among various programs, all of the errors were deflated by dividing them by the interpolated values for the mid-points of the programs.

CHART 3
Errors in Availability Estimates

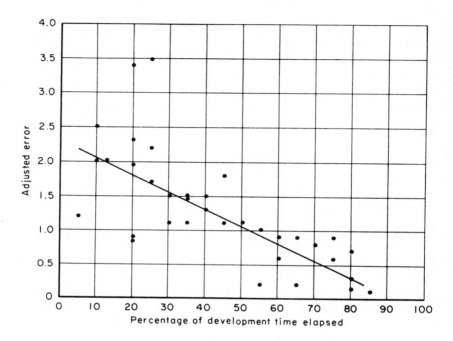

Percentage of development time elapsed

In order to test the early learning hypothesis the data were classified in two ways: according to the stage of development at which the estimate was made, and according to the ambitiousness of the advance sought in the program.[4] On the basis of the hypothesis, we should expect the variance in the cost estimates to decline in relation to the stage of development at which the estimate was made and to increase in relation to the degree of advance being sought.

The results of the investigation are summarized in Chart 4. Shown in each cell of the table are the summary numbers for the average errors $\dfrac{\text{(actual cost)}}{\text{(estimated cost)}}$ and the standard deviations and the number of observations on which they were based. The arrows indicate whether the direction of the changes observed in the average errors

[4] In order to decide whether the jump in the state-of-the-arts was "small," "medium," or "large," a panel of engineers was individually polled. Though in the case of a few programs there were considerable differences of opinion, on the whole the judgments on the degree of advance involved were fairly uniform.

CHART 4
Technological Advance

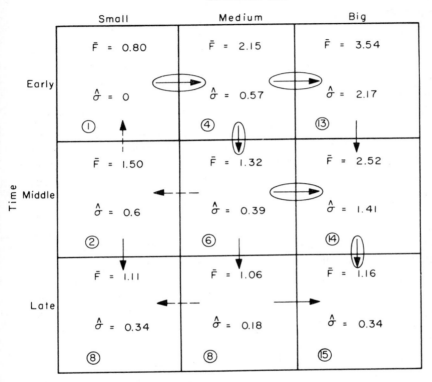

$$F = \frac{Actual\ cost}{Estimated\ cost}$$

and standard deviations, in looking across the rows and down the columns, is consonant or at variance with the double hypothesis. The solid arrows run in the direction predicted by hypothesis; the dashed arrows do not.[5]

It can be seen that 9 out of the 12 arrows point in the "right" direction and that 3 do not. However, only the encircled arrows indicate changes that are, roughly speaking, statistically significant—

[5] Though on the basis of the hypothesis the arrows should generally point to the right and downward, actually we should not expect to find significant differences among the bottom three rows. The accuracy of cost estimates made late in the development process should not be very different whether the particular project happened to involve a big advance or a small advance.

and it can be noted that all of these point either to the right or downward. As might be expected, although they are pretty much the same for the late time period, for the earlier two periods the size of the standard deviations appears to be highly correlated with the size of the technological advance being sought. And looking down the columns, the change in the standard deviation as well as the average error appears to be roughly linear. By taking a few liberties with the data, it might even be argued that the evidence is consistent with the assumption of a declining rate of error, but as someone once observed, "There is a limit to the amount of blood that can be squeezed out of a turnip."

It will be noted that I have expressed the errors in the availability and cost estimates as a function of development time rather than of development expenditures. Though it would have been more pertinent to make comparisons in terms of development expenditures, unfortunately we do not have that data for all the programs included. However, had it been possible to relate improvements in the accuracy of the estimates to development expenditures, there is little doubt that the results would have been somewhat more favorable to the hypothesis advanced earlier; that is, there is little doubt that as a function of development expenditures the accuracy of the estimates would have improved more rapidly. This is because the early stages of development are relatively inexpensive as compared with the later stages. We have found that by the time one-half of the development period has elapsed, the proportion of the total development bill that will have been spent is typically a good deal less than one-half.

To be sure, it would be desirable to have much more evidence on the rate that knowledge increases as development progresses. And we do hope that we will be able to push this kind of inquiry further, mainly because we believe it might provide some deeper insights into the nature of development. But I doubt that more evidence would sharply upset the proposition that, as development progresses, there is likely to be a more or less steady improvement in knowledge.

If the information used for making subsequent decisions can be markedly improved as development proceeds, progress in development should be much more rapid when the decision maker deliberately chooses a sequential decision making strategy. In comparing the results of the various development programs we studied, we think we have observed that there is a close relationship between the degree of success achieved and the willingness of the developer to undertake the project with the conviction that before it is finished he will have much to learn. In almost all the outstanding programs we have examined, the developer has started out with a very loose definition of the system he was trying to develop and has exhibited a considerable willingness to get hardware—even in rudimentary form—into test early in the program, and to pursue multiple approaches to difficult technical problems.

As a result of the work we have done, we are also coming to suspect that those firms that have been successful in research and development over a long period employ a kind of development strategy very different from that of firms whose success has been much more limited. For example, we have found that the "personalities" of the two firms that have been outstanding in jet engine development—Pratt and Whitney in this country, and Rolls Royce in Britain—are much alike, and that their approach in development tends to be a good deal more pragmatic than that of their competitors: "You develop an engine by testing it, and you never develop an engine with only one airplane in mind." In order to find out further whether there really is anything in the idea that the more successful firms in R and D go about the business differently from the less successful firms, we have initiated a project aimed at finding out as much as we can about the kinds of approaches private firms employ in research and development. We began with the highly successful firms (for the good reason that they were inclined to be much more cooperative in furnishing us information), and the results of our first investigation are reported in Thomas Marschak's paper "Strategy and Organization in a Systems Development Project." As it turned out, the manner in which Bell Telephone Laboratories went about developing a microwave relay system provides a first-rate example of sequential decision making.

EFFICIENCY IN DEVELOPMENT

If it is granted that the kind of strategy required to play the game of development is very different from that required to play the game of production (or other kinds of games in which the initial uncertainties have to be taken as given), the next question I would like to raise is this: are they really the same kind of games? I assert that they are not, and that the kind of behavior that will be efficient in one will not be in the other.

To make it clearer what I mean, let me take the problem of choosing an engine for an aircraft and ask, first, how the fellow who looks at the problem as a production decision would go about making the choice. Obviously, the first question he wants an answer to is, what kind of airplane?—for the engine characteristics well suited to one kind of plane may not be well suited to another. In bombers and transport planes, for example, fuel economy is a much more important factor relative to engine weight than it is in fighters, because in the former the weight of the fuel to be carried is very large in comparison with the weight of the engine. Moreover, for engines based on current technology these characteristics are highly substitutable.

Given this information, it is fairly obvious how the producer will make his decision. If I on Chart 5 represents the trade-off curve based on current technology, and if the plane in question is a bomber, he

CHART 5
Aircraft Engine Alternatives

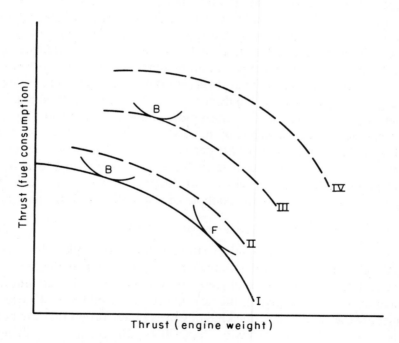

I — Current technology
II, III, IV — Advanced technology

will order engine B, and delivery of an engine possessing that particular combination of characteristics will meet his objective, on the other hand, if engine F is delivered to him he will be unhappy, for he will not have an optimal airframe-engine combination.

So far as the developer is concerned, he is primarily interested in developing a much better engine than any represented on I. His principal concern is whether he is likely to end up on a curve only slightly higher than can be provided by present technology (e.g., II) or a much higher one (e.g., IV) that will dominate an optimized present engine in all important respects. But within fairly wide limits, which particular point he finally manages to reach is of rather secondary importance to him.

Let us suppose, however, that the developer does make up his mind that he is going to have his cake and eat it, and that he sets for himself the firm objective of getting to point B on III. That he will be able to get there eventually there is little question. Given enough time and effort in development almost anything is possible. What I do question is whether in doing so he will have acted efficiently. With the same effort, I contend, the developer almost certainly could have gotten to some point on a higher opportunities curve, e.g., on IV. My proposition, in other words, is that efficiency in the usual sense of the word can be attained only after considerable sacrifice in progress, i.e., reaching a higher opportunities curve.

Unfortunately, in this paper I cannot provide the sort of evidence necessary to demonstrate to the skeptic that this is a reasonable proposition. But I would like to indicate briefly why I believe that it is.

One of the reasons—already pointed out—is that development projects tend not to come out as they were initially planned. For example, when we ask what the experience has been in aircraft development programs we find that airframes seldom do end up with the engines planned for them. As a matter of fact, engines that win the competitions, no matter which particular plane they were initially designed for, almost invariably dominate the losers in all important respects and are almost invariably used in a wide variety of planes, from commercial airplanes to supersonic fighters. In the case of missiles, it is astonishing how often successful systems are developed on the basis of technological components not originally intended for them. *Ex post*, a missile system can be reasonably defined as a system mainly made from components developed for other missile systems.

If it is accepted as a fact of life that nothing much can be done to combat the tendency of development projects not to come out as originally planned, the whole idea of attempting to reach some predetermined optimal point makes little sense. No matter whether an engine with a somewhat different combination of characteristics could have been developed, the best engine at the time the choice actually has to be made is the best one available.

The second reason back of my general proposition is that if it is not accepted as a fact of life that technology is ill mannered, it costs a good deal to force it to be well behaved. While the kind of efficiency practiced in production may be all right in its place, in development it is terribly expensive. When Marshall pointed out that the pain involved in carefully comparing costs with marginal utility can sometimes exceed the benefits, he was probably thinking of some of the calculations an individual might make before purchasing some item of personal consumption. But in development, optimization involves a good deal more than making some laborious calculations. For one thing, it involves putting tight constraints on the engineers who work on the various parts of the system, and, especially if the advances aimed for are ambitious, it enormously complicates their development task. For another, even if a great effort is made to have the individual pieces come out as originally planned, usually they do not; and this seriously complicates the job of coordinating the entire project, which even in the best circumstances is formidable. Hence my belief that the goal in development is not the same kind of efficiency one strives for in production.

Some Closing Observations

In observing that the decision making problem in development and in production are two very different sorts of things, I am merely calling attention to something that Schumpeter pointed out long ago, namely, that the conditions required for an efficient allocation of existing resources are not the same as the conditions required for rapid economic progress.[6] Out of this argument came his argument for monopolies, for which, certainly in recent years, he has become much more famous. But without wishing to argue the point here, I contend that no matter what one thinks of Schumpeter's views on monopoly, they do not necessarily follow from his central idea, and actually have had the effect of obscuring it. Even though everything

[6] J. A. Schumpeter, *The Theory of Economic Development*, Harvard University Press, 1911, Chap. II.

else he said may have been wrong, for this idea alone Schumpeter deserves a high place on the list of distinguished economists.

In 1909, when Schumpeter was writing his *Theory of Economic Development*, he was obviously not thinking of research and development as an organized activity. But the instinct to try out new ideas, as opposed to the instinct to satisfy existing wants efficiently, is of course not confined to research and development laboratories. Nor, obviously, is the experimental approach an approach used only by scientists. In other words, the classical theory of the firm provides a poor description of how the firm actually does behave—that is, the firm that gets ahead rapidly.

On the other hand, it may also be true that the forces making for efficiency in the narrower sense are deeply engrained in our society and stand in the way of more rapid progress. While economists have probably had little influence on business practices in research and development, the same cannot be said of cost accountants, management experts, and the growing army of business school graduates in general. And to their influence must be added the influence of the engineers. Despite the rise of experimental physics, a good many engineers are still trained in the tradition that it is sinful to design anything that might later have to be changed.

COMMENT

FREDERIC M. SCHERER, Harvard University Weapons Acquisition Research Project

My comments are addressed to Burton Klein's paper, "The Decision Making Problem in Development," and to the Marshall-Meckling paper which provides data upon which it is based. Specifically, I should like to make several observations on the nature of uncertainty in development decisions and on the possibilities for doing something about such uncertainty.

The efforts of Klein and his colleagues to determine empirically the rate of learning in development projects are highly commendable. If it can be demonstrated that the uncertainties in a development program can be substantially reduced early in the game (thus, the rate of learning function X in Klein's Chart 2), then the argument for multiple approaches and programs is strongly supported. Nevertheless, I think it necessary to emphasize that there are many different parameters whose values will be learned during a development effort, and each of these undoubtedly has a different rate of learning function. My own interpretation of data collected by the Harvard Weapons Acquisition Research Project suggests that uncertainties regarding technical feasibility and specific technical performance parameters do in fact decline sharply early in the development. However, accuracy in predicting development time and cost and production cost probably increases at a roughly linear rate over time, while uncertainties about reliability, operating cost, and military utility are usually not reduced substantially until late in the development effort (thus, the rate of learning function Y in Klein's Chart 2). If this is so, then the development approach chosen will depend upon which parameters happen to be particularly critical in the decision. For radical new innovations, learning about technical feasibility and performance may be most important, while for minor improvements, reliability and operating cost considerations may be paramount.

Secondly, I would disagree with any interpretation that the variances shown in the Marshall-Meckling paper are wholly the inevitable result of pressing an uncertain state of the art; that, as Klein suggests, "nothing much can be done to combat the tendency of development projects not to come out as originally planned." Granted, there will be unexpected technical difficulties or pleasant surprises, or both, during almost any advanced development effort. Granted, too, that it would be the height of foolishness not to include provision for unexpected contingencies in development plans, although the overt use of contingencies is usually prohibited by government contracting regulations. Nevertheless, the occurrence of truly unforeseeable and unavoidable technical difficulties represents only one of several variance causes. (By unforeseeable, I mean difficulties that could not have been anticipated by a good hard look at the state of the art—which has not been taken at the outset of all too many military programs.) Analysis of the Harvard group data shows that most of the variances from original time and cost predictions were man-made rather than caused by an ill-natured technology.

One common cause of prediction variances was unrealism in the original estimates, usually because of attempts to "sell" a program. Knowledgeable military decision makers usually apply heavy discount factors to such estimates.

Another major cause of variances was the intentional decision of military officials not to adhere to the original plan. Any development effort requires many major and minor compromises between essentially conflicting sets of objective functions—maximization of technical performance values and reliability on the one hand, and minimization of development time, and development, production, and operating costs on the other hand. The choice made in each individual case depends upon the relationship between the military utility of performance increments or time savings and the costs associated with those increments.[1]

Sometimes the need for a weapon may be so urgent that the system will be ordered into production as quickly as possible at the sacrifice of some technical perfection. In such cases, development cost and especially time predictions are apt to prove quite accurate, simply because maintaining the schedule was of vital importance. And typically, what is sacrificed is just a few percentage points in relevant performance values such as speed, range, CEP, operating ease, etc. It is commonly said that there is a diminishing returns phenomenon in development; that getting the last 10 per cent of performance or reliability takes 50 per cent of the effort. I have seen some evidence to support that hypothesis, although Klein and his associates might make a major contribution to our understanding of research and development economics by bringing their empirical data to bear on a rigorous test. In any event, attaining an additional ten per cent or so in performance or reliability, or both, may in certain cases be deemed so much more important than early tactical availability of the weapon that development time (and hence cost) will be *allowed* to exceed original predictions.

Let me use Klein's fighter-engine mating example to show what I mean about the man-made nature of these problems, taking one extreme example which is probably included in his sample of six fighters and which has been studied in detail by the Harvard group. This particular fighter was associated with four different engines during its development. The first-choice engine was dropped because it was heavily committed to a higher priority aircraft. The second choice (programmed for interim use only) was dropped when it fell a year behind schedule and because the engine manufacturer was unwilling to produce the very few engines that interim use implied. The third choice was used on a strictly interim basis until a better engine

---

[1] The theoretical relationship of these factors is discussed in Chapters IX and XVII of M. J. Peck and F. M. Scherer, *The Weapons Acquisition Process: An Economic Analysis*, (to be published in 1962).

became available. The fourth engine was programmed and actually used in the tactical version. Significantly, it was recognized right from the beginning that the fighter might use any of the engines; in other words, the engine question was not so uncertain that the problem could not be anticipated. It seems to me that this kind of situation has been more typical than the case in which an engine (or other subsystem) unexpectedly turns out to be unsuitable, as in the ill-fated F3H-1–J40 marriage.[2]

Another qualification needs to be made about Klein's six fighter illustration. The greater portion of all six developments took place during a period of relatively little international tension. The Korean conflict (which precipitated numerous performance sacrifices to get fighter aircraft into production quickly) had subsided, and we were not yet worried about the threat of high performance Russian bombers. We were well supplied with medium performance, yet adequate, interceptors and fighter-bombers. Under these circumstances, we could afford to change development plans in midstream in order to get the best possible engines, aerodynamic configurations, and electronic subsystems into our aircraft. Had the Korean conflict erupted into something bigger, we would have looked at such "nice to have" changes in a quite different light.

Other man-made causes of time and cost variances in weapons program outcomes included the lack of funds to implement production goals, bureaucratic decision making delays, and the failure of contractors to bring adequate human resources to bear (either because their organization lacked highly capable scientists and engineers or because those people were assigned to projects with greater promise of long term profits). This does not exhaust the list of causes I have observed, but at least it suggests that all variances from original predictions are not the result of a malevolent nature. If pressed for a quantitative estimate, I would guess that less than 30 per cent of the development time and cost variances experienced in development programs studied by the Harvard group were due to technical difficulties which were both unforeseeable and unavoidable.

If in fact development project outcomes are not nearly so far beyond human control as comparisons of original predictions with actual outcomes would suggest, then rather difficult conclusions about development approach and strategy are indicated. For one, I fail to

[2] Cf. *Navy Jet Engine Procurement Program*, H.R. Committee on Government Operations, 10th Intermediate Report, 1956.

share Klein's aversion to "putting tight constraints on the engineers who work on the various parts of the system," although our difference in this matter may hinge on semantic difficulties.

In the first place, clear and firm technical constraints are necessary to ensure that interrelated components fit together properly. Imagine what consternation would result from attempting to cram a 12 cubic foot bombing and navigation system into 9 cubic feet of airframe volume, or from feeding digital inputs into an analog computer, or when each of several component developers uses upon his individual item the whole error factor for a guidance system! Moreover, there are good psychological reasons for establishing a technical plan, even if it must later be modified. Most engineers, except perhaps the few really creative ones who ought to be engaged in basic and applied research, need to have a set of specific performance and time goals toward which they can work.

I think what Klein really means is that flexibility is required in developing basically new technical concepts. If so, I agree fully. Clearly, the development of a jet engine incorporating a radically new approach to compressor design should not be tightly constrained, at least not until the design's soundness has been demonstrated. But there comes a time in jet engine development when one must begin worrying about whether or not an afterburner will be used, about the kinds of air intake geometry to be employed, mounting arrangements, and the host of other details that must be solved (usually at a much greater expense in time and money than proving the basic concept required) before the engine can be mated with a specific airplane. When that time arrives, the world of loosely defined breakthroughs is forsaken for the more humdrum schedule, use, and cost oriented world of system development.

My observations about the controllability of development program outcomes also have implications regarding the use of multiple approaches to development problems. If systems development is not really so uncertain, then pursuing multiple approaches may not be as important on the average as Klein suggests. Furthermore, it should be recognized that there are costs other than dollar outlays to be weighed against the risk reduction benefits. One obvious cost is the dissipation of very scarce topflight technical talent. I think there are many cases in which it is preferable to focus all or most of the best talent available on one selected approach rather than to spread it over many efforts.

Another cost is related to the impact of multiple approaches upon decision making. There are two different processes going on simultaneously in a development effort: the creative process and the decision making or selective process. The creative process generates knowledge in the form of specific technical alternatives by defining problems, proposing solutions, and testing proposals. So long as this process indicates clearly which one alternative solution to any given problem is best, the decision making part is easy. But more frequently, alternatives are generated at a faster rate than best solutions can be identified. Usually the choice among alternatives is not obvious; one offers certain advantages and another, others, and so decision makers must indulge in time consuming evaluations before making their choices. If too liberal a use of multiple approaches is allowed, the decision making process can become overloaded and break down with consequent costly delays. Possibly this can be averted by superior organization, for example, through effective decentralization of decisions. Nevertheless, I have seen instances in which breakdowns did occur when the menu of technical alternatives became too rich for a project management group. Certainly, the theory of the firm has not yet abandoned the idea that the entrepreneurial (decision making) function imposes a limit on the scale of operations.

This does not mean that multiple approaches to development problems should be avoided. It merely means that they should be reserved for certain limited situations, the exact extent of their use depending upon the interrelationship of many factors: the kinds of uncertainties attached to specific problems, the rate of learning at which these uncertainties will be dispelled, the availability of technical talent to man individual projects, the monetary cost of additional approaches, the capacity of the decision making organization, the importance of minimizing development time, the military utility of marginal performance or reliability increments, etc.

One additional complication to the choice of a development strategy should be mentioned. A crucial factor in the decision whether or not to employ multiple technical approaches to a development problem is the probability distribution describing one group's chances of reaching an acceptable (in terms of time and technical parameters) solution. However, the introduction of interfirm competition will usually alter the original single-group probability distribution. Competition may improve the prospects for an acceptable solution if it incites the contractor to assign his best technical talent to the effort. It may impair those prospects if the contractor perceives his chances of coming up with the winning solution to be so poor relative to alternative opportunities for employing his resources that he allocates his talent into more promising areas.

What I have tried to show in these comments is that defining a single best approach to the development of advanced systems is exceedingly difficult, particularly since the historical evidence contains often obscure cause and effect relationships. This does not mean it should not be attempted, and the RAND group working on the problem should be complimented for its progress in the area. Nevertheless, I am afraid any theory of an optimal development strategy must necessarily be quite complex in order to reflect the vast range of situational factors involved.

REPLY BY KLEIN

Before taking up Frederic Scherer's specific charges, I would like to make this introductory comment: Contrary to the impression he apparently got from reading my piece, I certainly do not believe that the only kinds of uncertainties involved in making development decisions are technical uncertainties. The decision maker is uncertain not only about the kinds of performance that can be achieved, when, and at what cost—but also about what the military utility of particular capabilities will be some five to ten years in the future. Commonly, weapon systems go through a progression of changes during their development because earlier notions as to what can be achieved and what might be most useful *both* change. To be sure, in writing my paper I did give a good deal of attention to the technical uncertainties, but that was simply because it is these uncertainties that give development its special flavor.

Scherer's central criticism of my paper, I take it, is that I have considerably exaggerated the uncertainties in development. As he puts it, most of the variances from the initial predictions—about 70 per cent, he judges—were man-made rather than caused by an ill-natured technology. It would be nice if development were a much more predictable business than it seems to be, but before accepting Scherer's proposition I want a good deal more evidence. As it is, I am not even sure what he means when he says that "most of the variances were man-made." Does he mean that, after considering the nature of what was learned during the course of the development projects the Harvard Group reviewed, he personally has come to the conclusion that most of what was found out during the projects *could* have been known beforehand? I agree that in retrospect it usually turns out to be quite clear what decisions should have been made, but such findings have little relevance for how decisions should be made *ex ante*.

Scherer does give some particular reasons for believing that development is not nearly as unpredictable as it seems. One of his main arguments is that there is usually a good deal of optimism in the initial estimates of performance, cost, and availability; another is that military planners, in their quest for improvements in performance, intentionally do not stick to their initial plans. However, I find neither of these arguments very convincing.

As for the first, I will certainly agree that initial estimates are almost invariably optimistic. But if there are knowledgeable military decision makers who know what particular discount factors to apply to this estimate of cost, that estimate of performance, and so forth, I would like to know who they are. Our findings indicate that initial estimates contain not only a good deal of bias but also a good deal of variance. The problem, as it usually presents itself to the decision maker, is whether a particular system is likely to cost only 50 per cent more than the initial estimate, or 2 or 3 times as much; whether the bombing accuracy of a new missile might turn out to be, if not as good as that achieved by manned aircraft, "nearly" as good; whether the technical difficulties are likely to prove modest or major. The decision maker can, of course, consult impartial experts, and frequently he does. But having read dozens of reports prepared by various expert committees, I find that the chief result of such appraisals is only to tell the decision maker that, until development has been carried forward much further, the things he would like to know will remain very conjectural matters. This is not to say that such advice is often heeded.

Now let me turn to Scherer's second argument. I do not deny that plans are sometimes changed in the course of development in order to achieve what might be regarded as incremental gains in performance. But that such a striving for perfection is a major factor in explaining the many changes that do take place during the course of development, I simply refuse to believe. The particular evidence that Scherer gives in this connection does not seem to me, at least, to be very persuasive. He says that the six fighter programs I discussed were developed in a period of relatively little international tension, and when "we were not yet worried about the threat of high performance Russian bombers." I don't know whom he is referring to when he says "we," but it certainly is not the military officials who actually made the decisions. They regarded the development of supersonic fighters an urgent necessity and, as a matter of fact, four of the six programs were undertaken as high priority, development-production programs. Undertaking a program as a crash effort does not in itself, however, make the development problems involved any less real. The particular fighter whose development was most rapidly pressed, and whose initial funding was the largest, happened to be the one that underwent the most extensive modifications before it was put into operational use. And the modifications it underwent can hardly be described as modifications required only to get incremental gains in performance.

If it were normal in military development not to be in a hurry and to constantly strive for perfection, one would expect that occasionally the performance finally achieved would turn out to be better than that initially planned and that, when airplanes and missiles finally did go into operational use, they would more often than not, be in fine working order. Yet, we have been able to find very few cases when the first happened, and not many when the second happened. In the cases we looked into (which were many more than the fighter plane examples cited), many of the changes in the original designs were made to keep the programs from slipping more than they otherwise would have slipped to prevent major degradation in performance, and to assure that the equipment would be reasonably reliable (when I say "reasonably reliable" I do not mean the comparatively nearly perfect working order we require in our TV sets). These changes in turn often resulted in large cost increases.

When Scherer says that when a weapon is rushed into production, all that is typically sacrificed is "just a few percentage points in relevant performance values," I wonder if he includes among those relevant values: does the thing work? The experiences we have examined strongly suggest that there is much to be gained by rushing aircraft and missiles into test, but this is an entirely different matter from rushing them into production.

The basic difference between Scherer and myself comes out, I think, when he argues for the necessity of putting tight constraints on the engineers who are developing a system. There comes a point, he says, when the technical uncertainties will have been largely overcome and when detailed decisions on the final configuration have to be made. That this is so, I certainly agree, but I wonder if he is not defining development as an activity that starts at that point—presumably all that precedes it is research.

If one defines development in this way, certainly the nature of the activity will appear to be very different from its nature according to our broader definition. My reasons for not defining development as Scherer has are, first, that such a definition does not agree with what people in the business usually have in mind when they speak about development (though he prefers to regard designing a new compressor as a research problem, programs commonly referred to as development programs often involve several problems of comparable difficulty); and, second, that if economists accept this narrower definition, I am afraid they will not be able to get very far in explaining how progress comes about. Though the tools that economists have worked out are much more applicable if development is defined as an activity consisting of assembling known pieces of technology, I hope that we will not regard that as sufficient reason to so limit the scope of our inquiry.

Finally, let me say that I think Scherer is much too complimentary when he regards our work as an attempt to formulate "a single best approach to the development of advanced systems . . .". Actually, the aim of the paper I wrote was much less pretentious than that; it was simply to indicate that the character of the decision making problem in development is very different from that in production. This I would regard as a far cry from a positive theory and as the main shortcoming of our work thus far.

REJOINDER BY SCHERER

It is good that Burton Klein and I are still in disagreement, for disagreement is often the prelude to progress. What we need now, I think, are two things. First, we need a substantial body of empirical material on specific advanced system developments. Then it would be possible for us (and more important, for others interested in the economics of technological innovation) at least to isolate the factual and interpretational reasons for our disagreement. Unfortunately, proprietary and military security limitations are at present serious barriers to the publication of illuminating development case studies. But until more studies like those by Thomas Marschak and Richard Nelson are available, I am afraid we shall be led into the futile business of disagreeing on facts. Second, we need a better understanding of the kinds of trade-offs that can be made between performance, reliability, cost, and development time. Let me try to clear up some misunderstanding in this latter area.

As I said in my comment, substantial time and cost savings may often be obtained by making relatively small performance sacrifices. This does not imply only foregoing increments of performance above one's original objectives. It also means making do with a little less than was originally sought. If the original goals with respect to performance are optimistic, as is so often the case, it might be better to fall short and save considerable time and money. I realize there are institutional barriers to making such performance sacrifices. However, in the short space allowed for this reply, the medicine prescribed could be nothing more than a sugar pill, so I will not attempt to write a prescription.

Now, a word about reliability, that is, does the thing work? Let me say, first, that my "ordered into production as soon as possible" and Klein's "rushing into production" connote different time scales, at least in my mind. Achieving substantial performance advances and obtaining high reliability are usually antithetical, and a good deal of development effort is required to satisfy both objectives together. If, in the middle of a development program with ambitious performance goals, the system is rushed into production, it probably will not work, at least not very well. When early production is a major objective, then it is prudent *at the outset* to limit one's performance advancement goals to what can be obtained with high certainty. This means specifying already proven concepts and components, in other words, making early configuration decisions—just what Klein apparently condemns. If advancing the state of the art is the primary objective, then one *should* keep his technical plan flexible. But if a decision maker tries to have his cake and eat it, that is, to make big performance gains and still have an operational weapon in a very short time, he is begging for disappointment unless he is willing to spend a great deal on the insurance of multiple approaches. These are the most important optimization decisions in systems development, and they must be made early in the game. As the development progresses, the opportunities for making acceptable time-performance-reliability trade-offs become more and more constrained.

I do not want to argue with Klein over definitions of development. I do, however, want to make sure we are talking about the same thing. Plainly, there are all kinds of developments in terms of an a priori uncertainty classification. I have been referring to systems development, which might be defined very loosely as assembling known (although not always) pieces of technology. Most of Klein's examples are drawn from this sort of development, and most of our R and D money is spent on such activity. That behavior should be different for other kinds of development cannot be denied.

Rejoinder by Klein

If by "known technology" Frederic Scherer means "technology that does not involve any new scientific principles," then I agree that development can be defined as an activity involving the assembly of known pieces of technology. But, as I tried to emphasize in writing my paper, there is quite a difference between knowing that some idea, say, for a communications satellite system, does not violate any known scientific principles, and knowing when it can be ready for use, how much it will cost, how well it will operate, etc. (see, for example, Marschak's paper). And in this more relevant sense I insist that most of the money spent on R and D has not been spent on "known" technology. It seems to me that simply by reading the newspaper accounts about the B-70 bomber, about the Polaris missile, about the satellite warning system, about the missile that is supposed to shoot down ballistic missiles, about the Saturn development program, etc., one might deduce that capabilities aimed for in development are more than a little different from the things we have today.

Strategy and Organization
in a System Development Project

THOMAS A. MARSCHAK

THE UNIVERSITY OF CALIFORNIA, BERKELEY

OF THE $3.7 billion spent by private industry on research and development in 1953, about 4 per cent, the National Science Foundation estimates,[1] went to basic research.[2] A breakdown of the remainder by categories related to the degree of "appliedness" does not yet exist. It is safe to say, however, that a large proportion went to the development of what have come to be called systems.

There is no accepted unambiguous definition of a system. To call it a collection of interrelated components seems inadequate, for that is true of the simplest gadgets, down to the safety pin. Nor is it satisfactory to say that, compared to basic research, the uncertainties in developing a system are negligible and the goals precise. For, while a system is based on established principles which are the outputs of basic research, the difficulty of applying them to achieve a given performance goal may be highly uncertain, so that an initially selected goal may be substantially revised as development proceeds. Moreover, a system development project is generally larger than the average basic research project and more, in a sense, is at stake: in a system project a commitment may be based on a conjecture (about nature) whose uncertainty is negligible by the standard of basic research. But where, in a basic research project, a commitment might be an order for a dozen Bunsen burners, in a system project it is likely to be the task assignment of a large team of engineers, and sometimes it is heavy investment in production facilities. The uncertainties of system development may be niggling and prosaic compared to the deep mysteries of basic research, but it is urgent, all the same, to assess them carefully.

For our purpose it will suffice to think of a system as a complex aggregation of components, based on established principles. An aircraft is a system, and so are a color television set, a telephone exchange,

---

[1] *Science and Engineering in American Industry, Final Report on a 1953–1954 Survey,* National Science Foundation, 1956, Table A-13.

[2] Defined by the National Science Foundation as "Projects which are not identified with specific product or process applications, but rather have the primary objective of adding to the over-all scientific knowledge of the firm" (*ibid,* p. 18).

and a synthetic fiber plant. The established principles permit the confident assertion that (1) for some effort, or (2) for no effort, however large, the system can be made to attain a given performance. Knowledge of the effort needed in case (1) varies widely in accuracy from system to system and so, consequently, does the precision with which performance goals are specified when development of the system begins.

There is no need to go into the normative and positive questions about industrial research and development (and hence about technical change) for which a better understanding of system development is important. A major one: what is "efficient" system development and is it observed in American industry? The empirical study of system development could take at least three forms: an analysis, industry by industry, of relevant aggregates; a comparison of the conduct of system development as between industrial laboratories; or an examination of a number of system development projects in a variety of laboratories. Data for all three approaches are difficult to obtain. We are concerned here with the third approach: the intensive historical study of completed system development projects.

A sufficient number of such studies, over a sufficiently wide range of industries and project sizes, could help to provide first answers as to what sorts of development strategies and what types of project organization are likely to be associated with "successful" system development. By strategies we mean rules for making decisions as the project proceeds and knowledge is gained. The problem of measuring success is, of course, very troublesome. We shall be content to focus on certain observable and avoidable difficulties whose presence in the course of a project indicates "inefficiency" or less than maximum success.

While the accumulation of case studies would help to isolate the causes of these difficulties, some theoretical work on the nature of systems and on good organization and strategy for system projects would be in order as well.[3] For even without the peculiar role of uncertainty, a system would generally present a scheduling problem—the efficient scheduling of tasks, whose complexity goes beyond the existing results on scheduling problems arising in production.[4] With the introduction of uncertainty and of objective functions defined over a space of system performance parameters, the problem of good

---

[3] A first try at some formal theory is under way.
[4] E.g., on assembly-line scheduling.

strategy and organization becomes a completely new one, and a formal statement of it, at the least, seems essential.

We shall not attempt it here. The present paper merely illustrates the possibilities of case studies for the support of informally stated hypotheses about the types of strategy and organization which avoid or make likely specific types of difficulties. One case study is presented which is consistent with one such hypothesis.

The system we shall consider was developed at the Bell Telephone Laboratories. It is a microwave relay system for the transmission over long distances, via a chain of relay towers, of telephone conversations and television signals. Its development was complete and its manufacture had begun in 1958. The start of its development as a system can reasonably be dated 1952. The project built up to a peak of about ninety technical persons, and its man-power and other direct costs are roughly estimated at $15,000,000. In the Bell Telephone Laboratories it was one of the largest and most complex (nonmilitary) systems undertaken.

The materials available for the study were official project documents, informal memoranda and conference minutes, and some interviews. The written coverage of events was often sketchy and the time available for interviews to fill gaps was quite limited. It seems fair to say that for the major events in the project's history records exist (and were examined); for the others, the records and interviews covered, very roughly, a random sample. While it would be pleasant for the investigator of system development to come across a project in which a total history was kept—in which every idea, message, and decision was recorded on a punched card—one suspects that such a project would have drawbacks for the laboratory which, in its view, would outweigh the investigator's joy. If informality and partial independence of technical personnel are important attributes of successful projects, then, it may be conjectured, successful projects are far removed from the extreme of the punched card and are not easy to study. At any rate, even with the interest and cordial cooperation with which the study was received, much of the following account remains the writer's personal impression.

The following section gives a simplified layman's description of the system studied (known as the TH system). The second section is an "anonymous" history, concentrating on the general strategy of development and avoiding any mention of who was involved. It makes lavish use of the passive voice ("It was decided that . . ."), and might be the history of a one-man project. It is, of course, by no means complete, in the sense that very many events are omitted, but the strategy of development seems fairly portrayed. The fourth section contains some observations about the organization of the project (who did what). The last section is a recapitulation and a brief statement of a hypothesis about strategy and organization of system projects with which the case of TH seems consistent.

A Description of the TH System

The transmission of telephone conversations and television broadcasts over long (transcontinental) distances has been achieved in two ways —by coaxial cable and by microwave relay. The second method, the later of the two to be developed, dominates the former—for a given investment cost it provides far greater capacity (with comparable performance). A microwave relay network is composed of towers or repeater stations, a constant distance apart, each of which contains equipment that receives very high-frequency signals from the adjacent stations, equipment that amplifies the signals received, and equipment that transmits the amplified signals to the adjacent stations. At each end of a link in the microwave relay network originating telephone messages and TV broadcasts are transformed into signals of very high (microwave) frequency.

The first microwave relay system—the TD-2 system—was put into transcontinental operation by the American Telephone and Telegraph Company in 1951. Its microwave signals have frequencies around 4,000 megacycles per second (mc/sec). The TH system, with which we are concerned, operates at frequencies around 6,000 mc/sec. Its purpose is to greatly augment the capacity of TD-2, and it uses much equipment of totally new design. Its capacity is approximately 11,000 two-way telephone conversations (one television broadcast can be substituted for each 1,860 conversations)—roughly three times the capacity of TD-2.

We proceed now to a simplified description of TH—by a layman for laymen—which will serve as a reference base for the historical and organizational accounts that follow. Figure 1 provides a schematic portrayal of the system.

Consider the transmission of telephone conversations and TV broadcasts, via TH, from one location to another. At the first location we find a telephone central office in which groups of originating

FIGURE 1

Highly Simplified Schematic Diagram of TH System, Tracing Progress of One Signal, Covering One Channel

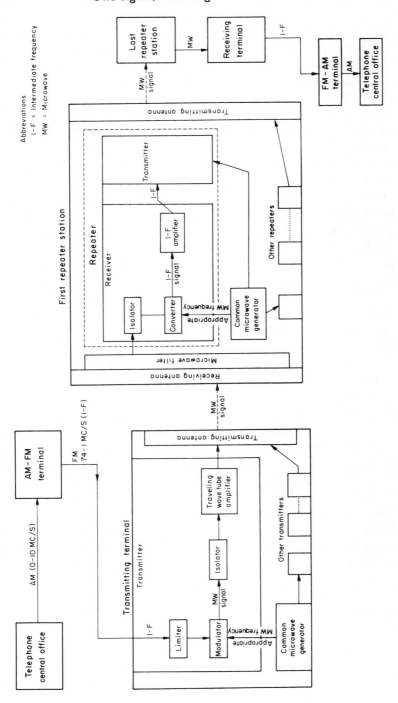

telephone conversations are transformed (by equipment developed some years before TH) into amplitude-modulated radio signals. These signals, together with television signals (which are also AM), are sent via cable to an *AM-FM terminal*. We shall trace the progress of one signal, conveying, say, a group of telephone messages (alternatively it could convey a TV program). The AM signal in question, like all the originating AM signals, uses the frequency band from 0 to 10 mc/sec, called the base band. At the AM-FM terminal it is converted, by equipment developed for TH, into a frequency-modulated signal whose center frequency is 74.1 mc/sec, called the intermediate frequency of i-f. The band of frequencies about the i-f, containing the modulations of the i-f which carry the group of messages in question, is 28 megacycles wide. This FM signal is fed, via cable, to a *transmitting terminal*.

Here the signal enters the *transmitting modulator*, where it is impressed on a microwave carrier signal, whose frequency is near 6,000 mc/sec; the microwave carrier signal, in other words, is frequency modulated so as to match (to carry the same information as) the incoming i-f FM signal. The source of the microwave carrier signal is a *common microwave generator* which provides all the microwave carrier frequencies needed in the transmitting terminal. The modulated microwave signal passes through a *ferrite isolator* (which attenuates undesired signals reflected back from subsequent components) and then goes to a *traveling-wave-tube amplifier;* the amplified signal finally reaches the transmitting terminal's *transmitting antenna*.

The microwave signal is detected at the first *repeater station*, containing a *receiving antenna*, several *repeaters*, and a transmitting antenna, and located some thirty miles away. Each repeater consists of a *receiver* and a *transmitter;* the components of the latter are identical with those just described for the transmitting terminal. After passing through the repeater station's receiving antenna, through an attached *wave guide*, and through a *microwave filter* which separates it from adjacent signals, the microwave signal goes to one of the repeaters. The first repeater component which it enters is an isolator (whose general purpose is as described above). It next goes to a receiving modulator or *converter*. Here it is impressed on a microwave signal of different frequency (obtained from the repeater's common microwave generator) in such a way that an FM signal at i-f emerges. The i-f signal contains the same information as the original received microwave signal, but like the received signal it is very weak. It is amplified in the *i-f amplifier*. The amplified i-f signal enters a trans-mitter; the transmitter's components have already been described.[5] The power needs of each repeater station are met by a *power supply*.

Following the final repeater station there is a *receiving terminal*, containing receivers (whose components have just been described). The amplified i-f signal which emerges is sent to an FM-AM terminal, where it is converted to the base band AM signal, and then sent to a telephone central office (or to a local TV transmitter if it conveys television).

The term "signal" needs to be made more precise. TH uses the 500-megacycle-wide microwave band between 5,925 and 6,245 mc/sec. This band is divided into 16 broad-band channels, each 28 mc wide, or 8 two-way broad-band channels, each composed of 2 nonadjacent broad-band channels. Of the 8, 6 are for regular service and 2 are protection channels. Each two-way broad-band channel will handle 1,860 two-way telephone conversations or one television program.[6]

It will be important for our purposes to clarify further the plac-ing of the two-way channels within the 500 mc band as well as their use. For the scheme of channel placement or frequency allocation was one of the major choices facing the developers of TH. Con-sider, for example, the two-way channel whose component chan-nels have the carrier frequencies 6,226.9 mc/sec, and 5,974.9 mc/sec when no messages are being transmitted. Now suppose the channel's complement of 1,860 telephone messages is sent from location A to location B via this two-way channel. This means that at the transmitting terminal a carrier signal of 5,974.9 mc/sec is frequency modulated—its frequency is altered at any instant of time above or below the carrier frequency so as to convey the information in these telephone messages. At the first repeater station, the frequencies conveying the messages are shifted upward (in the transmitting modulator) by 252 mc/sec, so that the unmodulated carrier frequency becomes 6,226.9 mc/sec and the telephone messages now cause deviations above and below

[5] The purpose of bringing the signal down to i-f at the repeater is to facilitate channel switching. See section below entitled "Generating Alternative Major System Characteris-tics Consistent with the Objectives."

[6] The width of each channel is determined by the width of the base band and (roughly) by the noise level to be tolerated in transmitting the information the base band signal contains.

this frequency. At the second repeater station the frequencies conveying the messages are shifted down to the original band centered at 5,974.9 mc/sec.

The alternation between the two components channels from repeater station to repeater station continues until the receiving terminal at B is reached. There is an analogous alternation in the opposite direction for the other part of the telephone conversation in question: the transmission of a message from B to A. The result is that at any repeater station one 28-mc frequency band carrying the telephone conversations in question is received from both directions and another (not adjacent to the first) is transmitted in both directions. For each two-way channel, there is, at a given repeater station, a distinct pair of transmitters and a distinct pair of receivers. All the transmitting frequencies in the repeater are grouped together and all the receiving frequencies are grouped together, the two groups being separated by a guard band 52 mc in width. The main purpose of this frequency-shift scheme is to avoid over-reach interference, which results when two successive repeaters transmit the same frequency band in the same direction. Figures 2 and 3 portray the scheme.

Very efficient use of the entire 500 mc band is made possible by *cross polarization* (portrayed in Figure 3). Any two adjacent one-way broad-band channels in a repeater station's transmitting group and any two in its receiving group are oppositely polar-

FIGURE 2

Frequency Shifting: One Two-Way Broad-Band Channel, Composed of One-Way Channels F₁ and F₂

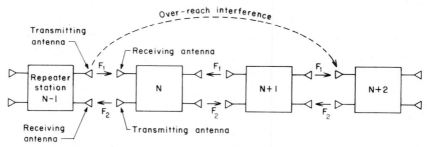

Arrows indicate direction of transmission.

Arrows indicate direction of transmission.

FIGURE 3

Two-Frequency Plan of Frequency Allocation, Using Cross-Polarization

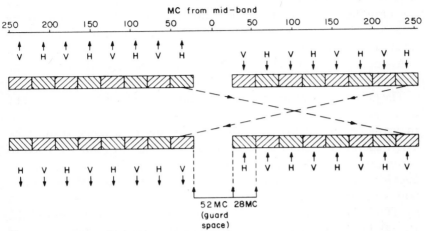

The crossing diagonal broken lines indicate a possible two-way broad-band channel at a given repeater station. Arrows indicate direction of transmission.

The crossing diagonal broken lines indicate a possible two-way broad-band channel at a given repeater station. Arrows indicate direction of transmission.

ized—if signals in the first channel travel in a horizontal plane to or from the next repeater, signals in the second travel in a vertical plane. This permits adjacent channels to be edge-to-edge without interference; without cross polarization there would have to be a guard band between two adjacent channels. Cross polarization also makes it possible to use one receiver and one transmitter for two adjacent (and oppositely polarized) one-way broad-band channels. Thus each repeater station contains in total eight repeaters (eight receivers and transmitters)—four for the eight one-way broad-band channels going in one direction and four for the eight going in the other direction.

An Anonymous History of the TH Project

ORIGINS

The TH system has, as we have seen, a predecessor—the TD-2 microwave relay system, first put into transcontinental operation in 1951. TD-2 operates at frequencies between 3,700 and 4,200 mc/sec.

It has five two-way broad-band channels; each channel's capacity is now 600 telephone conversations or one TV broadcast. (Each channel's capacity is less, per mc of width, than in TH, primarily because the amplifier used has much less power than TH's traveling-wave-tube amplifier.) The original transcontinental route has been paralleled and additional north-south and east-west fragments have been constructed so as to form a 25,000 mile network (densest in the eastern half of the country).

The growth in utilization of TD-2 was predicted at its inception to be quite steep. After the first two years of operation it was predicted that the capacity of some of its major links would be exhausted by 1960. The Federal Communications Commission had, in 1946, assigned to common carriers three microwave frequency bands for telephone and television transmission and to the Bell System the use of these three bands by transmitters at specific locations. One band was that used by TD-2. The remaining two were the 5,925–6,245 mc band and the 10,700–11,000 mc band. For accepted technical reasons[7] it was decided to use the latter band for a future short-haul feeder system and the former for the next long-haul relay system to be developed after TD-2.

It was clear at the time these decisions were made that a long-haul system operating in the 6,000 mc/sec range posed a major development task. Devices that accurately and reliably amplified signal channels in this range (each channel conveying a great deal of information) did not exist; there were at least two approaches to such devices and it was far from clear which was better. In addition to amplifiers, other important components of a future system were equally problematic. The future development task was conceived, moreover, as achieving an improvement over TD-2; it was to make more efficient use of its frequency band.

General exploratory work relevant to microwave transmission systems had been a continuing activity at Bell Laboratories for some years. Experimental tubes and other devices were constantly being built and investigated so as to provide an array of interesting component possibilities for unspecified future microwave systems. It seems to have been in 1949, however, that work was first specifically directed toward the components and techniques which were then the major puzzles of a future 6,000 mc/sec long-haul system. The

---

[7] Namely, that the difficulties of using the very high frequency band would be less serious in short-haul service.

years 1949-51 were primarily years of resolving fundamental uncertainties before the start of system planning and development.

1949–51: RESOLVING FUNDAMENTAL UNCERTAINTIES AND IDENTIFYING OBVIOUS BOTTLENECKS

1. The most extensive uncertainties concerned traveling wave tubes for amplification in the transmitter of a microwave relay system. The principles of the traveling wave tube had been developed just after World War II (largely in Britain and at Bell Laboratories) and experimental models had been built as early as 1947.[8] It seemed likely that traveling wave tube amplifiers with the required characteristics in the 6,000 mc/sec range could be developed. But it was highly uncertain how quickly the design of a satisfactory tube and an associated magnetic focusing structure could be found.

At the same time there existed an alternative to the traveling-wave-tube amplifier—an amplifier based on a planar triode. Such an amplifier had been developed for TD-2. There was a possibility that the TD-2 triode could be modified[9] to provide satisfactory amplification at 6,000 mc/sec. Attempts to do so were still underway, on a small scale, in 1949. But toward the end of 1949 the consensus was that the traveling wave tube held the greater promise.

There was interest concurrently in a low-noise traveling wave tube, a tube specially designed to have a much superior noise figure but a substantially smaller gain and smaller power output than the tube intended for the main transmitting amplifier. The low-noise tube would be used in the receiver to amplify the received microwave carrier signal before its conversion to an i-f signal in the converter. This promised to decrease significantly each repeater's contribution to the total noise in any future system in which signals were brought

---

[8] A very crude description of the tube is as follows. An electron gun, a helix (a coil of wire), and a collector are sealed in a long, thin glass tube. An electromagnetic wave to be amplified enters the tube through an input wave guide. The wave travels around the helix towards the collector with almost the speed of light; its effective speed through the tube, however, is less, roughly equalling the speed of the electrons which are sent through the helix from the gun by a voltage close to 2,000 volts. (The helix, in other words, "slows down" the electromagnetic wave by making it traverse a lengthy route to get from one end of the tube to the other.) The electrons and the wave travel along together, with the wave acting on the beam of electrons to group them in clusters which "match" the wave and which, in turn, act on it so as to amplify it. The waves can be visualized as waves on water and the electron stream as a breeze, which blows past the waves and raises them higher and higher as they travel. The amplified signal leaves the tube through an output waveguide. The direction of the electron stream must be very accurately maintained, and this is the function of a magnetic focussing structure surrounding the tube.

[9] Essentially by bringing the grid closer to the cathode.

down to an i-f at repeaters. Both traveling wave tubes under study through late 1951 were 4,000 mc/sec tubes built to match the only test equipment then available. It was expected that information obtained from tests at these frequencies could later be applied to higher frequency tubes. Only at the end of 1951 did work begin on 6,000 mc/sec versions of the two tubes.

2. Cross-polarization studies got under way in 1949. Cross polarization was known to have promise as a means for making more efficient use of a given microwave frequency band and experimental data were needed to estimate the difficulties of incorporating the techniques in the future system. Knowledge of waveguide and antenna designs permitting efficient cross polarization was obtained.

3. Frequency allocation studies were begun, to consider alternative ways of dividing up a future system's frequency band among channels and to deduce some of the broad requirements that each alternative would impose on the system.

4. Effort in the years 1949–51 was also directed at identifying and starting work on obvious potential bottlenecks which would arise in developing a future system unless work on them preceded the start of system development. By obvious bottlenecks we mean those that can be prevented by performing (before the start of system development) straightforward tasks whose magnitude is predictable with high confidence. Such tasks require no innovations and are independent of those properties of the final system which are initially very uncertain.

The chief obvious potential bottlenecks were certain items of test equipment. Conferences in 1949 formally emphasized the importance of these items. The highest-frequency test equipment then existing was in the 4,000 mc/sec range (largely developed for TD-2). The absence of 6,000 mc/sec test equipment was already constraining experimental traveling wave tube work. It would literally halt important work once a future system was in full development. To produce a variety of test equipment at 6,000 mc/sec, while a fairly straightforward engineering task, was apparently one that was sure to require substantial minimum time periods—up to a year and a half for some items. Allocation of more manpower to test-equipment development within the anticipated manpower limits could not, apparently, reduce the time required below these minima. Work on some of the major items consequently started in 1950 and 1951.

1952: PRELIMINARY SYSTEM PLANNING

In 1952 the planning of TH as a system began. The official authorization of preliminary planning meant that the accumulated information about the difficulty of developing TH, gained in the previous three years' attack on the system's fundamental puzzles, showed it to be certainly worth another one or two years' work at a great but still relatively low level of intensity.[10] At the end of the period it would be decided whether, in view of the predictions then possible about the roughly planned system and its development effort, and in view of the rising pressure on TD-2, a commitment to full-scale development should be made. A (partial) alternative still remaining at the time of that decision would be construction of additional TD-2 routes.

As a first step in planning, it was decided that TH would use the routes and towers of TD-2 and that the components of TD-2 should be used or adapted whenever possible. As a result of the work of 1949–51 it was also decided that microwave amplification would be based on the traveling wave tube; that cross polarization would be used together with an antenna type explored in 1949–51;[11] and that shifting of frequencies would occur at repeaters, as had been the case in TD-2.[12]

There then remained, at this stage, three major planning problems: formulating broad objectives; identifying alternative sets of major system characteristics consistent with these objectives; and formulating broad requirements for certain "key" components (those likely to require a long development time, or those that must be nearly completed before the development of important components can start). We shall discuss these problems in order.

Objectives

The system's purpose is to transmit information; its success in doing so depends, essentially, on the number of messages that can be simultaneously transmitted over any link in the system, the total noise expected over any link, and the reliability of any link. For a given

[10] Roughly 78 technical man-years were spent in 1952–1954 out of an estimated total of 345 spent on TH development by 1958. Further data on time path of expenditure are given at the end of this historical section.

[11] Horn-reflector antennas had been shown during this period to be much more efficient, especially for cross-polarization, than the delay-lens antennas of TD-2.

[12] But an important choice remained as to how many frequency bands each channel used in each direction. See below.

development effort and a given production and operating cost of the developed equipment, there is, in general, some scope for trade-off among these three magnitudes. For example, if each telephone conversation were assigned a larger portion of a two-way broad-band channel, a better signal-to-noise ratio could be attained, but fewer conversations could then be fitted into the given 500 mc band. To some extent, moreover, a greater development effort and a greater production and operating cost can "buy" better values of one or more of the three magnitudes.

In the early planning of the TH system, the objective with respect to noise was to meet standards previously set by the Bell System for long-haul telephone and television circuits. These specify a maximum acceptable total noise level for any long-haul link.[13] There was a corresponding goal with respect to messages transmitted: a minimum of six two-way broad-band channels each carrying at least 1,800 (two-way) telephone conversations or one TV broadcast.[14] The reliability goal was less precisely stated: a "very high" degree of reliability was to be obtained by making use of protection channels (two were planned) in addition to the six normal two-way broad-band channels. In the event of a breakdown in an item of equipment on which a given normal channel depends, one of the protection channels would be switched to automatically.[15] Alarm and control circuits would be used to signal the difficulty to maintenance personnel.

How binding were these objectives? The noise objective seems to have been the most critical. Even here, however, the view was certainly not that the entire development would be a failure should the final system not meet the noise objective. (The TD-2 system fell a little short of its noise objective, once fully utilized; further minor improvements are possible, moreover, even after a system is in operation, and such improvements were underway for TD-2 at the time of writing). The attitude toward the three goals might be summarized as follows: it seemed likely that for a reasonable development effort a system

[13] More precisely, a minimum signal-to-noise ratio at hours of peak system use under average atmospheric conditions.

[14] The goal of 1,800 telephone conversations per channel was reasonable, given the base-band width—10 mc—of the AM signal whose information content is transmitted over a channel. The 10 mc width was largely dictated by the existing equipment (developed for a coaxial-cable long-haul system) which could combine telephone conversations (1,800 of them, roughly) into an AM signal whose width was a bit less than 10 mc. The choice of 10 mc was also influenced by the possibility of a future demand for transmission of theater television, which would require a base-band of this width.

[15] It will be recalled that for each two-way broad-band channel there is, at each repeater station, a distinct pair of receivers and a distinct pair of transmitters.

could be obtained whose production cost was acceptable, whose noise came close to the noise objective, and whose message capacity and reliability were acceptably near the respective objectives (but further than the system's noise is from the noise objective). Development effort and production cost were to be increased, as became necessary, to reach acceptable values of the three performance magnitudes. Should a point in development be reached where an acceptable value of one of them could not be attained without a drastic increase in development effort or production cost, a decision whether or not to sacrifice performance significantly would be required. But that would be a bridge to be crossed when and if it appeared: there was no need to formulate beforehand a strategy for decision in the many conceivable contingencies of this sort.

No estimate of the total TH development effort was contained in the prospectus which, in 1952, accompanied official laboratory authorization of preliminary system planning. The prospectus did make a prediction about production cost, namely that the first cost of TH per channel-mile (using the existing TD-2 towers) would be about $1.25 less than for TD-2. (This prediction turned out, as we shall see, to be a moderate underestimate.)

Generating Alternative Major System Characteristics Consistent With the Objectives

The objectives having been formulated, many decisions remained as to certain important system characteristics. By a system characteristic we mean either (1) a number (or set of numbers) that characterizes the system (rather than any one component) but is distinct from the magnitudes defining the objectives; or (2) the specification which of several different ways of attaining the objectives is to be used (e.g., which of two possible, qualitatively different major components is to be used to perform a certain function). Alternative sets of characteristics consistent with the objectives were found, and choice among these sets was subsequently to be made. It was important to generate some alternatives at this stage, since uncertainty as to the effort required to realize any given set of characteristics was great. To formulate any set, however, is a costly analytical job, and many possible alternatives were never presented.[16]

[16] The final choice of system characteristics may reflect what system planners are fond of calling a "design philosophy"—i.e., a general approach to a wide class of problems

The most important characteristic was the frequency allocation plan. Two alternative plans were developed in 1952. One was the two-frequency plan finally adopted (a given signal traveling in a given direction uses two frequency bands, shifting from one to the other at each repeater station). This would allow, within the available 500 mc space, eight two-way broad-band channels and 52 mc of guard space. The other plan was a four-frequency plan wherein each two-way broad-band channel uses a separate pair of frequencies for each direction of transmission. Adjacent bands would be allowed to overlap somewhat in the latter plan but, even so, only six two-way broad-band channels could be fitted into the 500 mc space.[17] The first plan was therefore preferable, but its feasibility depended on further advances in the design of the antennas and the associated microwave filters. The difficulty of these advances was very much in doubt.

Another important pair of alternatives presented in 1952 were two repeater types. One possibility was an i-f type in which gain, regulation, and frequency shift are accomplished after bringing the signal down to i-f.[18] The other possibility was an all-microwave type where modifications of the signal are accomplished without bringing it down to i-f. The former type is necessary in any case at main repeater stations where channel switching[19] is required, but a choice between the types had to be made for all other repeater stations.

A third major pair of alternatives was to use or not use a low-noise traveling wave tube in the receivers.

A fourth very important set of alternatives consisted of the possible allocation of acceptable noise among major parts of the system so as to meet the total noise objective for telephone message and TV

posed by the system. In TH, for example, such a philosophy opposed the use of "mop-up" circuits following a component to correct undesirable distortions generated by the component; the component was to be designed, in general, so as to make mopping up unnecessary.

[17] In both plans the width of each one-way channel is 28 mc. Given the width of the AM base band other widths could have been explored (permitting more or fewer channels, with a penalty or gain in signal-noise ratios). But developing each alternative plan and exploring its consequences is expensive; it seemed reasonable to confine the comparison between two and four-frequency plans to the 28 mc width. In any case, 28 mc was regarded as a good bet for a width for which near-attainment of the noise and capacity objectives would be a reasonable development task.

[18] The precise intermediate frequency had not yet been chosen.

[19] I.e., switching a group of telephone conversations or a television broadcast from one specific two-way broad-band channel to another. This occurs at stations from which branches off the main trunk routes originate. Switching to a protection channel is a second kind of switching. Provision for either or both kinds is needed at two out of three stations.

transmission. A tentative "target" allocation was chosen in 1952. The acceptable noise contribution of central offices, terminals, and repeaters was specified. It "added up" to the total noise objective.[20] It was explicitly recognized that deviations from the target allocation would be permitted as they arose; if it turned out to be difficult not to exceed target noise for one source, the excess would be allowed, provided the noise in another source could be made to fall short of the target there by a roughly compensating amount.

Finally, a target requirement was set for system equalization. This magnitude measures, to put it crudely, the variation, as between a given channel's original amplitude-modulated base-band frequencies fed into a link of the system, of the strengths with which they emerge at the FM-AM terminal at the other end of the link, as well as their variation with respect to phase at the other end of the link. It is an important determinant of each channel's message capacity, given a maximum noise level, and it depends on the performance of a number of components. Some variation from the target value, initially set the same for each channel, was to be admitted.

Note that the system characteristics are closely interdependent: given the objectives to be met, and given all but one, the admissible values of the remaining characteristic are sharply constrained.

Broad Requirements for Major Components

The final planning task to get underway in 1952 was the formulation of broad requirements for major components consistent with each other, with the objectives, and with some of the alternative sets of system characteristics.

ANTENNAS. In the preferred two-frequency plan a repeater station N receiving a desired frequency from repeater station N + 1 will also receive interfering signals from repeaters N − 1 and N + 1. The only known way of discriminating against this interference is to improve antenna front-to-back ratios (very roughly the ratio of the antenna's efficiency in receiving or radiating

---

[20] The rule for totalling the contributions is more complex than simple addition. In addition to breaking down total noise into contributions of these three parts of the system it was also broken down into "types" of noise (fluctuation, intermodulation, and crosstalk noise). A given component may contribute one type of noise but not the others; the types are equally important to the total system noise. It goes without saying that attainment of a noise level for a part of the system below the target level for that part is desirable if it can be achieved with no additional effort.

energy in the desired direction to its efficiency in doing so in the reverse direction). Minimum requirements for antenna front-to-back ratios were computed such that, under the two-frequency arrangement, the "target" for each repeater station's contribution to system noise would be met—provided that reasonable requirements on other components are met.

TRAVELING WAVE TUBE AMPLIFIER. It was concluded that to guard against fading (which can periodically occur between any two repeater stations), while meeting the noise target for repeater stations and the message capacity goal for channels, each repeater should be capable of providing up to 100 db of gain and its traveling wave tube amplifier should have a power output of "about" five watts.

Requirements for the low-noise tube, on which development work was under way, were also formulated in case the alternative of using one should be adopted.

OTHER REPEATER COMPONENTS. Requirements on other major components of both i-f repeaters and all-microwave repeaters were roughly sketched. Some of these components were to be adaptations of TD-2 components, but others (e.g., the common microwave generator, the i-f amplifier) would require substantial development effort.

POWER SUPPLIES. Voltage requirements for each repeater station's power supply were formulated to meet the needs of the traveling wave tubes and other repeater components.

ALARM AND CONTROL CIRCUITS AND AUTOMATIC SWITCHING. A description was given of proposed alarm and control circuits, together with devices for automatic switching to protection channels. These features promised to meet the objectives for system reliability.

To summarize: The requirements drawn up for major components in this period were very broad and not rigid. They consisted generally of upper and lower limits to the main component characteristics. But they were consistent with each other, with the system objectives, and with some of the alternative sets of system characteristics. It could be stated with great confidence that, if major components meeting the requirements were developed, then the system objectives would be met. While there was considerable uncertainty about how difficult attainment of any requirement would turn out to be, the requirements seemed reasonable guides for the next stage of development. It was quite clear, however, that should a given requirement prove difficult to meet, another one might be substituted, perhaps a requirement consistent with different sets of system characteristics among the alternative sets previously generated, or even with different objectives, implying quite new system characteristics.

1953–54: CHOICE BETWEEN ALTERNATIVE MAJOR SYSTEM CHARACTERISTICS, FIRST DETAILED SYSTEM PLANNING, INITIAL COMPONENT DEVELOPMENT, AND DEVELOPMENT SCHEDULING

During the next stage in the development of TH, choice between major alternative system characteristics was made; the system was planned in detail for the first time (including requirements for a number of minor components); the development of major and minor components got well under way; and target dates for the main events in development were set. Finally, a tentative development budget was drawn up and allocated. All these activities overlapped in time.

Choice Between Alternative Major System Characteristics

Choice between alternative sets of major system characteristics was made possible in this stage because enough evidence had accumulated about the development difficulties implied by each. The evidence consisted of observations on experimental models of the key components which particular alternatives would require as well as further paper analysis of the requirements implied and the difficulty of attaining them.

LOW-NOISE TRAVELING WAVE TUBE. A decision not to use a low-noise tube in the receivers was made early in 1954. The noise figure obtained in some experimental tubes was not so low as had been hoped and at the same time the converter itself (using a newly developed crystal) promised a much better noise figure than anticipated earlier. Hence the advantage of incorporating a low-noise tube ahead of the converter appeared to be quite small and not worth additional development effort.

FREQUENCY PLAN. The two-frequency alternative was chosen. As a result of experimental work with antennas it appeared very likely that an antenna design yielding the required front-to-back ratios could be obtained. The precise spacing of channels was not decided upon until the end of 1954. (Given the channel width of 28 mc, previously chosen, it depended essentially on the width of the guard space between the two groups of eight one-way channels.)

REPEATERS (OTHER THAN MAIN REPEATERS): I-F VERSUS ALL-MICROWAVE. The possibility of all-microwave repeaters was rejected. The principal reasons were (1) difficulties discovered in achieving frequency shift in such repeaters, and (2) the increasingly likely prospect that, as the microwave network becomes denser, virtually all stations will become nodes of the network and will have to be provided with a channel switching ability.

NOISE ALLOCATION. By mid-1954 the noise objective had been slightly relaxed from that of two years earlier and the planned noise allocation had accordingly been changed slightly from the earlier target allocation. Now, moreover, it was given in somewhat greater detail. The target noise from repeater stations, in particular, was broken down into subtargets, corresponding to several repeater components. Early design work on noise-critical repeater components, undertaken in the intervening two years, had made this breakdown possible.

SYSTEM EQUALIZATION. A small relaxation from the original target was decided upon for certain specific channels and a slightly more stringent target was set for any channel carrying color television. The difficulty of achieving the revised targets was still very uncertain at the end of 1954, since it depended on the performance of a number of undeveloped components.

First Detailed System Planning

The end products of this period's detailed system planning were block diagrams of the system. They showed the path of the signals from component to component as well as specifications (requirements) for the components, stated in greater detail than before. This required choice of some minor system characteristics not dealt with before.

More Detailed Component Requirements

The choice of a major system characteristic was generally accompanied, as we have seen, by a more detailed statement of the alternative chosen. Similarly, requirements for major components, consistent with the chosen alternatives, were now formulated in considerably greater detail, involving in some cases specifications to be met by many of the smaller parts making up a major component. In addition, requirements were generated for minor components, not bothered with in the previous stage of development. The level of detail, however, was quite uneven—high for some (major or minor) components, low for others. This occurred for two main reasons; we shall discuss each in turn.

VARIATION IN DEVELOPMENT UNCERTAINTY OF COMPONENTS. The greater the uncertainty as to size of development effort needed to meet given requirements for a component, the less detailed, in general, were (1) the requirements formulated for it in this period, and (2) the requirements formulated for other components whose performance closely depended on it. Requirements for the components closely dependent on a highly uncertain component were stated broadly to provide consistency with a wide range of possible specifications for the component in question.

Consider, for example, the isolator and the common microwave generator. The isolator developed was a novel solution to the problem of blocking reflections from the antenna before they reach a repeater to which the antenna is connected. That the material (a ferrite) and the design would function properly became evident in 1953. Hence, in mid-1954, a precise minimum level of attenuation of the undesired antenna reflections was specified, as well as a maximum acceptable forward loss (i.e., loss of strength in the signal that passes through the isolator in the desired direction). In formulating those component requirements whose soundness depended on isolator performance, there was then no need to "hedge" to allow for alternative levels of isolator performance.

The common microwave generator, on the other hand, was a much more problematic component. Its critical property was reliability. The alternative to a common generator at each repeater station was a set of generators, one for each channel (this alternative was used in TD-2). The common generator's chief advantage is that it greatly reduces the number of tubes and other unreliable elements required for microwave generation (but requires a greater number of "passive" elements). Consequently the probability of failure of any single channel due to failure of its microwave supply at some repeater station is greatly reduced. The probability of failure of all channels, however, is somewhat increased, even with the use of a stand-by common generator at each repeater. The difficulty of reducing the latter probability to negligible levels was quite uncertain, and no requirement for the probability was decided upon in this stage of development. The many possible ways of generating the needed family of microwave frequencies[21] implied different generator reliabilities and a sufficiently wide exploration of these alternatives was far from complete at the end of 1954. In particular, a judicious choice of the i-f would make it possible to require only a small number of basic oscillator frequencies. Combinations of these could then be found which, when impressed on the i-f in the transmitters, yield the required family of 16 microwave carrier frequencies. The fewer the basic oscillator frequencies the common microwave generator is required to produce, the simpler and more reliable is the generator. The judicious choice of i-f was not made, however, until the end of 1954. The possibility of separate-channel generators was, in fact, still held in reserve until then.

VARIATION IN SYSTEM CRITICALITY OF COMPONENTS. Quite aside from having very uncertain development difficulties, a component may be highly "system critical"; its performance affects the appropriateness of a great many other components. In principle (though this probably rarely occurs in practice) a component could display virtual certainty about its development difficulties and yet be highly system critical. It was natural, in TH, to be particularly careful about prematurely issuing detailed requirements for highly critical components, even if their development difficulties were only moderately uncertain.

Choosing, at a given point in development, the appropriate level of detail for a critical component's requirements (which are taken as predictions about the component's final properties when planning other components) calls for a difficult balancing of two costs. A balance must be struck between the risk of having to revise the entire system when detailed predictions about the component turn out to be wrong, and the cost in total system development time of waiting to announce predictions (requirements) until this risk is small (because the component is already well into development). Since much depends on a critical component, planning and development cannot proceed without some prediction as to its final performance; but if too detailed predictions are taken too seriously too soon, costly revisions of the entire system are likely to be needed.

The isolator is a good example of a component which was relatively uncritical in the above sense. The power supply was an example of a critical component whose development uncertainties were moderate.

[21] The frequencies needed were precisely determined once the two-frequency plan had been decided on and a division of the 500 mc band into channels and guard space chosen.

The requirements on the power supply at the end of 1954 were still very broad, not so much because its development was a puzzle but because too much else depended on its precise performance.

Generation and Choice of Minor System Characteristics

Part of the process of formulating more detailed component requirements was the generation of alternative minor system characteristics —magnitudes which are not attributes of only a single component and which it was premature to consider in the previous stage of development. Among such magnitudes were, for example, the intermediate frequency and the channel guard space. The proposed alternative characteristics had to be consistent with the chosen values of the major characteristics. To formulate final component requirements, choice among the alternatives had to be made, though choice could in some cases be deferred until development of the dependent components was already under way. (Design work on the i-f amplifier, to meet certain requirements that did not depend on frequency, could and did precede final choice of the i-f.)

Initial Component Development

Requirements for a number of important components having been issued in 1953–54, the developers of these components had goals, though they varied widely in precision. By the end of 1954, designs of all major components had been proposed, and in several cases hardware had been constructed. We shall discuss the development of the principal components in the next section.

Scheduling Development and Allocating Manpower

In mid-1954 a schedule for development activities was released. For most components it showed a date for each of four events: completion of preliminary requirements (already attained in many cases); completion of a preliminary model (also known as a "breadboard model"); completion of a laboratory model (also known as a "brassboard model"); and release of manufacturing information. The fourth event was to occur by 1957 for all components. The distinction between the two kinds of models is difficult to characterize in a general way. For each component, the two models serve as checkpoints— their completion is an opportunity for a reassessment and, if this is worthwhile, a revision of the component's specifications (a last-chance opportunity, in the case of the laboratory model). Completion of each model for a component probably marks a sharp jump in knowledge about the components, i.e., in the accuracy of predictions about additional effort required to meet given specifications.

The schedule was a goal, in the same sense as component requirements were, but was probably regarded as still more likely to undergo later changes. At the same time rough estimates were made of the sequence of annual man-years (of technical personnel) needed to achieve the schedule, and the allocation of manpower between major tasks in each year. The total manpower estimates were: 53 technical man-years[22] in 1954, 62 in 1955 and 1956, and 59 in 1957.

1955–57: FULL-SCALE COMPONENT DEVELOPMENT AND FINAL SYSTEM PLANNING

By 1955 full-scale development of all components was underway. In 1955–57 the final system plan was worked out in detail. Even the most broadly stated component requirements issued in the preceding period were not immutable. Part of the task of a component's developers was to be continually alert to the possibility that a reasonable modification of the requirements might make the task of completing the components significantly easier and to propose such modifications. In developing some components, parallel exploration of alternative designs, all holding promise of meeting the (tentative) requirements, was undertaken.

We shall discuss most of the major components, but not all. The periods considered overlap the period treated in the preceding section.

Traveling-Wave-Tube Amplifier

While this was probably the most difficult component to develop, and one of the most system critical, it was, as we have seen above, one of the earliest to be started. The early experimental models of the traveling-wave tube operated at the wrong frequency and had many defects. In April 1953 experimental 6,000 mc/sec tubes became available, together with most of the required items of 6,000 mc/sec test equipment, but many difficulties remained. There were three major interrelated problem areas: the "matching"[23] of the waveguide (through which the signals to be amplified enter the tube) to the helix; the design of a suitable

---

[22] In obtaining these figures, a man-year for a technical assistant is counted as half of a man-year for a member of the technical staff.
[23] With respect to impedance.

magnetic focusing structure surrounding the tube; and the coupling of the amplifier to certain adjacent circuits. The requirements at which work in these three areas aimed were broadly stated through 1955. The goal was an amplifier of at least 25 db gain with a power output of about five watts[24] requiring very little adjustment and with noise characteristics and other properties "satisfactory."

By the end of 1953 two important but relatively easy decisions had been rather firmly made: the critical properties of the power supply for the tube had been chosen; and it had been decided to incorporate a limiter ahead of the tube so as to remove residual amplitude variations that would be turned into phase variations by the tube. This largely left the first two of the above three problem areas.

Much of the work on helix-waveguide matching had to await the availability, in mid-1954, of a crucial item of 6,000 mc/sec test equipment (a frequency generator for the entire 500 mc band). This permitted extensive experiments on various tube and waveguide designs; their general aim was wide-band matching (over the entire 500 mc band), which would make it possible to tune (adjust) the amplifier in the same way for all channels and to replace tubes without retuning. This was a reaction to the TD-2 situation where separate tuning was required for each channel and maintenance was complex. It was an early design goal for the amplifier, but it was not a formally stated requirement, on whose performance specification of many other parts of the system depended. After many trials (including experiments with the leading in and out of signals by coaxial cables and not by waveguide at all), a waveguide and tube design was attained (about the end of 1955) which achieved wide-band matching and, in combination with the magnetic focusing structure that had by then been developed, provided the gain aimed for at acceptable noise levels.[25]

The work on magnetic focusing structures was aimed at highly accurate focusing of the electron beam[26] by an easily maintainable

[24] Only the power output goal had been stated in 1952.

[25] I.e., at noise levels such that the goal for repeater noise announced in mid-1954 could be met, given the noise properties which now promised to characterize the other repeater components (most of which were nearly developed).

[26] I.e., at a longitudinal magnetic field parallel to the tube which is very strong relative to the cross field (perpendicular to the tube), the ratio of the two strengths being very precisely determined.

structure of reasonable weight; the focusing structure of the earliest experimental amplifiers had been very heavy and had required complex adjustment. The design tested up to the end of 1955 had proved unsatisfactory, and it became clear that the difficulty of the magnetic structure problem had been seriously underestimated. The requirements the magnetic field must satisfy in order to achieve the broad amplifier goals were still not well understood, and magnet designs meeting given field requirements were unexpectedly difficult to achieve. At several points measuring equipment not previously planned turned out to be essential and had to be quickly developed. The magnetic structure had to be shielded; a way had to be found to prevent the powerful field of the magnet from interfering with components adjacent to the traveling-wave-tube amplifier without disturbing the delicate focusing of the traveling-wave-tube's electron beam. A new approach to magnetic structure design was tried early in 1956—periodic-field focusing rather than the previous straight-field method. The hope was that the new approach might permit a smaller and more easily designed magnet assembly. The two approaches were pursued in parallel throughout 1956; periodic focusing was finally abandoned as too difficult.

Early in 1957 an amplifier design had been obtained achieving sufficiently accurate wide-band matching and beam focusing to attain the broad amplifier performance goals with a satisfactorily low maintenance effort.

To summarize, the traveling-wave-tube amplifier was critical to the planned system and highly uncertain as to development difficulties. It was itself a system, composed of several major and several minor components for each of which feasible requirements consistent with each other and with the broadly stated amplifier goals had to be found. The first requirements decided on were those most certain of attainment and least critical with respect to other requirements on amplifier components (power needs, properties of the limiter to be used ahead of the amplifier, cooling mechanism for the tube). In developing all major parts of the amplifier, alternative approaches were tried, some simultaneously, some successively.

The development of the amplifier ran into major unexpected difficulties. But the amplifier was so critical to the system—in the stage of development the system had already reached when these difficulties came to light—that the effort needed to resolve these difficulties appeared well worthwhile. An alternative might have been a major downward revision of the amplifier goals or the substitution of an amplifier not based on the traveling wave tube. Such a change would have required a major revision of the system and its development schedule, at a cost far outweighing the expected effort of resolving the traveling-wave-tube amplifier's difficulties. In retrospect, it might appear that a greater exploratory effort on magnetic focusing structures should have preceded any formulation of amplifier goals for use in planning the rest of the system. But it may be that the strategy pursued was generally sound (that it is a strategy the laboratory is content to pursue, in the light of experience, in all such situations). For it may be that the balance between the risk of system revision and the rewards of early planning of a critical component had been reasonably struck, and that the unexpected difficulties were improbable misfortunes.[27]

Shorter Notes on Some Other Components

I-F AMPLIFIER. Early work on a high figure-of-merit tube for the i-f amplifier had been undertaken in 1953 and was well under way even before the amplifier's critical requirements had been broadly formulated. Such a tube (which provides the amplifier with a high signal-to-noise ratio) would probably be useful in fulfilling any performance goals. Requirements had to await the decision as to i-f frequency and the allocation of the 500 mc band to broad-band channels. By mid-1954 goals for the i-f amplifier included the frequency band to be amplified,[28] the amplifier's contribution to total repeater noise, its gain, and its distortion characteristics. It was decided to design the amplifier so as to minimize the dependence of distortion on tube characteristics; this would avoid the tendency of the TD-2 system's i-f amplifier towards variation of distortion from repeater to repeater (whose amplifier tubes differ in age). The goals were, of course, not rigid. They were moderately critical with respect to goals for other parts of the system and were moderately uncertain of attainment.

Several important alternative design approaches were pursued in developing the amplifier. The amplifier tube first adopted

[27] An organizational interpretation of the difficulties that arose with respect to the magnetic focusing structure is given in a later section dealing with functional departments.
[28] A band 28 mc wide around the chosen i-f of 74.1 mc/sec. The width of 28 mc for each broad-band (microwave) channel had been chosen in 1952. See footnote 17, above.

turned out to have a cathode prone to warping and an amplifier design using a lower-performance tube and more stages was substituted. Two kinds of gain control—thermistor and grid—were explored, in part simultaneously, and the latter adopted. Two kinds of circuitry were explored in sequence: an attempt at printed circuitry proved very difficult and was dropped, in mid-1955, in favor of more conventional circuitry.

CONVERTER. Design of this component was finished early in 1954, subject to satisfactory completion of a crystal then still under development. The noise goal proposed (in 1952) for a converter preceded by a low-noise tube would then be more than met, and so the low-noise tube was dropped. Subsequent system planning essentially took converter performance as given, and the missing crystal became available, meeting expectations, in 1955.

POWER SUPPLY. Requirements for this component were chosen quite late—in 1955. They depended on those properties of many other components which determined the power needs of those components. Designing a required power source was a straightforward task. In formulating the power requirements, however, it was possible, to some extent, to simplify design of the power-using circuits by requiring the supply of a large variety of voltages. On the other hand, voltage requirements could be standardized, but this would require more complex using circuits. After preliminary study and debate, an approach in between the extremes of no voltage standardization and complete standardization was adopted.

FM TERMINALS, ENTRANCE LINKS, ALARM AND CONTROL CIRCUITS. Requirements for these components, like requirements for the power supply, were highly dependent on the system but were not uncertain with respect to development difficulty. Requirements for them were not chosen until well into 1955, and development was completed in 1956 and early 1957. Since the size of the development effort for these components was accurately predictable and goals for them could not be accurately specified until the system was well under way, the postponement of their development was reasonable.

Final System Planning and the Completion of System Development

By the middle of 1958 the block diagrams of the system had taken their final form and the component specifications had been completely filled in. Manufacturing information for nearly all components had been released and the remainder would shortly follow. The system displayed only very minor departures from the original system objectives. The system's production and operating costs will also be close, it appears, to predictions made in 1954.

With respect to the development schedule presented in 1954, there had been "slippage" for some components (particularly the traveling-wave-tube amplifier), but none of it much more than six months. The 1954 prediction as to manpower (and hence development cost), had, however, proven substantially optimistic. The actual total technical manpower used was roughly as follows: 56 man-years in 1954 (55 were predicted); 72 man-years in 1955 (62 predicted); 90 in 1956 (62 predicted); 88 in 1957 (59 predicted); and 95 in 1958. It would appear that the goal for total development effort was much more willingly sacrificed than the development schedule, and the latter more willingly modified than the objectives and the production and operating costs. The unplanned increase in development effort, moreover, seems to have been sufficient to "absorb" the system's unexpected difficulties, since the other goals did not need to be significantly relaxed.

Organization of TH Development

SYSTEMS ENGINEERING

Of the three major departments of the Bell Telephone Laboratories— Research, Development, and Systems Engineering—the latter two played a part in developing TH. The general function of the Systems Engineering Department is continually to explore the needs of the Laboratories' customers—the operating telephone companies—while at the same time keeping closely in touch with the technical possibilities for meeting these needs. From time to time this function culminates in a formal proposal, described in a prospectus, for a specific system to be developed. In consultation with the Systems Engineering Department and the Laboratories' management, A. T. and T. (the principal prospective user of the system) and Western Electric (its manufacturer) decide whether or not the Laboratories should be authorized to develop the proposed system. This is an economic decision, making use of forecasts in the prospectus about development time and cost, production and operating costs, and system performance. Generally, the forecasts as to development time and cost are the most cautiously worded and are violated with least regret. It is deeply understood by all parties to the decision that the final system performance and production and operating costs corresponding to a given development effort are initially uncertain.

In the case of TH, two or three persons from Systems Engineering prepared the first prospectus (in 1952), based on preliminary studies performed by personnel of Development. The prospectus estimated future demand for long-haul service and the operating savings which could be expected from TH, using existing TD-2 routes, as compared with building new TD-2 routes. After the prospectus appeared, the management of the Laboratories, A. T. and T., and Western Electric authorized initial development at a low level of intensity for two years (an upper limit on the technical man-years to be used was, in effect, imposed). In 1954 a second prospectus appeared. It made much more specific predictions, in the light of the work performed (in the Development Department) in the intervening years, about the final system and the development effort required. The development schedule described above was included. The same authorities who had approved the 1952 commitment now authorized completion of the TH development; they considered it sufficiently likely that the objectives described in the new prospectus could be closely approached for the predicted development time and cost. Some deviation from the latter, i.e., from the approved annual manpower targets (increasing over the project's remaining years), would be acceptable.

It is largely within the Development Department of the Laboratories that TH was developed and it is the organization of the task within that Department that we shall examine.

ORGANIZATION OF TH WITHIN THE DEVELOPMENT DEPARTMENT

Two broad classes of engineers were engaged in developing TH—the planners of the system and the developers of its components.[29] A TH System Analysis Group composed of planners was created in 1952, at the origin of the system, and maintained throughout its development. Its early function was to generate major system characteristics and rough block diagrams (showing the parts of the system and what

[29] Some individuals, of course, belonged to both classes.

each "does" to the signal transmitted, as well as broad specifications for major components). Its continuing task was to modify all of these and make them more detailed, as new knowledge appeared. The size of the group stayed close to five persons from 1954 on.

In contrast with the systems analysis group, the identity of some of the component groups shifts and fades through the years. Personnel switch back and forth between related components and some component groups appear to merge completely. This reflects not only the arbitrariness of any division of the system into components, but also a conscious policy, to be detailed below, of assigning broad component goals and encouraging the freest communication (and, to some extent, the making of agreements) between related groups.

The systems analysis group's role was not that of central decision making authority, issuing instructions to the component groups. Formal authority rested with what we may call an executive group of two or three individuals—the project engineer, the head of the section (Transmissions Systems) of the Development Department in which the bulk of TH effort took place, and (though he seldom exercised authority) the head of Development or his deputy.

The Organizational Ideal for TH

An ideal pattern, at which the formally designated leaders of TH seemed consciously to have aimed, was roughly as follows.

The systems analysis group formulates alternative major system characteristics consistent with the objectives[30] (which were formally issued by the Systems Engineering Department after preliminary consultation with the future developers of the system). It deduces from these a system plan, i.e., block diagrams with tentative requirements for the system's major components, consistent with one or more of the alternative sets of system characteristics and reasonable in the light of the information then available about the difficulty of attaining given requirements. The executive group approves these requirements as trial goals that are good "guesses" at the final ones, and tentatively assigns personnel to the component groups. The component groups start working toward the tentative requirements.

As soon as a component group is able to make a more confident estimate of the effort needed to meet the requirements it so informs

---

[30] The objectives themselves may later be changed, in accordance with the "trade-off" possibilities mentioned earlier; in the case of TH, as we have seen, this did not happen to a significant extent.

the executive group. It is, moreover, not only permitted but actively encouraged to tell the executive group as soon as it has evidence that a minor modification of its requirements (or a joint modification of its requirements and those of a related component group) would significantly ease its task (or the joint task of the two groups). This information from the component groups forms the basis for a series of "parliamentary" conferences, presided over by the executive group, with members of the component groups and the systems analysis group as participants. The conferences achieve a consensus as to the requirements for which modification should be attempted, as to a new tentative allocation of manpower[31] among groups and over time, and as to a tentative time schedule for completion of successive stages in each group's task.

The systems analysis group then works out the proposed modification of the system plan; the modification may call for replacing some of the system characteristics of the first plan with previously generated alternatives. Accompanying the modification, there is a greater detailing of major component requirements and the introduction of minor requirements. Both may be further modified later on, requiring, in turn, a further modification of the system plan and perhaps a further reallocation of manpower and a revision of schedules. The further changes are again settled in parliamentary conferences.

At all stages the executive group is easily accessible to the component groups. In the traditional informality of the Development Department (housed in a single building), conversations (face-to-face or by telephone) are generally as easy to arrange between members of different groups as between members of the same group. The members of the executive group, moreover, keep very well informed about the activities of the component and systems analysis groups, becoming, on occasion, part of certain of these groups working directly with them, for example, in compiling the evidence in favor of modifying their requirements. The executives might better be thought of, in fact, as central storers of information than as makers of decisions. Their knowledge of the status of all parts of the system is essential to decisions about changes in requirements, manpower allocations, and schedules, but the decisions are collectively made by the members of the parliamentary conferences (though formally

[31] That is, an allocation of the annual total manpower availabilities (increasing over the life of the project) approved by the laboratory management. These availabilities are "targets," which may later be revised if the system's progress should be slower or faster than anticipated.

issued, in memoranda or other documents, in the name of an executive).

Each component group is free to pursue its own ideas about the internal design of its component, exploring parallel approaches (or several approaches in sequence) if it wishes.

Finally, in the ideal organizational pattern, the relations between groups working on related components are very close. Each group can easily inform itself (and is kept informed through generally distributed memoranda) of the work of a related group; it does not need to proceed through the executive group in acquiring such information. Two related groups are encouraged to explore together designs for the two related components which would lessen their joint effort in meeting their (tentative) assigned goals, as well as to propose mutually compensating changes in these goals that would leave the system no worse off.

Among the better documented component developments in which the ideal organization pattern was closely approximated, several stand out. (1) Once the basic requirements for the common microwave generator—the frequencies it was to generate—were decided on, there remained a number of other requirements, which were tentatively chosen. The most troublesome one dealt with unwanted "tone products" (extraneous frequencies). A series of memos and minutes of conferences reveals the process of refining the requirement on tone products to obtain one that reasonable effort can achieve and the process of adjusting the system plan accordingly. (2) There is a similar process with respect to the more detailed requirements given the antenna design group. (3) There are memoranda from the executive group to the test equipment group documenting the ordering of test equipment and containing sentences such as this: "Any of these requirements that appear unduly difficult should be brought to our attention for possible modification." (4) The i-f amplifier group explored, as we saw, two major circuitry approaches. The idea for the first approach and the decision to drop it and pursue the second originated within the group.

There were, of course, continual minor exceptions to the ideal pattern—minor requirement modifications and minor reallocations of manpower, which appear in retrospect desirable, were thought of by component groups but never acted upon.

Functional Departments: the Major Exception to the "Ideal" Pattern

The major exceptions to the ideal pattern occurred with respect to some (but not all) of the functional departments (within the Development Department) that worked on TH. These are departments that perform specialized development tasks for all systems under development. The principal ones, in the case of TH, were the tube department, the magnetic devices department, the solid-state devices department (which developed the converter crystal), and the test-equipment department. During the TH development, these departments had to work on components for other systems than TH. The allocation of such a department's manpower to TH work, given the competing needs of other systems and the current total manpower targets for TH, was generally settled by negotiation between the head of the functional department and the TH executive group. Occasionally, one of the two or three executives of the Development Department was called upon to arbitrate. The solution sometimes involved assignment of TH personnel from outside the functional department to work with the functional department so that the total TH manpower target was not exceeded and the functional department was able to meet its competing needs.

Communication between the members of the functional departments working on TH and the groups working exclusively on TH, and vice versa, seems to have been, on significant occasions, more difficult than communication between the latter groups. This seems to have been because, in the first place, consultations on matters that held implications for the reallocation of manpower within the functional department often had to involve the head of the functional department—to whom its TH workers were responsible   and to be arranged through him. In the second place, a casual survey suggests that members of the functional department had their own internal loyalties and interests; they may sometimes have been motivated less by the specific desire to make TH work well than by the desire to perfect the devices which were their specialty independently of this particular using system. Communication by a functional department's TH workers of tentative notions for improving the component they were developing in the specific context of TH may have been less spontaneous and frequent than was true of the other TH groups.

Functional departments exist in a laboratory, however, because of the advantages they possess. There are distinct economies of scale in combining all development work on certain devices, versions of which are required again and again by many systems, into one development group. Moreover, it is an important Bell Laboratories policy to prepare for the systems of the future by developing and placing "on the shelf" laboratory models of components with new and interesting properties. This is a major responsibility of most of the functional departments. Whether these advantages outweigh the difficulties that some system projects experience in dealing with those departments is an important question, on which a single case study can shed no light.

In the history of TH there are several fairly well documented instances of major exceptions to the ideal organizational pattern resulting from a functional department's participation in the system project. The best documented instance centers around the magnetic focusing structure of the traveling-wave-tube amplifier. As we have seen, the task of developing an acceptable structure proved to be unexpectedly difficult. The problem had been entrusted to a functional department—a magnetic devices department which was simultaneously assisting other system projects. At the same time, developing the traveling-wave tube itself was primarily the responsibility of a group within another functional department—the tube development department. The magnet difficulties, when they arose, were partially attributed by the TH executives to insufficient allocation of manpower to magnetics and to poor coordination between the magnetics and tube groups (for example, the problem of physically mounting the magnetic structure on to the tube had been given insufficient attention, according to the TH executives). The TH executives were coming to feel that the magnetics work should be done not within a functional department but rather by a group set up to work exclusively on TH.

A series of conferences took place, attended by the TH executives, the heads of the two functional departments, and the principal developing engineers concerned. The outcome was as follows: magnetic structure work was to continue as a permanent functional responsibility and the TH project was to have its own temporary magnetics group (for which new manpower was authorized[32]), independent of the functional group. It was the TH magnetics group that

[32] The additional manpower would eventually show up as a small permissible increase in total target manpower unless compensated for by decreased use of manpower in other parts of the system.

developed the structure finally used in TH. The minutes of the final conference make the case for preserving the general functional responsibility thus:

> In considering the assignment of responsibility the following factors need to be weighed. The magnetic structure is an intricate and highly specialized kind of unit. It is an entity which has well defined natural boundaries. Design as well as exploratory work calls for highly specialized skills, which usually take a long time to develop, and also complicated and expensive testing gear. The same skills and equipment are probably needed to clear difficulties which might arise in production or in the field.
>
> Units of this kind will probably be required for projects which may be undertaken in a number of different locations in the Laboratories' organization and at different times. It is therefore desirable that the functional responsibility for these units reside in a single permanent organization. The alternative would be to set up essentially small magnetics groups and it is unlikely that these could retain a continuity of personnel or interest over an extended period of time.

The compromise reached in the case of TH, in other words, was not to be the general pattern for the future.

Some Difficulties Not Observed in the TH Project

Except for the difficulties associated with functional departments, the history of TH exhibits very few troubles which an organization patterned after a different ideal could have avoided. In particular, it fails to exhibit significantly the following troubles.

(1) Unnecessary effort, directed at (a) meeting requirements which are very difficult to fulfill and which could be modified to become easier without worsening the system, but are not; or (b) refinements of component design so as to exceed the requirements that suffice for satisfactory system performance[33]; or (c) unneeded parallel approaches to the component in question—approaches which do not serve to hedge against uncertainty since there exists a straightforward

---

[33] That is, refinements that either (1) permit attainment of system performance magnitudes superior to those chosen as system objectives but only at an effort which would not be considered worth making if the option arose as a conscious choice facing those responsible for the system's development; or (2) do not improve the performance magnitudes beyond those chosen as system objectives.

predictable approach to designing the component so as to meet requirements.

(2) What appears ex post as a more or less chaotic scheduling of tasks—some tasks being finished long before the information they provide is needed, while the start of others has to await the completion of still other tasks that could have been started earlier.

(3) The performance of component work that turns out to be useless because the component in question poorly "matches" related components.

These troubles have been observed in other system development projects.[34] While they require much further study it is fairly clear that their organizational pattern is different from the ideal pattern the TH project attempted to approximate. In important cases the pattern is something like the following. A system is planned at an early stage in considerable detail by a central authority. The authority schedules individual tasks and assigns them, together with an initial manpower allocation, to groups who, from lack of instructions to do so or because communication with the central authority is difficult, rarely question their assignments or suggest modifications. This leads to the difficulties described under 1.

Moreover, the original detailed plan and schedule rest on predictions about the outcome of each group's effort. These predictions often turn out to be wrong, but the enforced insularity of each group makes it hard for the central authority to "catch" a bad prediction as to the difficulty of reaching an original goal until the group has expended considerable effort toward it. The group may have guessed at the magnitude of the predictive error some time earlier but does not bother the central authority until the situation is serious. At that point it may be possible to salvage the original system plan and schedule by a massive injection of manpower into the group in question, or it may be better to relax the goal of the group in question and make compensating adjustments in the rest of the system plan. In either case there is an additional cost or delay not expected when the original plan and schedule were approved, and the troubles 2 and 3 appear in the project's history.

Thus a project organization in which a central authority makes all the system decisions and parcels out tasks to groups who try to perform them in comparative isolation seems to make the project more susceptible than does the organizational pattern approximated by

[34] Notably certain military ones with which the writer has acquaintance.

TH to the major difficulties observers have noted in system projects—overstaffing (unnecessary effort), and gambles which expensively fail (heavy commitments to system plans and schedules based on unreliable initial knowledge).[35]

A project so organized might perhaps have advantages over one like TH in the luckiest possible case. If all predictions turned out exactly right, and a highly detailed plan and schedule had been based on them, then each group's initially assigned task would be precisely fulfilled. There would be no need for any communications apparatus to link the groups with the central authority, and no need for a systems analysis group to stand by, ready to work out modifications of the plan if they become necessary. But such lucky cases are rare indeed.

Conclusion

The essential features of the general strategy of development portrayed in the history may be briefly sketched as follows. The laboratory management decides on a ranking over the space of system performance magnitudes and system production and operating costs. It may be a very coarse ranking: there may be indifference within very large regions of the space. Corresponding to each region, nevertheless, is a maximum development effort (defined by a time path of expenditure, or perhaps a number of indifferent time paths), which the management is willing to expend in order to reach the region. There are generally several regions for which there is a relatively high confidence of attainment for not more (but not much less) than the associated maximum admissible effort. One of these regions is initially chosen as goal.

Within the chosen region, an initial set of performance magnitudes is then chosen as system objectives. The number of ways of attaining them may be enormous and only a few can be explored. First are considered several "families" of ways, each family defined by a

---

[35] A further phenomenon that some have observed in certain system projects is the growth of project staffs, from project to project within a laboratory, in accordance with some sort of Parkinson's Law, each increment in staff depending as much on previous size of staff as on the minimum effort actually required to complete the new project. If the type of project organization just described leads to the difficulties 1 to 3, the project planners may decide that the only way to avoid these difficulties in the future is to be more liberal with manpower. This tends, however, to make the difficulties described under 1 more likely, since more manpower is now available for "unnecessary effort." Thus growth according to the Law may begin.

set of system characteristics. Bit by bit, each family considered is narrowed, as the alternative component specifications consistent with each family are explored and knowledge of their difficulty is gained (using parallel design approaches to them where there is much uncertainty). Gradually a choice of family and of one way (one set of component specifications) within that family is made.

Until the final choice is made, flexibility is maintained. Commitments of personnel to specific tasks are made only for small periods, and it continues to be generally easy to drop one family or one way and to shift effort to exploring another more intensively. (Commitments are kept particularly small while awaiting sharp jumps in knowledge, such as completion of "breadboard" models may provide.) An exception are system-critical component specifications, which are "frozen" somewhat before the complete system is specified (before the final way is chosen), but only after a careful balancing of the risks and the gains. In the background remains, until the final choice, the possibility of changing the system objectives or even the region of indifference aimed for. When the system is finally specified, a schedule for the remaining development tasks is drawn up (to choose a good one, for a complex system, may be quite difficult).

A strategy of this sort—pursued against a background of continually accumulating experimental data and components, placed "on the shelf" for future systems—is necessary, we conjecture, if a given stream of expenditures on system development is to yield a stream of "successful" systems. A successful system project is one in which there are no major revisions at great cost—of which it cannot be said that much less effort would have been needed to attain the performance realized if only certain commitments had awaited knowledge gained later in the system's development. An alternative strategy— early and massive commitment to one set of objectives and component specifications and one system schedule—will yield significantly more unsuccessful projects for the same expenditure stream.[36]

These opposing strategies could be pursued, in principle, by a single man working on a project all his own. When other persons are

[36] One recent study concerns a planning tool to be used when this alternative strategy is followed. Development of a very complex system is considered as the completion of a huge array of highly specified tasks; the tool permits their efficient scheduling. Nowhere is the possibility considered that some of these tasks may turn out to be the "wrong" ones. See D. G. Malcolm, J. H. Rosebloom, C. E. Clark, and W. Fazar, "Application of a Technique for R and D Project Evaluation," *Journal of the Operations Research Society of America*, September-October, 1959.

brought in, a choice of organizational pattern must be made. W further conjecture that the "ideal" organizational pattern describe above needs to be approximated in carrying out the first strateg described if a stream of successful projects is to be attained, wher the term unsuccessful is now enlarged to include specifically th difficulties (1) to (3) described above.

With this pair of informal conjectures, the experience of the TF project seems at least consistent.

The Link Between Science and Invention: The Case of the Transistor

RICHARD R. NELSON

THE RAND CORPORATION

Introduction

PURPOSE AND FORM OF THE PRESENT STUDY

THIS paper is a case study of basic research in industry. It focuses on the factors affecting the allocation of research resources in a science oriented industrial research laboratory.[1]

In the summer of 1948 the Bell Telephone Laboratories announced the invention of the point contact transistor—a small, efficient amplifying device. In 1951 the Laboratories announced the invention of the junction transistor, a device in most ways superior to the point contact transistor. In 1952 a Nobel prize was awarded to three of the principal participants in the research which led to these inventions.

The transistor was the result of the research of a group of extremely able scientists working close to the frontiers of scientific knowledge in one of the world's largest industrial research laboratories. As such, the invention of the transistor is a model of what many writers believe to be the coming norm. In another paper I have argued that the large industrial laboratory has by no means usurped the field of invention— the private inventor still is playing a very important role—and that many important inventions still are being made quite independently of closely preceding scientific advances.[2] But the role of the industrial laboratory is important and growing and it is likely that, particularly in the large laboratories, a growing share of inventive activity will be motivated by recent advances in fundamental science.

The inventive activity studied in this paper—the type which has led to such technical advances, in addition to the transistor, as nylon,

---

[1] This paper is one part of a continuing RAND-sponsored study of industrial research and development. The material in this paper was obtained from several published studies of the transistor and of the Bell Telephone Laboratories, from written laboratory records, from letters, and from a number of discussions with Bell Laboratories' scientists and administrators, to whom the author is deeply indebted. However, the views and opinions presented in this paper do not necessarily reflect the views of any Bell scientist, much less the consensus at Bell.

[2] R. R. Nelson, "The Economics of Invention: A Survey of the Literature," *Journal of Business*, April 1959.

dacron, hybrid corn, radar, and the new molecular electronics—
is not generally an activity motivated by, and directed toward, the
objective of a closely defined marketable product.[3] The research
scientists involved may have an idea of the practical fruits to which
their work may lead. But the research projects undertaken are far
less closely focused on a single objective than were, say, the projects
which led to the automatic cotton picker, the jet engine, and Koda-
chrome, where the scientists and technologists were aiming at one
particular target.[4]

While economic analysis of the demand for a new product and cost
of development and production seems to go a long way toward explaining the direction of inventive activity when that activity is aimed
at specific new products,[5] much less is known about the factors stimulating inventive activity of the sort which led to nylon and the transistor. While perceived demand certainly plays an important role,
advances in the state of scientific knowledge also seem to be extremely
important. But what are the mechanisms by which changing scientific
knowledge stimulates changes in inventive activity? It is hoped that
this paper will shed a little more light on the subject.

Little use of formal theory will be made in this paper because of the
constraint of space and because the formal theory itself is in a most
unsatisfactory state. It is hoped that at some later date this study,
and a number of complementary ones, can be recast within a framework of decision and organization theory. However, whatever specific
form the theoretical framework may subsequently take, it is reasonably clear now that certain variables will play a major role, and these
are the variables this study will stress.[6]

Decision theory examines problems relating to how a choice among
alternatives should be made. When there is uncertainty, decision
theory examines such questions as how much information should be
acquired before a final decision is made, and how alternatives should
be screened and narrowed down. The answers to the questions posed
by decision theory depend on such variables as the following: the
nature of the payoff function; the extent to which the best decision

---

[3] For very short histories of several of these inventions see J. Jewkes, D. Sawers, and
R. Stillerman, *The Sources of Invention*, London, Macmillan, 1958.

[4] *Ibid.*

[5] See Nelson, *op. cit.*

[6] The approach will be the schizophrenic one usual in economics. On the one hand the
analysis will be normative. The interest will be on how people should make decisions. On
the other hand the analysis will be predictive, under the assumption that most people
making the relevant decisions are quite rational.

differs depending on variables outside the decision maker's control or outside his knowledge, or both; the means and costs of reducing relevant uncertainties, i.e., the ability to learn; and the extent to which the decision maker can keep his set of alternatives open (not commit himself) until he receives more information.[7]

Organization theory examines problems relating to the interactions among a group of individuals who make decisions relevant to a possible pay-off. All the factors important in decision theory must, of course, enter the analysis of organization theory, but the focus of organization theory is on such questions as, what information should be communicated to what people, and who should make what decisions on the basis of what criteria. The answers to the questions posed by organization theory depend on the extent to which individual actions are interdependent, the nature of relevant information and the character of those who acquire it, the difficulty of effectively communicating information and orders, and other variables.[8]

The elements of the theory mentioned above will be used only informally in this paper. But pretend for the moment that the theory is in very good shape. What would be the implications for the organization of this paper, or for a paper incorporating several case studies of industrial basic research? I think the theory would suggest that it would be useful to organize the paper in three parts. First would be the case study or studies. These studies would be reasonably straightforward histories but focusing on the variables that theoretically determine the way decisions should be made and effort should be organized. The purpose of the histories would be to determine the values, or frequency distribution of values, these variables take on in industrial basic research. Second, the values of the variables would be plugged into the theory and the correct decision and organization policies deduced. Third, an organization, or a number of organizations, with a reputation for effective research management would be studied to see to what extent their policies corresponded to those which the theory indicated were sound. This would provide a quite useful check on the theory.

[7] Decision theory presently seems to be going in many different directions. See, for example: *Decision Processes*, R. M. Thrall *et al*, editors, New York, Wiley, 1954; A. Wald, *Statistical Decision Functions*, New York, Wiley, 1950; H. A. Simon, "Theories of Decision-Making in Economics and Behavioral Science," *American Economic Review*, June 1959; R. D. Luce and H. Raiffa, *Games and Decisions*, New York, Wiley, 1957.

[8] See, for example: J. G. March and H. A. Simon, *Organizations*, New York, Wiley, 1958; and T. Marschak, "Elements for a Theory of Teams," *Management Science*, January 1955.

Since theory is presently in such an inadequate state, this paper cannot be organized quite as sketched above. In the next section a reasonably straightforward history of the research which led to the transistor will be presented. The history will stress the pay-offs which were expected, the uncertainties involved, how new information came to light, how this new information affected the direction of the project, and the interaction of the several people working on the project. In a subsequent section a study of the organization and decision policies of the Bell Telephone Laboratories will be presented. There will be no formal theoretical section. However, the transistor history will conclude with an attempt to generalize on the characteristics of the research involved, and the organization study will be prefaced with an attempt to assess what these characteristics imply with respect to the problems of research management.

THE BELL TELEPHONE LABORATORIES AND THE TRANSISTOR

Although it is hoped that the analysis presented here has some general applicability, the paper is principally a single case study—a study of the research that led to the invention of the transistor and of the organization responsible for that research—the Bell Telephone Laboratories.

Bell Laboratories are jointly owned by the American Telephone and Telegraph Company and Western Electric, A. T. and T.'s production subsidiary. The Laboratories employ about 11,000 people, of whom about one-third are professional scientists and engineers, about one-third are technical aides, and about one-third, clerical and supporting personnel. About 85 per cent of the laboratory professionals are engaged in the development of specific devices and systems for use in the telephone system, or by the military. About 15 per cent of the professional scientists and engineers, about 500 people, constitute the research staff under William O. Baker, Vice-President in charge of research. Baker reports directly to James B. Fisk, President of the Laboratories. A large percentage of Baker's budget supports scientific research which is not tied to any specific practical objective. It is on this kind of research that this paper is focused.

The transistor was invented in the course of a research program started in 1946 at the Bell Telephone Laboratories. The transistor has several advantages over the triode vacuum tube, Lee De Forest's invention of half a century ago; it is much smaller than the vacuum tube, it requires much less energy input to do a given job, and in many applications it is much more durable. On the negative side, the performance of the transistor is much more sensitive to varying temperature than is that of the vacuum tube; at present the transistor is not as capable as the vacuum tube at high frequencies and in handling high power, and thus far, problems of quality control have proven quite serious in transistor manufacture.

The transistor has had its most significant impact not as a component replacing vacuum tubes in established products, but as a component of products which were uneconomical before the development of the transistor. There has been an increase in the use of electronic packages where the transistor's strong points are important. Very compact computers are the most striking example. Without transistors, computers of a given capability would have to be much larger both because vacuum tubes are larger than equivalent transistors and because cooling requirements are much greater for vacuum tubes. Almost all of our new airborne navigation, bombing, and fire control systems, for example, are transistorized. So are all of our satellite computers. And without transistors our large computers, which are playing an increasingly important role in science, engineering, and management, undoubtedly would be much more expensive—probably so much so that many of their present uses would not be economically sound.

Thus the transistor has stimulated growth, including the invention and innovation on a considerable scale of products which can profitably use transistors as components. The transistor has also stimulated research and development aimed at reducing the size of complementary electronic circuit elements. Much of the work in printed circuitry, for example, certainly fits this picture. Further, as we shall see, the research which led to the transistor also produced a number of other new and improved semiconductor devices. Thus, if it be argued that one of the indexes of the importance of an invention is the amount of inventive activity it stimulates, then, by this criterion, the transistor is a major invention indeed.

But while the transistor is playing an extremely important role in our more complex electronic equipment and in equipment where size is important, like hearing aids and portable radios, it has not superseded the vacuum tube in all uses. Dollar sales of vacuum tubes are still roughly double dollar sales of transistors. Given existing costs, vacuum tubes are now more economical in the bulk of those jobs in which size and efficiency are not particularly important. And since the birth of the transistor there have been substantial improvements in vacuum tubes, many of these improvements certainly stimulated by the competition of the transistor. Almost no invention eliminates all of its competition overnight, and the transistor is no exception. But there is reason to believe that the transistor may be one of the most important inventions of the twentieth century.

The History of the Transistor

HISTORY OF SEMICONDUCTOR RESEARCH BEFORE THE PROJECT AT BELL LABORATORIES

The transistor is a semiconductor device. The research at Bell which resulted in the invention took off from a base of knowledge about semiconductors built by several generations of scientists. Karl Popper has described the state of scientific knowledge at any time as the deposit of observations and conceptual schemes which have stood the test of time and which still are proving useful in explaining and predicting.[9] The current state of knowledge is the result of an evolutionary process operating on ideas. Therefore, in order to understand the post-World War II research at Bell, it is important to sketch the history of prior semiconductor research.[10]

The element germanium is a semiconductor. So are several other elements, including silicon, and a number of compounds, such as copper oxide and zinc oxide. By 1900 many scientists and experimenters with electricity knew that these metals had quite unusual properties. In particular, it was known that these materials conducted electricity although, as the name implies, not as well as conductors like metal. It also was known that the electrical resistance of these materials decreased with temperature. That is, when these materials were warm they conducted current more easily than when they were cold. This puzzling property set semiconductors apart from other conductors, like metals, which conducted more easily when cool than when warm. Also, it was known that these materials sometimes passed current more easily in one direction than in another. In other words, they rectified current.

In this section we shall see how these phenomena, and others, gradually came to be understood. We shall see how research led to a

[9] Karl R. Popper, *The Logic of Scientific Discovery*, Basic Books, 1959.
[10] The history that follows is primarily taken from G. L. Pierson and W. H. Brattain, "History of Semiconductor Research," *Proceedings of the Institute of Radio Engineers*, December 1955.

distinction between *n* type and *p* type semiconductors, and how it came to be realized that in a semiconductor there are both electrons and "holes." We shall see how, by the start of World War II, researchers had come to an understanding of semiconductors that was satisfactory in many respects. We shall also see that one important concept, that of "minority" carriers, was being neglected. This will set the stage for analysis of the research at Bell which led to the transistor.

Necessary Terms and Concepts

In order to understand the history of semiconductor research it is necessary to be familiar with a few terms and concepts, so before proceeding with the history let us leap ahead and consider a few aspects of modern-day theory.

Modern theory views a semiconductor as a crystal containing two different types of current carriers—electrons and holes. The electrons are negatively charged and the holes may be considered as positively charged. The number of holes and electrons which are free to carry current is an increasing function of the temperature of the crystal, which explains the negative coefficient of resistivity which had puzzled researchers around the turn of the century.

The proportion of holes and electrons in a semiconductor is a very sensitive function of its purity. By doping a germanium crystal with other elements a very great variation in the hole-electron ratio can be achieved. In some semiconductors there are many more electrons (negative charge carriers) than holes (positive charge carriers). Thus electrons are the "majority" carriers and holes are the "minority" carriers, and this type of crystal is called, conveniently enough, an *n* (for negative) semiconductor. In other crystals, holes are the majority carriers and this sort of semiconductor is called a *p* (for positive) type.

If a *p* and an *n* type crystal are placed end to end they form a "*p-n* junction." Such a *p-n* junction will conduct current much more easily in one direction than in the other, in other words, it is a rectifier. The theoretical explanation of rectification in *p-n* junctions rests on the fact that on one side of the junction (the *n* side) most of the charge carriers are negative, while on the other side of the junction (the *p* side) most of the charge carriers are positive. The explanation makes no use of the concept of minority carriers. However, as we shall see later, in the working of the transistor minority carriers play a key role. Without an understanding of the fact that there are minority carriers as well as majority carriers, the operation of the transistor cannot be comprehended.

Research Before World War II

Returning to our story, though by 1900 many scientists knew that the materials we now call semiconductors had interesting properties, they knew little about why. The birth of the radio industry created a practical demand for good rectifiers and quite early in the game "cat's whisker" rectifiers (semiconductors) became widely used. But, in large part because the vacuum tube rectifier was better understood and hence the direction of possible improvement more clearly indicated, the semiconductor rectifier declined in importance relative to the vacuum tube during the twenties and early thirties.

However, during this period research on semiconductors was far from stagnant. A number of experiments made it quite clear that in some semiconductors the charge carriers behaved as if they had a positive charge, and several scientists were coming to the belief that there were two quite different types of semiconductors.

During the thirties research workers in the field of radio waves and communications turned their interest to higher frequencies. The ordinary vacuum tube performed poorly at these higher frequencies, and attention returned to crystal detectors and hence to research on semiconductors. Improvements came rapidly. Techniques for producing very pure silicon were improved and metallurgists learned how to add very accurately measured quantities of impurities. At the Bell Laboratories it was learned that when silicon ingots were doped with certain elements (arsenic, phosphorous, antimony) the rectifying contact would conduct easily only when the crystal was negative relative to the metal, and that when silicon ingots were doped with certain other elements (aluminum, boron) the rectifying contact would conduct easily only when the crystal was positive relative to the metal. The first type of semiconductor came to be known as the *n* (for negative) type and the second as the *p* (for positive) type.[11]

Thus, before the war scientists at the Bell Telephone Laboratories

[11] The semiconductor types were named before theoretical understanding of the differences was achieved. Note that for the first type of semiconductor the rectifying contact conducts when the metal is positive relative to the crystal, so it could have been called *p* type, and similarly the second could have been called *n* type. Had they been, language use would have worked against the understanding of semiconductors. The situation would have been much like that in early 19th century electrical theory, where Franklin's convention of defining current flow direction as from plus to minus hindered understanding of electron flow.

and elsewhere were experimenting with *p* and *n* crystals and calling them that. Also before the war many scientists were thinking of making a semiconductor amplifier. The reasoning on the prospects for an amplifier was principally in terms of a simple analogy. Vacuum tubes rectified and, with the introduction of a grid, amplified. Semiconductors rectified. Therefore, somehow, they should be able to amplify. Indeed several workers suggested that a grid should be inserted into a semiconductor diode, but due to the extreme thinness of the rectifying area (rectification occurs in a region very close to the surface contact of cat's whisker rectifier, or at the *n-p* junction of a junction rectifier) this proved very difficult to do.

Meanwhile the conceptual scheme which we have described earlier and which would permit the workings of the semiconductor to be much better understood was gradually taking shape. Advances in quantum mechanics during the twenties set the stage for A. H. Wilson's quantum mechanical model of a solid semiconductor which was published in 1931. The Wilson model provided the basis for a theoretical explanation of the difference between *n* type and *p* type semiconductors, but, although the model was well known, few scientists saw this until after World War II. Indeed it seems that it was not until the postwar project at Bell Laboratories that the model was extended to apply to doped germanium and silicon. Further, and this is extremely important, though scientists in the field knew, or should have known from their feel for the above theory, that every semiconductor had both positive and negative charge carriers, their attention was focused almost exclusively on majority carriers. Thus *n* type germanium was pictured as having electrons carrying current, *p* type as having holes carrying current, and the minority carriers were ignored. The working of the transistor depends on minority carriers as well as majority carriers, and until both types were considered together understanding was sorely hindered.

To one who is not a physical scientist it is interesting that by the mid-1930's a well-known article, Wilson's, contained most of the essential ingredients for a rather complete understanding of semiconductors, but that almost all scientists missed some of the essential points. Similar instances in economic theory are legion. By the start of World War II, then, scientists understood quite well certain aspects of semiconductors, and were well on the road to understanding rectification. The essential theoretical foundations had been laid, but the phenomenon of minority carriers was being neglected. To many scientists doing research in the field the time seemed ripe for major breakthroughs.

The Start of the Project

In this section we shall follow the research work at the Bell Telephone Laboratories which led to the transistor. We shall see how difficulties with the first solid state amplifier design which interested Shockley led to a series of experiments which resulted, quite surprisingly, in the discovery of the transistor effect and the invention of the point contact transistor. We shall see how, in attempting to explain the transistor effect, the concept of minority carriers snapped into focus, and how this concept led to the invention of the junction transistor.[12]

The Bell Telephone Laboratories were deep in research in the field of semiconductors long before World War II. Bell's tradition in quantum mechanics was very strong. Several of the experiments which demonstrated the wave nature of electrons were conducted at the Laboratories during the thirties by Clinton J. Davisson; and Davisson and G. P. Thompson of England shared a Nobel prize for their efforts. William Shockley, Walter Brattain, Dean Wooldridge, and several other top-flight solid-state physicists were brought to the Bell Laboratories during the thirties. People in the Laboratories' metallurgy department were playing a major role in the advances then being made in producing pure crystals, and J. H. Scaff and others at Bell performed the experiment which led to the naming of *n* and *p* type crystals. Also, the pre-World War II work of the Laboratories in this area had led to the development of better crystal rectifiers, the thermistor—a circuit element whose resistance decreased with temperature—and other circuit elements.

During World War II research work in semiconductors continued at the Laboratories, but the war work was, of course, device oriented and several of the Bell scientists worked elsewhere. Semiconductor knowledge and technique played an extremely important role in the war-time work on radar. At Bell and at Purdue University research on germanium and silicon was pushed with the aim of developing better rectifiers, and important breakthroughs were made in techniques of

---

[12] The material in this section is taken from several sources, the most important of which are the Shockley and Bardeen Nobel Prize lectures.

producing very pure crystals and doping them to very close specifications.

During the summer of 1945, as it became evident that the war would soon be over, steps were taken to smooth the transition of the Laboratories to a peacetime basis. Shockley, who had been on leave from Bell during the war, believed strongly that the Laboratories should intensify its solid-state work, and in consultation with M. J. Kelly, then Director of Research, and others, was convincing enough so that it was agreed that it would be good research strategy to bring together in one department a number of people who had been working on solid-state physics, and perhaps to draw in some new talent. Within the solid-state research group, to be headed by Shockley and S. O. Morgan, a subgroup, including Shockley, was to work on semiconductors. It was felt that the greatly increased role of solid-state devices, particularly semiconductors, in communications technology warranted an increase in Bell's effort in this area. It was felt that advances in the understanding of semiconductors, including a better grasp of the meaning of the quantum mechanical model, had set the stage for major breakthroughs, and that the techniques of making crystals to close specifications promised materials which could be produced to fit the theoretical model. Improvements in rectifiers, and thermo- and photo-electric devices were judged a quite likely result of semiconductor research. Further, Shockley strongly believed that he could make a solid-state amplifier and his enthusiasm was contagious.

Shockley and Morgan were given hunting licenses and Brattain and Pearson were talked into joining the semiconductor research group. John Bardeen was hired from the outside. Later R. B. Gibney, a physical chemist, and H. R. Moore, a circuit expert, joined the group. The prime reason for establishing a special solid-state physics research group was the belief that the interaction of physicists, chemists, and metallurgists all interested in related problems would be instrumental in speeding the advance in understanding, and that the organization of a separate group would facilitate communication and mutual help. But it would be a mistake to believe that all the work on semiconductors going on at the Laboratories after 1946 was done by this subgroup. Throughout the period people in the metallurgy department were working on ways to make better crystals and rectifiers and there was considerable interplay between Shockley's group and the metallurgists. And scattered throughout the research divisions were people working in this area from time to time. All in all, the people playing a major role at one time or another in the work which led to the transistor discovery may have numbered about thirteen.

We have seen that the motives of the Bell Telephone Laboratories in establishing this new project were reasonably clear. Bell believed that major advances in scientific knowledge in this field were likely to be won and that advances in knowledge were likely to be fruitful in improving communications technology. One possible result was an amplifier. But improvements in rectifiers, thermistors, and other solid-state devices also were judged strong possibilities. It was the wide range of possible useful results which made the project attractive. The motives of the scientists on the project were, of course, much more complex. Several of the scientists involved were not much interested in or concerned with any practical applications their work might lead to. Their intellectual interests were focused almost exclusively on creating more knowledge about semiconductors. Others in the group were concerned with practical applications as well as with the underlying sciences. Shockley's interests were multiple. As a theorist he was fascinated by the prospect of developing a good theory of semiconductors. He also was fascinated with the prospects for a solid-state amplifier. Shockley's work was focused in a direction compatible with both these ends. That a good share of the work of the semiconductor research group was allocated so as to clear the way for an amplifier seems, in large part, to have been the result of Shockley's influence. But it is extremely difficult to say how much of this influence was "authority" and how much was Shockley's ability to interest others in what interested him.

Research Leading to the Discovery of the Transistor Effect

Stated in broad terms, the general scientific aim of the semiconductor research program was to obtain as complete an understanding as possible of semiconductor phenomena, not in empirical terms, but on the basis of atomic theory. Wilson's work was an important start for, as we have seen, a sound theoretical foundation already was partially built although it had not been fully exploited in thinking about doped germanium and silicon. With the wisdom of hindsight we know that one important roadblock to understanding of doped crystals was failure to consider minority carriers, the flow of electrons in p type germanium and holes in n type germanium. Also (though not to be discussed in this paper), the workers in the field were not adequately treating surface states, i.e., the fact that the properties of a solid at the surface can be (and usually are) quite different from the properties in the interior.

During the first few years of the solid-state physics project (the years we are considering here), the Shockley-Morgan group operated on a budget of roughly half a million dollars a year, about enough to support twenty to thirty scientists. Probably less than half of the group worked with Shockley on semiconductors. Both because the developing theory was simpler and better understood for simple crystals, and because the metallurgists at Bell had developed ways to produce very pure germanium crystals and to introduce impurities to close specifications, the work of the semiconductor research group focused on germanium at the start and later broadened to include silicon. During 1945 and 1946 much additional experience was gained in growing crystals, quite a bit was learned about semiconductor impurities, and rectification was studied. During the early years of the project research interest was quite diffuse. Considerable work, however, was focused on a solid-state amplifier.

At the early stages of the effort at Bell, Shockley's ideas on possible ways to make amplifiers shifted from placing a grid in the area of rectification (the strict analog of the vacuum triode) to influencing the number of movable electrons in a semiconductor (and hence the current flow) with an electric field imposed from the outside without actually touching the material. Shockley's calculations, based in large part on his developing extension of the Wilson model, indicated that a device based on the latter idea would amplify. Experiments were devised (in 1946 and 1947) to see if the gadget worked as theory indicated it should. It did not. Sometimes even the sign of the effect was off. When the sign was right the magnitude of the effect was roughly a thousandth of the theoretical effect.

To explain the negative result Bardeen proposed that the electrons affected by the field were not free inside the silicon, but were trapped at the surface in what he called surface states. Thus the application of an electric field would not significantly affect the number of free charge carriers in the semiconductor. Other scientists, including Shockley himself, had previously suggested the possibility of surface states at the free surface of a solid, but no one had realized the importance of this phenomenon to the properties of semiconductors. Bardeen's theory very effectively explained failure of amplification in the field effect experiments and also significantly increased understanding of rectification at the junction of a semiconductor and a metal (cat's whiskers), but for our purposes it is not necessary to describe the theory.

What is important for our purposes is that, to test the Bardeen theory and to attempt to find a way to neutralize the surface states so that a useful field effect amplifier could be built, Shockley, Bardeen, and Brattain, often with the collaboration of others in the group performed a number of experiments. The physical phenomena involved seem to have drawn a great deal of interest.

A set of experiments by Bardeen and Brattain play the key role in our story. These experiments did yield observed amplification from a field effect. But more important, in one of the experiments two contacts were placed quite close together on a germanium crystal. (Figure 1). It does not matter here just why this particular experiment

FIGURE 1

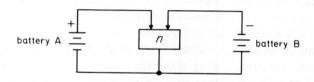

was performed. What is significant is that it was not performed with the hope of observing the most important result it yielded. For in the course of the experiment it was observed that connecting up the A battery increased the current flow in the B battery circuit. The device amplified. This was the first indication of the transistor effect.

The research workers were very well aware of the importance of their discovery. Experiments motivated, in part at least, by a desire to make a field effect amplifier work had resulted in the discovery of an amplifier working on quite different principles, an amplifier which, as it was developed and perfected in subsequent work, came to be called a "point contact" transistor.

The most obvious explanation for the current flow increase in the B circuit induced by connecting the A circuit was hole flow from the left top contact to the right top contact. The key concept in the modern explanation is the flow of minority carriers in a crystal, holes in n type germanium. Although the latter was not seen immediately, gradually it came to be accepted.

This description of the discovery of the point contact transistor in late 1947 and very early 1948 is too neat and simple, and the outline of the development of the ideas which explained it is much too orderly to be accurate. Indeed, there still is no really adequate quantitative theory explaining the working of the point contact transistor. But what is important for us is that the experiments were conducted by men who had amplification as their goal, who observed something that they were not looking for or expecting which indicated the possibility of building an amplifier of a design very different from the one they had in mind, and who explained the working of this new amplifier in terms of injected minority carriers.

For the observation that minority carriers are important in semi-conductor current flow provided the key which enabled Shockley to propose still another design for an amplifier, a junction transistor. Thus the field effect experiments led to two amplifier designs. They led directly to the point contact transistor and, through theory, to the junction transistor.

The Junction Transistor

Shockley spent most of 1949 writing his *Electrons and Holes in Semiconductors*. Much of the book is a contribution to theoretical physics, but in it he describes the principles of the junction transistor. Unlike the point contact transistor which, as we have seen, was invented partially by accident, the junction transistor was predicted theoretically and then built. Essentially the theory was the invention.

An *n-p-n* junction transistor consists of a germanium or silicon crystal with two *n* regions separated by a thin *p* region (Figure 2).

FIGURE 2

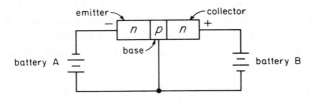

The contacts to the *n*, *p*, and *n* layers are referred to as the emitter terminal, the base terminal, and the collector terminal. Shockley showed that an increase in the voltage across the A circuit would lead to an increase in the flow of electrons between the emitter and the collector, the electrons flowing right through the central *p* region. And he showed that, for appropriate battery biases, the resulting change in voltage across the B circuit would exceed the inducing change across the A circuit. Or, the transistor would amplify.

Notice that minority carriers, electrons flowing through the *p* type base region (injected from the *n* type emitter region), are of crucial importance to the working of the junction transistor. If only holes could conduct in *p* type germanium then the transistor would not work. As we have seen, it took the semiaccidental discovery of the point contact transistor to focus attention on minority carriers. Until the experiments which resulted in the point contact transistor, Shockley did not see clearly that they were important. But once he did, he soon could see that an *n-p-n* junction connected as in Figure 2 would amplify.

Research After the Discovery of the Transistor Effect

The discovery of the transistor effect and the consequent invention of the point contact and junction transistors acted to focus much more closely the interests of the semiconductor research group. Funds for this group came from the broader solid-state research group budget, and although the budget of the solid-state group was not dramatically increased for a year or so, it appears that the proportion of the research effort of the Shockley-Morgan group which was directed to semiconductor research definitely increased. Further, a special semiconductor development group under J. A. Morton was organized shortly after the birth of the point contact transistor. And the allocation of research in metallurgy definitely was affected.

Within the semiconductor research group Shockley, as we have seen, directed his attention to working out the theory of holes and electrons in semiconductors. Others directed their experimental and theoretical work to minority carriers. Since an effective amplifier of the junction design requires very pure and orderly crystals, people in Shockley's group, as well as in Morton's group and in metallurgy, intensified their research on this problem. Methods for pulling single crystals from a melt of germanium were developed by G. K. Teal and J. B. Little, and a method known as zone refining was invented by W. G. Pfann. During 1949 and 1950 better and better junction transistors were made and the construction of a reliable junction transistor is conventionally dated 1951.

It should be stressed here that the breakthrough in knowledge about semiconductors led to research and development of several other devices in addition to the transistor. The theory led directly to the development of better rectifiers and thermo-electric devices. Parametric amplifiers, amplifiers quite different from the transistors, rest on the principles treated by Shockley's theory. The Bell solar battery, developed a bit later, also rests on the theory. Although many of the new semiconductor devices were invented in laboratories other than Bell, Bell Laboratories has continued to be in the forefront of semiconductor developments. Thus, though the transistor breakthrough tended for a while to draw together the interests of the semiconductor research group, the new theory carried within itself the seeds of subsequent research diversification. For the application and value of the theory and the new light it shed on semiconductors far exceeded its specific application to junction transistors.

1948 and 1951 are given as the standard dates when handbuilt point contact and junction transistors were first publicly demonstrated. But generally—and the transistor is no exception—the road is long and difficult between the first demonstrator model of a new invention, and a reliable, producible, economic product. In the early days of the transistor, its performance was likely to change if someone slammed a door. All transistors used were laboriously constructed by hand. No one quite knew in what uses the transistor would prove economic.

Much money and talent were spent in improving the operating characteristics of transistors and making them more predictable and reliable, in developing new circuits and designs to take advantage of the transistor's strong points, and in developing an economic production technology. More money has been spent at the Bell Telephone Laboratories on these problems than was spent on the project which was described in the preceding section, but this is beyond our story.

NATURE OF THE RESEARCH ACTIVITY

Although one case study is insufficient support for confident generalization, in this section I will attempt to sketch certain characteristics of the transistor research history which seem to have relevance to the policy decisions of an organization undertaking basic research.[13]

[13] Several other studies of basic research show much the same pattern as the transistor history. See, for example, "Nylon," *Fortune*, July 1940; I. B. Cohen, *Science, Servant of Man*, Boston, Little Brown, 1948; James B. Conant, *Science and Common Sense*, Yale

Some implications of these characteristics will be very briefly examined in the introduction to the section treating the actual research policies of the Bell Telephone Laboratories.

Uncertainty and Learning

At the start of the semiconductor research project there was considerable uncertainty whether an amplifier could be achieved at all, and if so, what was the best way of achieving it. Shockley believed he could make a solid-state amplifier but was not quite sure how, and several other people were not so optimistic. Because of the great uncertainties involved, much of the research effort was directed toward learning rather than toward the achievement of a specific and well-defined result. Shockley and others, however, certainly hoped to achieve an amplifier and allocated much of their research time accordingly. And the direction of research changed dramatically in response to what was learned.

To illustrate these points, recall the chronology of the research. At the start of the project much of the semiconductor research was quite generally oriented; only as knowledge accumulated did the amplifier interest tend to predominate. And in the course of the project, three different amplifier designs were considered. In the early stages, almost all amplifier oriented research was concerned with the field effect amplifier, but this design did not work as hoped and expected. Indeed, the results of the critical experiments in this area were sufficiently unexpected that a new theory had to be formulated to explain them—Bardeen's theory of surface states. The allocation of experimental effort was shifted to check the theory. The second amplifier design, the point contact, was discovered as a more or less surprising result of the surface-state experiments. Further, in order to explain the results of the experiments, attention turned to minority carriers, and once the importance of minority carriers was clearly realized, Shockley was able to design a junction amplifier. Thus, only toward the end of the project was the design which has proved most successful clearly perceived.

This last point needs to be stressed. There never seems to have been an attempt to list all research alternatives and to pick the best on

---

University Press, 1951; H. D. Smyth, *Atomic Energy for Military Purposes*, Princeton, 1946. Many other references could be cited, though few deal in any detail with specific research projects.

the basis of some formal calculation. Rather, the *discovery* of new ideas and alternatives occurred often in the program. It does not seem an adequate representation to say that what was learned from the surface-state experiments made the junction transistor a more promising alternative. Before the experiments, the path to an amplifier by way of junctions and minority carriers just was not clearly perceived.

Interaction

A number of different people with different skills contributed to the research, but the exact nature of the interaction could not have been predicted and planned for in advance. Bardeen's analysis of surface states and Brattain's experimental skill were key factors, but no one at the start of the program could have predicted that these particular experiments would be performed, much less the importance of the results. Throughout the course of the program there seems to have been a great deal of informal exchange of ideas, and quite a bit of cooperation on experimental work.

The major requirements for effective interaction seem to have been easy communication and the ability of individuals to drop what they were doing to help with problems their colleagues brought up, if these problems seemed interesting and important. There is little evidence of closely programmed and directed team work, or of any requirement for it. Unfortunately, I have not been able to uncover much in the way of specific examples to illustrate these points.

Goals

As we have seen the research program was not justified in its early stages by prospects for the invention of a specific device. Indeed, the early project reports do not even mention amplifiers. Instead the purpose of the project is stated in the early reports as the advancement of knowledge about semiconductors. Of course, this does not mean that the research workers, themselves, had no ideas about possible specific practical results; they certainly did. An amplifier was one. Rectifiers and thermoelectric devices were others. But these devices were listed in the early project reports as "for instances" of the possible practical payoffs. And, as we have seen, the research did in fact lead to a number of technical advances in addition to the transistor.

Research Management at the Bell Telephone Laboratories

THE PROBLEMS OF RESEARCH MANAGEMENT

This section will examine the way that basic research decisions are made at the Bell Telephone Laboratories. But first it seems worthwhile to discuss very briefly a few of the implications, with respect to research policy, of the characteristics of basic research sketched in the preceding section.

Given the resources an industrial laboratory intends to allocate to basic research, there are a vast number of projects to which laboratory personnel can be allocated. Clearly somehow some of these projects must be selected and the number of persons working on them be decided. The nature of basic research imposes serious constraints on the policies the laboratory can pursue in making these decisions.

Criteria

In order that some projects be selected and others rejected, some criteria must be used. The choice of good criteria must rest on the realization that a successful basic research project promises major advances in scientific understanding and that major advances in scientific understanding are likely to stimulate a wide range of practical inventions, though just what these technical advances will be it is very difficult to specify in advance. A project which is likely to have payoffs in a wide range of applications should not be justified on the basis of any one in particular, especially if it is not at all clear that the specific objective selected will be achieved. Indeed, for many organizations it just does not make very good sense to sponsor basic research at all. The outcomes of most basic research efforts are too unpredictable for a firm with a small range of products and processes to have confidence that the results will be of use to it. But, if the range of products and technology is wide, the firm may have some confidence that the results will be of practical value.[14]

Perhaps it can be assumed, as a first approximation, that for a company with a wide technological base there is a high correlation between the value to the company of the technical advances generated by research and the scientific advances achieved by research. Certainly

[14] For an extension and elaboration of this line of argument, see R. R. Nelson, "The Simple Economics of Basic Scientific Research," *Journal of Political Economy*, June 1959.

there are major qualifications to this. Probably the criterion should be amended by the requirement that the area of research be one where applications to the technology of the company seem quite possible. But for a company with a wide enough technological base to support basic research at all, the criterion of "scientific promise" is probably better than one that stresses the value of specific predicted practical inventions.

The criterion "scientific promise," subjective though it may be, does seem operational. Recall that before the start of the transistor work a number of scientists agreed that the time was ripe for major advances in knowledge of semiconductors. And the restriction that the research be in fields where applications to company technology seem possible also is operational. Recall that scientists were able to list a number of applications which might result from a major break-through in knowledge of semiconductors, and many of their proph-ecies were fulfilled.

Authority

But who is to apply the criterion? Who is to decide which scientists will work on which projects? For reasons which will be discussed later, that criterion, if adopted, argues for a decentralized decision making structure. And the nature of the basic research activity, the changing knowledge which is the scientific goal of research, also argues against centralization. Further, the type of interaction we have noted in the transistor project requires that individuals be free to help each other as they see fit. If all allocation decisions were made by a centrally situated executive, the changing allocation of research effort called for as perceived alternatives and knowledge change would place an impossible information processing and decision making burden on top management. Clearly the research scientists must be given a great deal of freedom, and the type of decision which must be cleared through a central authority must be quite limited.

It is earnestly hoped that the preceding discussion, and the study of Bell Laboratories which follows, is more than a pious restatement of the old saws, "scientific knowledge in itself pays off" and "in research, freedom is good." It is true that I believe the theme generally is valid. However, I trust that this paper sheds a little more light on why it is valid, and what its limitations are. In particular, it is clear that a policy involving decentralized decision making (research freedom), and the acceptance of the criterion of scientific promise must somehow be complemented by policies designed to constrain research to those areas where application to the technology of the company seems promising.

Bell has developed policies which seem to cope with this problem adequately. There is evidence that several other companies noted for their success in basic research management have similar policies.

RESEARCH POLICY OF THE BELL TELEPHONE LABORATORIES

The research philosophy of the Bell Telephone Laboratories has been stated succinctly by James B. Fisk, president of the Laboratories. "Our fundamental belief is that there is no difference between good science and good science relevant to our business. Among a thousand scientific problems, a hundred or so will be interesting, but only one or two will be truly rewarding—both to the world of science and to us. What we try to provide is the atmosphere that will make selecting the one or two in a thousand a matter of individual responsibility and essentially automatic." There are two aspects then to Bell's policy toward research. First, scientific worth is assumed to be highly correlated with potential technical value. And second, the individual scientist is to be free to choose the projects he considers of greatest interest. In short, the management philosophy of Bell Laboratories corresponds to the one we have just stated. How does this policy work out in practice? How serious are the problems introduced by the possible divergence of individual scientific interests from the interests of Bell Laboratories? How does Bell cope with the problem? As we shall see, the policy is not quite as simple and clear-cut as it seems. The fact that Bell is in the communications business does play a very major role in determining the type of research that is undertaken.

Freedom of Research Choice

It is well to dwell a bit here on what is meant by freedom in research. Freedom clearly involves a range of alternatives among which choice can be made but, equally clearly, the range of alternatives in any real situation is constrained in many ways. The training of the research scientist, the equipment available to him, the state of knowledge in the field in which he is interested, all are constraints on his choice. The imagination of the research scientist, of his peers in the laboratory, and of research management also affect the range of his perceived alternatives.

If we use the expression "degree of research freedom" to mean the extent to which constraints are imposed upon the range of choice open to a research scientist as a matter of company policy, then from the point of view of the company it is rational to give the research scientist wide freedom of choice if it is believed that he will tend to do more valuable work, on the average, if he selects his projects as he sees fit than if some higher authority provides him with a much more constrained range of choice. In a way, the arguments for freedom of choice for the research scientist resemble and rest on the same assumptions as the arguments for a free enterprise economic system do.

Let us assume for the moment that institutional arrangements and the system of incentives are such that individual and group aims coincide. This is one of the prerequisites for research freedom, but it is not enough. In addition it must be assumed that the individual has more information about the choices open to him—their relative prospects and their costs—than a central authority has. Usually this assumption is violated in situations where there is strong interdependence among the actions of a large number of different individuals. Where there is such interdependence one person's decision should be made in the light of knowledge about what everyone else is doing. This is the kind of information that a central executive has, but that, if the number of people involved is large, the individual may not have. However, in basic research it seems that the number of persons among whom coordination is required is small at any one time, and the individual scientist is likely to know quite well what his colleagues are doing. In the transistor project this kind of knowledge was facilitated by the policy of bringing most of the scientists doing semiconductor research into one group. And as to the promise of his own line of research, the working scientist is likely to know much more than the laboratory management possibly can know.

Philosophers and Gestalt psychologists have argued convincingly that people do not observe the same things unless those things are in the same context, and at the frontiers of science what is missing is a clear context. A scientist working on a research project often has a "feel" for the promise of his work but is not capable of expressing his intuition, his embryonic theory, in language. Others working in the same area may have the same feel, but often not. Yet one of the marks of a good scientist is that his hunches prove right. The approaches he sees as promising but which he cannot in the beginning describe precisely blossom into useful hypotheses and conceptual schemes.

Often, after the fact, he can state clearly a plausible reason why he thought his work promising when he started it, and why he did things the way he did. But it is more than likely that, if you had queried him *ex ante*, he would not have given such a good set of reasons for why he was doing what he was doing and why he felt it important. If this point of view is accepted, a research director is likely to be a much poorer judge than the scientist working on a project is of the scientific promise of the project. The scientist has information that the research director cannot have, and much of the information is not in a solid enough form to permit easy communication.

Allocation of Resources

Given the nature of scientific research, and an organization where individual scientists have a wide degree of freedom, the allocation of the scientific staff among competing alternatives is likely to be accomplished by an evolutionary, or a natural selection process. We have argued that uncertainty and learning are key aspects of research. Consider a laboratory at a moment of time. Scientists are working on many research projects at many different stages. Some research work has been running for a long time and many of the original objectives have been achieved. Some research work started but a short time ago is looking quite unpromising already. But some research work which has just started is looking extremely promising and interesting, and some research work is producing new answers, new prospects, and new questions. An alert scientist working on a project which is looking increasingly unpromising or on a project which appears to be running into sharply diminishing returns has very strong incentives—his professional reputation, his scientific curiosity, and his future at the laboratories—to phase out his current work and phase in research in a more promising area—a new project or a going project which has exciting prospects.

The above description sounds very much like the economist's model of a changing economy. Some industries are dying and others are thriving. An astute entrepreneur spurred by a higher expected return will leave the dying industry and enter the thriving industry. And, as in the economist's picture of a changing economy, luck plays a great role. The structure of economic demand may change again, and the dull entrepreneur who sticks with the industry his more alert colleague thought declining will *ex post* have been shown to be the wiser. Meanwhile the alert entrepreneur may find that the skills he applied in the old industry are of little use in the new. And in the laboratory, as in the economy, there are transfer costs. The scientist who jumps from project to project, like the entrepreneur who jumps from industry to industry, may be not very wise.

However, the analogy is weak when incentives and signals are compared. In the economist's model of the market economy, perceived profit opportunities are viewed as the prime motive, and cost and demand are the factors determining profit. Cost and demand are assumed to be clearly signaled by the structure of prices. The incentives of the scientist are much more complex than the incentives of the entrepreneur of economic theory; though perhaps they are no more complex than the incentives of the entrepreneurs of real life. The furthering of a reputation as a scientist among scientists and the satisfaction of intellectual curiosity are certainly as important, perhaps more important, dimensions of the research worker's goals as are financial advance and status within an organization.

Other Advantages of Decentralization

In addition to allocating research scientists among alternative projects, the mechanism described above seems especially well suited for generating new ideas, projects, and alternatives. Even if the performance of the mechanism in allocating men among known alternatives was believed to be far from optimal, this latter attribute would be a strong argument for research freedom. It is quite likely that it is even more important to the success of a laboratory for it to generate good new ideas than it is for it to allocate very efficiently its resources among a given set of alternatives.

Decision making by evolution, in addition to providing greater flexibility and speed than would be possible under a more formal and centralized structure, has another extremely important advantage. The traditions of the scientific community are extremely strong where freedom to pursue research interests is concerned. To be told just what line of research to follow—to have it made clear that the goal of the research is company profit, not increased knowledge or benefit to mankind—to realize all too plainly that a few individual supervisors, not a wide jury of scientific peers, are to evaluate the work—strikes hard at the traditions of science. Since World War II there seems to have been a striking reduction in the intensity with which scientists cling to these traditions. But their force is still strong, and many of the most outstanding scientists feel that to engage in industrial research would prostitute their heritage.

The Bell Telephone Laboratories, perhaps more than any other industrial laboratory, has avoided establishing a decision and control system which would run against the traditions of the scientific community. For this reason the Laboratories have a great advantage, relative to similar institutions, in recruiting people. Many scientists who would work in no other industrial laboratory, will work at Bell. This fact explains the extremely high quality of the laboratory staff that Bell has managed to maintain. Bell salaries are not particularly high by industrial laboratory standards.

Because a scientist at the Laboratories is not forced to abandon the traditions of the scientific community, Bell scientists tend to maintain very strong links with the academic world. Many Bell scientists have taught at universities, and many Bell scientists are actively sought by university faculties. The quantity and quality of Bell's scientific publications is matched only by the best of universities.

In the work which led to the transistor, Shockley, Bardeen, and others were in close touch with members of the university community working in the field of solid-state physics. There were visits and many letters. Clearly, this close link with the main stream of the scientific community is of major importance to the Laboratories for the flow both of ideas and of men.

Management Controls: Environment and Employment

Although as a broad generalization it may be reasonable to argue that the scientific merit of a project is a good index of potential profit, clearly, from the point of view of the company, advances in some areas of science are likely to be much more profitable than advances in other areas of science. The argument that the results of research are uncertain does not imply that these areas cannot be specified. Thus from the point of view of Bell Laboratories, advances in knowledge of the magnetic properties of material are almost certain to prove more important than advances in botany, and probably more important than advances in organic chemistry. At the start of the semiconductor research project it was clear that if there were significant scientific breakthroughs, the payoffs for communications equipment would be great.

Further, though basic research projects should not be justified in terms of specific practical objectives, we have seen from the case of the transistor that it is sometimes possible to perceive certain practical advances which may result from research. And from the point of view of the company, these objectives should be given some weight in research project selection.

Clearly it is in the interests of the company to have procedures for guiding research so that the most promising areas of science are stressed, and so that practical objectives are not completely suppressed in the research project selection mechanism. The Bell Telephone Laboratories are in the communications industry, and the research work undertaken there reflects this fact, though the research scientists are subject to few, if any, more constraints than their university peers.

Areas of Research

There are no geneticists working at the Laboratories. There are few organic chemists. At present (though this may be changed shortly) there is no group working in nuclear physics. In 1946 there was but a handful of men at Bell who were working in the field of solid-state physics. Today there are many more. While the choice of the research area of the scientists in the research department is seldom subject to strong executive pressure, formal executive decisions strongly affect the allocation of research effort through the hiring process. The growing promise of the research work in the field of semiconductors definitely strengthened the force of Shockley's requests for more people to work with him. And though "promising" is a difficult word to define in this context, prospects for improving communications equipment certainly do not hurt the promise of an area of research.

The decision to hire or not to hire new men certainly does not rest exclusively on evaluation of prospects for advances in different fields applicable to communications technology, but the areas of scientific research which are growing at Bell Laboratories are in general those in which significant advances are expected to have some application to communications technology. And as we have seen, changes in prospects are generated in the course of research activity itself. The striking success of the rather small semiconductor research group led to an expansion in the number of solid-state scientists working at Bell (as well as to an increase in the proportion of the veteran Bell staff interested in and working in solid-state physics). Thus the composition of Bell's scientific staff makes the starting of research work in a field not related to communications technology unusual.

But what happens when a member of the research staff at Bell, hired because at that time he was doing work in a field of interest to the company, becomes interested in a new field (as he sometimes does)? Several factors must be considered here. First, few at the Laboratories will be so rash as to state that research in a particular area of science certainly will not result in knowledge of use in the design of communications systems. Of course, this is not to say that certain areas are not considered much more promising than others. Second, the best way to find out whether a new area of science looks promising is to do some work in the area. Third, a policy of applying strong formal pressure to dissuade a scientist from working in a certain area would, if used as a matter of course, undermine the general philosophy of research direction at Bell which has proved so successful in the past, and further, would tend to make the Laboratories a much less attractive place to top-flight scientists. Therefore laboratory policy is to avoid pressuring a man not to work in an area of interest to him.

If the new work of an individual proves of significant interest, both scientifically and in possible communications applications, then it is likely that others in the laboratory will also initiate work in the field, and that people from the outside will be brought in. Thus a new area of laboratory research will be started. If the work does not prove of interest to the Laboratories, eventually the individual in question will be requested to return to the fold, or leave. It is hoped that pressure can be informal. There seems to be no consensus about how long to let a man wander, but it is clear that young and newly hired scientists are kept under closer reins than the more senior scientists. However even top-flight people, like Jansky, have been asked to change their line of research. But, in general, the experience has been that informal pressures together with the hiring policy are sufficient to keep A. T. and T. and Western Electric more than satisfied with the output of research.

Interest in Devices

The hiring process is also an important mechanism for keeping the laboratory alert to the possibilities for new devices. The Bell Telephone Laboratories tend to attract scientists who are also interested in devices. Shockley is a case in point. Further, problems relating to practical devices are often very interesting ones. Bardeen and Brattain found the problem of why Shockley's field effect amplifier did not work extremely exciting as a scientific one. And results worthwhile from the purest scientific point of view came from their efforts to explain the failure of the amplifier. The fact that the research department is housed in the same building with the development and systems engineering departments also seems important in keeping the research people alert to the device needs of the Telephone Company. There are many interdepartmental seminars and formal talks. But perhaps informal contact is the most important link.

Device consciousness on the part of the research staff can lead to a serious misallocation of research effort if device oriented work is permitted to cut back sharply the effort directed toward advancing scientific knowledge. For this reason, though the research scientists are encouraged to be device conscious, laboratory policy discourages research people from working on a device beyond the building of a simple working model.

Thus, early in 1948, very shortly after the discovery of the point contact transistor, a development group under the direction of J. A. Morton was established. By 1950 there were more people engaged in development work than in research. The ultimate role of Morton's group was to create new devices for the systems development groups to use in creating new systems for Bell Telephone and for the military. The early objectives of the development group were to improve the point contact amplifier, examine and test a wide range of possible applications, and to produce a number of transistors to achieve these purposes. Later the development group began to concern itself with problems of cost.

But the research group that created the transistor did not participate in this work. The history of the solid-state research group after the transistor experiments is a good illustration of the evolutionary allocation mechanism which has been described. In 1951, with the advances achieved in junction transistors, the solid-state physics group began to grow rapidly, and in addition to the work on the junction transistor and underlying physics, work in other areas was intensified. As germanium and silicon were better understood, research in that area ran into diminishing returns and research on more complex semiconductors grew more promising. Similarly, research on magnetics and dielectrics was increased. In 1952 a separate transistor physics department was organized, headed by Shockley. Semiconductors research, once a subsection headed by Shockley under the solid-state physics group of Shockley and Morgan, which in turn was under physical research, is now a separate major department.

Concluding Thoughts

There is a limit to what can be learned from one case study. Generalizations are hazardous. However, it seems worthwhile to speculate on several aspects of industrial research which recently have been the subject of much public interest.

"TEAMWORK" IN RESEARCH

Much of the recent literature on industrial research has stressed the "team" aspect of this activity.[15] Many writers have expressed sharp discomfort with the idea of the research team, and have argued that industrial research which stresses teamwork is likely to be scientifically arid. As I have emphasized before, the transistor is just one case, but nonetheless it seems worthwhile to examine what teamwork meant in the case of the transistor.

First of all, we have seen that it meant interaction and mutual stimulation and help. Shared intense interest in the general field, ease of communication, differences in the viewpoints and experience of different scientists—these elements naturally call for interaction and make interaction fruitful for scientific advance. The purpose of bringing together the people doing work in solid-state physics was to achieve this end, and from the history of the project it seems that the close interaction of several people definitely contributed to the advance achieved. But several people outside the team also interacted in an important way. In particular, the metallurgists' work in developing ways to produce pure crystals was both an important link at many places in the chain of research and an activity in large part stimulated by the solid-state research effort of the team.

Second, we have seen that teamwork in the case of the transistor did not mean a closely directed project with an assigned devision of labor in the form of tasks and schedules for each of the team members. There were no closely defined goals shared by all members of the group. All were interested in understanding semiconductors but, at least at the start, all were not excited by amplifiers. The project was marked by flexibility—by the ability to shift directions and by the rather rapid focusing of attention by several people on problems and phenomena unearthed by others.

Third, we have seen that teamwork in the case of the transistor did mean a more concentrated effort than probably would have developed

---

[15] "Team" is used here in the popular sense, not in the sense of the theory of teams.

had the individuals involved not been brought together in one group. Shockley's interest in amplifiers definitely tended to draw the research interests of the group toward his focus. The research work of the transistor team, despite its very loose formal structure, was definitely affected by the fact that the men were working very closely together. In the case of the transistor this pulling together of interests proved extremely fruitful. Yet in many cases a more diversified attack might prove rewarding.

One wonders whether an invention like the transistor which came about as a direct result of an advance in scientific theory ever can be a team effort, if invention refers to a basic idea, and team refers to a group of people whose work is closely coordinated and planned by a team leader. It appears that the type of coordination required in an organization emphasizing fundamental science and the practical devices that might be created from advances in fundamental science is achieved quite effectively without planned coordination of effort and central control. Indeed it seems unlikely that a more formal control structure would be flexible enough to achieve anything like the type of coordination that marked the work of the research group on semiconductors. No one could have predicted the course of new knowledge or planned ahead to assure the right type of help at the right time. The informality of the decision structure played a very important role in permitting speedy cooperative response to changing ideas and knowledge. Thus the transistor was a team invention, but not in the sense of the term which has grown fashionable in recent years.

THE ROLE OF THE LARGE CORPORATION

In contrast to the public dismay about "teamwork" in research, many people have argued that the research laboratories of the large corporation are the only possible source of such inventions as the transistor. To what extent is an invention like the transistor dependent upon a sponsoring organization like the Bell Telephone Laboratories? How did the size of the Laboratories and the size of the corporations owning the Laboratories affect the project? Could the transistor have been developed at a significantly different institution, say, a laboratory owned by a much smaller company? My feeling is that devices like the transistor, based on fundamental new scientific knowledge, can come from small industrial laboratories or from universities, but that a large industrial laboratory like Bell does have a comparative advantage in this business.

The ingredients which seem to have played such an important role in the success of the semiconductor research project include the close interaction of a group of top-flight scientists, a great deal of freedom in the course of research, and an extremely strong interest on the part of at least one member of the group in inventing a practical device. This is high-priced talent at work, and when the project was initiated no guarantees were given as to the profits which would result. And for about two years before the transistor was invented, the group was kept free from pressure to produce practical results. This is not the type of project a small industrial laboratory is likely to be able to afford.

On the other hand, a university with strong science departments would have the resources to support work like the semiconductor research project. During World War II, and for a time after the war, work was going on at Purdue University under Lark-Horowitz which might have led to the transistor. The idea that an amplifier could be constructed from semiconductors was quite widely held by people working in the field. But, if my interpretation of the Bell project is correct, device minded scientists are essential if a laboratory is to develop devices such as the transistor. Shockley's theory, on which rests the design of the junction transistor, was in large part motivated by the desire to design a transistor. Further, it seems likely that if the identical theory had been developed by someone not interested in amplification, it would have taken some time for another worker to see that an amplifier could be designed on the basis of the theory. The popular image of the university scientist is that of a pure scholar, not interested in practical devices. If all university scientists were so, universities could hardly be the source of inventions like the transistor. For better or for worse, many university scientists do not fit that image, but are quite interested in devices. It is my feeling that the university with strong science departments, including scientists with a major interest in devices—not the laboratory of the small industrial corporation—is the major alternative source to the large industrial laboratory for inventions like the transistor.

ECONOMIC FACTORS AFFECTING THE DIRECTION OF SCIENTIFIC RESEARCH

It has often been argued that the rate and direction of advance in pure science must be considered as an autonomous factor in any theory of the factors affecting the rate and direction of inventive activity. And it is likely that any analysis describing the motives of the scientists who played the key roles in advancing quantum mechanics (Bohr, de Broglie, Schrodinger, Heisenberg, Pauli, Dirac, and others) as involving, in an important way, prospects for advancing practical technology, would be farfetched. But our case study has shown that the laboratories of large corporations may be effective institutions for drawing scientific research to areas where the importance of practical advances is great. And recall that the science of thermodynamics was, in large part, called forth by the development of steam engines, not vice versa. Advances in technology itself certainly affect the direction of scientific research.

The tremendous increase in the number of students taking undergraduate and graduate training in solid-state physics clearly has been strongly influenced by improved income prospects resulting from the increased use of solid-state physicists in industry and government sponsored research and development. This is not the whole explanation. Solid-state physics is much more scientifically fashionable now than it was. But even what is "fashionable" is strongly affected by applications. Since the birth of the transistor the proportion of articles relating to solid-state physics has significantly increased, and many scientists believe that the correlated change in the allocation of research effort was, in considerable part, due to the invention of the transistor and the consequent spotlighting of the field. Of course the same statements could be made about nuclear physics and the bomb. The direction of scientific advance is not independent of economic and practical factors.

WHAT IS BASIC RESEARCH?

One of the most important things which can be learned from the history of the transistor is that the distinction between basic research and applied research is fuzzy. In the transistor project the results included both an advance in fundamental physical knowledge and the invention and improvement of practical devices. The scientists involved, though many of them were not interested in devices, were able to predict roughly the nature of the practical advances; indeed in some instances they were able to predict quite closely. And several of the scientists were motivated by the hope both of scientific advance and practical advance. Thus the project was marked by duality of results, and of motives. Yet by the standards of the National Science Foundation the Bell semiconductor research work most certainly would be considered basic research.

I have a feeling that duality of interests and results is far from unusual. I wonder how many scientists—university scientists—doing basic research do not think now and then about the possible practical applications of their work. I wonder how many are completely uninfluenced in their choice of research by consideration of possible practical benefit to mankind? By posing these questions I am not implying that the answer to both is "none." But the answer may be "only a small proportion."

I have the feeling that many scientists in industrial research laboratories, including—perhaps, particularly including—men with considerable executive authority, are defensive and internally torn about the dual nature of the research work. Unlike the management of most other industrial laboratories, the administration at the Bell Telephone Laboratories is strongly imbued with a belief in the value of fundamental research to the telephone company and with the understanding that people doing fundamental research, to be effective, must be kept free from day-to-day practical problems. Since the telephone laboratories were among the first industrial laboratories to undertake fundamental research, and since Bell's record has been so outstanding, the organization likes to toot its horn now and then. People in the Laboratories like to stress the extent to which much of their research is fundamental, and how fundamental research yields big payoffs. When it is suggested that much of the fundamental research is not conducted with "pure" motives, there is a tendency to get defensive, for the scientific community has long been accustomed to separate fundamental research from applied research on the basis of purity of motive. If research is conducted solely to advance man's knowledge it is fundamental; if it is conducted to help achieve a practical objective, it is applied, and somehow less intellectually respectable. And many people at Bell who are defenders of the fundamental research program are cut on this intellectual saw.

Shockley, however, suffers from no such intellectual split. In his Nobel lecture he states, "Frequently, I have been asked if an experiment I have planned is pure or applied science; to me it is more important to know if the experiment will yield new and probably enduring knowledge about nature. If it is likely to yield such knowledge, it is, in my opinion, good fundamental research; and this is more important than whether the motivation is purely esthetic satisfaction on the part of the experimenter on the one hand or the improvement of the stability of a high-power transistor on the other."

Much of the history of science bears out Shockley's view. Some of the greatest scientific advances resulted from the research of men who were much concerned with the practical implications of their work, and their work was in large part motivated by the desire to benefit mankind.

The fuzzy nature of the boundary between basic and applied research does not imply, however, that some projects are not clearly more basic than some others. Nor does it imply that there are no important distinctions between the industrial research laboratory and the university laboratory. Basic research undertaken at industrial laboratories must somehow be related to expected company profit. And many of the greatest scientists have taken pride in the "purity" of their research motives and in the apracticality of fundamental science. Much of the foundation of modern physics was laid by men who chose science as a career in part because it offered an escape from the materialistic world. Although these men were often able to predict roughly the practical implications of their research, such practical aspects were unimportant, or even repugnant, to them. For these men the industrial research laboratory would seem a poor home. An industrial laboratory is not and probably should not be the equivalent of a university science department. It is risky to speculate how much of the "pure" research conducted at universities is "purer" than the "pure" research conducted at the Telephone Laboratories, but I believe that Einstein would have been unhappy at Bell, and Bell would be most unhappy if most of their research scientists were as intellectually pure as Einstein. It is probably best for all that this is so.

PART VI
WELFARE ECONOMICS AND
INVENTIVE ACTIVITY

Inventive Activity: Government Controls and the Legal Environment

JESSE W. MARKHAM

PRINCETON UNIVERSITY

Introduction

INVENTIVE activity, perhaps more than any other single economic endeavor, mirrors our "mixed" economy. The government has assumed primary responsibility for research relating to the Navy since 1789, and for research in agriculture since the creation of the Department of Agriculture and the land-grant college system in 1862.[1] It has participated directly in the design of weapons, surface craft, aircraft, missiles and rockets, in the development and control of atomic energy, radio and telecommunications, and in the promotion of science and public health. Except for these areas, and perhaps a few additional ones, control of inventive activity traditionally has been left to a system of private incentives which the government affects only indirectly through the institutions of public law.

An assessment of the impact of government controls and the legal environment on inventive activity in the United States requires, therefore, at the outset a systematic classification of such activity according to the prevailing direct and indirect means of public control (Table 1). From such a classification it immediately becomes clear that inventive activity is subject to a wide variety of controls, and that these controls vary greatly according to type and source of inventive activity.

Research financed and performed directly by the government is subject to the system of political controls applicable to budget items generally. The total sums expended are therefore determined by what the President proposes and Congress approves, and in turn by how serious each considers the "present need" to be. For example, in the decade preceding World War II the federal government spent on the average less than $40 million per year on research and development; the annual average for 1941–45 was $500 million,[2] reflecting

---

[1] The federal government had assumed responsibility for dissemination of plants, seeds, and certain information relating to agriculture as early as 1839.

[2] *Science and Public Policy*, the President's Scientific Research Board, 1947, Vol. 1, p. 10.

TABLE 1

CLASSIFICATION OF INVENTIVE ACTIVITY ACCORDING TO
MEANS OF PUBLIC CONTROL

Inventive Activity	Means of Public Control
GOVERNMENT	
Direct research	Budgetary process
Research contracted to the private sector	Budgetary process and patent, antitrust and taxation laws
Support of scientific education	Budgetary process and educational institution policy
PRIVATE INDIVIDUALS AND BUSINESS FIRMS	
Self-financed research	Patent, antitrust and taxation laws
Financed under government contract	Budgetary process and patent, antitrust and taxation laws
Research contracts with and donations to educational institutions and nonprofit organizations	Educational institution policy and tax laws
EDUCATIONAL AND NONPROFIT INSTITUTIONS	
Self-financed	Educational institution policy
Government financed	Budgetary process and educational institution policy
Business financed	Educational institution policy and tax laws

the need for massive military research. The federal government in the pre-Sputnik years 1952–57 spent on the average $76 million per year on space exploration and flight technology. The 1960 fiscal year budget called for expenditures of $325 million and the proposed 1961 budget, the first to follow the Soviet Union's successful lunar probe, called for $600 million.[3] These figures serve only to emphasize the point that the level of government supported inventive activity is determined as much by the forces of politics as it is by "pure" economic considerations. This is true not only because the dollar magnitude of specific items in the federal budget must be politically acceptable, but also because research and development expenditures for such purposes as defense, space exploration, public health, and so on, are not readily determinable by marginal social cost—marginal social benefit analysis. It is impossible even to measure in terms of current dollars the marginal cost to society of a given increase in taxes, much less the marginal social benefit of a successful flight to the moon in 1962 as compared with 1965.

[3] President Eisenhower's Budget Message to Congress, January 18, 1960, as reproduced in the *New York Times*, January 19, 1960, p. 17.

Government research contracted to private firms is also controlled primarily by the budgetary process, although such aspects of the legal environment as the patent, antitrust, and taxation laws are not totally inapplicable. Government research contracts sometimes specify that patentable discoveries made in the course of such research belong to the government, and hence are not patentable by the contracting firms. Some contracts permit firms to patent but provide that the government may obtain royalty-free licenses.[4] In either case the patent incentive is somewhat weakened. But, as Usher has persuasively argued, any achievement of large social importance involves the cumulative synthesis of several strategic inventions.[5] The prohibition, or the provision for royalty-free licensing to the government, applies to the contracted research but not to the subsequent synthesis which may produce a patentable invention. Similarly, while the antitrust laws may not be directly applicable to research performed under a particular government contract, the distribution of prime contracts by size of firm and the effect the research may have on the future market position of the contracting firm raise antitrust considerations. The effect the corporate income tax has on such research is not readily discernible but will depend, among other factors, on the contracting firm's current profit position and on whether it would have engaged in similar research activities on its own.

Government research contracted to educational and other non-profit organizations is controlled by the budgetary process and the policies of the recipient institutions. In the case of universities such policies usually relate to the issues of academic freedom, the compatibility of the contract research with the university's overall research program, the special research interests of the scientists involved, and so on.

Research expenditures for inventive activity conducted by private firms (and individuals) are governed by the profit motive subject to incentives and constraints that inhere in the legal environment. The patent laws, which are essentially a means for making new knowledge public in exchange for a 17-year right to monopolize the use of an invention, are designed to serve as a stimulus; they provide the inventor with an alternative to secrecy, an alternative he would not have in

[4] *Cf.* Gayle Parker, "Comparison of the Patent Provisions of the NASA Act and AEC Act," *Patent, Trademark, and Copyright Journal of Research and Education*, Fall 1959, pp. 303–316.

[5] Abbott P. Usher, *A History of Mechanical Inventions*, rev. ed., Harvard University Press, 1954, pp. 68–69.

their absence. Presumably the corporate income tax serves both as an incentive and as a constraint. Corporations, because they are permitted to expense rather than capitalize research expenditures, may with some justification reason that each dollar spent on research reduces profits after taxes by only $0.48.[6] On the other hand, the income tax significantly reduces what Schumpeter has called the pool of uncommitted retained earnings which corporations may use for new and untried ventures. It can be said that, on balance, the corporate income tax acts as an incentive if an increase of $1.00 in after-tax profits would lead to new expenditures on research of less than $0.48, and as a constraint if more than $0.48. A similar line of reasoning applies to corporate donations to universities and other nonprofit institutions for research purposes. The impact of the antitrust laws, the complexity of which defies the brevity an introductory statement imposes, is generally supposed to be favorable to inventive activity on the ground that it stimulates competitive effort, which often takes the form of an innovational race against competitors.

Of the three principal seats of research activity given attention in this study the educational and nonprofit institutions are the least affected by economic, political, and legal controls. They are by definition nonprofit organizations and for this reason are liberated from profits maximizing incentives. While both scientist and institution have patented certain of their inventions, patentability is not an important consideration in the conduct of their research. A few, but probably only a few, are affected by political criteria of the sort that determine the research items in the federal government's budget. They are unaffected by the antitrust laws and, although they may be favorably affected by income tax regulations, they are not guided in their research to any considerable extent by tax considerations. Even in their conduct of research under government contract such institutions generally have held out for a minimum of contractual constraints.[7] This relative freedom from control is, from an analytical point of view, not an unmixed blessing. Because nonprofit institutions are free to pursue within very broad limits whatever research they wish, what they in fact will pursue is highly unpredictable. They are susceptible

[6] It has been argued that such expenditures should be capitalized. *cf.* National Science Foundation, *Proceedings of a Conference on Research and Development and Its Impact on the Economy*, 1958, p. 122.

[7] Some universities have voiced apprehension over the increasing amount of contract research and the limitations it imposes on the freedom of individual research scientists. See Harold W. Dodds on "Projectitis" in *Official Register of Princeton University: The President's Report, 1952–53*, January 1, 1954, pp. 19–24.

to neither political nor economic analysis since they presumably are motivated by neither political nor economic incentives.

In sum, inventive activity in the United States is affected by a wide variety of incentives and legal institutions. The array of incentives includes what the government considers to be in the public interest and politically feasible, the profit motive, the quest for knowledge, the urge to create, and pure humanitarianism. Institutions that act to constrain or release these motives include the budgetary process, the patent system, the income tax laws, the antitrust laws, and what may be loosely defined as the policies of educational and other nonprofit institutions.

Quantitative Importance of Incentives and Controls

By historical coincidence estimates of advertising and of research and development outlays both reached the $10 billion mark in 1957. Data on advertising are voluminous; those on research and development—though technological change is the principal source of the American economy's sustained increase in productivity[8]—are intolerably inadequate. In part the problem is one of coverage: all surveys exclude individual inventors, and most exclude small firms. In part it is one of definition: a thin line separates technical effort from technical effort to create. As Dexter Keezer has put it, when Joe fixes a tractor it is repair; if he fails to fix it it is research.[9] Even references to federal government research outlays do not always distinguish between funds obligated and funds expended, or between calendar and fiscal years. And data from different sources, even from the same source, are not easily reconciled.[10]

But in spite of these inadequacies the data unmistakably show significant shifts in the relative importance of the various financial sources of inventive activity, and hence in the various means of social control (Table 2). In 1930 industry accounted for 70 per cent of total research and development expenditures, nonprofit institutions (mainly universities) for 16 per cent, and the federal government for only 14 per cent. In 1959 the federal government financed 60 per cent of total

[8] Some estimates of the contribution technological change has made to productivity run as high as 87 per cent. See Robert M. Solow, "Technological Change and the Aggregate Production Function," *Review of Economics and Statistics*, August 1957, pp. 312–320. Those who think this estimate too high generally consider technological change to be the most important single factor. See Richard Nelson, "The Economics of Invention: A Survey of the Literature," *Journal of Business*, April 1959, p. 102.

[9] National Science foundation, *op. cit.*, p. 146.

[10] See note to Table 2.

TABLE 2

RESEARCH AND DEVELOPMENT EXPENDITURES BY GOVERNMENT, INDUSTRY,
AND NONPROFIT INSTITUTIONS, SELECTED YEARS, 1930–59
(millions of dollars)

Source and Nature of Expenditure	1930	1941–45 average	1953	1956	1959
Government	23	500	2,810	5,234	7,200
Research performed in government	n.a.	n.a.	970	1,400	1,600
Research contracted to private sector	n.a.	n.a.	1,840	3,834	5,600
Industry	n.a.	n.a.	1,500	3,134	4,600
University	n.a.	n.a.	340	700	1,000
Other	n.a.	n.a.			
Business firms	116	80	3,870	6,000	9,100
Self-financed	n.a.	n.a.	2,370	2,900	4,500
Government financed	n.a.	n.a.	1,500	3,134	4,600
Donations to nonprofit institutions	n.a.	n.a.	10	—	—
Educational and other nonprofit institutions					
University	20	10 ⎫	530	1,000	1,300
Other	7[a]	10 ⎭			
Self-financed	n.a.	n.a.	180	300	300
Government financed	n.a.	n.a.	340	700	1,000
Business financed and other sources	n.a.	n.a.	10	n.a.	n.a.
Totals (duplications eliminated)	166	600	5,400	9,000	12,000

SOURCE: National Science Foundation, *Proceedings of a Conference on Research and Development and its Impact on the Economy*, 1958, pp. 170–178; *Science and Public Policy*, a Report to the President by John R. Steelman, Chairman, President's Scientific Research Board, 1947, Vol. 1, p. 10; *Business Plans, 1956–1959*, Prepared by the McGraw-Hill Department of Economics, New York, McGraw Hill, 1956, p. 13; and Dexter M. Keezer, Douglas Greenwald, and Robert P. Ulin, "The Outlook for Expenditures on Research and Development During the Next Decade," *American Economic Review*, May 1960, p. 355. Where estimates varied, as they usually did, the most recent compilation was used.

[a] Includes state government.
n.a. = Not available.

research and development expenditures, industry 38 per cent, and nonprofit institutions less than 3 per cent. A corresponding shift has occurred in the relative importance of the instruments of control over the private and public sectors of the economy. In 1930 and up to the outbreak of World War II, approximately 70 per cent of all inventive activity occurred in industry, which nominally was subject to the profit motive and the patent and antitrust laws; in recent years this share has been reduced to less than 40 per cent. Meanwhile, the share controlled by federal budgetary considerations had risen by 1959 from 14 per cent to 60 per cent. In decisions concerned with the financing of inventive activity, therefore, political feasibility and what the government considers to be the public need have become the principal instruments of control, replacing private profit incentives and the traditional legal instruments of antitrust laws and the patent system.

No similar shift has occurred in research and development *performance*. In 1953 private industry performed 72 per cent of all inventive activity as measured by research and development funds expended, the federal government 12 per cent, and nonprofit institutions, such as universities, 10 per cent. In 1956 industry performed 70 per cent, and in 1959 76 per cent. This pattern of performance does not differ significantly from that of the thirties. Data on inventive activity, like that on corporate ownership, reveal what may be called the "Berle and Means effect"—a divorcement of control over research finance and research performance.

The sharp difference in the pattern of research performance and research financing is explained by the pronounced increase in federal government research appropriations and the use of such funds to support research in the private sector of the economy. In 1959 the government contracted 78 per cent of its total appropriations for research and development out to the private sector—64 per cent to industry and 14 per cent to nonprofit institutions. These contracted funds accounted for 51 per cent of the total inventive activity performed by industry and for 77 per cent of that performed by nonprofit institutions.

The impact of government-supported research is spread far from evenly throughout American industry. For the total research and development performed by industry and financed by government in 1956, 58 per cent of the funds went for aircraft and parts, 23 per cent for electrical equipment, 8 per cent for machinery, and 3 per cent for professional and scientific instruments. The four industries alone accounted for 92 per cent of the total research and development funds supplied by government to industry. Telecommunications and broadcasting accounted for an additional 2 per cent. In these five industries, all of which are vitally tied up with the Nation's defense effort, government sponsored research accounts for from 40 per cent to nearly 90 per cent of total research expenditures. The remaining 6 per cent of government-sponsored research in industry—federal funds of $136 million—appears to be spread thinly and evenly over the rest of the private sector of the economy.

One side effect of these developments deserves emphasis. Through-out the 1930's universities accounted for slightly less than 25 per cent of all research expenditures. Since it is generally agreed that during this period universities were primarily preoccupied with basic research, and that government and business made only a modest contribution at that level, it seems reasonable to conclude that basic research accounted for something in excess of one-quarter of total research expenditures. In 1953 basic research expenditures amounted to $435 million,[11] more than was spent on all types of research in the 1930's but still only 8 per cent of total research expenditures in 1953. Relative to total research, therefore, basic research has declined. And the sources of funds for basic research, as in the case of total research, have on an increasing scale become divorced from the locus of research performance. In 1953 the federal government financed 36 per cent but performed only 11 per cent of all basic research; colleges and universities financed only 14 per cent but performed slightly more than 47 per cent; other nonprofit institutions financed about 9 per cent and performed 3 per cent; and industry financed 41 per cent and performed slightly less than 39 per cent.[12] Only in industry, which performs less than two-fifths of the total, is the decision to engage in basic research tied directly to the decision to finance it.

What effect have these recent trends had on the traditional incentives for, and instruments of control over, inventive activity? The data strongly suggest that they play a relatively less important role in the inventive process than they formerly did. Even if we make some allowance for the possibility that industry takes on a portion of the government financed research with an eye toward increasing its patent holdings and profits in the distant future, it can still be reasonably concluded that the traditional incentives and institutional controls governing inventive activity have given considerable ground to the political, welfare, and defense (the three are not mutually exclusive) considerations which come into play in the federal budgetary process.

It does not follow from this, of course, that approximately two-fifths of all research outlays are prompted by commercial incentives and governed by the patent system and the antitrust laws. The above

---

[11] National Science Foundation, *op. cit.*, p. 171.

[12] *Ibid.* These data probably understate the extent of divorcement. Industry receives substantial sums for basic research from the federal government and supplies substantial sums to universities and other nonprofit organizations. The gross difference between basic research financed and basic research performed by industry would be considerably greater than the net difference.

data omit altogether the activity of the free-lance inventor. While his contribution to total inventive effort has unquestionably undergone a relative decline over the past half-century,[13] there are no grounds for writing it off as insignificant.[14] And, as pointed out earlier, research financed by government but performed by industry may not be completely divorced from the traditional incentives and instruments of public control. Finally, a significant portion of the research financed by industry would probably be carried on in the absence of patent protection. The eleventh annual McGraw-Hill survey of 1956 showed that about 50 per cent of all reporting companies were conducting research on new products, 41 per cent were conducting research on product improvement, and only 11 per cent reported research on new processes.[15] Research on new products and processes may be motivated by patentability, but the bulk of the research on product improvement probably reflects the exertion of competitive effort to keep abreast or move ahead of rivals in established markets. Such research effort is a normal aspect of product competition, much of which is carried on without the incentives afforded by the patent system.[16] If we were to make the rather heroic assumption that such competitive research just about offset the unreported research carried on by free-lance inventors, and the further assumption that the patent system had a negligible effect on industry research financed by government, it could be concluded that the patent and antitrust laws were applicable to approximately two-fifths of all inventive activity.[17] Since there are no satisfactory means for testing the validity of either assumption, the soundest conclusion is that in recent years no more than one-

[13] Evidence of the relative decline in the role of what is romantically referred to as the attic inventor is found in patent assignments. According to data supplied by P. J. Frederico of the United States Patent Office, in 1900 over 80 per cent of all patents issued were assigned directly to individuals and less than 20 per cent to corporations; in 1955 about 39 per cent were assigned to individuals, 59 per cent to corporations, and slightly over 2 per cent to the government.

[14] The press frequently reports inventions patented by individuals. See report on new carbonated beverage bottle cap patented in January 1960 by Clyde A. Tolson, top aid to J. Edgar Hoover, *New York Times*, January 23, 1960, p. 26.

[15] National Science Foundation, *op. cit.*, p. 123.

[16] A. F. Ravenshear drew this distinction between "intensive inventions" (that lower the costs of existing goods) and "originative inventions" (that produce a new result) more than a half-century ago, and concluded that the former did not require the patent incentive. See his *The Industrial and Commercial Influence of the English Patent System*, London, 1908, pp. 52–55.

[17] It can be assumed with some justification that free-lance inventors are affected by the patent system but not the antitrust laws, that the normal product-improving research of industrial firms is affected by the antitrust laws but not the patent system, and that both are motivated primarily by commercial incentives.

quarter to one-half of total inventive activity in the United States is governed by the profit incentive and the traditional means of public control as embodied in patent and antitrust policies;[18] until two decades ago the share so governed was significantly greater, probably as much as three-quarters to four-fifths.

These major shifts in the sources of financial support for inventive activity, and the corresponding shifts in relative importance of the instruments of public control, appear to be more or less permanent. The McGraw-Hill forecast for 1969 estimates that government will finance 56 per cent of total research and development costs, industry 40 per cent, and colleges and other nonprofit institutions 4 per cent.[19] Of the total research and development activities performed by industry, it is estimated that government will finance 45 per cent and industry 55 per cent. The estimated slight increase in the share financed by industry is based on the assumptions that (1) diplomacy will reduce the intense arms race which has characterized the past decade, and (2) industry will increase its outlays on fundamental (basic) research. But even under these rather optimistic assumptions less than one-half of total inventive activity would be governed by the traditional private incentives and public instruments of control in 1969. The already perceptible decline in the relative importance of those incentives and the correspondingly larger role played by the budgetary process can therefore scarcely be viewed as mid-twentieth century ephemera.

Inventive Activity, Incentives, and Public Policy

THE PATENT SYSTEM

Public policy toward inventive activity in the United States can be dated from the Constitution of 1787, which gave Congress the power "to promote the progress of Science and useful Arts, by securing for limited times to Authors and Inventors the exclusive Right to their respective Writings and Discoveries." Congress exercised that power in 1790 by enacting a law establishing a patent system, which was to be virtually the sole instrument of public policy on inventions until

[18] The author emphasizes the word "governs" and urges that it not be confused with "induces." How much inventive activity the patent system induces is taken up later on.

[19] Dexter M. Keezer, Douglas Greenwald, and Robert Ulin, "The Outlook for Expenditures on Research and Development During the Next Decade," *American Economic Review*, May 1960, p. 355.

the enactment of the Sherman Act a century later,[20] and the primary instrument until it became eclipsed by the budgetary process at the outset of World War II. It is still the principal instrument of public policy toward inventive activity financed and performed by private industry although, as will be shown later, the patent system has itself been governed in no small way by antitrust policy.

While the rationale of patent systems varies from country to country[21]—and even from time to time within each country—most students of the United States patent system appear to agree that it finds its principal justification in terms of the following premises.

1. Prospective rewards to the inventor during the seventeen-year period of protection will often exceed the costs of research, adaptation, and disclosure. The prospective rewards would exceed such costs in fewer cases were the seventeen-year property right not granted. Hence, the patent system induces inventive activity which would not otherwise be undertaken. Stated differently, in the absence of patent protection the social benefits of inventive activity often exceed the private rewards; the patent system is designed to narrow the difference.

2. Prospective gains to society in the form of new products, processes, and disclosed knowledge the patent system encourages exceeds the social costs of the seventeen-year monopoly grant.

It is in terms of these two premises that the patent system, as distinct from abuses of the system, must be assessed. If the system accounts for a net increase in inventions having a value to society exceeding the costs society pays for them, the patent system is justifiable in economic terms. It is worth pointing out that fulfillment of this condition justifies the system irrespective of how much inventive activity the system encourages, provided the costs of maintaining the system itself is included among the costs society incurs. In this sense the patent system is not unlike any other incentive-creating public policy, for example, a change in interest rates by the monetary authorities. Conceptually, the system performs optimally if it produces marginal social benefits equal to the marginal social costs it imposes, irrespective of the level of activity at which this equality occurs.

Most of the thoughtful views expressed on the patent system—of

[20] Exceptions, as already pointed out, were the federal government's early research activities in agriculture and defense, which until 1940 accounted for a small part of total research.

[21] For an excellent discussion of this question see Fritz Machlup, *An Economic Review of the Patent System*, study of the Subcommittee on Patents, Trademarks, and Copyrights of the Senate Committee on the Judiciary, 85th Cong. 2nd sess., 1958, pp. 20 ff.

which there are many—have not been especially relevant to an appraisal of the system in terms of these criteria. Those who apparently accept the system as it presently exists lean heavily on the logical appeal of the proposition that patent protection is necessary to induce inventive activity and the requisite investment to exploit it commercially.[22] Few economists who subscribe to this view regard the patent system as an unmixed blessing, and some approve its retention only because no superior substitute has yet been offered.[23] It is emphasized, however, that this position finds its principal support in the intuitive appeal of the a priori logic of the case rather than in any empirical proof of the premises on which the case rests.

This does not mean that there is no factual information on how the patent system affects inventive effort, but rather that the existing facts scarcely add up to a reliable empirical test of the important hypothesis. Several industry studies have developed persuasive evidence that the patent system has promoted technological progress in selected industries, often by making possible the entry of new firms to compete with established, and patent protected, processes and products.[24] And at least one recent study offers evidence that business men regard the patent system as an important stimulus to research by their respective companies and, because of the disclosure requirement, to the growth in usable knowledge and a reduction in wasteful duplication of research effort.[25] While all these studies point in the direction of the idea that firms undertake research when the resulting discoveries may be patented (which they would not otherwise undertake), and that the disclosure requirement enhances both the level and exchange of patentable knowledge, the studies have developed

[22] See especially citations of J. B. Clark, A. T. Hadley, Irving Fisher, Ludwig von Mises, John Jewkes, F. W. Taussig, A. F. Ravenshear, F. von Weiser, and A. C. Pigou in Fritz Machlup. *op. cit.*, pp. 33–40.

[23] See John Jewkes, David Sawers, and Richard Stillerman, *The Sources of Invention*, London, Macmillan, 1958, pp. 251–253.

[24] See W. Rupert Maclaurin, *Invention and Innovation in the Radio Industry*, New York, 1949; Arthur A. Bright, Jr., *The Electric-Lamp Industry: Technological Change and Economic Development from 1800 to 1947*, New York, 1949; Harold C. Passer, *The Electrical Manufacturers, 1875–1900: A Study in Competition, Entrepreneurship, Technical Change and Economic Growth*, Harvard University Press, 1953; and in *Patent, Trademark, and Copyright Journal of Research and Education*, June 1957: Nathan Belfer and Irving H. Siegel, "Patent and Other Factors in the Development of Firms in the Custom Heat-Treating Industry," pp. 57–73; and Weldon Welfling and Irving H. Siegel, "Patent and Other Factors in the Growth of the Electronics Industry in the Boston Area," pp. 119–126.

[25] Jesse W. Markham, James S. Worley, and Dwight S. Brothers, "The Value of the American Patent System: An Inquiry into Possible Approaches to Its Measurement," *Patent, Trademark, and Copyright Journal*, June 1957, pp. 20–56.

relatively little information on the social costs at which these positive benefits of the patent system are obtained.

Critics of the patent system have tended to direct their attack toward the system's "abuse," and have only incidentally questioned the system's logical basis. Hence, much criticism of the system envisages the policy remedy of patent reform rather than the more drastic remedies of outlawing the system altogether or replacing it with another set of incentives and controls. The reasons generally advanced for calling in question the premises on which the patent system rests may be summarized as follows:[26]

1. The patent system was designed for the individual inventor, but over the years research has become concentrated in the large corporation. This shift in location of inventive activity has rendered the patent system obsolete.

2. The rise of institutional research—notably government, non-profit organization, and institutionalized corporate research—has rendered the patent system inapplicable to a large portion of inventive activity.

3. Interfirm competition has become the primary stimulus to inventive activity; the patent system is therefore no longer necessary.

4. The rise of monopoly has provided the business firm with sufficient means of protection without resorting to patenting.

5. The purely formal test for the novelty of an invention has encouraged the inventor, especially the large corporation, to keep many important aspects of an invention secret. Further, to avoid impairing the novelty of possible future patent claims, business firms refrain from publishing scientific discoveries. In these ways the patent system encourages secrecy rather than the publication of knowledge.

6. In an age characterized by publicity and efficient communications it is impossible to keep important scientific discoveries secret. Hence, under a patent system, society trades valuable monopoly grants for information which it could get for nothing.

These six objections to the patent system are neither mutually

---

[26] These criticisms, in slightly different language, may be found in the following references: Sir Arnold Plant, "The Economic Theory Concerning Patents for Inventions," *Economica* (new series), 1934, pp. 44–46; Michael Polanyi, "Patent Reform," *Review of Economic Studies*, 1944, p. 71; Alfred E. Kahn, "Deficiencies of American Patent Law," *American Economic Review*, 1940, p. 479; Seymour Melman, *The Impact of the Patent System on Research*, study of the Subcommittee on Patents, Trademarks, and Copyrights of the Senate Committee on the Judiciary, 85th Cong. 2nd sess., pp. 8, 18; S. C. Gilfillan, "The Prediction of Technical Change," *Review of Economics and Statistics*, November 1952, pp. 376–377; and Machlup, *op. cit.*, pp. 28–52.

exclusive nor internally consistent. In some cases conclusions follow from unsupportable premises, and some observations which may be factually true do not negate the traditional rationale for the patent system. For example 5 and 6 obviously are inconsistent; if one is true the other must be false. To a lesser extent so are 3 and 4: if it can be stated as a general proposition that inventive activity is the primary means of interfirm competition, it is difficult to see how protected monopolistic positions have rendered unnecessary the additional protection the patent system affords. A world of firms vigorously competing through innovations and one made up of firms with monopoly power insulated from competitive forces obviously are two different worlds. Moreover, although the prevailing level of monopoly power may exceed that consistent with a competitively regulated economy, there is no persuasive evidence that it has risen perceptibly over the past half-century.[27] It is probably true for a variety of reasons—one of which was dealt with at length in the preceding section—that a smaller proportion of inventive activity is governed by the patent system than was the case in earlier years. However, the justification for the system as an instrument of public policy does not lie in the share of total inventive activity it governs.

Since almost all those who question the logical basis of the patent system have either explicitly or implicitly based their conclusions on historical changes in industrial organization, it is essential to inquire into how these changes may have altered the relative social benefits and social costs of the system.

Corporate enterprise has undoubtedly displaced the solo inventor as the primary performer of inventive activity.[28] It does not clearly follow from this, however, that the social costs of the patent system have increased relative to its social benefits. Uncertainty, it is generally agreed,[29] is the essential characteristic of inventive activity. A traditional rationale for the patent system is that, by holding out the possibility of greater rewards for inventive activity that turns out to be commercially successful, it encourages inventors to incur the costs of uncertainty. Corporate enterprise obviously has not eliminated the risks of uncertainty, as is sometimes claimed, but has simply transferred them from the individual scientist—now largely an

---

[27] See G. Warren Nutter, *The Extent of Enterprise Monopoly in the United States,* University of Chicago Press, 1952.

[28] See footnote 13, *supra.*

[29] Cf. Charles J. Hitch, "Research and Development and the Economy," in National Science Foundation, *Proceedings, op. cit.,* p. 132.

employable factor—to the corporation itself. However, in at least one way the rise of the large corporate research laboratory has reduced uncertainty. The outcome of any one of the several dozen research projects a large corporation may launch in a given time period may be as uncertain now as it would have been fifty years ago, but it may be relatively certain that at least one or two will turn out to be commercial successes. Hence, the large corporate laboratory can, on the insurance principle, reduce uncertainty through greater coverage and larger numbers and, accordingly, can predict with greater reliability the probable returns on its research outlays. But the expected returns are themselves enhanced by the possibility of patent protection. Hence, if it can be assumed that the marginal costs of inventive activity turn upward at some point, it can be concluded that the patent system stimulates some research that private firms otherwise would not undertake—presumably the more costly and more uncertain projects.

The statistical evidence, while far from satisfactory, suggests either that the research required to produce a patentable invention, or that the research which does not lead to patents, increased substantially over the past half-century. It probably suggests a combination of both. In 1900 one patent was issued for every 1.7 scientists and engineers in the United States; in 1954 one patent was issued for every 20.5 scientists and engineers.[30] Research outlays by business firms have increased, especially since 1930, more rapidly than the population of scientists and engineers. Hence, the scientific manpower and dollar costs per patentable invention or nonpatentable inventive effort, or both, have increased enormously.[31] Much of the high-cost research characterized by uncertainty may have been stimulated by the patent system; much of the research that was directed toward small product and process innovations led to relatively few patents and probably would have occurred in the absence of the patent system. The absolute decline in recent years in the number of patents issued while research

[30] Melman, *op. cit.*, p. 29. Melman infers from these data that the patent system is no longer justified, or not as much justified as it once was.

[31] The rate of patenting in industry groups relating to the mechanical and industrial arts has declined while that in industry groups relating to chemistry and physics has increased. Cf. Alfred B. Stafford, "Trends of Invention in Material Culture: A Statistical Study of the Class-wise Distribution of Inventive Effort in the United States as Determined by Patents Granted During the Period 1914–1945," unpublished Ph.D. thesis, University of Chicago, 1950. This shift may have accounted for a portion of the increase in research costs per patentable invention.

outlays in the private sector registered large increases is consistent with this interpretation.[32]

It is highly improbable that a single inflexible patent system can apply optimally both to costly research contemplating major technological breakthroughs and to competitive research aimed at maintaining or strengthening a firm's market position in an established product line. The existence of these two broad classes of inventive activity suggests the advisability of a dual patent system, in principle analogous to the familiar rationale for price discrimination. The system would provide for relatively long periods of protection for major technological breakthroughs, because they are of high value and involve uncertainty and large research costs. It would also provide for much shorter-term protection for inventive effort generally considered to be an integral part of dynamic competition, and productive of incremental changes no one of which adds substantially to society's total stock of knowledge. Such a dual system would no doubt more nearly equate the marginal social costs of both classes of inventive activity with their corresponding marginal social rewards and, however great the administrative difficulties, would go a long way toward resolving important inconsistencies and conflicts in public policy—especially those existing between patent and antitrust policies.

ANTITRUST POLICY AND THE PATENT SYSTEM

The insulation from the forces of competitive imitation the patent system provides may raise no special problem and extract no unusual social cost in economies where public policy regards monopoly as neutral, or possibly even as desirable. But under United States antitrust policy the patent laws give to firms a protection from competitive forces they cannot themselves erect with impunity. In short, it is primarily because of antitrust policy that the protection the patent system provides can be regarded as a serious social cost. In the language of the late Joseph A. Schumpeter, such protection may be necessary to induce those innovations which strike "not at the margins of the profits and the outputs of the existing firms but at their foundations and their very lives."[33] But to accord the same protection to innova-

[32] Throughout the 1930's annual average patent increases amounted to 48,520; in 1954 patent increases amounted to only 33,872 (Melman, *op. cit.*, p. 29). However, data issued by the United States Patent Office since this paper was first written show that patent increases in 1958 reached 48,405.

[33] *Capitalism, Socialism, and Democracy*, 2nd ed., New York, Harper, 1947, p. 84. Those who may be tempted to invoke the authority of Schumpeter in defense of liberal use of patent protection will meet with disappointment. Although Schumpeter defined

tions of a much lower order, and which may result from the normal course of vigorous interfirm competition in existing markets, compromises unnecessarily the principles of antitrust policy.[34]

Early United States patent policy logically surrounded the patent with what at that time were considered to be effective safeguards: exclusive use was limited to fourteen years; the patent applicant was required to specify exactly what he claimed to have discovered and fully to disclose it; and patents were to be issued only for technological devices sufficiently useful and important to merit the reward of limited exclusive use.[35] Statutory safeguards were further strengthened by the institutional environment to which they were addressed. In 1790 invention was almost entirely a matter of individual tinkering within the area of the mechanical arts. Limitations on the individual's inventive genius and financial resources assured society that no one person alone could monopolize an industry through patenting or patent accumulation.

In the hundred years that separated the first patent statute and the Sherman Act—and for a decade or two thereafter—these safeguards were substantially weakened by legislative revision, administrative procedures, judicial interpretation, and unchecked abuse of the system by private parties. In 1861 Congress lengthened the period of exclusive use from fourteen to seventeen years, and through other statutory amendments over the years enlarged the area of patent coverage. In an 1817 case Justice Story construed "useful" to mean any invention not "mischievous" or "immoral."[36] The Patent Office adopted procedures which encouraged both the proliferation and abuse of patent rights.[37] Business firms adjusted their practices to the weaker safeguards and, as an impressive list of court cases shows, often overstepped the liberal legal boundaries. Two students of the problem, summing up the situation as it existed in the first decade of the twentieth century, stated that ". . . the patent system had become a special sanctuary for trusts, pools, and trade confederacies."[38] Another observed that ". . . the

innovation as any alteration of existing production functions, his empirical observations were confined almost entirely to those that brought on revolutionary changes, e.g., the automobile, rayon, the chemical industries, and so on. These appear to be the innovations he had in mind when he sought to justify temporary protection by private and public means.

[34] This conflict between the patent right and antitrust policy is evidently being resolved more and more in favor of antitrust; see below.

[35] See George W. Stocking and Myron W. Watkins, *Monopoly and Free Enterprise*, New York, Twentieth Century Fund, 1951, pp. 450–452.

[36] Lowell v. Lewis, 15 Fed. Cases 1018 (1817), p. 1019.

[37] Stocking and Watkins, *op. cit.*, pp. 455–456, 58–59.

[38] *Ibid.*, p. 454.

protection of patent franchises had enabled big business to circumvent the basic law prohibiting monopoly."[39] These pronouncements probably exemplify the more extreme diagnosis but they are backed by serious and responsible studies which make it clear that the patent system, if left unchecked by a vigorous antitrust policy, can be made an effective vehicle for the spread of monopoly power. Until 1890, indeed until several decades thereafter, antitrust policy was something less than effective. In consequence, the social cost of the patent system unquestionably was enhanced, and no doubt some would argue that the social rewards of the system were reduced.

Over the past three or so decades an unpublicized but discernible trend has developed toward resolving conflicts between the past lax patent policy and the recent relatively vigorous antitrust policy in favor of the latter. Evidence of this trend is found in myriad sources, but its specific content is more readily identifiable in selected court cases. Decisions arising out of such cases have tended to (1) curtail extension of the effects of the patent beyond the invention described in the patent claim; (2) establish higher standards for patentable inventions; and (3) prescribe compulsory licensing—sometimes royalty-free licensing—of patents used, and abused, to further monopoly power.

In 1912 the Supreme Court approved in the A. B. Dick case a restriction the patentee imposed on an unpatented material used in the patented device.[40] It expressly withdrew this approval in the Motion Pictures Patent case[41] in 1917; in a series of cases decided in the 1940's the Court established doctrines that the licenses could not fix the prices of unpatented products produced by patented processes or machines or where only a part of the product is patented;[42] and in 1948 struck down a royalty provision based on the sale of an unpatented as well as a patented commodity as an illegal price-fixing device.[43]

Unless they result in industrywide price fixing, price restrictions imposed by the patentee on the licensee are generally held, as in the General Electric case, to be legal on the grounds that they are "nor-

[39] Walton H. Hamilton, *Patents and Free Enterprise*, TNEC Monograph No. 31, Washington, 1941, p. 62.

[40] Henry v. A. B. Dick Co., 224 U.S.-1 (1912).

[41] Motion Picture Patents Co. v. Universal Film Mfg. Co., 243 U.S.-502, 510 (1917).

[42] See *Report of the Attorney General's National Committee to Study the Antitrust Laws*, Washington, 1955, p. 234.

[43] United States v. United States Gypsum Co., 333 U.S. 364, 384–385 (1948).

mally and reasonably adapted to secure pecuniary reward for the patentee's monopoly."[44] In recent years considerable effort has been exerted to overturn this doctrine. In the Lime Material decision[45] the failure to obtain a majority of the Supreme Court resulted in neither affirming nor overruling General Electric. However, a district court found illegal the particular price-fixing license before it in *Newburgh Moire Co.* v. *Superior Moire Co.* in 1952.[46] Several members of the Attorney General's National Committee to Study the Antitrust Laws argued strongly that such price-fixing clauses not only should be proscribed, but in fact have been proscribed in more recent Supreme Court interpretations of the scope of patent rights.[47] And in a series of decisions beginning in 1942 the Court overturned a long-standing rule of patent law to the effect that a licensee is not free to contest the validity of the licensed patent. In these decisions the Court held that the licensee did not forego this freedom where the license included a price-fixing clause.[48]

In the last three decades the mortality rate for patents before the various courts has substantially increased. It is not entirely clear whether the increase in invalidations is attributable to a relaxation of standards at the Patent Office or to a stiffening of the standards used by the courts; however, most evidence supports the view that the courts have begun to set higher standards of patentability—a view the courts themselves seem to share.[49] It would appear that Congress has also imposed higher standards on the patent applicant. The test set forth in the early patent statutes was whether the discovery was "new and useful—or a new and useful improvement thereon not known or used before." In *Hotchkiss* v. *Greenwood* the Supreme Court had added the additional criterion that "an improvement in the prior art must involve more ingenuity and skill than would be obvious to an ordinary mechanic in the art."[50] Congress appears to have approved this test in the Patent Act of 1952:[51]

---

[44] United States v. General Electric Cò., 272 U.S. 476 (1926).

[45] United States v. Lime Material Co., 333 U.S. 287 (1948).

[46] 105 F. Supp. 372. (D.N.J. 1952).

[47] *Report of the Attorney General's National Committee to Study the Antitrust Laws*, pp. 235–236.

[48] *Ibid.*, p. 234 at n. 49.

[49] See Gay Chin, "The Statutory Standard of Invention: Section 103 of the 1952 Patent Act," *Patent, Trademark, and Copyright Journal of Research and Education*, Fall 1959, pp. 317–329, especially p. 318.

[50] *Ibid.*, citing 52 U.S. 247 (1850).

[51] 35 U.S.C. 103. The courts appear to be divided on whether this higher legislative test is as high as that the courts themselves have established (see Chin, *op. cit.*, pp. 320–323).

A patent may not be obtained—if the differences between the subject matter sought to be patented and the prior art are such that the subject matter as a whole would have been obvious at the time the invention was made to a person having ordinary skill in the art to which said subject matter pertains.

The courts have also shown a decided tendency in recent years to deny the patentee exclusive use where it results in significant monopoly power. According to S. Chesterfield Oppenheim, between 1941 and 1957 over 100 judgments, involving more than 300 antitrust defendants, provided for compulsory licensing or the outright dedication of as many as 35,000 patents.[52] Because many of these were consent judgments the judicial rationale for the trend toward compulsory licensing and dedication of patents must be inferred from a small number of decisions. However, in a few cases the courts have spoken with clarity. In the United Shoe Machinery case Judge Wyzanski stated:[53]

Defendant is not being punished for abusive practices respecting patents, for it engaged in none, . . . It is being required to reduce the monopoly power it has, not as a result of patents, but as a result of business practices. And compulsory licensing, on a reasonable royalty basis, is in effect a partial dissolution on a non-confiscatory basis . . .

Judge Forman in ordering dedication of certain patents in the General Electric case stated:[54]

In view of the fact that General Electric achieved its dominant position in the industry and maintained it in great measure by its extension of patent control the requirement that it contribute its existing patents to the public is only a justified dilution of that control made necessary in the interest of free competition in the industry.

In the 1956 A. T. & T. consent decree[55] all the patents owned by defendents A. T. & T. and Western Electric Company were made subject

[52] *Patent, Trademark, and Copyright Journal,* June 1957, pp. 135–136.
[53] 110 F. Supp. 295, 351 (D. Mass. 1953), aff'd. per curiam 374 U.S. 521 (1954).
[54] 115 F. Supp. 835 (D.N.J. 1953).
[55] United States v. Western Electric Inc., civil action 17–49 (D.N.J.), decree entered January 24, 1956.

to compulsory licensing to all domestic applicants, and about 8,600 patents involved in licence exchange agreements with three other large electronic companies were made subject to royalty-free compulsory licenses. The decree was hailed as "a sweeping patent victory" that "will open up the electronics and television industry to competition."[56]

These are a few of the recent compulsory licensing and patent dedication decrees based almost entirely on antitrust considerations. In others, the issues of patent abuse and monopoly have often been intertwined, but the resulting decrees have generally contemplated remedies of the sort antitrust policy envisages; see, for example, the 1952 I. C. I. decree.[57] This is a discernible break with traditional patent adjudication, where relief usually consisted of an injunction against the enforcement of patent licenses used to effectuate monopolistic control.[58]

The constraints antitrust policy has placed on patent usage are of relatively recent origin and reflect the increased vigor of antitrust law administration over the past two decades.[59] In view of what is known and, more importantly, what is not known about the operation of the patent system, a strong argument can be made for assigning this role to antitrust policy. The principle social costs of the patent system are the temporary monopoly positions to which it gives legal protection. Antitrust policy has provided the traditional means for mitigating the excesses of monopoly to which such costs are attributable.

Summary

In the past two decades two significant developments have brought about fundamental changes in the institutional environment of inventive activity in the United States. (1) the share of total research and development expenditures financed by government rose from 13 per cent to a staggering 60 per cent; and (2) antitrust policy was strengthened and administered with increasing vigor. A concomitant of the first was a large-scale substitution of the budgetary process for the

---

[56] *Business Week*, January 28, 1956, p. 160.

[57] United States v. Imperial Chemical Industries, 105 F. Supp. 215, 222 (S.D.N.Y. 1952).

[58] *Cf.* "Compulsory Licensing by Antitrust Decree," *Yale Law Journal*, 1946, pp. 77–81.

[59] There is little doubt that the trend since the late 1930's has been toward a more vigorous antitrust policy. See Edward S. Mason, *Economic Concentration and the Monopoly Problem*, Harvard University Press, 1957, p. 400; Jesse W. Markham, "United States Antitrust Policies: How Effective Have They Been?" *Southern Economic Journal*, July 1959, p. 61.

private profit incentive and the patent system as a means of governing inventive activity. The second led to resolution of conflicts between traditional patent policy and recent antitrust policy in favor of the latter. Accordingly, the patent right has become relatively less important, and the protection it affords less absolute, than it once was. While these developments have not rendered obsolete the historical debate over the merits of the patent system they have clearly made it less compelling.

The ascendency of government in inventive activity may be largely explained in terms of national defense requirements, but the impact of the research it sponsors is felt throughout the economy generally. Just as the peaceful tin can may be drafted for war, so may atomic energy, missile science, space photography, electronic computors, and so on, be turned to peaceful purposes. The fundamental laws of nature, and many of their applications, are unaffected by the state of politics. With well over one-half of total inventive activity subject to government control the budgetary process assumes paramount importance. In a large area it has supplanted the traditional economic incentives to invent. The economic and political considerations integral to the budgetary process will play a major role in shaping the course of inventive activity in the forseeable future. What these considerations are and how they may be assimilated in welfare economics should be an interesting and challenging subject for the political economist.

Economic Welfare and the Allocation of Resources for Invention

KENNETH J. ARROW

THE RAND CORPORATION

INVENTION is here interpreted broadly as the production of knowledge. From the viewpoint of welfare economics, the determination of optimal resource allocation for invention will depend on the technological characteristics of the invention process and the nature of the market for knowledge.

The classic question of welfare economics will be asked here: to what extent does perfect competition lead to an optimal allocation of resources? We know from years of patient refinement that competition insures the achievement of a Pareto optimum under certain hypotheses. The model usually assumes among other things, that (1) the utility functions of consumers and the transformation functions of producers are well-defined functions of the commodities in the economic system, and (2) the transformation functions do not display indivisibilities (more strictly, the transformation sets are convex). The second condition needs no comment. The first seems to be innocuous but in fact conceals two basic assumptions of the usual models. It prohibits uncertainty in the production relations and in the utility functions, and it requires that all the commodities relevant either to production or to the welfare of individuals be traded on the market. This will not be the case when a commodity for one reason or another cannot be made into private property.

We have then three of the classical reasons for the possible failure of perfect competition to achieve optimality in resource allocation: indivisibilities, inappropriability, and uncertainty. The first problem has been much studied in the literature under the heading of marginal-cost pricing and the second under that of divergence between social and private benefit (or cost), but the theory of optimal allocation of resources under uncertainty has had much less attention. I will summarize what formal theory exists and then point to the critical notion of information, which arises only in the context of uncertainty. The

NOTE: I have benefited greatly from the comments of my colleague, William Capron. I am also indebted to Richard R. Nelson, Edward Phelps, and Sidney Winter of The RAND Corporation for their helpful discussion.

economic characteristics of information as a commodity and, in particular, of invention as a process for the production of information are next examined. It is shown that all three of the reasons given above for a failure of the competitive system to achieve an optimal resource allocation hold in the case of invention. On theoretical grounds a number of considerations are adduced as to the likely biases in the misallocation and the implications for economic organization.[1]

Resource Allocation under Uncertainty

The role of the competitive system in allocating uncertainty seems to have received little systematic attention.[2] I will first sketch an ideal economy in which the allocation problem can be solved by competition and then indicate some of the devices in the real world which approximate this solution.

Suppose for simplicity that uncertainty occurs only in production relations. Producers have to make a decision on inputs at the present moment, but the outputs are not completely predictable from the inputs. We may formally describe the outputs as determined by the inputs and a "state of nature" which is unknown to the producers. Let us define a "commodity-option" as a commodity in the ordinary sense labeled with a state of nature. This definition is analogous to the differentiation of a given physical commodity according to date in capital theory or according to place in location theory. The production of a given commodity under uncertainty can then be described as the production of a vector of commodity-options.

This description can be most easily exemplified by reference to agricultural production. The state of nature may be identified with the weather. Then, to any given set of inputs there corresponds a number of bushels of wheat if the rainfall is good and a different number if rainfall is bad. We can introduce intermediate conditions of rainfall

---

[1] For other analyses with similar points of view, see R. R. Nelson, "The Simple Economics of Basic Scientific Research," *Journal of Political Economy*, 1959, pp. 297–306; and C. J. Hitch, "The Character of Research and Development in a Competitive Economy," The RAND Corporation, p. 1297, May 1958.

[2] The first studies I am aware of are the papers of M. Allais and myself, both presented in 1952 to the Colloque International sur le Risque in Paris; see M. Allais, "Généralisation des théories de l'équilibre économique général et du rendement social au cas du risque," and K. J. Arrow, "Rôle des valeurs bousières pour la répartition la meilleure des risques," both in *Econométrie*, Colloques Internationaux du Centre National de la Recherche Scientifique, Vol. XL, Paris, Centre National de la Recherche Scientifique, 1953. Allais' paper has also appeared in *Econometrica*, 1953, pp. 269–290. The theory has received a very elegant generalization by G. Debreu in *Theory of Values*, New York, Wiley, 1959, Chap. VII.

in any number as alternative states of nature; we can increase the number of relevant variables which enter into the description of the state of nature, for example by adding temperature. By extension of this procedure, we can give a formal description of any kind of uncertainty in production.

Suppose—and this is the critical idealization of the economy—we have a market for all commodity-options. What is traded on each market are contracts in which the buyers pay an agreed sum and the sellers agree to deliver prescribed quantities of a given commodity *if* a certain state of nature prevails and nothing if that state of nature does not occur. For any given set of inputs, the firm knows its output under each state of nature and sells a corresponding quantity of commodity-options; its revenue is then completely determined. It may choose its inputs so as to maximize profits.

The income of consumers is derived from their sale of supplies, including labor, to firms and their receipt of profits, which are assumed completely distributed. They purchase commodity-options so as to maximize their expected utility given the budget restraint imposed by their incomes. An equilibrium is reached on all commodity-option markets, and this equilibrium has precisely the same Pareto-optimality properties as competitive equilibrium under certainty.

In particular, the markets for commodity-options in this ideal model serve the function of achieving an optimal allocation of risk bearing among the members of the economy. This allocation takes account of differences in both resources and tastes for risk bearing. Among other implications, risk bearing and production are separated economic functions. The use of inputs, including human talents, in their most productive mode is not inhibited by unwillingness or inability to bear risks by either firms or productive agents.

But the real economic system does not possess markets for commodity-options. To see what substitutes exist, let us first consider a model economy at the other extreme, in that no provisions for reallocating risk bearing exist. Each firm makes its input decisions; then outputs are produced as determined by the inputs and the state of nature. Prices are then set to clear the market. The prices that finally prevail will be a function of the state of nature.

The firm and its owners cannot relieve themselves of risk bearing in this model. Hence any unwillingness or inability to bear risks will give rise to a nonoptimal allocation of resources, in that there will be discrimination against risky enterprises as compared with the optimum. A preference for risk might give rise to misallocation in the opposite direction, but the limitations of financial resources are likely to make underinvestment in risky enterprises more likely than the opposite. The inability of individuals to buy protection against uncertainty similarly gives rise to a loss of welfare.

In fact, a number of institutional arrangements have arisen to mitigate the problem of assumption of risk. Suppose that each firm and individual in the economy could forecast perfectly what prices would be under each state of nature. Suppose further there were a lottery on the states of nature, so that before the state of nature is known any individual or firm may place bets. Then it can be seen that the effect from the viewpoint of any given individual or firm is the same as if there were markets for commodity-options of all types, since any commodity-option can be achieved by a combination of a bet on the appropriate state of nature and an intention to purchase or sell the commodity in question if the state of nature occurs.

References to lotteries and bets may smack of frivolity, but we need only think of insurance to appreciate that the shifting of risks through what are in effect bets on the state of nature is a highly significant phenomenon. If insurance were available against any conceivable event, it follows from the preceding discussion that optimal allocation would be achieved. Of course, insurance as customarily defined covers only a small range of events relevant to the economic world; much more important in shifting risks are securities, particularly common stocks and money. By shifting freely their proprietary interests among different firms, individuals can to a large extent bet on the different states of nature which favor firms differentially. This freedom to insure against many contingencies is enhanced by the alternatives of holding cash and going short.

Unfortunately, it is only too clear that the shifting of risks in the real world is incomplete. The great predominance of internal over external equity financing in industry is one illustration of the fact that securities do not completely fulfill their allocative role with respect to risks. There are a number of reasons why this should be so, but I will confine myself to one, of special significance with regard to invention. In insurance practice, reference is made to the moral factor as a limit to the possibilities of insurance. For example, a fire insurance policy cannot exceed in amount the value of the goods insured. From the purely actuarial standpoint, there is no reason for this limitation;

the reason for the limit is that the insurance policy changes the incentives of the insured, in this case, creating an incentive for arson or at the very least for carelessness. The general principle is the difficulty of distinguishing between a state of nature and a decision by the insured. As a result, any insurance policy and in general any device for shifting risks can have the effect of dulling incentives. A fire insurance policy, even when limited in amount to the value of the goods covered, weakens the motivation for fire prevention. Thus, steps which improve the efficiency of the economy with respect to risk bearing may decrease its technical efficiency.

One device for mitigating the adverse incentive effects of insurance is coinsurance; the insurance extends only to part of the amount at risk for the insured. This device is used, for example, in coverage of medical risks. It clearly represents a compromise between incentive effects and allocation of risk bearing, sacrificing something in both directions.

Two exemplifications of the moral factor are of special relevance in regard to highly risky business activities, including invention. Success in such activities depends on an inextricable tangle of objective uncertainties and decisions of the entrepreneurs and is certainly uninsurable. On the other hand, such activities should be undertaken if the expected return exceeds the market rate of return, no matter what the variance is.[3] The existence of common stocks would seem to solve the allocation problem; any individual stockholder can reduce his risk by buying only a small part of the stock and diversifying his portfolio to achieve his own preferred risk level. But then again the actual managers no longer receive the full reward of their decisions; the shifting of risks is again accompanied by a weakening of incentives to efficiency. Substitute motivations whether pecuniary, such as executive compensation and profit sharing, or nonpecuniary, such as prestige, may be found, but the dilemma of the moral factor can never be completely resolved.

A second example is the cost-plus contract in one of its various forms. When production costs on military items are highly uncertain, the military establishment will pay, not a fixed unit price, but the cost of production plus an amount which today is usually a fixed fee. Such a contract could be regarded as a combination of a fixed-price contract with an insurance against costs. The insurance premium could be

---

[3] The validity of this statement depends on some unstated assumptions, but the point to be made is unaffected by minor qualifications.

regarded as the difference between the fixed price the government would be willing to pay and the fixed fee.

Cost-plus contracts are necessitated by the inability or unwillingness of firms to bear the risks. The government has superior risk bearing ability and so the burden is shifted to it. It is then enabled to buy from firms on the basis of their productive efficiency rather than their risk bearing ability, which may be only imperfectly correlated. But cost-plus contracts notoriously have their adverse allocative effects.[4]

This somewhat lengthy digression on the theory of risk bearing seemed necessitated by the paucity of literature on the subject. The main conclusions to be drawn are the following: (1) the economic system has devices for shifting risks, but they are limited and imperfect; hence, one would expect an underinvestment in risky activities; (2) it is undoubtedly worthwhile to enlarge the variety of such devices, but the moral factor creates a limit to their potential.

Information as a Commodity

Uncertainty usually creates a still more subtle problem in resource allocation; information becomes a commodity. Suppose that in one part of the economic system an observation has been made whose outcome, if known, would affect anyone's estimates of the probabilities of the different states of nature. Such observations arise out of research but they also arise in the daily course of economic life as a by-product of other economic activities. An entrepreneur will automatically acquire a knowledge of demand and production conditions in his field which is available to others only with special effort. Information will frequently have an economic value, in the sense that anyone possessing the information can make greater profits than would otherwise be the case.

It might be expected that information will be traded in, and of course to a considerable extent this is the case, as is illustrated by the numerous economic institutions for transmission of information, such as newspapers. But in many instances, the problem of an optimal allocation is sharply raised. The cost of transmitting a given body of information is frequently very low. If it were zero, then optimal allocation would obviously call for unlimited distribution of the informa-

---

[4] These remarks are not intended as a complete evaluation of cost-plus contracts. In particular, there are, to a certain extent, other incentives which mitigate the adverse effects on efficiency.

tion without cost. In fact, a given piece of information is by definition an indivisible commodity, and the classical problems of allocation in the presence of indivisibilities appear here. The owner of the information should not extract the economic value which is there, if optimal allocation is to be achieved; but he is a monopolist, to some small extent and will seek to take advantage of this fact.

In the absence of special legal protection, the owner cannot, however, simply sell information on the open market. Any one purchaser can destroy the monopoly, since he can reproduce the information at little or no cost. Thus the only effective monopoly would be the use of the information by the original possessor. This, however, will not only be socially inefficient, but also may not be of much use to the owner of the information either, since he may not be able to exploit it as effectively as others.

With suitable legal measures, information may become an appropriable commodity. Then the monopoly power can indeed be exerted. However, no amount of legal protection can make a thoroughly appropriable commodity of something so intangible as information. The very use of the information in any productive way is bound to reveal it, at least in part. Mobility of personnel among firms provides a way of spreading information. Legally imposed property rights can provide only a partial barrier, since there are obviously enormous difficulties in defining in any sharp way an item of information and differentiating it from other similar sounding items.

The demand for information also has uncomfortable properties. In the first place, the use of information is certainly subject to indivisibilities; the use of information about production possibilities, for example, need not depend on the rate of production. In the second place, there is a fundamental paradox in the determination of demand for information; its value for the purchaser is not known until he has the information, but then he has in effect acquired it without cost. Of course, if the seller can retain property rights in the use of the information, this would be no problem, but given incomplete appropriability, the potential buyer will base his decision to purchase information on less than optimal criteria. He may act, for example, on the average value of information in that class as revealed by past experience. If any particular item of information has differing values for different economic agents, this procedure will lead both to a nonoptimal purchase of information at any given price and also to a nonoptimal allocation of the information purchased.

It should be made clear that from the standpoint of efficiently distributing an existing stock of information, the difficulties of appropriation are an advantage, provided there are no costs of transmitting information, since then optimal allocation calls for free distribution. The chief point made here is the difficulty of creating a market for information if one should be desired for any reason.

It follows from the preceding discussion that costs of transmitting information create allocative difficulties which would be absent otherwise. Information should be transmitted at marginal cost, but then the demand difficulties raised above will exist. From the viewpoint of optimal allocation, the purchasing industry will be faced with the problems created by indivisibilities; and we still leave unsolved the problem of the purchaser's inability to judge in advance the value of the information he buys. There is a strong case for centralized decision making under these circumstances.

Invention as the Production of Information

The central economic fact about the processes of invention and research is that they are devoted to the production of information. By the very definition of information, invention must be a risky process, in that the output (information obtained) can never be predicted perfectly from the inputs. We can now apply the discussion of the preceding two sections.

Since it is a risky process, there is bound to be some discrimination against investment in inventive and research activities. In this field, especially, the moral factor will weigh heavily against any kind of insurance or equivalent form of risk bearing. Insurance against failure to develop a desired new product or process would surely very greatly weaken the incentives to succeed. The only way, within the private enterprise system, to minimize this problem is the conduct of research by large corporations with many projects going on, each small in scale compared with the net revenue of the corporation. Then the corporation acts as its own insurance company. But clearly this is only an imperfect solution.

The deeper problems of misallocation arise from the nature of the product. As we have seen, information is a commodity with peculiar attributes, particularly embarrassing for the achievement of optimal allocation. In the first place, any information obtained, say a new method of production, should, from the welfare point of view, be available free of charge (apart from the cost of transmitting information). This insures optimal utilization of the information but of course provides no incentive for investment in research. In an ideal socialist economy, the reward for invention would be completely separated from any charge to the users of the information.[5] In a free enterprise economy, inventive activity is supported by using the invention to create property rights; precisely to the extent that it is successful, there is an underutilization of the information. The property rights may be in the information itself, through patents and similar legal devices, or in the intangible assets of the firm if the information is retained by the firm and used only to increase its profits.

The first problem, then, is that in a free enterprise economy the profitability of invention requires a nonoptimal allocation of resources. But it may still be asked whether or not the allocation of resources to inventive activity is optimal. The discussion of the preceding section makes it clear that we would not expect this to be so; that, in fact, a downward bias in the amount of resources devoted to inventive activity is very likely. Whatever the price, the demand for information is less than optimal for two reasons: (1) since the price is positive and not at its optimal value of zero, the demand is bound to be below the optimal; (2) as seen before, at any given price, the very nature of information will lead to a lower demand than would be optimal.

As already remarked, the inventor will in any case have considerable difficulty in appropriating the information produced. Patent laws would have to be unimaginably complex and subtle to permit such appropriation on a large scale. Suppose, as the result of elaborate tests, some metal is discovered to have a desirable property, say resistance to high heat. Then of course every use of the metal for which this property is relevant would also use this information, and the user would be made to pay for it. But, even more, if another inventor is stimulated to examine chemically related metals for heat resistance, he is using the information already discovered and should pay for it in some measure; and any beneficiary of his discoveries should also pay. One would have to have elaborate distinctions of partial property rights of all degrees to make the system at all tolerable. In the interests of the possibility of enforcement, actual patent laws sharply restrict the range of appropriable information and thereby reduce the incentives to engage in inventive and research activities.

[5] This separation exists in the Soviet Union, according to N. M. Kaplan and R. H. Moorsteen of The RAND Corporation (verbal communication).

These last considerations bring into focus the interdependence of inventive activities, which reinforces the difficulties in achieving an optimal allocation of the results. Information is not only the product of inventive activity, it is also an input—in some sense, the major input apart from the talent of the inventor. The school of thought that emphasizes the determination of invention by the social climate as demonstrated by the simultaneity of inventions in effect emphasizes strongly the productive role of previous information in the creation of new information. While these interrelations do not create any new difficulties in principle, they intensify the previously established ones. To appropriate information for use as a basis for further research is much more difficult than to appropriate it for use in producing commodities; and the value of information for use in developing further information is much more conjectural than the value of its use in production and therefore much more likely to be underestimated. Consequently, if a price is charged for the information, the demand is even more likely to be suboptimal.

Thus basic research, the output of which is only used as an informational input into other inventive activities, is especially unlikely to be rewarded. In fact, it is likely to be of commercial value to the firm undertaking it only if other firms are prevented from using the information obtained. But such restriction on the transmittal of information will reduce the efficiency of inventive activity in general and will therefore reduce its quantity also. We may put the matter in terms of sequential decision making. The a priori probability distribution of the true state of nature is relatively flat to begin with. On the other hand, the successive a posteriori distributions after more and more studies have been conducted are more and more sharply peaked or concentrated in a more limited range, and we therefore have better and better information for deciding what the next step in research shall be. This implies that, at the beginning, the preferences among alternative possible lines of investigation are much less sharply defined than they are apt to be later on and suggests, at least, the importance of having a wide variety of studies to begin with, the less promising being gradually eliminated as information is accumulated.[6] At each stage the decisions about the next step should be based on all available information. This would require an unrestricted flow of informa-

[6] The importance of parallel research developments in the case of uncertainty has been especially stressed by Burton H. Klein; see his, "A Radical Proposal for R. and D.," *Fortune*, May 1958, p. 112 ff.; and Klein and W. H. Meckling, "Application of Operations Research to Development Decisions," *Operations Research*, 1958, pp. 352–363.

tion among different projects which is incompatible with the complete decentralization of an ideal free enterprise system. When the production of information is important, the classic economic case in which the price system replaces the detailed spread of information is no longer completely applicable.

To sum up, we expect a free enterprise economy to underinvest in invention and research (as compared with an ideal) because it is risky, because the product can be appropriated only to a limited extent, and because of increasing returns in use. This underinvestment will be greater for more basic research. Further, to the extent that a firm succeeds in engrossing the economic value of its inventive activity, there will be an underutilization of that information as compared with an ideal allocation.

Competition, Monopoly, and the Incentive to Innovate

It may be useful to remark that an incentive to invent can exist even under perfect competition in the product markets though not, of course, in the "market" for the information contained in the invention. This is especially clear in the case of a cost reducing invention. Provided only that suitable royalty payments can be demanded, an inventor can profit without disturbing the competitive nature of the industry. The situation for a new product invention is not very different; by charging a suitable royalty to a competitive industry, the inventor can receive a return equal to the monopoly profits.

I will examine here the incentives to invent for monopolistic and competitive markets, that is, I will compare the potential profits from an invention with the costs. The difficulty of appropriating the information will be ignored; the remaining problem is that of indivisibility in use, an inherent property of information. A competitive situation here will mean one in which the industry produces under competitive conditions, while the inventor can set an arbitrary royalty for the use of his invention. In the monopolistic situation, it will be assumed that only the monopoly itself can invent. Thus a monopoly is understood here to mean barriers to entry; a situation of temporary monopoly, due perhaps to a previous innovation, which does not prevent the entrance of new firms with innovations of their own, is to be regarded as more nearly competitive than monopolistic for the purpose of this analysis. It will be argued that the incentive to invent is less under monopolistic than under competitive conditions but even in the latter case it will be less than is socially desirable.

We will assume constant costs both before and after the invention, the unit costs being c before the invention and $c' < c$ afterward. The competitive price before invention will therefore be c. Let the corresponding demand be x_c. If r is the level of unit royalties, the competitive price after the invention will be $c' + r$, but this cannot of course be higher than c, since firms are always free to produce with the old methods.

It is assumed that both the demand and the marginal revenue curves are decreasing. Let $R(x)$ be the marginal revenue curve. Then the monopoly output before invention, x_m, would be defined by the equation,

$$R(x_m) = c .$$

Similarly, the monopoly output after invention is defined by,

$$R(x'_m) = c' .$$

Let the monopoly prices corresponding to outputs x_m and x'_m, respectively, be p_m and p'_m. Finally, let P and P' be the monopolist's profits before and after invention, respectively.

What is the optimal royalty level for the inventor in the competitive case? Let us suppose that he calculates p'_m, the optimal monopoly price which would obtain in the postinvention situation. If the cost reduction is sufficiently drastic that $p'_m < c$, then his most profitable policy is to set r so that the competitive price is p'_m, i.e. let,

$$r = p'_m - c' .$$

In this case, the inventor's royalties are equal to the profits a monopolist would make under the same conditions, i.e. his incentive to invent will be P'.

Suppose, however, it turns out that $p'_m > c$. Since the sales price cannot exceed c, the inventor will set his royalties at,

$$r = c - c' .$$

The competitive price will then be c, and the sales will remain at x_c. The inventor's incentive will then be, $x_c(c - c')$.

The monopolist's incentive, on the other hand, is clearly $P' - P$. In the first of the two cases cited, the monopolist's incentive is obviously less than the inventor's incentive under competition, which is P', not $P' - P$. The preinvention monopoly power acts as a strong disincentive to further innovation.

The analysis is slightly more complicated in the second case. The monopolist's incentive, $P' - P$, is the change in revenue less the change in total cost of production, i.e.,

$$P' - P = \int_{x_m}^{x'_m} R(x)\, dx - c'\, x'_m + c\, x_m .$$

Since the marginal revenue $R(x)$ is diminishing, it must always be less than $R(x_m) = c$ as x increases from x_m to x'_m, so that,

$$\int_{x_m}^{x'_m} R(x)\, dx < c\, (x'_m - x_m),$$

and,

$$P' - P < c\,(x'_m - x_m) - c'\, x'_m + c\, x_m = (c - c')\, x'_m .$$

In the case being considered, the postinvention monopoly price, p'_m, is greater than c. Hence, with a declining demand curve, $x'_m < x_c$. The above inequality shows that the monopolist's incentive is always less than the cost reduction on the postinvention monopoly output, which in this case is, in turn, less than the competitive output (both before and after invention). Since the inventor's incentive under competition is the cost reduction on the competitive output, it will again always exceed the monopolist's incentive.

It can be shown that, if we consider differing values of c', the difference between the two incentives increases as c' decreases, reaching its maximum of P (preinvention monopoly profits) for c' sufficiently large for the first case to hold. The ratio of the incentive under competition to that under monopoly, on the other hand, though always greater than 1, decreases steadily with c'. For c' very close to c (i.e., very minor inventions), the ratio of the two incentives is approximately x_c/x_m, i.e., the ratio of monopoly to competitive output.[7]

[7] To sketch the proof of these statements quickly, note that, as c' varies, P is a constant. Hence, from the formula for $P' - P$, we see that,

$$d(P' - P)/dc' = dP'/dc' = R(x'_m)\,(dx'_m/dc') - c'(dx'_m/dc') - x'_m = -x'_m ,$$

since $R(x'_m) = c'$. Let $F(c')$ be the difference between the incentives to invent under competitive and under monopolistic conditions. In the case where $p'_m < c$, this difference is the constant P. Otherwise,

$$F(c') = x_c\,(c - c') - (P' - P),$$

so that

$$dF/dc' = x'_m - x_c .$$

For the case considered, we must have $x'_m < x_c$, as seen in the text. Hence, $dF/dc' \le 0$, so

The only ground for arguing that monopoly may create superior incentives to invent is that appropriability may be greater under monopoly than under competition. Whatever differences may exist in this direction must, of course, still be offset against the monopolist's disincentive created by his preinvention monopoly profits.

The incentive to invent in competitive circumstances may also be compared with the social benefit. It is necessary to distinguish between the realized social benefit and the potential social benefit, the latter being the benefit which would accrue under ideal conditions, which, in this case, means the sale of the product at postinvention cost, c'. Clearly, the potential social benefit always exceeds the realized social benefit. I will show that the realized social benefit, in turn, always equals or exceeds the competitive incentive to invent and, a fortiori, the monopolist's incentive.

Consider again the two cases discussed above. If the invention is sufficiently cost reducing so that $p'_m < c$, then there is a consumers' benefit, due to the lowering of price, which has not been appropriated by the inventor. If not, then the price is unchanged, so that the consumers' position is unchanged, and all benefits do go to the inventor. Since by assumption all the producers are making zero profits both before and after the invention, we see that the inventor obtains the entire realized social benefit of moderately cost reducing inventions but not of more radical inventions. Tentatively, this suggests a bias against major inventions, in the sense that an invention, part of whose costs could be paid for by lump-sum payments by consumers without making them worse off than before, may not be profitable at the maximum royalty payments that can be extracted by the inventor.

---

that $F(c')$ increases as c' decreases.

Let $G(c')$ be the ratio of the incentive under competition to that under monopoly. If $p'_m \leqslant c$, then,

$$G(c') = P'/(P' - P),$$

which clearly decreases as c' decreases. For $p'_m > c$, we have,

$$G(c') = x_c (c - c')/(P' - P).$$

Then,

$$dG/dc' = [-(P' - P) x_c + x_c (c - c') x'_m]/(P' - P)^2.$$

Because of the upper bound for $P' - P$ established in the text, the numerator must be positive; the ratio decreases as c' decreases.

Finally, if we consider c' very close to c, $G(c')$ will be approximately equal to the ratio of the derivatives of the numerator and denominator (L'Hopital's rule), which is, x_c/x'_m, and which approaches x_c/x_m as c' approaches c.

Alternative Forms of Economic Organization in Invention

The previous discussion leads to the conclusion that for optimal allocation to invention it would be necessary for the government or some other agency not governed by profit-and-loss criteria to finance research and invention. In fact, of course, this has always happened to a certain extent. The bulk of basic research has been carried on outside the industrial system, in universities, in the government, and by private individuals. One must recognize here the importance of nonpecuniary incentives, both on the part of the investigators and on the part of the private individuals and governments that have supported research organizations and universities. In the latter, the complementarity between teaching and research is, from the point of view of the economy, something of a lucky accident. Research in some more applied fields, such as agriculture, medicine, and aeronautics, has consistently been regarded as an appropriate subject for government participation, and its role has been of great importance.

If the government and other nonprofit institutions are to compensate for the underallocation of resources to invention by private enterprise, two problems arise: how shall the amount of resources devoted to invention be determined, and how shall efficiency in their use be encouraged? These problems arise whenever the government finds it necessary to engage in economic activities because indivisibilities prevent the private economy from performing adequately (highways, bridges, reclamation projects, for example), but the determination of the relative magnitudes is even more difficult here. Formally, of course, resources should be devoted to invention until the expected marginal social benefit there equals the marginal social benefit in alternative uses, but in view of the presence of uncertainty, such calculations are even more difficult and tenuous than those for public works. Probably all that could be hoped for is the estimation of future rates of return from those in the past, with investment in invention being increased or decreased accordingly as some average rate of return over the past exceeded or fell short of the general rate of return. The difficulties of even ex post calculation of rates of return are formidable though possibly not insuperable.[8]

The problem of efficiency in the use of funds devoted to research

---

[8] For an encouraging study of this type, see Z. Griliches, "Research Costs and Social Returns: Hybrid Corn and Related Innovations," *Journal of Political Economy*, 1958, pp. 419–431.

is one that has been faced internally by firms in dealing with their own research departments. The rapid growth of military research and development has led to a large-scale development of contractual relations between producers and a buyer of invention and research. The problems encountered in assuring efficiency here are the same as those that would be met if the government were to enter upon the financing of invention and research in civilian fields. The form of economic relation is very different from that in the usual markets. Payment is independent of product; it is governed by costs, though the net reward (the fixed fee) is independent of both. This arrangement seems to fly in the face of the principles for encouraging efficiency, and doubtless it does lead to abuses, but closer examination shows both mitigating factors and some explanation of its inevitability. In the first place, the awarding of new contracts will depend in part on past performance, so that incentives for efficiency are not completely lacking. In the second place, the relation between the two parties to the contract is something closer than a purely market relation. It is more like the sale of professional services, where the seller contracts to supply not so much a specific result as his best judgment. (The demand for such services also arises from uncertainty and the value of information.) In the third place, payment by results would involve great risks for the inventor, risks against which, as we have seen, he could hedge only in part.

There is clear need for further study of alternative methods of compensation. For example, some part of the contractual payment might depend on the degree of success in invention. But a more serious problem is the decision as to which contracts to let. One would need to examine the motivation underlying government decision making in this area. Hitch has argued that there are biases in governmental allocation, particularly against risky invention processes, and an excessive centralization, though the latter could be remedied by better policies.[9]

One can go further. There is really no need for the firm to be the fundamental unit of organization in invention; there is plenty of reason to suppose that individual talents count for a good deal more than the firm as an organization. If provision is made for the rental of necessary equipment, a much wider variety of research contracts with individuals as well as firms and with varying modes of payment, including incentives, could be arranged. Still other forms of organiza-

[9] *Op. cit.*

tion, such as research institutes financed by industries, the government, and private philanthropy, could be made to play an even livelier role than they now do.

COMMENT

C. J. HITCH, The RAND Corporation

There is, I think, one important aspect of government policy with respect to research and development that Markham failed to discuss—the government's contracting and management policies in this area. The problems here are related to Arrow's discussion of incentives, particularly his remarks concerning risk bearing and the adverse allocative effects of cost-plus contracts.

Let me illustrate one set of such problems by contrasting the management policies used by the Army Air Corps before World War II in developing new combat aircraft with the policies now used by the Air Force in developing aircraft and missiles.

Before the war the Air Corps would typically announce a competition for a new aircraft type, the desired characteristics of which would be described in general terms. Any aircraft company that wanted to enter the competition would develop and build, with its own funds, the required number of prototypes (usually one to three). The competition consisted in flying and testing, at Dayton, the prototypes entered by the companies. The prize for the winner was a production contract. The losers lost their stake.

Now, typically, the competition occurs at the design stage. The competing companies enter drawings, with their estimates of performance (and time and cost of development). The winner of the design competition is awarded a development contract which, if things go favorably, is transformed later into a production contract. Occasionally, if the program is considered very important, two competing designs may be approved for development or even production (cf. the Atlas and Titan). But usually the development of more than one model is considered too expensive.

In fact, the greatly increased cost of development is the reason given for this change in policy. When the cost of developing a new vehicle is from \$0.5 billion to \$2.0 billion, it seems evident that no aircraft company can assume the risk, and perhaps also that even the government can not finance multiple developments.

Nevertheless, the new policy appears far from ideal. The aircraft companies risk nothing (even the cost of preparing designs is usually reimbursed). Because of the great uncertainties involved in any major development, it is hard to make a wise selection at the design stage. Companies have a natural tendency to be optimistic in estimating performance, cost, and availability at this stage—sometimes much more so than at other stages as Klein and Marshall and Meckling have shown. And the Air Force has a natural tendency to favor the more optimistic proposals. As a result, the specifications in the development contract are sometimes unrealistic to the point of causing inordinate delay.

Moreover, once the winner has been selected, there is no more competition. The company may put its best team on the development for the sake of patriotism or its own long term reputation, but the powerful incentive of competition is lacking. Partly for this reason the Air Force, locked to a sole source with a cost-plus contract, has to exercise a kind and degree of control during the development process that is inconsistent with management prerogatives as they are understood and practiced in other parts of the free enterprise economy.

I believe the inefficiencies resulting from these policies and procedures are serious, and worthy of much more attention by economists. It does no good simply to inveigh against the iniquities of cost-plus contracting and government risk bearing when we are unable to propose a practical alternative. Perhaps part of the answer lies in some form of risk sharing. What is badly needed here is an economics invention or, more probably, several of them. The government is going to be in the business of supporting research and development on a large scale for a long time, and it is important that it use policies that take advantage of the incentives present in the economy.

SUBJECT INDEX

(Includes inventors' names)

Academic research:
  engineering, 426-429, 438
  medicine, 420-426, 437-438
  natural science, 410-420, 436-437
Adams, Joseph H., 301-302, 311, 313
Agricultural research, factors directing, 429-434, 438
Agriculture, determinants of inventions and investment in, 199, 216, 219-221
Aircraft industry, 261, 274, 282, 287-288
  government support of R and D in, 240, 243, 593
  as leader in R and D, 238-240, 243, 246, 251
  size of firm and R and D, 245, 248
Allocation of inventive activity:
  in academic and agricultural research, 410-440
  alternative forms of organization for, 623-625
  effect of monopoly and competition compared, 619-622
  under uncertainty, 14, 609-619, 623-626
  See also Market Structure
Aluminum alloys, 292
Aluminum industry:
  sources of inventions in, 284-286, 292-293
  aluminum alloys, 292
  brazing process, 287
  Croning process, 289-290
  forging press, 290-291
  heilarc process, 287
  Koldweld process, 286-288
  Properzi casting process, 290
  Soderberg process, 296-297
  structure of industry (effect on inventions), 279-284
Antitrust policy, and patent system, 602-608
Apparel industry, 274
Applied research, defined, 43, 46, 581-583

Baker, William O., 552
Bardeen, John, 559, 561-562, 566-567, 574, 576
Basic research, defined, 43, 46, 581-583
Bayer process, 296 n., 297
Bell Telephone Laboratories:
  development of T H system, 509-548

development of transistor, 549-567
  management and policies on research, 568-577
  organization of, 552
Brazing process, 287
Bromide process, *see* Tetraethyl lead
Burton cracking process, 300-301, 305-306, 311, 318-319
Burton, W. M., 300, 311, 313

Capital-saving inventions:
  definition of, 176-177
  directed by market, *see* Factor prices
Carothers, Wallace, 333, 335, 341
Casale process, 329
Catalytic cracking process, 302-303, 311-312
  See also Petroleum industry
Cellophane, 325, 328-331, 343-344
Chemical industry, 257-258, 264
  among leaders in R and D, 238-240, 246, 249, 275
  effect of R and D on productivity in, 95-141
  government support of R and D in, 240
  research spending as per cent of sales, 274
  size of firm and R and D in, 245, 248
Chloride process, *see* Tetraethyl lead
Claude process, 329
Competition, *see* Market structure
Continuous casting process, *see* Aluminum industry
Cracking processes, 300-306, 310-313, 317-321
Croning process, 289-290
Cross cracking process, 301-302, 305, 311, 314 n.
Cross, R. and W., 301-302, 312-313
Cultural base theory, 66-68

Dacron, 325, 341, 343-344
Decision-making process:
  effect of science on (case of the transistor), 549-567
  organization and values affecting:
    in academic research, 410-429, 436-438
    in agricultural research, 429-434, 438

627

ratio of rejects to gross output of, 163-165, 167-168

relation to demand and investment, 6-7, 11-12, 197-224
See also Productivity, effect of investment on

effect of science on, *see* Science

sources of Du Pont's innovations, 323-346

supply (curve) of, 6, 8, 143-168
elasticity of, 167, 197

T H system, *see* T H system

time interval between inventions and innovations, 304-310

timing due to identification of technical problem, 211-215

transistor, *see* Transistor

Inventive activity:
allocation of, *see* Allocation of inventive activity

directed by factor prices, *see* Factor prices

direction affected by monopsony, *see* Monopsony

economies of scale in, 15, 94-96, 100, 125-130, 155-163, 266-267, 420, 425, 618-619

effect of profits on, 6, 8, 11-12, 95, 118-122, 350-353, 377

effect of uncertainty on welfare, 14, 609-619, 623-626

locational differences in, 253-267

measuring input and output of, 24-42, 48-51, 53-90, 152, 162-165, 229-232, 256-257

population and employment groups giving rise to, 5-6, 12, 31-32, 56-57, 60-61, 253-267

social vs. private, cost of, 151, 193-194
See also Inventions, supply curve of

Inventors:
distribution of patents to, 5-6, 56-57, 61-62

motives and intellect of, 144-146, 212, 361-384

measuring quality differences in, 34, 50-51, 57-58

quality differences and supply curve of, 147-151

population and employment groups giving rise to, *see* Inventive activity

Koldwell process, 386-387

Labor-saving inventions:
effected by market, *see* Factor prices

definition of, 176-177

effect on employment, *see* Employment, level of

Machinery industry, 257, 263-264, 274, 593
source of inventions in aluminum industry, 279, 282-293
See also Electrical machinery

Manley, F. T., 300, 311, 313

Market structure:
effect on benefits of patent system, 599-608

effect on output of inventions, 183, 185, 279-284, 293-298, 353, 355-356, 579-580, 619-625
See also Research and development, size of firm as a determinant of

effect on productivity, 94-95, 130-137

Methodology:
measuring input and output of inventive activity, 24-42, 48-51, 53-90, 152, 162-165

problems in preparing industrial patent series, 229-232, 256-257

Midgeley, Thomas, Jr., 327

Monopoly, effect on output of inventions, *see* Market structure

Monopsony:
effect in direction of inventive effort, 181-184, 187
See also Market structure

Motor vehicle industry, 257, 261, 274
R and D expenditures in, 240

Multiple approaches in R and D, 9-11, 501-502, 505
See also Decision-making process, problems arising in R and D

Nylon, 325, 334-337, 343-344, 354

Odell, W. W., 303, 312-313, 320

Oligopoly, *see* Market structure

Orlon, 325, 339-340, 343-344

Paper industry, 238, 248, 274
determinants of inventions and investment in, 199, 216, 221-224

Patents:
characteristics of patent receivers, 5-6, 56-58, 61-62

measuring output of inventions, 36-41, 68-85, 229-232, 256-257
See also Inventive activity, measuring input and output

AUTHOR INDEX

Abramovitz, M., 3 n., 93 n., 198 n.
Agriculture, Department of, 429 n.
Aitchison, J., 305 n.
Allais, M., 610 n.
Allen, Francis R., 54 n. 66 n.
Allport, G. W., 375
Arrow, K. J., 9, 13-15, 193, 610 n.
Ashby, Eric, 411 n.
Avery, Robert W., 385 n.

Bagehot, Walter, 227
Baldwin, G. B., 308
Ball, Carleton R., 429 n.
Barber, Bernard, 448 n.
Barger, Harold, 209
Barnes, W. A., 286 n.
Beaton, Kendall, 300 n., 301 n.
Belfer, Nathan, 598 n.
Bello, Francis, 450 n.
Bennett, W. B., 168 n., 377
Berle, A. A., 4 n.
Beveridge, W. I. B., 443 n.
Bichowsky, F. R., 7 n.
Blank, David M., 240, 243 n., 275
Bolton, E. K., 335 n., 336-337
Borenstein, Israel, 217
Boring, E. G., 448 n.
Brattain, W. H., 554 n., 558-559, 562, 576
Bright, A. A., 5 n., 308, 598 n.
Brillouin, L., 446 n.
Brothers, Dwight S., 598 n.
Brown, J. A. C., 305 n.
Brownlee, O. H., 44 n.
Brozen, Yale, 6 n., 12
Bruner, J. S., 446 n.
Buchanan, Andrew E., 342
Burgess, Ralph E., 55 n.
Bush, George P., 61 n.

Carter, C., 6 n., 153 n., 164 n., 165 n.
Census Bureau, 246 n., 254, 262 n.
Cherington, Paul W., 13
Chin, Gay, 605 n., 606 n.
Church, F. L., 289 n., 291 n.
Clark, C. E., 547 n.
Clark, Colin, 450 n.
Clark, J. B., 598 n.
Cohen, I. Bernard, 391 n., 416, 419, 443 n., 444 n., 448 n., 565 n.
Commerce, Department of, 258, 262, 297 n.

Committee on Armed Services, House, 400
Committee on Armed Services, Senate, 403
Committee on Government Operations, House, 398 n., 399 n., 500 n.
Committee on the Judiciary, House, 323 n.
Conant, James B., 431 n.
Cook, P., 442 n.
Cootner, Paul H., 210
Cotton, Donald B., 385 n.
Creamer, Daniel, 217

Dahl, Robert A., 433
Daum, A. R., 219 n.
Debreu, G., 610 n.
Dobrovolsky, Sergei, 217
Dodds, Harold W., 590 n.
Domar, Evsey, 184-185
Douglas, P. H., 357
Downs, Anthony, 433
Du Pont de Nemours & Company, 327, 337 n.-342 n.
Dupree, A. Hunter, 429 n.
Dutton, William S., 332 n.

Easterlin, Richard A., 198 n.
Eisenhower, Dwight D., 401, 588 n.
Eliot, E., 290 n.
Ellis, Carleton, 300 n.
Enos, J. L., 11, 312, 317-318, 319 n., 350
Epstein, R. C., 317

Farber, Eduard, 442 n.
Farrell, E. A., 291 n.
Fazar, W., 547 n.
Federal Trade Commission, 235, 274 n.
Fellner, William, 8-9
Field, Phillip M., 234 n., 246 n.
Finch, James Kip, 426-427
Fisher, Irving, 598 n.
Fortune magazine, 235, 237, 324 n., 325 n., 338, 341, 565 n.
Friedland, Seymour, 241 n.

Galbraith, J. K., 4 n., 6 n.
Gee, E. A., 340
Gershinowitz, Harold, 417
Ghiorso, Albert, 444 n.

634